AN INTRODUCTION TO THE
THEORY OF FUNCTIONS
OF A
COMPLEX VARIABLE

AN
INTRODUCTION TO THE
THEORY OF FUNCTIONS
OF A
COMPLEX VARIABLE

BY

E. T. COPSON
M.A. (OXON.), D.Sc. (EDIN.)

Professor of Mathematics at University
College, Dundee, in the University of
St. Andrews

OXFORD UNIVERSITY PRESS
LONDON : GEOFFREY CUMBERLEGE

OXFORD UNIVERSITY PRESS
AMEN HOUSE, E.C. 4
London Edinburgh Glasgow New York
Toronto Melbourne Cape Town Bombay
Calcutta Madras
GEOFFREY CUMBERLEGE
PUBLISHER TO THE UNIVERSITY

First edition 1935

Reprinted photographically in Great Britain in 1944 (corrected),
1946. by LOWE & BRYDONE, PRINTERS. LTD., LONDON, from sheets
of the first edition

PREFACE

THIS book is based on courses of lectures given to undergraduates in the Universities of Edinburgh and St. Andrews, and is intended to provide an easy introduction to the methods of the theory of functions of a complex variable. The reader is assumed to have a knowledge of the elements of the theory of functions of a real variable, such as is contained, for example, in Hardy's *Course of Pure Mathematics*; an acquaintance with the easier parts of Bromwich's *Infinite Series* would prove advantageous, but is not essential.

The first six chapters contain an exposition, based on Cauchy's Theorem, of the properties of one-valued differentiable functions of a complex variable. In the rest of the book the problem of conformal representation, the elements of the theory of integral functions and the behaviour of some of the special functions of analysis are discussed by the methods developed in the earlier part. The book concludes with the classical proof of Picard's Theorem.

No attempt has been made to give the book an encyclopaedic character. My object has been to interest the reader and to encourage him to study further some of the more advanced parts of the subject; suggestions for further reading have been made at the end of each chapter.

I am especially indebted to Mr. W. L. Ferrar, who read the manuscript of the whole book in its original and revised forms, and suggested many improvements. My grateful thanks are also due to Professor E. T. Whittaker, F.R.S., for his kindly criticism during the early stages of the preparation of this work and for his constant encouragement.

Finally, I have to thank Dr. H. S. Ruse and Professor J. M. Whittaker for their careful reading of the proof sheets and many valuable suggestions.

E. T. C.

GREENWICH,
July 1935

CONTENTS

CHAPTER I

COMPLEX NUMBERS

1.1. The introduction of complex numbers into algebra

IN arithmetic, we understand by a real number a magnitude which can be expressed as a decimal fraction. If the decimal terminates or recurs, the real number is said to be rational, since it is then the ratio of two whole numbers. But if the decimal does not terminate or recur, the number is not the ratio of two whole numbers and is said to be irrational. We shall assume that the reader is acquainted with Dedekind's method of founding the theory of rational and irrational numbers on a sound logical basis.†

Elementary algebra is concerned with the application of the operations of arithmetic to symbols representing real numbers. The result of any sequence of such operations is always a real number.

A difficulty, however, soon arises in the theory of equations. If a, b, and c are real numbers, the quadratic equation $ax^2+2bx+c=0$ has two distinct roots if $b^2 > ca$ and two equal roots when $b^2 = ca$. But if $b^2 < ca$, there is no real number x which satisfies the equation, since the square of every real number is positive. It is customary to introduce a new symbol $\sqrt{(-1)}$, whose square is defined to be -1, and then to show that the equation is formally satisfied by taking

$$ax = -b \pm \sqrt{(ac-b^2)}\sqrt{(-1)},$$

when $b^2 < ca$.

When this new symbol has been added to the algebra of real numbers, every quadratic equation is formally satisfied by two expressions of the form $\alpha+\beta\sqrt{(-1)}$, where α and β are real numbers. Such expressions are called complex numbers.

If we suppose that the symbol $\sqrt{(-1)}$ obeys all the laws of algebra, save that its square is -1, we can develop a consistent algebra of complex numbers which includes the algebra of real numbers as a particular case and which also possesses a character of completeness which is lacking in the simpler theory. This

† See, for example, Chapter I of Hardy's *Pure Mathematics* (1921).

B

completeness is well illustrated by the theorem which states that every equation of degree n has precisely n roots—a result which is true in the algebra of complex numbers but is false in the algebra of real numbers.

The present book is concerned essentially with the application of the methods of the differential and integral calculus to complex numbers.

1.2. An algebra of ordered pairs of real numbers

Before we proceed to elaborate the algebra of complex numbers, it is very desirable that we should provide a definition of such numbers which depends only on real numbers, instead of the formal introduction of the symbol $\sqrt{(-1)}$ of elementary algebra. Such a definition is suggested by the following geometrical considerations.

In the analytical geometry of the Euclidean plane, the equations† $x' = ax$, $y' = ay$ define a transformation of any configuration of points into a new configuration which is obtained by a very simple geometrical construction. When a is positive, the transformation magnifies all distances from the origin in the ratio $a : 1$, whilst when a is negative, there is a magnification in the ratio $-a : 1$ together with a rotation about the origin through two right angles.

If we write the equations of transformation in the form $(x', y') = (x, y) a$, we see that a real number is the symbol of a certain geometrical transformation.

These transformations are, however, merely particular cases of the more general transformation $x' = ax - by$, $y' = bx + ay$, depending on two real parameters a and b. This transformation magnifies all distances from the origin in the ratio $\sqrt{(a^2 + b^2)} : 1$ and rotates all rays from the origin through an angle $\tan^{-1}(b/a)$. The two equations defining the transformation may be combined by writing‡

$$(x', y') = (x, y)\begin{pmatrix} a, & b \\ -b, & a \end{pmatrix};$$

---

† The axes of coordinates are supposed to be at right angles.

‡ The notation is that of the algebra of matrices. The reader is warned against confusing the matrix $\begin{pmatrix} a, & b \\ -b, & a \end{pmatrix}$ with the determinant $\begin{vmatrix} a, & b \\ -b, & a \end{vmatrix}$. A matrix has no numerical value, but is merely an array of numbers.

here the multipliers for x' occur in the first column of the two-rowed symbol, those for y' in the second. We shall now construct an algebra of these two-rowed symbols and shall show that this provides the desired definition of a complex number.

In the first place, we say that two symbols are equal if the corresponding transformations are the same; thus

$$\begin{pmatrix} a, & b \\ -b, & a \end{pmatrix} = \begin{pmatrix} a', & b' \\ -b', & a' \end{pmatrix}$$

holds if and only if $a = a'$ and $b = b'$. Secondly, we define the sum of the two symbols by the equation

$$\begin{pmatrix} a, & b \\ -b, & a \end{pmatrix} + \begin{pmatrix} a', & b' \\ -b', & a' \end{pmatrix} = \begin{pmatrix} a+a', & b+b' \\ -b-b', & a+a' \end{pmatrix}.$$

From the definition of addition it follows that

$$\begin{pmatrix} a', & b' \\ -b', & a' \end{pmatrix} + \begin{pmatrix} a-a', & b-b' \\ -b+b', & a-a' \end{pmatrix} = \begin{pmatrix} a, & b \\ -b, & a \end{pmatrix};$$

accordingly we define subtraction by

$$\begin{pmatrix} a, & b \\ -b, & a \end{pmatrix} - \begin{pmatrix} a', & b' \\ -b', & a' \end{pmatrix} = \begin{pmatrix} a-a', & b-b' \\ -b+b', & a-a' \end{pmatrix}.$$

The definition of the product of two symbols is not quite so obvious, but it is suggested by analogy with the simpler case in which the transformation $(x', y') = (x, y) ab$ is the result of applying successively the two transformations $(x', y') = (x'', y'') b$ and $(x'', y'') = (x, y) a$. Accordingly, we define the product of the symbols

$$\begin{pmatrix} a, & b \\ -b, & a \end{pmatrix}, \qquad \begin{pmatrix} a', & b' \\ -b', & a' \end{pmatrix}$$

to be the symbol of the transformation obtained by applying successively the transformations

$$(x', y') = (x'', y'') \begin{pmatrix} a', & b' \\ -b', & a' \end{pmatrix}, \qquad (x'', y'') = (x, y) \begin{pmatrix} a, & b \\ -b, & a \end{pmatrix}.$$

It follows that†

$$\begin{pmatrix} a, & b \\ -b, & a \end{pmatrix} \begin{pmatrix} a', & b' \\ -b', & a' \end{pmatrix} = \begin{pmatrix} aa'-bb', & ab'+a'b \\ -ab'-a'b, & aa'-bb' \end{pmatrix}.$$

† It should be observed that the rule for multiplication is the same as that for multiplying two determinants; elements of a row of the first symbol are multiplied by the corresponding elements of a column in the second symbol.

The symbol

$$\begin{pmatrix} 0, & 0 \\ 0, & 0 \end{pmatrix}$$

is called the zero symbol, for it plays the part of zero in this algebra, since the difference of two equal symbols or the product of any symbol and the zero symbol is always the zero symbol. Similarly we call

$$\begin{pmatrix} 1, & 0 \\ 0, & 1 \end{pmatrix},$$

which corresponds to the identical transformation

$$(x', y') = (x, y),$$

the unit symbol, since every symbol is unaltered by multiplication by the unit symbol.

Finally, given any non-zero symbol

$$\begin{pmatrix} a, & b \\ -b, & a \end{pmatrix},$$

we can deduce from the law of multiplication a unique symbol, namely

$$\begin{pmatrix} a/(a^2+b^2), & -b/(a^2+b^2) \\ b/(a^2+b^2), & a/(a^2+b^2) \end{pmatrix},$$

whose product with the given symbol is the unit symbol. The second symbol is said to be the reciprocal of the first. We now define division by a non-zero symbol to be multiplication by its reciprocal.

Having defined the operations of addition and multiplication, together with the inverse operations of subtraction and division, we must next consider whether these operations obey the commutative, associative, and distributive laws of algebra.† The reader will easily verify that this is the case by showing that, if A, B, C denote any three of these two-rowed symbols, then

$$A+B = B+A,$$
$$AB = BA,$$
$$(A+B)+C = A+(B+C),$$
$$(AB)C = A(BC),$$
$$A(B+C) = AB+AC.$$

Moreover, if AB is identical with the zero symbol, so also is at

† See G. Chrystal, *Algebra*, **1** (1910), 2–24.

least one of A and B. It follows, therefore, that operations in this algebra of two-rowed symbols are carried out in precisely the same manner as in ordinary algebra.

In particular, the algebra of symbols of the form $\begin{pmatrix} a, & 0 \\ 0, & a \end{pmatrix}$ is identical with that of the real numbers a. Even though the two-rowed symbols of this type are logically distinct from the real numbers, no useful purpose is served by keeping a special notation for them.† With this convention, we may write

$$\begin{pmatrix} a, & b \\ -b, & a \end{pmatrix} = a + ib,$$

where

$$i = \begin{pmatrix} 0, & 1 \\ -1, & 0 \end{pmatrix}.$$

We easily see, by means of the rule for multiplication, that

$$i^2 = \begin{pmatrix} -1, & 0 \\ 0, & -1 \end{pmatrix} = -1;$$

in other words, i has all the properties formally assigned to $\sqrt{(-1)}$ in elementary algebra.

We now define a *complex number* to be a two-rowed symbol of the form $\begin{pmatrix} a, & b \\ -b, & a \end{pmatrix}$ or $a + ib$, which obeys the laws of combination prescribed above. It follows that *we can perform all the operations of algebra with complex numbers in exactly the same way as with real numbers, provided that we treat the symbol i as a number and replace its square by -1 whenever it occurs.*

1.3. The modulus and argument of a complex number

The geometrical transformation

$$(x', y') = (x, y)\begin{pmatrix} a, & b \\ -b, & a \end{pmatrix}$$

associated with the complex number $a + ib$ magnifies all distances from the origin in the ratio $+\sqrt{(a^2 + b^2)} : 1$, and rotates all rays from the origin through a certain angle α. The magni-

---

† It will be recalled that a similar point arises in connexion with Dedekind's theory of the real numbers, where the real rational number x (defined by a Dedekind section of the rational numbers) is logically distinct from the corresponding rational number. See Hardy, *Pure Mathematics* (1921), 14.

fication factor $+\sqrt{(a^2+b^2)}$ is called the *modulus* of the complex number $a+ib$ and is denoted by $|a+ib|$.

The number α which is determined by the two equations

$$a = |a+ib|\cos\alpha, \qquad b = |a+ib|\sin\alpha,$$

is called the *argument*† of $a+ib$, and is written $\arg(a+ib)$. If the modulus of a complex number $a+ib$ is not zero, its argument has an infinite number of values; for if α is a value of $\arg(a+ib)$, so also is $\alpha+2n\pi$, n being any integer. The principal value of $\arg(a+ib)$ is defined to be that which satisfies the inequality

$$-\pi < \arg(a+ib) \leqslant \pi.$$

If, however, $|a+ib|$ is zero, then a and b are both zero, and the equations to determine α are satisfied identically; the argument of the complex number 0 is thus indeterminate.

Let us now suppose that the complex number $A+iB$ is the product of $a+ib$ and $a'+ib'$. Since the geometrical transformation corresponding to $A+iB$ is the result of applying successively the transformations corresponding to $a+ib$ and $a'+ib'$, it follows at once that

$$|A+iB| = |a+ib|\,.\,|a'+ib'|,$$

and also that a value of $\arg(A+iB)$ is the sum of the principal values of the arguments of $a+ib$ and $a'+ib'$.

1.31. The real and imaginary parts of a complex number

It is convenient to denote a complex number $x+iy$ by a single letter, z say. If $z = x+iy$, where x and y are real, we call x and y the real and imaginary parts of z, and frequently write

$$x = \mathrm{Rl}\,z, \qquad y = \mathrm{Im}\,z.$$

It is easily seen that

$$-|z| \leqslant \mathrm{Rl}\,z \leqslant |z|, \qquad -|z| \leqslant \mathrm{Im}\,z \leqslant |z|.$$

From the definition of the equality of two of the symbols of § 1.2, it follows that two complex numbers z and z' are equal if and only if $\mathrm{Rl}\,z = \mathrm{Rl}\,z'$, $\mathrm{Im}\,z = \mathrm{Im}\,z'$. Again, from the rule for addition, we see that

$$\mathrm{Rl}(z+z') = \mathrm{Rl}\,z + \mathrm{Rl}\,z', \qquad \mathrm{Im}(z+z') = \mathrm{Im}\,z + \mathrm{Im}\,z'.$$

† Alternatively, the *amplitude* of $a+ib$.

1.32. Conjugate complex numbers

If $z = x+iy$, where x and y are real, the number $x-iy$ is said to be *conjugate* to z and is denoted by $\bar{z}$. Obviously, the number conjugate to $\bar{z}$ is z itself. Moreover, the numbers conjugate to z_1+z_2 and $z_1 z_2$ are evidently $\bar{z}_1+\bar{z}_2$ and $\bar{z}_1\bar{z}_2$ respectively.

The proofs of many theorems regarding complex numbers can often be greatly simplified by the use of conjugate complex numbers, if we remember the easily-proved formulae

$$|z|^2 = z\bar{z}, \qquad 2\,\mathrm{Rl}\,z = z+\bar{z}, \qquad 2i\,\mathrm{Im}\,z = z-\bar{z}.$$

First of all, if z_1 and z_2 are any two complex numbers, we have

$$|z_1 z_2|^2 = z_1 z_2 \,\overline{z_1 z_2} = z_1 \bar{z}_1 \, z_2 \bar{z}_2 = |z_1|^2 |z_2|^2,$$

and so
$$|z_1 z_2| = |z_1|\,.\,|z_2|,$$

the positive square root being taken since the modulus of a complex number is never negative. Therefore *the modulus of the product of two complex numbers* (and hence, by induction, of any number of complex numbers) *is equal to the product of their moduli.*†

Again, we have

$$\begin{aligned}
|z_1+z_2|^2 &= (z_1+z_2)(\bar{z}_1+\bar{z}_2) \\
&= z_1\bar{z}_1+z_1\bar{z}_2+\bar{z}_1 z_2+z_2\bar{z}_2 \\
&= |z_1|^2+2\,\mathrm{Rl}(z_1\bar{z}_2)+|z_2|^2 \\
&\leqslant |z_1|^2+2|z_1\bar{z}_2|+|z_2|^2 \\
&= (|z_1|+|z_2|)^2,
\end{aligned}$$

and so‡
$$|z_1+z_2| \leqslant |z_1|+|z_2|.$$

Hence the modulus of the sum of two complex numbers (and so, by induction, of any number of complex numbers) *cannot exceed the sum of their moduli.*

On the other hand, we also have

$$\begin{aligned}
|z_1-z_2|^2 &= |z_1|^2-2\,\mathrm{Rl}(z_1\bar{z}_2)+|z_2|^2 \\
&\geqslant |z_1|^2-2|z_1\bar{z}_2|+|z_2|^2 \\
&= (|z_1|-|z_2|)^2,
\end{aligned}$$

† An alternative proof was given in § 1.3.

‡ It should be observed that the sign of equality occurs only when $z_1\bar{z}_2$ is real and positive; this is the case if and only if z_1 and z_2 have the same argument.

so that $$|z_1-z_2| \geqslant |(|z_1|-|z_2|)|,$$

an important inequality of which frequent use will be made.

Example. Show that $\arg z + \arg \bar{z} = 2n\pi$, where n is an integer or zero.

1.4. The geometrical representation of complex numbers

The usual method of representing real numbers geometrically is by means of points on a line, the real number x corresponding to the point of abscissa x, according to some given scale, referred to a fixed origin on the line. In a similar way, we shall represent a complex number z by a point in a plane whose rectangular Cartesian coordinates are (Rl z, Im z); the complex number z is then called the *affix* of the point which represents it. The straight line whose equation is Im $z = 0$ is called the *real axis*, since the affix of each point on it is a real number; similarly we call the line Rl $z = 0$ the *imaginary axis*.

This geometrical picture, which is often called the Argand diagram, enables us to describe properties of complex numbers by means of geometrical language, as all the operations of the algebra of complex numbers have simple geometrical interpretations in this scheme.

Example 1. If P, Q, R are the points of affix z, z', $z+z'$ respectively, show that $OPRQ$ is a parallelogram.

Example 2. Prove that the polar coordinates of the point of affix z are $(|z|, \arg z)$, referred to the origin as pole and the real axis as initial line. Deduce a geometrical construction for the point of affix zz'.

Example 3. Prove that $|a-b|^2 + |a+b|^2 = 2|a|^2 + 2|b|^2$. Interpret this result geometrically.

1.41. The point at infinity

In the Euclidean geometry of the plane, 'points at infinity' do not occur; two straight lines intersect in a point except in the case when the lines are parallel. It is, however, usual to postulate, at a later stage, that there exists an infinite number of points at infinity, each being defined as the point of intersection of a pencil of parallel lines.

Now, if we take a pencil of curves through the point of affix c in the Argand plane, the transformation $z' = 1/z$ turns them into a pencil of curves through the point of affix $1/c$, provided that c is not zero. To avoid the difficulty of this exceptional case, we now postulate that there is a single point at infinity in the Argand plane; this point at infinity is defined to be the point corresponding to the origin in the transformation $z' = 1/z$.

The nature of the Argand plane at the point at infinity is made much clearer by the use of Riemann's spherical representation of complex numbers, which depends on stereographic projection.

In order to map a spherical surface stereographically on a plane, we take a point on the sphere as vertex of projection and its equatorial plane as plane of projection. Then to any point of the sphere save the vertex of projection, there corresponds a unique point of the plane; conversely, to each point of the plane, there corresponds a unique point of the sphere.

If we project the points on the sphere $\xi^2 + \eta^2 + \zeta^2 = 1$ stereographically on the plane $\zeta = 0$, taking the point $(0, 0, 1)$ as vertex of projection, we find that the point $(x, y, 0)$ of the plane corresponds to (ξ, η, ζ) on the sphere if

$$x = \xi/(1-\zeta), \qquad y = \eta/(1-\zeta),$$

or, writing z for $x+iy$,

$$z = (\xi+i\eta)/(1-\zeta).$$

Conversely, (ξ, η, ζ) on the sphere corresponds to the point of affix z in the plane if

$$\xi + i\eta = \frac{2z}{z\bar{z}+1}, \qquad \zeta = \frac{z\bar{z}-1}{z\bar{z}+1}.$$

These equations provide a continuous one-to-one correspondence between the complex numbers and points on a spherical surface.

Now if (ξ, η, ζ) corresponds to the point of affix z, $(\xi, \eta, -\zeta)$ corresponds to z', where

$$z' = \frac{\xi+i\eta}{1+\zeta} = \frac{1-\zeta}{\xi-i\eta} = \frac{1}{\bar{z}},$$

since $\xi^2 + \eta^2 = 1 - \zeta^2$. But obviously $\arg z = \arg z'$ and $|z| \cdot |z'| = 1$, so that z and z' are inverse points with respect to the unit circle with centre at the origin. Thus points of the Argand plane which are inverse with respect to the circle $|z| = 1$ correspond to points of the Riemann sphere which are symmetrical with respect to the plane $\zeta = 0$.

In particular, when $z = 0$, z' is, by definition, the point at infinity, and so the point $(0, 0, 1)$ of the Riemann sphere corresponds to the point at infinity of the Argand plane. We have thus set up a one-to-one correspondence between the points of the Argand plane, completed by the addition of the point at infinity, and the points of the whole Riemann sphere. Any geometrical property involving the point at infinity in the Argand plane can thus be easily visualized by means of this spherical representation of complex numbers.

REFERENCES†

G. H. HARDY, *Pure Mathematics*‡ (Cambridge, 1921), Chap. III.

B. A. W. RUSSELL, *Introduction to Mathematical Philosophy* (London, 1919), Chap. VII.

MISCELLANEOUS EXAMPLES

1. Show that the equation of a straight line in the Argand plane is

$$b\bar{z} + \bar{b}z = c,$$

where b and c are constants, c being real. Deduce the condition for the collinearity of three points.

Prove also that z' is the reflection of z in this line if $b\bar{z} + \bar{b}z' = c$.

2. Find the area of the triangle whose vertices are the points of affix z_1, z_2, z_3.

3. Show that the triangles whose vertices are z_1, z_2, z_3 and z_1', z_2', z_3' are similar if

$$\begin{vmatrix} z_1 & z_1' & 1 \\ z_2 & z_2' & 1 \\ z_3 & z_3' & 1 \end{vmatrix} = 0.$$

4. Prove that the equation of a circle in the Argand plane is

$$az\bar{z} + b\bar{z} + \bar{b}z + c = 0,$$

where a ($\neq 0$), b and c are constants, a and c being real.

Show that§ z and z' are inverse points with respect to this circle if

$$az'\bar{z} + b\bar{z} + \bar{b}z' + c = 0.$$

---

† At the end of each chapter, references will be given to suggest further reading.

‡ It is important to notice that, although Hardy's definition of a complex number is quite different from that adopted here, both depend on constructing an algebra with certain symbols involving two real numbers arranged in a certain manner. As the laws of combination are the same for both sets of symbols, the two constructions lead to the same algebra of complex numbers.

§ This implies that inversion with respect to the degenerate circle $0z\bar{z} + b\bar{z} + \bar{b}z + c = 0$ is reflection in the line $b\bar{z} + \bar{b}z + c = 0$.

5. Show that the equations

$$\left|\frac{z-a}{z-b}\right| = \lambda, \qquad \arg\frac{z-a}{z-b} = \alpha,$$

where λ and α are variable parameters, represent two orthogonal families of coaxal circles.

6. Prove that the homographic transformation

$$Z = \frac{\alpha z + \beta}{\gamma z + \delta},$$

where α, β, γ, δ are complex constants, turns circles in the z-plane into circles in the Z-plane, straight lines being regarded as degenerate circles.

7. Prove that a homographic transformation is a one-to-one transformation of the complete z-plane into the complete Z-plane, which leaves the angle between any two intersecting curves unaltered. Show also that the cross-ratio of the affixes of four points

$$\frac{(z_1-z_2)(z_3-z_4)}{(z_1-z_3)(z_2-z_4)}$$

is invariant under a homographic transformation.

8. Show that every homographic transformation may be generated by an even number of inversions with respect to circles or straight lines.

9. Show that there are two points which are invariant with respect to a homographic transformation. Hence show that, if these invariant points are distinct, the transformation is expressible in the form

$$\frac{Z-z_1}{Z-z_2} = k\frac{z-z_1}{z-z_2},$$

where k is a constant, and that, if the invariant points are coincident, the transformation is

$$\frac{1}{Z-z_1} = \frac{1}{z-z_1} + b,$$

where b is a constant.

10. Determine the regions of the z-plane specified by

$$\left|\frac{z-a}{1-\bar{a}z}\right| < 1, \quad = 1, \quad \text{or} > 1,$$

where a is a constant of modulus less than unity.

11. Find the regions of the z-plane for which

$$\left|\frac{z-a}{z+\bar{a}}\right| < 1, \quad = 1, \quad \text{or} > 1,$$

where the real part of a is positive.

12. Show that the equation $(a\bar{z}+\bar{a}z)^2 = 2(b\bar{z}+\bar{b}z)+c$, where c is real, represents the most general parabola in the complex plane.

13. Two points, whose affixes are z_1 and z_2, move independently round an ellipse with a focus at the origin. Show that the region in which the

point of affix z_1/z_2 lies is bounded by a curve whose polar equation is

$$(1+r^2)(1-\epsilon^2)-2r(1-\epsilon^2\cos\theta) = 0,$$

where ϵ is the eccentricity of the ellipse. Sketch this curve and indicate the region in which z_1/z_2 must lie. What is the corresponding result for a parabola? [Oxford: Junior Scholarship, 1929.]

14. Prove that, in stereographic projection, straight lines in the plane correspond to small circles on the sphere which pass through the vertex of projection.

Show also that the great circles through the ends of a fixed diameter of a sphere project into a family of coaxal circles with real common points, and that the small circles whose planes are perpendicular to this diameter project into the orthogonal system of coaxal circles.

15. If $d\sigma$ be the element of length of a curve on the sphere $\xi^2+\eta^2+\zeta^2 = 1$ and ds the element of length of its stereographic projection on the plane $\zeta = 0$, prove that

$$ds = \frac{d\sigma}{1-\zeta}.$$

Hence show that stereographic projection maps a sphere conformally† on a plane.

16. Show that the points z_1, z_2 are the stereographic projections of the ends of a diameter of the Riemann sphere if $z_1\bar{z}_2 = -1$.

If the Riemann sphere be rotated through an angle θ about this diameter, prove that the corresponding transformation of the Argand plane is given by

$$\frac{z'-z_1}{z'-z_2} = (\cos\theta+i\sin\theta)\frac{z-z_1}{z-z_2}.$$

17. Prove that the necessary and sufficient condition that a transformation of the Argand plane correspond to a rotation of the Riemann sphere about a diameter is that it be of the form

$$z' = \frac{az-\bar{c}}{cz+\bar{a}}.$$

18. A rotation of the Riemann sphere about a diameter through the point of spherical polar coordinates $(1,\theta_0,\phi_0)$ moves the point $(1,\theta,\phi)$ to $(1,\theta',\phi')$. Prove that‡

$$\cot\tfrac{1}{2}\theta'\, e^{i(\phi'-\phi_0-\alpha)} = \frac{\cot\theta_0\cosec\alpha\cot\tfrac{1}{2}\theta\, e^{i(\phi-\phi_0+\alpha)}+i}{\cot\theta_0\cosec\alpha+i\cot\tfrac{1}{2}\theta\, e^{i(\phi-\phi_0+\alpha)}}.$$

Determine the relation between the angle of rotation and the parameter α.

† A method of mapping is said to be *conformal* if it preserves the angle of intersection of every pair of intersecting curves. See Chapter VI.
‡ $e^{i\psi}$ is here used as a convenient abbreviation for $\cos\psi + i\sin\psi$. See § 3.51.

CHAPTER II

THE CONVERGENCE OF INFINITE SERIES

2.1. Sets of points in the Argand plane

As we saw in the last chapter, we can describe properties of complex numbers in geometrical language by using the Argand diagram or the Riemann sphere. In the present chapter, we consider from this geometrical standpoint some of the properties of sets of complex numbers.

By a *neighbourhood* of a point z_0 in the Argand plane we mean the set of all points z such that $|z-z_0| < \epsilon$; we call ϵ the radius of this neighbourhood. Under the transformation $z' = 1/z$, the neighbourhood of the origin of radius ϵ becomes the set of all points z for which $|z| > 1/\epsilon$. Accordingly, we define a neighbourhood of the point at infinity to be the part of the z-plane outside a circle $|z| = R$. It should be observed that the portion of the Riemann sphere which corresponds to this neighbourhood of the point at infinity is the interior of the small circle cut off by the plane $\zeta = (R^2-1)/(R^2+1)$.

A point z_0 is said to be a *limiting point* of a set of points S in the Argand plane if every neighbourhood of z_0 contains a point of S distinct from z_0. For example, the points $\pm 1 + i$ are limiting points of the set of points of affix

$$(-1)^n + \frac{ni}{n+1} \quad (n = 1, 2, 3, \ldots),$$

whilst the point at infinity is a limiting point of the set of points of affix
$$n^2 + 2in \quad (n = 1, 2, 3, \ldots).$$

This definition implies that *every neighbourhood of a limiting point z_0 of a set of points S contains an infinite number of points of S*. For the neighbourhood $|z-z_0| < \epsilon$ contains a point z_1 of S distinct from z_0; next, the neighbourhood $|z-z_0| < |z_1-z_0|$ contains a point z_2 of S distinct from z_0, and so on indefinitely.

2.11. Closed and open sets of points

The limiting points of a set are not necessarily points of the set. For example, the limiting points $\pm 1 + i$ of the set of points of affix

$$(-1)^n + \frac{ni}{n+1} \quad (n = 1, 2, 3, \ldots)$$

are certainly not members of the set. If, however, every limiting point of the set belongs to the set, we say that the set is *closed*.

Limiting points are divided into two classes, *interior points* and *boundary points*. A limiting point z_0 of a set S is said to be an interior point if there exists a neighbourhood of z_0 which consists entirely of points of S.† A limiting point which is not an interior point is called a boundary point. Thus, if S consists of all points for which $|z| < 1$, points on the circle $|z| = 1$ are boundary points, whilst each point of the set is an interior point.

A set which consists entirely of interior points is said to be *open*. It should be observed that sets exist which are neither open nor closed; a simple set of this type consists of the point $z = 1$ and all points for which $|z| < 1$.

Example. Show that, if a set S' consists of all the limiting points of a given set S, then a limiting point of S' necessarily belongs to S'.

2.12. Jordan curves

The equation $\qquad z = x(t) + iy(t),$

where $x(t)$ and $y(t)$ are real continuous functions of the real variable t, defined in the range $t_0 \leqslant t \leqslant T$, determines a set of points in the Argand plane which we call a continuous arc. A point z_1 is said to be a multiple point of the arc if the equation $z_1 = x(t) + iy(t)$ is satisfied by more than one value of t in the given range.

A continuous arc without multiple point is called a *Jordan arc*. A simple example of a Jordan arc is the polygonal arc which consists of a finite chain of straight segments.

A continuous arc which has but one multiple point, a double point corresponding to the terminal values t_0, T of t, is called a *simple closed Jordan curve*. For example, the arc

$$z = \cos t + i \sin t,$$

where $0 \leqslant t \leqslant 2\pi$, is a simple closed Jordan curve, the double point‡ being $z = 1$, corresponding to $t = 0$ and $t = 2\pi$.

---

† This, of course, implies that z_0 belongs to S.

‡ It should, however, be observed that it is not a double point in the sense understood in the theory of higher plane curves.

2.13. Bounded sets

A set of points is said to be bounded if there exists a positive number K with the property that the inequality $|z| \leqslant K$ is satisfied by the affix z of each point of the set. If there exists no such number K, the set is said to be unbounded.

2.14. The definition of a domain

A set of points in the Argand plane is said to be *connex* if every pair of its points can be joined by a polygonal arc which consists only of points of the set. An open connex set of points is called an *open domain*. If we add to an open domain its boundary points, the resulting set is called a *closed domain*.

Two open domains which have no point in common are said to be separated. Obviously every polygonal arc which joins a point of an open domain to a point of another open domain separated from the first must contain boundary points of the sets.

2.15. The Jordan curve theorem

It is easily shown that the circle $|z| = 1$ divides the Argand plane into two separated open domains, namely the sets defined by the inequalities $|z| < 1$ and $|z| > 1$, which have the circle as common boundary. This result is a particular case of the Jordan curve theorem,† which states that *a simple closed Jordan curve divides the plane into two open domains which have the curve as common boundary.* One of these domains is bounded and is called the interior domain; the other is unbounded and is called the exterior domain.

The two domains into which the plane is divided by a simple closed Jordan curve C are distinguished by a simple analytical property. If a is a point of the exterior domain, $\arg(z-a)$ returns to its original value when z goes once round C. On the other hand, if b is a point of the interior domain, $\arg(z-b)$ increases by $\pm 2\pi$. If the increase is $+2\pi$, we say that z describes C in the positive or counter-clockwise sense.

Although the results we have just stated seem quite obvious,

† Jordan's original proof will be found in his *Cours d'Analyse*, **3** (Paris, 1887), 587. He assumed the truth of the theorem for a polygon.

their proof is extremely complicated and far too difficult to give here.† For the most part, we shall only use simple closed Jordan curves composed of straight lines and circular arcs, and we shall rely upon geometrical intuition, which does not, in fact, lead us astray. Actually the proofs of the theorem in these elementary cases are generally quite straightforward.

2.2. Nests of intervals and rectangles

The set of all real numbers x such that $a \leqslant x \leqslant b$ is called an *interval*. If we represent the real numbers by points on a straight line in the usual manner, this interval is represented by a segment of the line of length $b-a$, the end-points being included in the segment. It is convenient to use the same word, interval, for such a set of real numbers and for the corresponding segment on a line.

A sequence‡ of intervals $I_1, I_2,..., I_n,...$ is said to form a *nest*§ if each interval I_{n+1} consists only of points of I_n and if the length of I_n tends to zero as $n \to \infty$. We shall now show that *there is one and only one point which belongs to all the intervals of a nest.*

For suppose that the interval I_n consists of all points x such that $a_n \leqslant x \leqslant b_n$. Then, by the definition of a nest, $a_n \leqslant a_{n+1} < b_1$ for all values of n, and so the numbers a_n form a non-decreasing bounded sequence. Hence, as $n \to \infty$, a_n tends to a finite limit ξ. Moreover, since $a_n \leqslant a_{n+p}$ for every positive integer p, we see, by making $p \to \infty$, that $a_n \leqslant \xi$. Similarly we can show that b_n tends to a limit ξ', and that $b_n \geqslant \xi'$, for every finite value of n.

But since $b_n - a_n$ tends to zero by hypothesis, a_n and b_n must tend to the same limit ξ. We have thus shown that there exists a number ξ such that the inequality $a_n \leqslant \xi \leqslant b_n$ holds for every

---

† See P. Dienes, *The Taylor Series* (Oxford, 1931), 177–97; G. N. Watson, *Complex Integration and Cauchy's Theorem* (Cambridge, 1914), 3–16; M. H. A. Newman, *Topology of Plane Sets* (Cambridge, 1939).

‡ By a *sequence* we mean, throughout this book, a set of infinitely many objects which can be put into one-to-one correspondence with the set of positive integers.

§ This term is suggested in R. C. Young's translation of Knopp, *Theory and Application of Infinite Series* (London, 1928).

finite value of n. In other words, the point of coordinate ξ lies in every interval of the nest.†

A similar theorem is true of complex numbers; we state it in a geometrical form. A sequence of closed rectangles R_1, R_2,..., R_n,..., whose sides are parallel to the real and imaginary axes, is called a nest if each rectangle R_{n+1} consists only of points of R_n and if also the lengths of the sides of R_n tend to zero as $n \to \infty$. Then, as we shall now show, there is one and only one point which lies in all the rectangles of the nest.

Let us suppose that the rectangle R_n consists of all points of affix z such that

$$a_n \leqslant \mathrm{Rl}\, z \leqslant b_n, \qquad a'_n \leqslant \mathrm{Im}\, z \leqslant b'_n.$$

Then, by definition, we have

$$a_n \leqslant a_{n+1} < b_{n+1} \leqslant b_n, \qquad a'_n \leqslant a'_{n+1} < b'_{n+1} \leqslant b'_n,$$

where $b_n - a_n$ and $b'_n - a'_n$ both tend to zero as $n \to \infty$.

These conditions, however, imply that the intervals

$$a_n \leqslant x \leqslant b_n \quad (n = 1, 2, 3, ...)$$

form a nest. Hence there is exactly one point ξ on the real axis such that the inequality $a_n \leqslant \xi \leqslant b_n$ holds for all values of n. Similarly there is precisely one point $i\eta$ on the imaginary axis such that $a'_n \leqslant \eta \leqslant b'_n$ for all positive integers n. It follows that the point of affix $\xi + i\eta$ is the one and only point which lies in all the rectangles of the nest.

Example. $A_1 B_1 C_1$ is a triangle, which is divided into four congruent triangles by joining the mid-points of its sides. $A_2 B_2 C_2$ is one of these smaller triangles, chosen according to some definite rule. $A_3 B_3 C_3$ is obtained from $A_2 B_2 C_2$ in the same manner, and so on indefinitely. Prove that there is one and only one point which lies within or on all the triangles of this sequence.

2.21. The Bolzano-Weierstrass theorem

The fundamental property of bounded sets of points is contained in the theorem of Bolzano and Weierstrass, which runs

---

† It is necessary for the truth of the theorem that the end-points of an interval should belong to the interval. For example, if J_n denotes the set of points such that $0 < x < 1/n$, there is no point which belongs to all the sets $J_1, J_2, ..., J_n, ...$.

as follows. *If a set S is bounded and contains infinitely many points, then it possesses at least one limiting point.*[†]

By hypothesis, there exists a closed square R_0, with vertices $\pm K \pm iK$, to which every point of the set S belongs. The imaginary axis divides this square into two equal rectangles. One of these, regarded as a closed set, must contain an infinite number of points of S; if both do, we take the right-hand one. Again, the real axis divides the selected rectangle into two congruent squares. One of these squares, regarded as a closed set, contains an infinite number of points of S; if both do, we take the upper square.

In this way we obtain a closed square R_1, of side K, which is contained in R_0 and which contains an infinite number of points of S. We now treat R_1 in the same way. We divide R_1 into two congruent rectangles by a line parallel to the imaginary axis. One of these rectangles, regarded as a closed set, contains an infinite number of points of S; if both do, we take the right-hand one. The selected rectangle is then divided into two equal squares by a line parallel to the real axis. Again, one of these squares, regarded as a closed set, contains an infinite number of points of S; if both do, we take the upper one. We thus obtain a closed square R_2, of side $K/2$, which is contained in R_1 and which contains an infinite number of points of S. The square R_2 is then treated in the same manner, and so on indefinitely. The process never terminates since we never reach a square which contains only a finite number of points of S.

Now the squares R_0, R_1,..., R_n,... form a nest, since R_{n+1} consists only of points of R_n and the length of each side of R_{n+1} is $K/2^n$, which tends to zero as $n \to \infty$. Accordingly there exists one and only one point ζ which lies in all the squares of the nest; we now show that ζ is a limiting point of S. For if ϵ is any assigned positive number, we can choose an integer N such that the diagonal of the square R_N is less than ϵ; then the neighbourhood of ζ of radius ϵ contains the square R_N and hence contains an infinite number of points of S. This proves the theorem.

---

† Two proofs of this theorem for the case when all the points lie on a straight line will be found in Hardy, *Pure Mathematics* (1921), 30, 134. The proof given here in the two-dimensional case is similar to Hardy's second proof.

2.3. The convergence of complex sequences

A sequence of complex numbers $z_1, z_2, ..., z_n, ...$ is said to be convergent if the corresponding set of points in the Argand plane has one and only one limiting point, whose affix z is finite; when this is the case, the number z is called the limit of the sequence. We denote this symbolically by writing '$z_n \to z$ as $n \to \infty$', or $\lim_{n \to \infty} z_n = z$.

The definition implies that z is the limit of the sequence if and only if every neighbourhood of the point of affix z contains all but a finite number of points of affix z_n. In other words, *z is the limit of the sequence $z_1, z_2, ..., z_n, ...$ if, given any positive number ϵ, we can find an integer N such that the inequality $|z_n - z| < \epsilon$ holds for all integers $n \geqslant N$*. It follows that a convergent sequence is necessarily bounded.

A sequence which is not convergent is said to be divergent. A divergent sequence either has more than one limiting point, in which case it is said to oscillate, or else has a single limiting point at infinity.

If the points of the sequence $z_1, z_2, ..., z_n, ...,$ having a single limiting point at infinity, lie on a branch of a curve which has the line $\arg z = \alpha$ as asymptote, it is sometimes convenient to denote this fact by writing† $z_n \to \infty . e^{\alpha i}$. Thus $n + i/n \to +\infty$, and $1 + ni + 1/n \to 1 + \infty i$. This convention does not violate the postulate that there is but one point at infinity in the Argand plane; it is merely a simple way of specifying the manner in which the limiting point at infinity is approached.

2.31. Cauchy's principle of convergence

It can be easily shown that a sequence of complex numbers. $z_1, z_2, ..., z_n, ...$ is convergent if and only if the two sequences of real numbers $x_1, x_2, ..., x_n, ...,$ and $y_1, y_2, ..., y_n, ...,$ where $x_n = \mathrm{Rl}\, z_n$, $y_n = \mathrm{Im}\, z_n$, are convergent, and so theorems concerning the convergence of complex sequences can be deduced from the corresponding theorems for real sequences. It is, however, usually much more convenient to make use of Cauchy's principle of convergence, which runs as follows. *The necessary and sufficient condition for the convergence of a complex sequence $z_1, z_2, ..., z_n, ...$ is that, given any positive number ϵ, there should*

† $e^{\alpha i}$ is used here to denote $\cos \alpha + i \sin \alpha$.

exist an integer N, depending on ϵ, such that the inequality $|z_{N+p}-z_N| < \epsilon$ *holds for every positive integer p.*

The condition is necessary; for if $z_n \to z$, there exists an integer N, depending on the given number ϵ, such that the inequality $|z_n-z| < \frac{1}{2}\epsilon$ holds when $n \geqslant N$. Hence, if p is any positive integer, we have

$$|z_{N+p}-z_N| \leqslant |z_{N+p}-z|+|z_N-z| < \epsilon.$$

The condition is also sufficient. For if it is satisfied, the given sequence is bounded, since all save a finite number of its points lie in the neighbourhood of z_N of radius ϵ; hence, by the Bolzano-Weierstrass theorem, the sequence possesses at least one limiting point. Now if the sequence is not convergent, it must possess at least two finite limiting points, z' and z'', say. Accordingly, there exist integers q and r, depending on the given number ϵ, such that

$$|z'-z_{N+q}| < \epsilon, \qquad |z''-z_{N+r}| < \epsilon.$$

With these values of N, q, r, we have

$$|z'-z''| = |(z'-z_{N+q})+(z_{N+q}-z_N)-(z_{N+r}-z_N)-(z''-z_{N+r})|$$
$$\leqslant |z'-z_{N+q}|+|z_{N+q}-z_N|+|z_{N+r}-z_N|+|z''-z_{N+r}|$$
$$< 4\epsilon.$$

This is, however, impossible, since z' and z'' were supposed to be distinct limiting points of the sequence, whilst ϵ is quite arbitrary. Hence the sequence does not possess more than one limiting point; this completes the proof of the sufficiency of the condition.

Example 1. Determine the limiting points of the sequence of complex numbers

$$z_n = \left(1+\frac{1}{n}\right)\left(\cos\frac{n\pi}{\alpha} + i\sin\frac{n\pi}{\alpha}\right),$$

where α is (i) real and rational,
    (ii) real and irrational.

Example 2. If $z_n \to z$, $z'_n \to z'$, prove that $z_n+z'_n \to z+z'$, $z_n z'_n \to zz'$, and also that, if z' is not zero, $z_n/z'_n \to z/z'$.

2.32. The maximum and minimum limits of a sequence of real numbers

We shall now show that a sequence of real numbers x_1, x_2,..., x_n,... possesses a greatest and a least limiting point. In the cases when $x_n \to x$, $x_n \to +\infty$, $x_n \to -\infty$, the sequence has but one limiting point and there is nothing to be proved. Accordingly, we may restrict our attention to oscillating sequences.

Let us suppose, in the first place, that the sequence is bounded above, that is, there exists a real number K such that the inequality $x_n < K$ holds for all values of n. We now divide the real numbers into two classes L and R in the following manner. The number x belongs to R if there are only a finite number of members of the sequence greater than x, and belongs to L in the contrary case. Evidently the class R exists, since every number greater than K belongs to it.

Now if every real number belonged to the R class, all save a finite number of members of the sequence would be less than $-x$, no matter how large x was; but this would imply that $x_n \to -\infty$, which we are supposing is not the case. Hence the L class also exists.

Moreover, this classification of the real numbers satisfies the conditions for a Dedekind section, namely,

(i) every number belongs to L or R;

(ii) each class exists;

(iii) any member of L is less than any member of R.

Hence, by Dedekind's theorem,[†] there exists a real number ξ such that all numbers less than it belong to L and all numbers greater than it to R.

Now if ϵ is any positive number, $\xi + \frac{1}{2}\epsilon$ belongs to R; there are, therefore, only a finite number of members of the sequence greater than $\xi + \frac{1}{2}\epsilon$, and so $\xi + \epsilon$ is certainly not a limiting point. Hence the sequence does not possess a limiting point greater than ξ.

On the other hand, $\xi - \epsilon$ belongs to L; there are, therefore, an infinite number of members of the sequence between $\xi - \epsilon$ and $\xi + \epsilon$, and so ξ is a limiting point of the sequence.

We have thus shown that a sequence of real numbers, bounded above, possesses a greatest limiting point ξ. We call ξ the maximum limit of the sequence, and write

$$\xi = \overline{\lim} x_n.$$

If, however, the sequence is unbounded above, it is usual to write

$$\overline{\lim} x_n = +\infty.$$

† See Hardy, *Pure Mathematics* (1921), 29.

The minimum limit of the sequence, which is denoted by $\underline{\lim} x_n$, is defined by the equation

$$\underline{\lim} x_n = -\overline{\lim}(-x_n).$$

If $\underline{\lim} x_n$ has a finite value ξ', ξ' is the least limiting point of the sequence; but if $\underline{\lim} x_n = -\infty$, the sequence is unbounded below.

Finally, it is evident that the equation

$$\underline{\lim} x_n = \overline{\lim} x_n$$

holds only in the cases when $x_n \to x$, $x_n \to +\infty$ or $x_n \to -\infty$.

2.4. Infinite series

The symbol
$$a_0 + a_1 + a_2 + \ldots + a_n + \ldots,$$

which involves the addition of an infinite number of complex numbers, has, in itself, no meaning. In order to assign a meaning to the sum of such an infinite series, we consider the associated sequence of partial sums $s_0, s_1, s_2, \ldots, s_n, \ldots$, where

$$s_n = a_0 + a_1 + a_2 + \ldots + a_n.$$

If this sequence tends to a finite limit s, we say that the infinite series is convergent and that its sum is s; in this case, we write

$$\sum_{n=0}^{\infty} a_n = s.$$

But if the sequence of partial sums does not tend to a finite limit, we say that the infinite series is divergent.

The necessary and sufficient condition for the convergence of an infinite series is provided by Cauchy's principle of convergence. There are, however, numerous sufficient conditions which may be deduced from this general principle.

An alternative procedure is to make the theory of the convergence of complex series depend on the corresponding theory for real series, with which we shall assume the reader is acquainted.† For the sequence of partial sums $s_0, s_1, s_2, \ldots, s_n, \ldots$

---

† See, for example, Hardy, *Pure Mathematics* (1921), chapters 4, 8; Bromwich, *Theory of Infinite Series* (1926), chapters 1–4; Knopp, *Theory and Application of Infinite Series* (1928), chapters 3, 4, 9, 10.

of a complex series is convergent if and only if $\mathrm{Rl}\, s_n$ and $\mathrm{Im}\, s_n$ tend to finite limits, that is, if and only if the two real series

$$\sum_0^\infty \mathrm{Rl}\, a_n, \qquad \sum_0^\infty \mathrm{Im}\, a_n$$

are convergent.

2.41. Absolutely convergent series

An infinite series $\sum_0^\infty a_n$ of complex terms is said to be absolutely convergent if the series $\sum_0^\infty |a_n|$ is convergent. We now show that *absolute convergence implies convergence, but not conversely.*

Let us suppose that the series $\sum_0^\infty a_n$ is absolutely convergent, and let us write

$$s_n = a_0 + a_1 + a_2 + \ldots + a_n, \qquad \sigma_n = |a_0| + |a_1| + |a_2| + \ldots + |a_n|.$$

Then, given any positive number ϵ, we can find an integer N, depending on ϵ, such that the inequality

$$|\sigma_{N+p} - \sigma_N| < \epsilon$$

holds for every positive integer p. Now

$$
\begin{aligned}
|s_{N+p} - s_N| &= |a_{N+1} + a_{N+2} + \ldots + a_{N+p}| \\
&\leqslant |a_{N+1}| + |a_{N+2}| + \ldots + |a_{N+p}| \\
&= \sigma_{N+p} - \sigma_N.
\end{aligned}
$$

But, since $\sigma_{N+p} - \sigma_N$ is positive, this gives

$$|s_{N+p} - s_N| \leqslant |\sigma_{N+p} - \sigma_N| < \epsilon.$$

Hence, by Cauchy's principle of convergence, the absolutely convergent series $\sum_0^\infty a_n$ is convergent.

To complete the proof of the theorem, we need only observe that the series

$$\frac{i}{1} + \frac{i^2}{2} + \frac{i^3}{3} + \ldots + \frac{i^n}{n} + \ldots$$

is convergent, but not absolutely convergent.

The most important property of an absolutely convergent series is that its sum is not altered by changing the order of its terms in any manner, a property which is not possessed by non-

absolutely convergent series. This follows from the corresponding well-known theorem concerning real series.†

2.42. Sufficient conditions for absolute convergence

We shall now prove that *the series $\sum a_n$ of complex terms is
absolutely convergent if* $\overline{\lim} |a_n|^{1/n} < 1$, *but is divergent if*
$\overline{\lim} |a_n|^{1/n} > 1$. This test, which is due to Cauchy, is of great
importance in the theory of power series.

For if $\overline{\lim} |a_n|^{1/n} = 1 - 2c$, where $0 < c \leqslant \frac{1}{2}$, then the in-
equality $|a_n|^{1/n} \leqslant 1 - c$ is true for all save a finite number of
values of n. There exists, therefore, an integer M such that
$|a_n| \leqslant (1-c)^n$ when $n \geqslant M$.

If, now, σ_n denotes the nth partial sum of the series $\sum |a_n|$,
we have, when $n \geqslant M$,

$$|\sigma_{n+p} - \sigma_n| \leqslant (1-c)^{n+1} + (1-c)^{n+2} + \ldots + (1-c)^{n+p}$$
$$\leqslant \frac{(1-c)^{n+1} - (1-c)^{n+p+1}}{c} < \frac{(1-c)^{n+1}}{c}.$$

Since this last expression tends to zero as $n \to \infty$, we may assign
an arbitrary positive number ϵ and then choose an integer
$N (> M)$ such that the inequality $|\sigma_{N+p} - \sigma_N| < \epsilon$ is true for
all positive integers p. Hence, by Cauchy's principle of con-
vergence, the series $\sum |a_n|$ is convergent.

On the other hand, if $\overline{\lim} |a_n|^{1/n} = 1 + 2d$, where $d > 0$, the
inequality $|a_n|^{1/n} \geqslant 1 + d$ is true for an infinite number‡ of
values of n. This, however, implies that $|a_n| \geqslant (1+d)^n$ for an
infinite number of values of n, and so a_n does not tend to zero
as $n \to \infty$. Hence the series $\sum a_n$ is divergent.

Another test, which is somewhat easier to apply, is d'Alembert's ratio-test, which states that *the series $\sum a_n$ of complex
terms is absolutely convergent if* $\overline{\lim} |a_{n+1}/a_n| < 1$, *but is divergent
if* $\underline{\lim} |a_{n+1}/a_n| > 1$. The proof of this is left to the reader. It
should, however, be observed that d'Alembert's ratio-test is
definitely less powerful than Cauchy's nth root test. For, since§

$$\overline{\lim} |a_{n+1}/a_n| \geqslant \overline{\lim} |a_n|^{1/n} \geqslant \underline{\lim} |a_n|^{1/n} \geqslant \underline{\lim} |a_{n+1}/a_n|,$$

† See Bromwich, loc. cit. 71, or Knopp, loc. cit. 138–9.
‡ But not necessarily for all sufficiently large values of n.
§ For a proof of this inequality, see Bromwich, loc. cit. 421–2; Knopp, loc.
cit. 277–8.

a series $\sum a_n$ may be absolutely convergent in virtue of the fact that $\overline{\lim} |a_n|^{1/n} < 1$, even though $\overline{\lim} |a_{n+1}/a_n| > 1$; the series

$$1+a+b^2+a^3+b^4+...,$$

where $0 < |a| < |b| < 1$, is a case in point. A similar remark applies to the ratio-test for divergence.

If, however, $|a_{n+1}/a_n|$ tends to unity, d'Alembert's ratio-test fails. We may then have recourse to Raabe's test, which states that *the series $\sum a_n$ is absolutely convergent if*

$$\overline{\lim}\, n \left\{ \left| \frac{a_{n+1}}{a_n} \right| - 1 \right\} < -1.$$

For if the value of this maximum limit is $-1-2c$, where c is positive, the inequality

$$n \left\{ \left| \frac{a_{n+1}}{a_n} \right| - 1 \right\} \leqslant -1 - c$$

holds for all save a finite number of values of n, and so is certainly true when $n \geqslant N$, say. If we write this inequality in the form

$$c|a_m| \leqslant (m-1)|a_m| - m|a_{m+1}| \qquad (m = N, N+1, ..., n)$$

and add, we find that, when $n \geqslant N$,

$$c\{|a_N| + |a_{N+1}| + ... + |a_n|\} \leqslant (N-1)|a_N| - n|a_{n+1}| < (N-1)|a_N|.$$

But since $(N-1)|a_N|$ does not depend on n, the series $\sum |a_n|$ of positive terms has bounded partial sums and so is convergent. Hence $\sum a_n$ is absolutely convergent.

The three tests for absolute convergence given in this section will be found quite adequate to deal with the series used in this book. For a discussion of more refined tests, we refer the reader to the works of Bromwich and Knopp already cited.

2.43. A test for non-absolute convergence

Of the various sufficient conditions for the convergence of a series of complex terms which does not converge absolutely, the following test, due to Dedekind, is one of the most important. *The series $\sum a_n v_n$ is convergent if*

   (i) *the series $\sum a_n$ has bounded partial sums,*

   (ii) *the series $\sum (v_n - v_{n+1})$ is absolutely convergent; and*

   (iii) $v_n \to 0$ *as* $n \to \infty$.

This test is closely related to the tests of Abel and Dirichlet for real series,† and its proof, like theirs, depends on Abel's method of partial summation.

Let us write
$$s_n = a_0 + a_1 + \ldots + a_n,$$
$$S_n = a_0 v_0 + a_1 v_1 + \ldots + a_n v_n.$$

Then there exists, by hypothesis, a constant K such that $|s_n| < K$, for all values of n.

Now if p is any positive integer, we obtain by partial summation

$$
\begin{aligned}
S_{n+p} - S_n &= a_{n+1} v_{n+1} + a_{n+2} v_{n+2} + \ldots + a_{n+p} v_{n+p} \\
&= (s_{n+1} - s_n) v_{n+1} + (s_{n+2} - s_{n+1}) v_{n+2} + \ldots + \\
&\qquad\qquad\qquad\qquad + (s_{n+p} - s_{n+p-1}) v_{n+p} \\
&= -s_n v_{n+1} + \sum_{r=n+1}^{n+p-1} s_r (v_r - v_{r+1}) + s_{n+p} v_{n+p},
\end{aligned}
$$

and so

$$
\begin{aligned}
|S_{n+p} - S_n| &\leqslant K \left\{ |v_{n+1}| + \sum_{r=n+1}^{n+p-1} |v_r - v_{r+1}| + |v_{n+p}| \right\} \\
&\leqslant K \left\{ |v_{n+1}| + |v_{n+p}| + \sum_{r=n+1}^{\infty} |v_r - v_{r+1}| \right\}.
\end{aligned}
$$

But if ϵ is any given positive number, then, since $\sum |v_r - v_{r+1}|$ is convergent, we can find an integer N_1, depending on ϵ, such that

$$\sum_{r=n+1}^{\infty} |v_r - v_{r+1}| < \frac{\epsilon}{3K}$$

when $n \geqslant N_1$. Moreover, since v_n tends to zero, we can also find an integer N_2 such that $|v_n| < \frac{1}{3}\epsilon/K$ when $n \geqslant N_2$. Hence, if N is the greater of N_1 and N_2, we have

$$|S_{N+p} - S_N| < \epsilon$$

for every positive integer p, and so, by Cauchy's principle of convergence, the series $\sum a_n v_n$ is convergent.

Example. Show that, if $n \geqslant m$,
$$S_{n+p} - S_n = -(s_n - s_m) v_{n+1} + \sum_{r=n+1}^{n+p-1} (s_r - s_m)(v_r - v_{r+1}) + (s_{n+p} - s_m) v_{n+p},$$
in the notation of the previous section.

Deduce that the series $\sum a_n v_n$ is convergent if
  (i) the series $\sum a_n$ converges, and
  (ii) the series $\sum (v_n - v_{n+1})$ is absolutely convergent.

---

† Bromwich, loc. cit. 58–60; Knopp, loc. cit. 314–15.

2.5. Double sequences

A set of complex numbers $s_{m,n}$ where m and n take all positive integral values is called a *double sequence*. It is said to converge to the value s if, given any positive number ϵ, we can find an integer N, depending on ϵ, such that the inequality $|s_{m,n}-s| < \epsilon$ holds whenever m and n exceed N. The finite number s is then called the limit of the double sequence and is denoted by $\lim\limits_{m,n\to\infty} s_{m,n}$. A double sequence which does not converge is said to be divergent.

The fundamental theorem in the theory of double sequences is Stolz's principle of convergence, which may be stated as follows. *The necessary and sufficient condition for the convergence of the double sequence $s_{m,n}$ is that, given any positive number ϵ, there should exist an integer M depending on ϵ, such that the inequality $|s_{p,q}-s_{m,n}| < \epsilon$ holds whenever $p > m > M$ and $q > n > M$.*

The condition is obviously necessary. To show that it is also sufficient, we observe that it implies that the simple sequence $s_{1,1}, s_{2,2},..., s_{n,n},...$ converges to a finite limit s, say. Accordingly, there exists an integer N_1 such that $|s-s_{n,n}| < \frac{1}{2}\epsilon$ when $n > N_1$. But, by hypothesis, there also exists an integer N_2 such that $|s_{n,n}-s_{p,q}| < \frac{1}{2}\epsilon$ when $p > n > N_2$, $q > n > N_2$. Hence, if N is the greater of N_1 and N_2, we have $|s-s_{p,q}| < \epsilon$ when $p > N$, $q > N$, and so $s_{p,q}$ converges to the limit s.

It follows immediately from the definition that *if $s_{m,n}$ be a convergent double sequence for which both the repeated limits*

$$\lim_{m\to\infty}\left(\lim_{n\to\infty} s_{m,n}\right), \qquad \lim_{n\to\infty}\left(\lim_{m\to\infty} s_{m,n}\right)$$

exist, each repeated limit is equal to the limit of the double sequence.

For if s is the limit of the double sequence $s_{m,n}$, the inequality $|s_{m,n}-s| < \epsilon$ holds when m and n exceed a certain integer M. But since $\lim\limits_{n\to\infty} s_{m,n}$ exists, this gives

$$\left|\lim_{n\to\infty} s_{m,n}-s\right| \leqslant \epsilon$$

when $m > M$. This, however, implies that

$$\lim_{m\to\infty}\left(\lim_{n\to\infty} s_{m,n}\right) = s.$$

A similar argument shows that the other repeated limit is also equal to s.

The existence and equality of the repeated limits of a double sequence do not imply that the sequence is convergent. For instance, if

$$s_{m,n} = \frac{mn}{(m+n)^2},$$

both repeated limits are equal; but since

$$s_{n,n} = \tfrac{1}{4}, \qquad s_{2n,n} = \tfrac{2}{9},$$

the double sequence is not convergent. Again, the example

$$s_{m,n} = (-1)^{m+n}\left(\frac{1}{m} + \frac{1}{n}\right)$$

shows that a double sequence may be convergent even though neither repeated limit exists.

2.51. Double series

By a double series, we understand an array of complex numbers of the form

$$a_{0,0} + a_{0,1} + a_{0,2} + \dots$$
$$+ a_{1,0} + a_{1,1} + a_{1,2} + \dots$$
$$+ a_{2,0} + a_{2,1} + a_{2,2} + \dots$$
$$+ \quad . \quad . \quad . \quad . \quad .,$$

there being an infinite number of rows, each containing an infinite number of terms. Associated with such an array is the double sequence of partial sums

$$s_{p,q} = \sum_{m=0}^{p} \sum_{n=0}^{q} a_{m,n},$$

where p and q are positive integers. The double series is said to be convergent if the double sequence $s_{p,q}$ converges to a finite limit s. We then call s the sum of the series and write

$$s = \sum_{m,n=0}^{\infty} a_{m,n}.$$

A double series which is not convergent is said to be divergent.

If the repeated limit

$$\lim_{p\to\infty}\left(\lim_{q\to\infty} s_{p,q}\right) = \sum_{m=0}^{\infty}\left(\sum_{n=0}^{\infty} a_{m,n}\right)$$

exists, its value is called the sum by rows of the double series. Similarly, if

$$\lim_{q\to\infty}\left(\lim_{p\to\infty} s_{p,q}\right) = \sum_{n=0}^{\infty}\left(\sum_{m=0}^{\infty} a_{m,n}\right)$$

exists, it is called the sum by columns. It follows from § 2.5 that *if a double series is convergent and is summable by rows and by columns, all three sums are equal.* (Pringsheim's theorem.)

Example. Prove that the sum of a convergent double series of positive terms can be obtained by summing by rows or by columns.

2.52. Absolutely convergent double series

A double series $\sum a_{m,n}$ of complex terms is said to be absolutely convergent if $\sum |a_{m,n}|$ is convergent. *An absolutely convergent double series is convergent.*

For if we denote by $\sigma_{p,q}$ the sum of the moduli of the terms which occur in $s_{p,q}$, then, by Stolz's principle of convergence, if we are given a positive number ϵ, we can find an integer N such that the inequality $0 < \sigma_{p,q} - \sigma_{m,n} < \epsilon$ holds when $p > m > N$, $q > n > N$. But since $|s_{p,q} - s_{m,n}| \leqslant \sigma_{p,q} - \sigma_{m,n}$, this gives $|s_{p,q} - s_{m,n}| < \epsilon$ when $p > m > N$ and $q > n > N$; hence the double series converges.

We shall now show that *an absolutely convergent series may be summed by rows or by columns.* For since

$$\sum_{s=0}^{n} |a_{r,s}| \leqslant \sum_{r,s=0}^{\infty} |a_{r,s}|,$$

no matter how large n may be, the series $\sum_{s=0}^{\infty} a_{r,s}$ converges absolutely; let us denote its sum by A_r. Then

$$\sum_{r=0}^{m} |A_r| \leqslant \sum_{r=0}^{m} \sum_{s=0}^{\infty} |a_{r,s}| \leqslant \sum_{r=0}^{\infty} \sum_{s=0}^{\infty} |a_{r,s}|,$$

no matter how large m may be. But this last expression is finite, since a convergent double series of positive terms can be summed by rows. Hence $\sum A_r$ is absolutely convergent, and so the sum by rows of $\sum a_{r,s}$ exists; similarly the sum by columns also exists. The required result now follows by Pringsheim's theorem (§ 2.51).

Example 1. The double series $\sum a_{r,s}$ is absolutely convergent with sum S. Show that, if

$$S_n = \sum_{r+s \leqslant n} a_{r,s},$$

then $S_n \to S$ as $n \to \infty$.

Example 2. Show that, if $\sum\limits_1^\infty a_n$ and $\sum\limits_1^\infty b_n$ are two absolutely convergent series with sums A, B respectively, then

$$\sum_1^\infty (a_1 b_n + a_2 b_{n-1} + \ldots + a_{n-1} b_2 + a_n b_1)$$

is absolutely convergent and has sum AB. (CAUCHY.)

REFERENCES

Theory of sets of points:

P. DIENES, *The Taylor Series* (Oxford, 1931), Chap. VI.

E. W. HOBSON, *Functions of a Real Variable*, **1** (Cambridge, 1921), Chap. II.

Convergence of infinite series of complex terms:

T. J. I'A BROMWICH, *Infinite Series* (London, 1926), Chap. X.

E. C. FRANCIS and J. E. LITTLEWOOD, *Examples in Infinite Series, with Solutions* (Cambridge, 1928).

K. KNOPP, *Theory and Application of Infinite Series* (Glasgow, 1928), Chap. XII.

Double Series:

T. J. I'A BROMWICH, loc. cit., Chap. V.

MISCELLANEOUS EXAMPLES

1. Show that the series $\sum z^n/n^\mu$ converges absolutely when $|z| < 1$ and also when $|z| = 1$ and $\mathrm{Rl}\,\mu > 1$, but that it diverges when $|z| > 1$.

Prove also that if $|z| = 1$, $z \neq 1$, the series converges, but not absolutely, when $0 < \mathrm{Rl}\,\mu \leqslant 1$; and that it diverges when $\mathrm{Rl}\,\mu < 0$.

Finally show that, when $z = 1$, the series converges only if $\mathrm{Rl}\,\mu > 1$, when it is absolutely convergent.

2. Prove that, if a_n is never zero and

$$\frac{a_{n+1}}{a_n} = 1 + \frac{\mu}{n} + \frac{\omega_n}{n^p},$$

where ω_n is bounded, $p > 1$, and μ is a complex constant, then $a_n n^{-\mu} \to l$ ($\neq 0$) as $n \to \infty$.

Hence show that the series $\sum a_n$ converges if and only if $\mathrm{Rl}\,\mu < -1$, and that it is then absolutely convergent.

3. Prove that the binomial series

$$1 + \nu z + \nu(\nu-1)\frac{z^2}{2!} + \nu(\nu-1)(\nu-2)\frac{z^3}{3!} + \ldots$$

converges absolutely when $|z| < 1$ and diverges when $|z| > 1$. Show also that, on $|z| = 1$, the series is absolutely convergent if $\mathrm{Rl}\,\nu > 0$, convergent if $-1 < \mathrm{Rl}\,\nu \leqslant 0$ and $z \neq -1$, and divergent if $\mathrm{Rl}\,\nu \leqslant -1$.

4. Show that the hypergeometric series

$$1 + \sum_{n=1}^{\infty} \frac{(\alpha)_n (\beta)_n}{(\gamma)_n . n!} z^n,$$

where $(\alpha)_n = \alpha(\alpha+1)(\alpha+2)...(\alpha+n-1)$, converges absolutely when $|z| < 1$ and also when $|z| = 1$ and $\text{Rl}(\gamma - \alpha - \beta) > 0$, but that it diverges when $|z| > 1$. Discuss also the convergence of the series on $|z| = 1$ when $\text{Rl}(\gamma - \alpha - \beta) \leqslant 0$.

5. Prove that, if $\sum a_n n^{-\mu}$ is convergent and $\text{Rl} z > \text{Rl} \mu$, then $\sum a_n n^{-z}$ is also convergent. Show by an example that the latter series is not necessarily convergent when $\text{Rl} z = \text{Rl} \mu$.

6. Show that, if

$$f(z,n) = \frac{z(z-1)(z-2)...(z-n+1)}{n!}$$

and z is not zero or a positive integer, the series $\sum a_n f(z,n)$ and $\sum a_n(-1)^n/n^{1+z}$ are either both convergent or both divergent.

7. Prove that, if

$$F(z,n) = \frac{n!}{z(z+1)(z+2)...(z+n)}$$

and z is not zero or a negative integer, the series $\sum a_n F(z,n)$ and $\sum a_n n^{-z}$ are either both convergent or both divergent.

8. Show that, if $A_n \to A$ as $n \to \infty$, then

$$(A_1 + A_2 + ... + A_n)/n \to A.$$

More generally, prove that, if $A_n \to A$, $B_n \to B$, then

$$(A_1 B_n + A_2 B_{n-1} + ... + A_n B_1)/n \to AB.$$

9. The series $\sum_1^{\infty} a_n$, $\sum_1^{\infty} b_n$ are convergent with sums A and B respectively. Show that, if

$$c_n = a_1 b_n + a_2 b_{n-1} + ... + a_{n-1} b_2 + a_n b_1,$$

and

$$C_n = c_1 + c_2 + ... + c_n,$$

then

$$\lim_{n \to \infty} (C_1 + C_2 + ... + C_n)/n = AB.$$

Deduce that, if $\sum_1^{\infty} c_n$ is convergent, its sum is AB. (Abel's theorem.)

10. Show that it is sufficient for the convergence of the series $\sum c_n$ of Ex. 9, that one of the series $\sum a_n$, $\sum b_n$ be absolutely convergent.† (Merten's theorem.)

† Compare the result of § 2.52, Ex. 2.

CHAPTER III

FUNCTIONS OF A COMPLEX VARIABLE

3.1. The definition of a function

WHEN we say that w is a function of the complex variable z, defined in a domain D of the Argand plane, we mean that we can calculate the value of w at each point z of D by a given rule or set of rules. For example, the greatest integer less than $|z|$ is a function of the complex variable z in this general sense.

This definition is, however, far too wide for our present purposes. For it implies that, if $z = x+iy$, then w is of the form $u(x,y)+iv(x,y)$, where u and v are real functions of the real variables x and y of the most general possible type. In the present chapter we consider how this definition may be modified so that the methods of the differential calculus of functions of a single real variable may also be applicable, as far as possible, to functions of a complex variable.

3.2. Continuous functions

A function $f(z)$, defined in a bounded closed domain D of the Argand plane, is said to tend to a limit l as z tends to a point z_0 of D along any path in D, if, given any positive number ϵ, no matter how small, we can find a number δ, depending on ϵ and z_0, such that the inequality

$$|f(z)-l| < \epsilon$$

holds for all points z of D, other than z_0, which belong to the region $|z-z_0| < \delta$. When this is the case, we write

$$\lim_{z \to z_0} f(z) = l.$$

This definition says nothing whatever about the value of $f(z)$ at z_0, and, in general, l need not be equal to $f(z_0)$. But if $f(z_0) = l$, we say that the function is continuous at z_0. In other words, *the function $f(z)$, defined in the bounded closed domain D, is said to be continuous at a point z_0 of D, if, given any positive number ϵ, we can find a number δ, depending on ϵ and z_0, such that the inequality*

$$|f(z)-f(z_0)| < \epsilon$$

holds at all points z of D in the neighbourhood $|z-z_0| < \delta$ of z_0.

If a function is continuous at every point of a bounded closed domain D, it is said to be continuous in D.

It should be observed that a function of the complex variable $z = x+iy$, continuous in a domain D, is necessarily a continuous function of x when y is constant and also a continuous function of y when x is constant. But continuity with respect to x and y separately does not imply continuity with respect to z. An instance of this is provided by the function

$$f(z) = xy/(x^2+y^2) \qquad (z \neq 0),$$
$$= 0 \qquad (z = 0),$$

which is a continuous function of x and y separately. But since $f(z) = m/(1+m^2)$ on the line $y = mx$, $f(z)$ is certainly not a continuous function of z at the origin.

Example 1. Show that the function defined by the equations

$$f(z) = \frac{xy^3}{x^2+y^6} \quad (z \neq 0), \qquad f(0) = 0$$

is discontinuous at the origin.

Example 2. Show that the function defined by the equations

$$f(z) = x^2/(x^2+y^2)^{\frac{1}{2}} \quad (z \neq 0), \qquad f(0) = 0$$

is continuous at the origin.

Example 3. The functions $f(z)$ and $g(z)$ are continuous at z_0. Show that $f(z)+g(z)$ and $f(z)g(z)$ are also continuous there. Prove also that $f(z)/g(z)$ is continuous at z_0 if $g(z_0)$ is not zero.

3.21. Uniform continuity

We have seen that, if $f(z)$ is continuous in the bounded closed domain D, then, given any positive number ϵ and any point z of D, we can find a positive number $\delta(\epsilon, z)$, depending on ϵ and z, such that the inequality

$$|f(z')-f(z)| < \epsilon$$

holds whenever z' is a point of D in the neighbourhood $|z'-z| < \delta(\epsilon, z)$ of the point z. In point of fact, there are an infinite number of such numbers $\delta(\epsilon, z)$; for if the property holds with $\delta(\epsilon, z) = \delta'$, say, it also holds when $\delta(\epsilon, z) < \delta'$. Let us now denote by $\Delta(\epsilon, z)$ the largest† of the numbers $\delta(\epsilon, z)$; it is a positive function of the complex variable z defined at each point of D.

† The existence of the largest of the numbers $\delta(\epsilon, z)$ is readily proved by means of a Dedekind section of the real numbers.

There are two possibilities regarding the behaviour of $\Delta(\epsilon, z)$ in the domain D. Either there exists a positive number $\eta(\epsilon)$, depending only on ϵ, such that the inequality $\Delta(\epsilon, z) \geqslant \eta(\epsilon)$ holds at every point of D, or else there exist points of D at which $\Delta(\epsilon, z)$ takes values as small as we please.

If the second alternative is true, we can find a sequence of points $z_1, z_2, ..., z_n, ...$ of D, for which $\Delta(\epsilon, z_n) < (\frac{1}{2})^n$. Since D is bounded, this sequence possesses at least one limiting point ζ, by the Bolzano-Weierstrass theorem; moreover, since D is closed, ζ is a point of D.

But since $f(z)$ is continuous at ζ, there exists a positive number δ such that the inequality

$$|f(z) - f(\zeta)| < \tfrac{1}{2}\epsilon$$

holds whenever z is a point of D in the region $|z - \zeta| < 2\delta$. Now let z be any point of D for which $|z - \zeta| < \delta$. Then, for all points z' of D such that $|z' - z| < \delta$, we have $|z' - \zeta| < 2\delta$, and so

$$|f(z') - f(z)| \leqslant |f(z') - f(\zeta)| + |f(\zeta) - f(z)| < \epsilon.$$

From this it follows that $\Delta(\epsilon, z) \geqslant \delta$, whenever z is a point of D in the neighbourhood $|z - \zeta| < \delta$ of the limiting point ζ. But this is impossible, since there are points of the sequence $z_1, z_2, ...$ in every neighbourhood of ζ. The second alternative is thus untenable.

We have thus shown that, *if $f(z)$ is continuous in the bounded closed domain D, then given any positive number ϵ, we can find a positive number $\eta(\epsilon)$, depending only on ϵ, such that the inequality $|f(z') - f(z)| < \epsilon$ holds for every pair of points z, z' of D for which $|z - z'| < \eta(\epsilon)$.* In other words, we can choose the number $\delta(\epsilon, z)$ so that it has the same value at each point of D. This property is usually stated in the following form: a function which is continuous in a bounded closed domain is *uniformly continuous* there.[†]

3.22. Bounded functions

A function $f(z)$, defined in a domain D, is said to be *bounded* in D if there exists a positive constant K such that the inequality $|f(z)| < K$ holds at each point z of D.

[†] For the equivalent theorem concerning functions of a real variable, see Hardy, *Pure Mathematics* (1921), 189–90 (Theorem II).

If $f(z)$ is continuous in a bounded closed domain D, it is bounded in D. For if not, we could find a sequence of points $z_1, z_2, ..., z_n, ...$ of D such that $|f(z_n)| \geqslant 2^n$, and this sequence would possess at least one limiting point ζ belonging to D. This is, however, impossible since $f(z)$ tends to a finite limit as $z \to \zeta$. Hence the result. It should be observed that this result is not necessarily true if the domain is not closed; for example, $1/(1-z)$ is continuous when $|z| < 1$, but is not bounded there.

3.23. The symbols O and o

The notation '$f(z) = O(1)$ as $z \to \alpha$' means that $f(z)$ is bounded in a neighbourhood of the point α; more precisely, there exist positive numbers A and δ, independent of z, such that $|f(z)| < A$ when $|z-\alpha| < \delta$. Similarly '$f(z) = O(1)$ as $z \to \infty$' means that $f(z)$ is bounded in a certain neighbourhood of the point at infinity.

If $f(z)/\phi(z) = O(1)$ as $z \to \alpha$, we shall sometimes write $f(z) = O(|\phi(z)|)$.

When, however, $f(z)/\phi(z)$ tends to zero as $z \to \alpha$, it is usual to write $f(z) = o(|\phi(z)|)$. Thus $z^2 = o(|z|)$ as $z \to 0$, but $z = o(|z|^2)$ as $z \to \infty$.

3.3. Differentiability

We shall now consider whether the definition of the derivative of a function of a single real variable is applicable in the theory of functions of a complex variable. If $f(z)$ is a one-valued function, defined in a domain D of the Argand plane, we say that $f(z)$ is differentiable at a point z_0 of D if the increment-ratio

$$\frac{f(z)-f(z_0)}{z-z_0}$$

tends to a finite limit as z tends to z_0 in any manner, provided that z always remains a point of D.

More precisely, we require that there should exist a number l with the following property: given any positive number ϵ, no matter how small, there must exist a positive number δ, depending on ϵ and possibly on z_0, such that the inequality

$$\left| \frac{f(z)-f(z_0)}{z-z_0} - l \right| < \epsilon$$

holds whenever z is a point of D in the neighbourhood $|z-z_0| < \delta$

of the point z_0. When this is the case, we call l the derivative of $f(z)$ at z_0, and denote it by $f'(z_0)$.

In order that a function should be differentiable at a certain point, it must be continuous there; for otherwise the increment ratio would certainly not tend to a finite limit. On the other hand, continuity does not imply differentiability. A simple instance of this is provided by the continuous function $|z|^2$, which is differentiable at the origin, but nowhere else. For when $z \neq z_0$ and $z_0 \neq 0$, we have

$$\frac{|z|^2 - |z_0|^2}{z - z_0} = \frac{z\bar{z} - z_0 \bar{z}_0}{z - z_0} = \bar{z} + z_0 \frac{\bar{z} - \bar{z}_0}{z - z_0}$$

$$= \bar{z} + z_0 (\cos 2\alpha - i \sin 2\alpha),$$

where $\alpha = \arg(z - z_0)$, and this expression does not tend to a unique limit as $z \to z_0$ in any manner; but when z_0 is zero, the increment ratio is $\bar{z}$, which tends to zero with z.

Example. Show that $|z|$ and $\arg z$ are not differentiable anywhere.

3.31. The definition of an analytic function

If a function is one-valued and differentiable at every point of a domain D of the Argand plane, save possibly for a finite number of exceptional points, we say that it is *analytic* in the domain D. The exceptional points are called the *singular points* or *singularities* of the function.

If, however, no point of D is a singularity of the analytic function, we then say that it is *regular* in D.

When we are dealing with functions which are analytic or regular in a domain, we shall often find it more convenient to use the ordinary notation

$$\frac{d f(z)}{dz}$$

for the derivative of $f(z)$, instead of $f'(z)$.

Example 1. Show that, if $f(z)$ and $g(z)$ are analytic functions, regular in a domain D, then $f(z) + g(z)$ and $f(z) g(z)$ are also regular in D, and that their derivatives may be calculated by the ordinary rules of the calculus.

Prove also that $f(z)/g(z)$ is regular in D, provided that $g(z)$ does not vanish there.

Example 2. Prove that, if w is a regular function of ζ, which is itself a regular function of z, then w is a regular function of z and

$$\frac{dw}{dz} = \frac{dw}{d\zeta}\frac{d\zeta}{dz}.$$

3.32. Polynomials and rational functions

One of the simplest analytic functions is z^n, where n is a positive integer. This function is regular in every bounded domain, and has derivative nz^{n-1}; for when $z \neq z_0$,

$$\frac{z^n - z_0^n}{z - z_0} = z^{n-1} + z^{n-2}z_0 + \ldots + zz_0^{n-2} + z_0^{n-1} \to nz_0^{n-1}$$

as $z \to z_0$. Similarly, we can show that z^{-n}, where n is a positive integer, is analytic in every bounded domain and has but one singularity, the origin; its derivative is $-nz^{-n-1}$.

By using the result of § 3.31, Ex. 1, we find that the function $a_0 + a_1 z + a_2 z^2 + \ldots + a_n z^n$, where n is a positive integer and the coefficients a_r are constants, is also an analytic function, regular in every bounded domain. Such a function is called a *polynomial* in z of degree n. It will be shown in § 6·21 that this polynomial is expressible uniquely in the form†

$$a_n(z - z_1)(z - z_2)\ldots(z - z_n),$$

where the numbers $z_1, z_2, \ldots, z_n$ are certain constants, depending only on the coefficients a_r. Since the polynomial vanishes when $z = z_r$, we call $z_1, z_2, \ldots, z_n$ the zeros of the polynomial.

The quotient of two polynomials is called a *rational function*. Such a function is also an analytic function, its only singularities being the zeros of the denominator.

3.33. Power series

An infinite series, proceeding in ascending integral powers of z, of the form

$$a_0 + a_1 z + a_2 z^2 + \ldots + a_n z^n + \ldots,$$

where the coefficients a_0, a_1, $a_2, \ldots$ are all constant, is called a *power series.*‡ By Cauchy's nth root test (§ 2.42), this series

---

† See also Hardy, *Pure Mathematics* (1921), 83, 433–7.
‡ The conclusions of this section will also be true of power series of the form $\sum\limits_{0}^{\infty} a_n(z - \alpha)^n$, the obvious changes being made.

converges absolutely when $\overline{\lim} |a_n z^n|^{1/n} < 1$ and diverges when $\overline{\lim} |a_n z^n|^{1/n} > 1$. Hence, if

$$\underline{\lim} |a_n|^{-1/n} = R,$$

the series is absolutely convergent when $|z| < R$ and divergent when $|z| > R$. The number R is called the *radius of convergence* of the power series; the circle $|z| = R$ is its *circle of convergence*.

There are three cases to be considered, viz. (i) $R = 0$, (ii) R finite, (iii) R infinite. The first case is quite trivial, since the series is then convergent only when $z = 0$. In the third case the series converges for every finite value of z.

We shall now show that, *if a power series has a non-zero radius of convergence, its sum is an analytic function regular within its circle of convergence.*

Let $f(z)$ be the sum of the power series $\sum_0^\infty a_n z^n$ which has a non-zero radius of convergence R. Obviously $f(z)$ is one-valued when $|z| < R$; we have to show that it is continuous and differentiable at every point of the domain $|z| \leqslant R_1$, where R_1 is any finite positive number definitely less than R.

Now choose a number R_2 such that† $0 < R_1 < R_2 < R$. If $|z| \leqslant R_1$ and $|h| \leqslant R_2 - R_1$, we have $|z+h| \leqslant R_2$, and so

$$f(z+h) - f(z) = \sum_0^\infty a_n (z+h)^n - \sum_0^\infty a_n z^n$$

$$= h \sum_1^\infty a_n \{(z+h)^{n-1} + (z+h)^{n-2} z + \ldots + \\ + (z+h) z^{n-2} + z^{n-1}\}.$$

From this, it follows that

$$|f(z+h) - f(z)| < |h| \sum_1^\infty n |a_n| R_2^{n-1}.$$

But this series of positive terms is convergent, since‡

$$\overline{\lim} \{n |a_n| R_2^{n-1}\}^{1/n} = \frac{R_2}{R} < 1.$$

Hence $$|f(z+h) - f(z)| < A |h|,$$

where A is independent of z and h, and therefore $f(z)$ is continuous when $|z| \leqslant R_1$.

---

† If R is infinite, it is conventional to interpret the inequality as meaning that R_2 is finite and greater than R_1.

‡ We use here the well-known result that $\lim\limits_{n \to \infty} n^{1/n} = 1$.

Now the increment ratio $\{f(z+h)-f(z)\}/h$ tends formally to $\sum_1^\infty na_n z^{n-1}$ as $h \to 0$. Accordingly, we consider the expression

$$I = \frac{f(z+h)-f(z)}{h} - \sum_1^\infty na_n z^{n-1} = \sum_1^\infty a_n \left\{ \frac{(z+h)^n - z^n}{h} - nz^{n-1} \right\},$$

where z and h satisfy the same conditions as before. By the use of the binomial theorem, we see that

$$\frac{(z+h)^n - z^n}{h} - nz^{n-1} = h \sum_2^n {}_nC_r z^{n-r} h^{r-2},$$

and so

$$\left| \frac{(z+h)^n - z^n}{h} - nz^{n-1} \right| \leqslant |h| \sum_2^n {}_nC_r |z|^{n-r} |h|^{r-2}$$

$$= |h| \sum_0^{n-2} {}_nC_{s+2} |z|^{n-s-2} |h|^s$$

$$\leqslant \tfrac{1}{2}n(n-1)|h| \sum_0^{n-2} {}_{n-2}C_s |z|^{n-s-2} |h|^s$$

$$= \tfrac{1}{2}n(n-1)|h|\{|z|+|h|\}^{n-2}$$

$$\leqslant \tfrac{1}{2}n(n-1)|h|R_2^{n-2}.$$

Hence $|I| \leqslant \tfrac{1}{2}|h| \sum_1^\infty n(n-1)|a_n|R_2^{n-2} = B|h|,$

say, where B is finite and independent of z and h, since the series $\sum n(n-1)|a_n|R_2^{n-2}$ is convergent. But this implies that I tends to zero with h. We have thus shown that

$$f'(z) = \sum_1^\infty na_n z^{n-1},$$

provided that $|z| \leqslant R_1$, where R_1 is any number less than the radius of convergence of the given power series. This completes the proof of the theorem.

Now, since $\varliminf |na_n|^{-1/n} = \varliminf |a_n|^{-1/n},$

the series $\sum na_n z^{n-1}$ has the same radius of convergence R as the series $\sum a_n z^n$ whose sum is $f(z)$. Hence, if we apply the theorem to the derived series, we see that $f'(z)$ is itself an analytic function, regular when $|z| < R$, and that its derivative is $\sum n(n-1)a_n z^{n-2}$; and so on. Thus the derivative of $f(z)$ of any order p is regular when $|z| < R$, and is given by the formula

$$\frac{d^p}{dz^p} f(z) = \sum_{n=p}^\infty {}_nC_p a_n z^{n-p}.$$

In other words, *a power series can be differentiated term by term as often as we please at any point within its circle of convergence.*

Example. Show that, if $|a_n/a_{n+1}| \to R$ as $n \to \infty$, then R is the radius of convergence of the power series $\sum a_n z^n$. (This result often provides a simple method of calculating the radius of convergence of a power series.)

3.4. The Cauchy-Riemann equations

We have just seen that the sum of a power series with a non-zero radius of convergence is an analytic function, regular within its circle of convergence. The converse theorem, that an analytic function, regular in a neighbourhood of a point z_0, can be expressed as a power series of the form

$$\sum_0^\infty a_n(z-z_0)^n$$

with non-zero radius of convergence, is also true, and will be proved in § 4.5. Thus the whole of the theory of analytic functions can be made to depend on power series.

For some purposes it is, however, more convenient to make use of an alternative method of defining analytic functions which depends on the theory of continuous functions of two real variables. We shall suppose that the reader is acquainted with the elements of this theory.†

Let us suppose that, when $z = x+iy$, the function $f(z)$ is expressed in the form $u(x,y)+iv(x,y)$, where u and v are real functions of the two real variables x and y. Now if $f(z)$ is differentiable at a given point z, the increment ratio $\{f(z+h)-f(z)\}/h$ tends to the limit $f'(z)$ as $h \to 0$. If we take h to be real, this implies that the expression

$$\frac{u(x+h,y)-u(x,y)}{h} + i\,\frac{v(x+h,y)-v(x,y)}{h}$$

tends to $f'(z)$ as $h \to 0$. Hence the two partial derivatives u_x, v_x must exist at the point (x,y), and the derivative is then given by

$$f'(z) = u_x(x,y)+iv_x(x,y).$$

---

† See, for example, Dockeray, *Elementary Treatise on Pure Mathematics* (London, 1934), Chap. VII; Gibson, *Advanced Calculus* (London, 1931), Chap. IV; Hardy, *Pure Mathematics* (Cambridge, 1921), 274–81; or Phillips, *Course of Analysis* (Cambridge, 1930), Chap. IX.

Similarly we find, by taking h to be purely imaginary, that u_y, v_y must exist at (x, y) and that

$$f'(z) = v_y(x, y) - iu_y(x, y).$$

The two expressions for $f'(z)$ so obtained must, however, be identical. Equating real and imaginary parts, we find that

$$u_x = v_y, \qquad u_y = -v_x.$$

These two relations are called the *Cauchy-Riemann differential equations*. We have thus shown that *for the function* $f(z) = u + iv$ *to be differentiable at* $z = x + iy$, *it is necessary that the four partial derivatives* u_x, v_x, u_y, v_y *should exist and satisfy the Cauchy-Riemann differential equations*.

That the conditions of this theorem are not sufficient is shown by considering the function† defined by the equations

$$f(z) = \frac{x^3(1+i) - y^3(1-i)}{x^2 + y^2} \quad (z \neq 0), \qquad f(0) = 0.$$

This function is continuous at the origin, and the four partial derivatives exist there and have values‡

$$u_x = 1, \qquad u_y = -1, \qquad v_x = 1, \qquad v_y = 1,$$

satisfying the Cauchy-Riemann equations; yet, as the reader will easily verify, the derivative $f'(0)$ does not exist.

3.41. Sufficient conditions for a function to be regular

We shall now show that *the continuous one-valued function* $f(z) = u + iv$ *is an analytic function of* $z = x + iy$, *regular in a domain* D, *if the four partial derivatives* u_x, v_x, u_y, v_y *exist, are continuous, and satisfy the Cauchy-Riemann equations at each point of* D.

Let $z = x + iy$ and $z' = x' + iy'$ be two points of D. Then, since u_x, u_y exist and are continuous, we have, by the mean-value theorem for functions of two variables,

$$u(x', y') - u(x, y) = \{u_x(x, y) + \epsilon\}(x' - x) + \{u_y(x, y) + \eta\}(y' - y),$$

---

† This example is due to Pollard, *Proc. London Math. Soc.* (2) **28** (1928), 159–60.

‡ It should be remembered that $u_x(0, 0)$ is, by definition, equal to

$$\lim_{x \to 0} \{u(x, 0) - u(0, 0)\}/x = \lim_{x \to 0} (x/x) = 1.$$

Similarly for the other derivatives.

where ϵ and η tend to zero as $z' \to z$. Similarly,

$$v(x',y')-v(x,y) = \{v_x(x,y)+\epsilon'\}(x'-x) + \{v_y(x,y)+\eta'\}(y'-y),$$

where ϵ' and η' also tend to zero. Hence, by the Cauchy-Riemann equations, we obtain

$$f(z')-f(z) = \{u_x(x,y)+iv_x(x,y)\}(z'-z)+\omega,$$

where

$$\omega = (\epsilon+i\epsilon')(x'-x)+(\eta+i\eta')(y'-y),$$

and so

$$\frac{f(z')-f(z)}{z'-z} = u_x+iv_x+\frac{\omega}{z'-z}.$$

Now

$$\left|\frac{\omega}{z'-z}\right| \leqslant (|\epsilon|+|\epsilon'|)\frac{|x'-x|}{|z'-z|}+(|\eta|+|\eta'|)\frac{|y'-y|}{|z'-z|}$$

$$\leqslant |\epsilon|+|\epsilon'|+|\eta|+|\eta'|.$$

Hence

$$\frac{f(z')-f(z)}{z'-z} \to u_x+iv_x$$

as $z' \to z$. Thus $f(z)$ is differentiable at each point of D; this completes the proof of the theorem.

Example. The function $f(z)$ is regular in a domain D, where its derivative is identically zero. Show that $f(z)$ is constant in D.

3.5. The exponential function

We now introduce the exponential, logarithmic, and trigonometric functions of a complex variable by means of power series. We shall assume that the reader is well acquainted with the properties of the corresponding functions of a real variable, and shall show how these properties can be extended into the complex domain.

The exponential function $\exp z$ is defined by the power series

$$\exp z = 1+\sum_{n=1}^{\infty}\frac{z^n}{n!}.$$

By using the ratio-test (§ 3.33, Ex.), we find that the radius of convergence of this power series is infinite. Hence $\exp z$ is an analytic function which has no singularities in any bounded domain in the z-plane.

When x is a real number, $\exp x$ is identical with the function e^x of elementary algebra. We shall often find it convenient to write e^z for $\exp z$, when z is complex, since $\exp z$ obeys the multiplication law

$$\exp z \, \exp z' = \exp(z+z'),$$

which is of the same form as the law of indices in algebra.

To prove this, we observe that, if we differentiate term by term, we find that the derivative of $\exp z$ is $\exp z$. Hence, if a be any finite constant, the derivative of the function

$$f(z) = \exp z \, \exp(a-z)$$

is identically zero, and so $f(z)$ is a constant whose value, $\exp a$, is found by putting $z = 0$. We have thus shown that

$$\exp z \, \exp(a-z) = \exp a,$$

or, writing z' for $a-z$, that

$$\exp z \, \exp z' = \exp(z+z').$$

This result is usually called the *addition theorem of the exponential function*.[†]

An important consequence of the addition theorem is that $\exp z$ never vanishes. For if $\exp z$ vanished when $z = z_1$, the equation

$$\exp z_1 \, \exp(-z_1) = 1$$

would give an infinite value for $\exp(-z_1)$, which is impossible.

3.51. The trigonometrical functions

It follows from the geometrical definition of the trigonometrical functions of an angle of circular measure x that[‡]

$$\sin x = \sum_{n=0}^{\infty} (-1)^n \frac{x^{2n+1}}{(2n+1)!}, \qquad \cos x = \sum_{n=0}^{\infty} (-1)^n \frac{x^{2n}}{(2n)!},$$

for all values of the real variable x. We now define the trigonometrical functions of a complex variable z by the equations

$$\sin z = \sum_{n=0}^{\infty} (-1)^n \frac{z^{2n+1}}{(2n+1)!}, \qquad \cos z = \sum_{n=0}^{\infty} (-1)^n \frac{z^{2n}}{(2n)!}.$$

Since the radius of convergence of each of these power series is infinite, $\sin z$ and $\cos z$ are analytic functions of z, regular in every bounded domain of the Argand plane. Moreover, we see

---

† The addition theorem can also be proved by using Cauchy's theorem on the product of two absolutely convergent series (§ 2.52, Ex. 2).

‡ See, for example, Hobson, *Plane Trigonometry* (Cambridge, 1911), 131–4.

at once by term-by-term differentiation that the derivatives of $\sin z$ and $\cos z$ are $\cos z$ and $-\sin z$.

The other trigonometrical functions are then defined by the equations

$$\tan z = \frac{\sin z}{\cos z}, \quad \cot z = \frac{\cos z}{\sin z}, \quad \sec z = \frac{1}{\cos z}, \quad \operatorname{cosec} z = \frac{1}{\sin z}.$$

Obviously $\sin z$, $\operatorname{cosec} z$, $\tan z$ and $\cot z$ are odd functions of z, $\cos z$ and $\sec z$ even functions.

If we use the result of § 3.31, Ex. 2, we find that $\tan z$ and $\sec z$ are analytic functions, regular in any domain in which $\cos z$ never vanishes, their derivatives being $\sec^2 z$ and $\sec z \tan z$ respectively. Similarly $\cot z$ and $\operatorname{cosec} z$ are regular in any domain in which $\sin z$ never vanishes and have derivatives $-\operatorname{cosec}^2 z$ and $-\operatorname{cosec} z \cot z$ respectively.

If we denote $\exp(iz)$ by e^{iz} in accordance with the convention of § 3.5, the equations defining the sine and cosine become

$$\sin z = (e^{iz} - e^{-iz})/2i, \qquad \cos z = (e^{iz} + e^{-iz})/2.$$

From these formulae and the addition theorem for $\exp z$, it easily follows that the fundamental identity

$$\sin^2 z + \cos^2 z = 1$$

and the addition theorems

$$\sin(z+z') = \sin z \cos z' + \cos z \sin z',$$
$$\cos(z+z') = \cos z \cos z' - \sin z \sin z',$$

still hold when z is complex. As all the elementary identities of trigonometry are algebraical deductions from the fundamental identity and the addition theorems, these identities still hold for the trigonometrical functions of a complex variable.

Example. Prove that, if $z = x+iy$, where x and y are real,
$$e^z = e^x(\cos y + i \sin y).$$

3.52. The hyperbolic functions

When z is real, the hyperbolic functions are defined by the equations

$$\sinh z = \tfrac{1}{2}(e^z - e^{-z}), \quad \cosh z = \tfrac{1}{2}(e^z + e^{-z}), \quad \tanh z = \sinh z/\cosh z,$$
$$\operatorname{cosech} z = 1/\sinh z, \quad \operatorname{sech} z = 1/\cosh z, \quad \coth z = 1/\tanh z.$$

We now define the hyperbolic functions for all real or complex values of z by these equations, the symbol e^z being now interpreted as meaning the function $\exp z$.

The hyperbolic functions of the complex variable z are all analytic functions, and their derivatives have the same form as in the theory of the hyperbolic functions of a real variable. It should be observed that $\sinh z$ and $\cosh z$ are regular in every bounded domain. On the other hand, $\tanh z$ and $\operatorname{sech} z$ have singularities at the points where $\cosh z$ vanishes, and $\coth z$ and $\operatorname{cosech} z$ at the points where $\sinh z$ vanishes.

The equations

$$\sin iz = i\sinh z, \qquad \cos iz = \cosh z,$$
$$\sinh iz = i\sin z, \qquad \cosh iz = \cos z,$$

which the reader will easily prove, are of great importance as they enable us to deduce the properties of the hyperbolic functions from the corresponding properties of the trigonometrical functions.

3.53. The zeros of $\sin z$ and $\cos z$

If $z = x+iy$, where x and y are real, we have

$$\sin z = \sin x \cosh y + i\cos x \sinh y,$$

and so $\sin z$ vanishes if and only if

$$\sin x \cosh y = 0, \qquad \cos x \sinh y = 0.$$

But since $\cosh y \geqslant 1$ when y is real, the first equation implies that $\sin x$ is zero, and so $x = n\pi$, where n is an integer or zero. The second equation then becomes $\sinh y = 0$, and this has but one root, $y = 0$, since $\sinh y$ increases steadily with y. We have thus proved that $\sin z$ vanishes if and only if $z = n\pi$, where n is a positive, zero, or negative integer. Moreover, by using the addition theorem for $\sin z$, we see that

$$\frac{\sin z}{z-n\pi} = (-1)^n \frac{\sin(z-n\pi)}{z-n\pi} = (-1)^n \sum_{r=0}^{\infty} (-1)^r \frac{(z-n\pi)^{2r}}{(2r+1)!}$$

which tends to $(-1)^n$ as $z \to n\pi$.

It follows that the only singularities of $\cot z$ and $\operatorname{cosec} z$ are at the points $z = n\pi$. The behaviour of these functions near a singularity is exhibited by the equations

$$(z-n\pi)\operatorname{cosec} z \to (-1)^n, \qquad (z-n\pi)\cot z \to 1$$

as $z \to n\pi$; the proof of this is left to the reader.

Similarly we can show that $\cos z$ vanishes if and only if $z = (n+\frac{1}{2})\pi$, where n is an integer or zero. It follows that the only singularities of $\tan z$ and $\sec z$ are at the points $z = (n+\frac{1}{2})\pi$, and that

$$\{z-(n+\tfrac{1}{2})\pi\}\tan z \to -1, \qquad \{z-(n+\tfrac{1}{2})\pi\}\sec z \to (-1)^{n+1}$$

as $z \to (n+\frac{1}{2})\pi$.

Example 1. Show that the only singularities of $\operatorname{cosech} z$ and $\coth z$ are at the points $z = n\pi i$, where n is a positive, zero or negative integer, and that, as $z \to n\pi i$,

$$(z-n\pi i)\operatorname{cosech} z \to (-1)^n, \qquad (z-n\pi i)\coth z \to 1.$$

Example 2. Prove that the only singularities of $\operatorname{sech} z$ and $\tanh z$ are at the points $z = (n+\frac{1}{2})\pi i$, where n is a positive, zero or negative integer, and that, as $z \to (n+\frac{1}{2})\pi i$,

$$\{z-(n+\tfrac{1}{2})\pi i\}\operatorname{sech} z \to i(-1)^{n+1}, \qquad \{z-(n+\tfrac{1}{2})\pi i\}\tanh z \to 1.$$

3.54. The periodicity of $\exp z$

The real or complex number γ is said to be a *period* of the function $f(z)$ if the equation $f(z+\gamma) = f(z)$ holds for all values of z. We shall now show that $\exp z$ *is a periodic function, its periods being* $2n\pi i$, *where n is an integer*.

For, if $\gamma = \alpha+i\beta$ be a period of $\exp z$, we have, by the addition theorem,

$$\exp z = \exp(z+\gamma) = \exp z \exp \gamma,$$

so that $\exp \gamma = 1$. But this equation, when written in the form $e^\alpha(\cos\beta+i\sin\beta) = 1$, implies that

$$e^\alpha \cos\beta = 1, \qquad e^\alpha \sin\beta = 0.$$

If we square and add, we find that $e^{2\alpha} = 1$, and so $\alpha = 0$. The number β is thus given by the equations

$$\cos\beta = 1, \qquad \sin\beta = 0.$$

Hence $\beta = 2n\pi$, where n is an integer. This proves the theorem.

3.55. The logarithmic function

When x is real and positive, the equation $e^u = x$ has one real solution, which is called the logarithm of x and is denoted by $\log x$. When, however, z is complex, the corresponding equation $\exp w = z$ has an infinite number of solutions, as we shall now show; each solution of this equation is called a logarithm of z.

To find the solutions of this equation we write $w = u+iv$, where u and v are real, so that

$$e^u(\cos v + i \sin v) = z.$$

From this it follows that v is one of the values of $\arg z$, whilst $e^u = |z|$ and so $u = \log |z|$. Every solution of the equation is thus of the form

$$w = \log |z| + i \arg z.$$

Since $\arg z$ has an infinite number of values, there are an infinite number of logarithms of the complex number z, each pair differing by a multiple of $2\pi i$.

We shall write

$$\text{Log } z = \log |z| + i \arg z,$$

so that $\text{Log } z$ is a function with an infinite number of values corresponding to each value of z. Each determination of $\text{Log } z$, obtained by making a special choice of the many-valued function $\arg z$, is called a branch of the logarithm. The most important branch is the *principal value of the logarithm of z*, which is obtained by giving to $\arg z$ its principal value. We shall denote this principal value by $\log z$, since it is identical with the ordinary logarithm when z is real and positive.

Now the function $\log |z|$ is continuous except at the origin; but as $z \to 0$, $\log |z| \to -\infty$. Again the principal value of $\arg z$ is continuous except at points on the negative half of the real axis; for, if $x < 0$, $y > 0$, we have

$$\lim_{y \to 0} \arg(x+iy) = \pi \qquad \lim_{y \to 0} \arg(x-iy) = -\pi$$

Hence, if $z \neq 0$ and $z' \to z$ along any path which does not cross the negative half of the real axis, then $\log z' \to \log z$. But if the path from z' to z crosses the negative half of the real axis once, $\log z' \to \log z \pm 2\pi i$, where the sign is $+$ or $-$ according as the path crosses from above to below or from below to above. Thus we can pass from the principal value to any other branch of $\text{Log } z$ by making a sufficient number of circuits about the origin. For this reason, the origin is called the *branch point* of $\text{Log } z$.

To avoid this difficulty, we now make a *cut* along the real axis from $-\infty$ to 0, across which it is impossible to pass. Then, if D is any bounded domain in this cut plane which does not possess the origin as boundary point, $\log z$ is one-valued and continuous in D. If z and z' are any two points of D and if w and w' denote $\log z$ and $\log z'$ respectively, then $w' \to w$ as $z' \to z$ along any path in D. Hence

$$\frac{w'-w}{z'-z} = \frac{w'-w}{\exp w' - \exp w} = 1 \bigg/ \frac{\exp w' - \exp w}{w'-w}$$

$$\to 1/\exp w = 1/z$$

as $z' \to z$. Thus $\log z$ is an analytic function, regular in D, which has the function $1/z$ for derivative.

Example 1. Prove that a value of the logarithm of zz' is $\log z + \log z'$, but that this is not necessarily the principal value.

Example 2. Show that $\log(1-z^2)$ is a regular analytic function provided that the z-plane is cut along the real axis from $-\infty$ to -1 and from $+1$ to $+\infty$. Discuss how the function behaves when circuits are made about the points 1 and -1.

3.56. The power series for $\log(1+z)$

We have just seen that $\log(1+z)$ is an analytic function which is regular in the z-plane, supposed cut along the real axis from $-\infty$ to -1, and which has derivative $1/(1+z)$. In the region $|z| < 1$ this derivative can be expanded as a convergent power series

$$1-z+z^2-z^3+\dots.$$

But, by § 3.33, the sum of this power series is the derivative of the function

$$f(z) = z - \frac{z^2}{2} + \frac{z^3}{3} - \dots + (-1)^n \frac{z^{n+1}}{n+1} + \dots$$

whenever the latter series converges.

Now the radius of convergence of the power series defining $f(z)$ is unity. Hence

$$F(z) = f(z) - \log(1+z)$$

is an analytic function which is regular and has zero derivative when $|z| < 1$. It follows that $F(z)$ is a constant, whose value is found to be zero by putting $z = 0$. We have thus shown that $\log(1+z)$ can be represented by a power series

$$\log(1+z) = z - \frac{z^2}{2} + \frac{z^3}{3} - \dots + (-1)^n \frac{z^{n+1}}{n+1} + \dots,$$

convergent when $|z| < 1$.

3.57. The function z^α

It follows from the definition of $\text{Log}\, z$ that, when p is any integer, the function $\exp(p\,\text{Log}\, z)$ is a one-valued function of z, being equal to z^p, even though $\text{Log}\, z$ is many-valued. If q is any other integer, the function

$$w = \exp\!\left(\frac{p}{q}\,\text{Log}\, z\right)$$

is, therefore, a solution of the equation $w^q = z^p$, so that we might denote any branch of it by $z^{p/q}$. We shall, however, reserve this notation for the principal value of w, namely

$$z^{p/q} = \exp\!\left(\frac{p}{q}\log z\right).$$

The other solutions of the equation are then of the form

$$w = z^{p/q}e^{2k\pi i/q},$$

where $k = 1, 2, 3, ..., q-1$. Obviously each of these solutions can be obtained from $z^{p/q}$ by making circuits about the branch-point 0 of $\log z$.

We now define z^α, for any real or complex value of α, by the equation
$$z^\alpha = \exp(\alpha \log z).$$

With this definition the law of indices still holds; for

$$z^\alpha z^\beta = \exp(\alpha \log z)\exp(\beta \log z) = \exp\{(\alpha+\beta)\log z\} = z^{\alpha+\beta}.$$

We saw in § 3.55 that $\log z$ is discontinuous on the negative half of the real axis, and that it suddenly decreases by $2\pi i$ as we cross this line from above to below. Hence, if $x < 0$ and $y > 0$, then

$$\frac{(x+iy)^\alpha}{(x-iy)^\alpha} \to e^{2\alpha\pi i}$$

as $y \to 0$; thus z^α is also discontinuous when z is real and negative, except in the case when α is an integer. It is, however, one-valued and continuous in every bounded domain D of the z-plane, supposed cut along the real axis from $-\infty$ to 0. Moreover, if we write the equation defining z^α in the form $z^\alpha = e^{\alpha\zeta}$ where $\zeta = \log z$, we see, by § 3.31, Ex. 2, that z^α is regular in D, its derivative being given by

$$\frac{dz^\alpha}{dz} = \frac{de^{\alpha\zeta}}{d\zeta}\frac{d\zeta}{dz} = \alpha e^{\alpha\zeta}\frac{1}{z} = \alpha z^{\alpha-1}.$$

Example 1. Show that it is not necessarily the case that

$$z_1^\alpha z_2^\alpha = (z_1 z_2)^\alpha.$$

Example 2. Determine the branches and branch-points of the function $(1-z^2)^{1/2}$.

REFERENCES

Power series:

T. J. I'A BROMWICH, *Theory of Infinite Series* (London, 1926), Chap. X.

P. DIENES, *The Taylor Series* (Oxford, 1931), Chap. V.

The exponential, logarithmic and trigonometrical functions:

G. H. HARDY, *Pure Mathematics* (Cambridge, 1921), Chap. X.

E. W. HOBSON, *Plane Trigonometry* (Cambridge, 1911), Chap. XV.

E. T. WHITTAKER and G. N. WATSON, *Modern Analysis* (Cambridge, 1920), Appendix.

MISCELLANEOUS EXAMPLES

1. If $$f(z) = \frac{x^3 y(y - ix)}{x^6 + y^2} \quad (z \neq 0), \qquad f(0) = 0,$$

prove that the increment ratio $\{f(z) - f(0)\}/z$ tends to zero as $z \to 0$ along any radius vector, but not as $z \to 0$ in any manner.

2. If $z = re^{\theta i}$, $f(z) = u + iv$, where r, θ, u, v are real and $f(z)$ is a regular analytic function, show that the Cauchy-Riemann differential equations are

$$\frac{\partial u}{\partial r} = \frac{1}{r}\frac{\partial v}{\partial \theta}, \qquad \frac{\partial v}{\partial r} = -\frac{1}{r}\frac{\partial u}{\partial \theta}.$$

3. Verify that the real and imaginary parts of $\log z$ satisfy the Cauchy-Riemann equations when z is not zero.

4. Prove that the function

$$f(z) = 1 + \sum_{n=1}^{\infty} \frac{\alpha(\alpha-1)\ldots(\alpha-n+1)}{n!} z^n$$

is regular when $|z| < 1$ and that its derivative is $\alpha f(z)/(1+z)$. Hence show that the derivative of $(1+z)^{-\alpha}f(z)$ is zero, and deduce that

$$f(z) = (1+z)^\alpha.$$

5. If n is any positive or negative integer or zero, and if $0 < \epsilon < \frac{1}{2}\pi$, prove that $|e^z/z^n|$ tends to infinity as z tends to infinity in the angle $-\frac{1}{2}\pi + \epsilon \leqslant \arg z \leqslant \frac{1}{2}\pi - \epsilon$, but that $|e^z/z^n|$ tends to zero as z tends to infinity in the angle $\frac{1}{2}\pi + \epsilon \leqslant \arg z \leqslant \frac{3}{2}\pi - \epsilon$.

6. Prove that, if n is a positive integer and $|z| \leqslant \frac{1}{2}n$,

$$n \log\left(1 + \frac{z}{n}\right) = z + f_n(z)$$

where $$|f_n(z)| \leqslant \frac{|z|^2}{n}.$$

Deduce that
$$\left(1+\frac{z}{n}\right)^n \to e^z$$

as $n \to \infty$, when z lies in any bounded domain of the z-plane.

7. Show that the general solution of the equation $z = \tan w$ is
$$w = \frac{1}{2i}\operatorname{Log}\frac{1+iz}{1-iz}.$$

Prove that each branch of this many-valued function is an analytic function, regular in the z-plane, supposed cut along the imaginary axis from $-\infty i$ to $-i$ and from i to ∞i, and that the derivative of each such branch is $1/(1+z^2)$.

Show also that, when $|z| < 1$, the principal branch is
$$w = z - \frac{z^3}{3} + \frac{z^5}{5} - \dots .$$

8. Prove that the conjugates of the complex numbers $\sin z$ and $\cos z$ are $\sin \bar{z}$ and $\cos \bar{z}$ respectively. Hence show that
$$|\sin z|^2 = \tfrac{1}{2}(\cosh 2y - \cos 2x), \qquad |\cos z|^2 = \tfrac{1}{2}(\cosh 2y + \cos 2x).$$

9. Prove that
$$\sinh|\operatorname{Im} z| \leqslant \left|\frac{\sin}{\cos}z\right| \leqslant \cosh(\operatorname{Im} z).$$

Deduce that $|\sin z|$ and $|\cos z|$ tend to infinity as z tends to infinity in either of the angles $\epsilon \leqslant \arg z \leqslant \pi - \epsilon$, $\pi + \epsilon \leqslant \arg z \leqslant 2\pi - \epsilon$, where $0 < \epsilon < \tfrac{1}{2}\pi$.

10. If $f(z) = u + iv$ is an analytic function, regular in a domain D where $f'(z)$ does not vanish, prove that the curves $u = $ constant, $v = $ constant form two orthogonal families.

Verify that this is the case when (i) $f(z) = z^2$, (ii) $f(z) = \sin z$.

CHAPTER IV

CAUCHY'S THEOREM

4.1. Rectifiable arcs

BEFORE discussing Cauchy's theorem on the integration of analytic functions of a complex variable, it is desirable to consider briefly how the length of a Jordan arc, whose equation is $z = x(t) + iy(t)$, where $t_0 \leqslant t \leqslant T$, may be defined. Let z_0, z_1, z_2,..., z_n be the points of this arc which correspond to the values t_0, t_1, t_2,..., t_n of the parameter t, where

$$t_0 < t_1 < t_2 < \ldots < t_{n-1} < t_n = T.$$

The polygonal arc which is obtained by drawing straight lines from z_0 to z_1, from z_1 to z_2, and so on, is of length

$$\Sigma = \sum_{r=1}^{n} |z_r - z_{r-1}|.$$

If Σ tends to a unique limit l as $n \to \infty$ and the greatest of the numbers $t_r - t_{r-1}$ tends to zero, we say that the arc is *rectifiable* and that its length is l.

It can be shown that the necessary and sufficient condition for a Jordan arc to be rectifiable is that the sums Σ should be bounded for all possible modes of subdivision of the range of values of the parameter.† In the present book, we shall, in general, be concerned only with rectifiable arcs of a more special type, namely Jordan arcs with continuously turning tangent. Such curves we shall call *regular arcs*. A regular arc is characterized by the fact that the derivatives $\dot{x}(t)$ and $\dot{y}(t)$ exist and are continuous over the whole range of values of t.

We shall now prove that *a regular arc is rectifiable* by showing that the sum Σ does, in fact, tend to the limit

$$\int_{t_0}^{T} \{\dot{x}^2 + \dot{y}^2\}^{1/2}\, dt.$$

The first step in the proof is to show that Σ can be made to

† Proofs of this are given, for example, by P. Dienes, *The Taylor Series* (Oxford, 1931), 199–201; E. W. Hobson, *Functions of a Real Variable* (Cambridge, 1921), **1**, 318–20; E. G. Phillips, *Course of Analysis* (Cambridge, 1930), 208–10.

differ by as little as we please from the sum

$$\Sigma_1 \equiv \sum_{r=1}^{n} |\dot{x}(t_r) + i\dot{y}(t_r)|(t_r - t_{r-1}),$$

by making the greatest of the numbers $t_r - t_{r-1}$ sufficiently small.

We start with the inequality

$$|\{|Z| - |Z'|\}| \leqslant |Z - Z'|$$

of § 1.32, which obviously implies that

$$|\{|Z| - |Z'|\}| \leqslant |\mathrm{Rl}(Z - Z')| + |\mathrm{Im}(Z - Z')|.$$

Hence we have

$$I_r \equiv |\{ |z_r - z_{r-1}| - |\dot{x}(t_r) + i\dot{y}(t_r)|(t_r - t_{r-1}) \} |$$
$$\leqslant |(x_r - x_{r-1}) - \dot{x}(t_r)(t_r - t_{r-1})| + |(y_r - y_{r-1}) - \dot{y}(t_r)(t_r - t_{r-1})|,$$

where x_r denotes $x(t_r)$, and so on.

Now, by the mean-value theorem of the differential calculus,

$$x_r - x_{r-1} = \dot{x}(\tau_r)(t_r - t_{r-1}), \qquad y_r - y_{r-1} = \dot{y}(\tau'_r)(t_r - t_{r-1}),$$

where τ_r and τ'_r lie between t_{r-1} and t_r, and so

$$I_r \leqslant (t_r - t_{r-1})\{|\dot{x}(\tau_r) - \dot{x}(t_r)| + |\dot{y}(\tau'_r) - \dot{y}(t_r)|\}.$$

But, by hypothesis, the functions $\dot{x}(t)$ and $\dot{y}(t)$ are continuous and hence also uniformly continuous. We can therefore assign arbitrarily a positive number ϵ, as small as we please, and then choose another positive number δ, depending only on ϵ, such that
$$|\dot{x}(t) - \dot{x}(t')| < \epsilon, \qquad |\dot{y}(t) - \dot{y}(t')| < \epsilon$$

whenever $|t - t'| < \delta$. If the greatest of the numbers $t_r - t_{r-1}$ is less than δ, we find that

$$I_r < 2\epsilon(t_r - t_{r-1}),$$

and hence that

$$|\Sigma - \Sigma_1| \leqslant \sum_{r=1}^{n} I_r < 2\epsilon \sum_{r=1}^{n} (t_r - t_{r-1}) = 2\epsilon(T - t_0).$$

Finally, by the definition of the integral of a continuous function, the sum Σ_1 tends to the limit

$$\int_{t_0}^{T} |\dot{x}(t) + i\dot{y}(t)| \, dt = \int_{t_0}^{T} \{\dot{x}^2 + \dot{y}^2\}^{1/2} \, dt,$$

as n tends to infinity and the greatest of the numbers $t_r - t_{r-1}$ tends to zero. Since, however, $|\Sigma - \Sigma_1|$ can be made as small as we please by making δ sufficiently small, Σ must also tend to the same limit. We have thus shown that a regular arc is rectifiable and that its length is

$$\int_{t_0}^{T} \{\dot{x}^2 + \dot{y}^2\}^{1/2} \, dt.$$

4.11. Contours

If AB and BC are two rectifiable arcs of lengths l and l' respectively, which have only the point B in common, the arc AC is evidently also rectifiable, its length being $l+l'$. From this it follows that a Jordan arc which consists of a finite number of regular arcs is rectifiable, its length being the sum of the lengths of the regular arcs forming it. Such an arc we call a *contour*.

By a *closed contour* we mean a simple closed Jordan curve which consists of a finite number of regular arcs. Obviously a closed contour is rectifiable.

4.12. Riemann's definition of integration

The fundamental operation of the calculus known as integration arises in two distinct ways. The determination of the indefinite integral may be regarded as the operation inverse to that of differentiation. But in the applications of the calculus to geometry or physics, it is the definite integral, defined as the limit of a sum, which is of importance. In the theory of functions of a complex variable we start with the definition of an integral as the limit of a sum, and, later on, deduce the connexion between the operations of differentiation and integration.

Although this definition of the definite integral had its origin in the work of the Greek mathematicians, it only attained a precise arithmetical form, satisfying modern standards of rigour, in the nineteenth century at the hands of Riemann.[†] We shall now explain Riemann's definition of an integral, not, indeed, in its original form, but in one more suited for our present purposes.

Let us consider a function $f(z)$ of the complex variable z, which is not necessarily analytic but which has a definite finite value at each point of a rectifiable arc L. Let the equation of this arc be $z = x(t) + iy(t)$, where $t_0 \leqslant t \leqslant T$. We subdivide this

---

[†] In his inaugural address of 1854 on trigonometric series. This is reprinted in his collected works (German edition (1876), 213–51).

arc into n smaller arcs by the points $z_0, z_1, z_2, ..., z_{n-1}, z_n \; (= Z)$, which correspond to the values

$$t_0 < t_1 < t_2 ... < t_{n-1} < t_n = T$$

of the parameter t, and then form the sum

$$\sum = \sum_{r=1}^{n} f(\zeta_r)(z_r - z_{r-1}),$$

where ζ_r is a point of L between z_{r-1} and z_r.

If this sum $\sum$ tends to a unique limit J as n tends to infinity and the greatest of the numbers $t_r - t_{r-1}$ tends to zero, we say that $f(z)$ *is integrable*† *from* z_0 *to* Z *along the arc* L, and we write

$$J = \int_L f(z)\, dz.$$

The direction of integration is from z_0 to Z, since the point of affix $x(t) + iy(t)$ describes the arc L in this sense when t increases. Thus the numbers Z, z_0 play in this theory much the same parts as the upper and lower limits in the definite integral of a function of a real variable. Nevertheless, we do not write

$$J = \int_{z_0}^{Z} f(z)\, dz;$$

for, as we shall soon see, the value of J depends, in general, not only on the initial and final points of the arc L but also on its actual form.

The complex integral of a function $f(z)$ along a rectifiable arc L, defined in this way, exists under quite general conditions, a sufficient, but not necessary, condition being that $f(z)$ should be continuous on L. There is no need whatever to assume that the derivatives $\dot{x}(t)$ and $\dot{y}(t)$ exist. We shall not, however, prove this general result,‡ but shall only consider in detail the case when L is a contour.

Example 1. If L is any rectifiable arc joining the points z_0 and Z, prove that

$$\int_L dz = Z - z_0, \qquad \int_L z\, dz = \tfrac{1}{2}(Z^2 - z_0^2).$$

---

† In particular, if L is a segment of the real axis, this definition reduces to the ordinary definition of the integral of a bounded function of a real variable.

‡ For a proof of this, see, for example, Watson, *Complex Integration and Cauchy's Theorem* (Cambridge, 1914), 17–25.

Both integrals exist since the integrand is, in each case, continuous on L.

In the first case, we have

$$\sum_{r=1}^{n} f(\zeta_r)(z_r - z_{r-1}) = \sum_{r=1}^{n} (z_r - z_{r-1}) = Z - z_0,$$

from which the result stated follows at once.

In the second, we have to find the limit of

$$\sum_{r=1}^{n} \zeta_r(z_r - z_{r-1}).$$

This is necessarily the same as the limits of

$$\Sigma_1 = \sum_{r=1}^{n} z_r(z_r - z_{r-1}), \qquad \Sigma_2 = \sum_{r=1}^{n} z_{r-1}(z_r - z_{r-1}),$$

and so is also the same as the limit of $\frac{1}{2}(\Sigma_1 + \Sigma_2)$. But

$$\tfrac{1}{2}(\Sigma_1 + \Sigma_2) = \tfrac{1}{2}\sum_{r=1}^{n}(z_r^2 - z_{r-1}^2) = \tfrac{1}{2}(Z^2 - z_0^2).$$

Hence
$$\int_L z \, dz = \tfrac{1}{2}(Z^2 - z_0^2).$$

It should be observed that in both these examples the value of the integral is independent of the path from z_0 to Z.

Example 2. If $f(z)$ is integrable along the two rectifiable arcs AB and BC which have only the point B in common, prove that $f(z)$ is integrable along the arc AC and that

$$\int_{AC} f(z) \, dz = \int_{AB} f(z) \, dz + \int_{BC} f(z) \, dz.$$

Example 3. If $f(z)$ is integrable along L, and if L' is the same arc described in the opposite sense, show that

$$\int_{L'} f(z) \, dz = - \int_{L} f(z) \, dz.$$

Example 4. If $f(z)$ and $g(z)$ are integrable along L, and a and b are constants, prove that

$$\int_L \{af(z) + bg(z)\} \, dz = a \int_L f(z) \, dz + b \int_L g(z) \, dz.$$

4.13. Integration along a regular arc

Let us suppose that $f(z)$ is continuous on the regular arc L whose equation is $z = x(t) + iy(t)$, where $t_0 \leqslant t \leqslant T$. We prove that $f(z)$ is integrable along L and that

$$\int_L f(z) \, dz = \int_{t_0}^{T} F(t)\{\dot{x}(t) + i\dot{y}(t)\} \, dt,$$

where $F(t)$ denotes the value of $f(z)$ at the point of L of parameter t.

In the notation of § 4.12 we have to consider the sum

$$\Sigma \equiv \sum_{r=1}^{n} f(\zeta_r)(z_r - z_{r-1}),$$

where ζ_r is a point of the arc between z_{r-1} and z_r. If τ_r is the parameter of ζ_r, τ_r obviously lies between t_{r-1} and t_r. Writing $F(t) = \phi(t) + i\psi(t)$, where ϕ and ψ are real, we find that

$$\Sigma = \sum_{r=1}^{n} \phi(\tau_r)(x_r - x_{r-1}) + i \sum_{r=1}^{n} \psi(\tau_r)(x_r - x_{r-1}) +$$
$$+ i \sum_{r=1}^{n} \phi(\tau_r)(y_r - y_{r-1}) - \sum_{r=1}^{n} \psi(\tau_r)(y_r - y_{r-1}).$$

We consider these four sums separately.

By the mean-value theorem of the differential calculus the first term is

$$\Sigma_1 \equiv \sum_{r=1}^{n} \phi(\tau_r)(x_r - x_{r-1}) = \sum_{r=1}^{n} \phi(\tau_r)\dot{x}(\tau_r')(t_r - t_{r-1}),$$

where τ_r' lies between t_{r-1} and t_r. The first step is to show that Σ_1 can be made to differ by as little as we please from

$$\Sigma_2 \equiv \sum_{r=1}^{n} \phi(t_r)\dot{x}(t_r)(t_r - t_{r-1})$$

by making the greatest of the numbers $t_r - t_{r-1}$ sufficiently small.

Now, by hypothesis, the functions $\phi(t)$ and $\dot{x}(t)$ are continuous. As continuous functions are necessarily bounded, there exists a positive number K such that the inequalities $|\phi(t)| \leqslant K$, $|\dot{x}(t)| \leqslant K$, hold when $t_0 \leqslant t \leqslant T$. Moreover, the functions are also uniformly continuous; we can, therefore, assign arbitrarily a positive number ϵ, as small as we please, and then choose a positive number δ, depending only on ϵ, such that

$$|\phi(t) - \phi(t')| < \epsilon, \qquad |\dot{x}(t) - \dot{x}(t')| < \epsilon,$$

when $|t - t'| < \delta$. Hence, if the greatest of the numbers $t_r - t_{r-1}$ is less than δ, we have

$$|\phi(\tau_r)\dot{x}(\tau_r') - \phi(t_r)\dot{x}(t_r)|$$
$$= |\phi(\tau_r)\{\dot{x}(\tau_r') - \dot{x}(t_r)\} + \dot{x}(t_r)\{\phi(\tau_r) - \phi(t_r)\}|$$
$$\leqslant |\phi(\tau_r)| \cdot |\dot{x}(\tau_r') - \dot{x}(t_r)| + |\dot{x}(t_r)| \cdot |\phi(\tau_r) - \phi(t_r)| < 2K\epsilon,$$

and therefore
$$|\Sigma_1 - \Sigma_2| < 2K\epsilon(T-t_0).$$

By the definition of the integral of a continuous function of a real variable, Σ_2 tends to the limit

$$\int_{t_0}^{T} \phi(t)\dot{x}(t)\, dt$$

as n tends to infinity and the greatest of the numbers $t_r - t_{r-1}$ tends to zero. Since, however, $|\Sigma_1 - \Sigma_2|$ can be made as small as we please by taking δ small enough, Σ_1 must also tend to the same limit. Similarly the other terms of Σ tend to limits.

Combining these results we find that Σ tends to the limit

$$\int_{t_0}^{T} (\phi\dot{x} - \psi\dot{y})\, dt + i \int_{t_0}^{T} (\psi\dot{x} + \phi\dot{y})\, dt = \int_{t_0}^{T} F(t)\{\dot{x}(t) + i\dot{y}(t)\}\, dt,$$

and so $f(z)$ is integrable along the regular arc L.

This result is not merely of theoretical importance as an existence theorem. It is also of practical use in that it reduces the problem of evaluating a complex integral to the integration of two real continuous functions of a real variable.

More generally, it can be shown without difficulty that, if $f(z)$ is continuous on a contour C, it is integrable along C, the value of its integral being the sum of the integrals of $f(z)$ along the regular arcs of which C is composed.

Example 1. Find the value of the integral of $1/(z-a)$ round the circle C, whose equation is $|z-a| = R$.

The parametric equation of C is $z = a + R\cos t + iR\sin t$, where t varies from 0 to 2π as z describes C once in the positive sense. Hence

$$\int_C \frac{dz}{z-a} = \int_0^{2\pi} \frac{1}{R\cos t + iR\sin t}(-R\sin t + iR\cos t)\, dt$$

$$= \int_0^{2\pi} i\, dt = 2\pi i.$$

Example 2. Show that the integral of $1/z$ along a semicircular arc from -1 to $+1$ has the value $-\pi i$ or πi according as the arc lies above or below the real axis.

4.14. The absolute value of a complex integral

If $f(z)$ is continuous on a contour C of length l, where it satisfies the inequality $|f(z)| \leqslant M$, then

$$\left| \int_C f(z)\, dz \right| \leqslant Ml.$$

In proving this theorem we evidently only need to consider the case when C is a regular arc.

Now if $\phi(t)$ is any complex continuous function of the real variable t, we have

$$\left| \sum_{r=1}^{n} \phi(t_r)(t_r - t_{r-1}) \right| \leqslant \sum_{r=1}^{n} |\phi(t_r)|(t_r - t_{r-1}),$$

and so, on proceeding to the limit,

$$\left| \int_{t_0}^{T} \phi(t)\, dt \right| \leqslant \int_{t_0}^{T} |\phi(t)|\, dt.$$

In the notation of § 4.13, $f(z) = F(t)$ on C, and so $|F(t)| \leqslant M$. Hence

$$\left| \int_C f(z)\, dz \right| = \left| \int_C F(t)(\dot{x} + i\dot{y})\, dt \right|$$

$$\leqslant \int_{t_0}^{T} |F(t)|(\dot{x}^2 + \dot{y}^2)^{1/2}\, dt$$

$$\leqslant M \int_{t_0}^{T} (\dot{x}^2 + \dot{y}^2)^{1/2}\, dt = Ml.$$

4.2. Cauchy's theorem

Let $f(z)$ be an analytic function, regular in a simply connected domain D. Let z_0 and z_1 be two points of D, joined by a rectifiable arc L lying in D. Then the integral of $f(z)$ along L certainly exists since $f(z)$ is continuous on L. The fundamental property on which the theory of analytic functions depends is that the value of this integral is a function of z_0 and z_1 alone and is quite independent of the particular arc L which joins the two given points.

An equivalent form of this result is *Cauchy's theorem*, which states that, if C is a simple closed rectifiable arc lying in D, then the integral of $f(z)$ round C is zero. For any two points of C divide it into two rectifiable arcs L and L_1, say. If L_2 denotes the arc L_1 described in the opposite sense, the integrals of $f(z)$ along L and L_2 are equal. Hence we have, by § 4.12, Exx. 2, 3,

$$\int_C f(z)\,dz = \int_L f(z)\,dz + \int_{L_1} f(z)\,dz = \int_L f(z)\,dz - \int_{L_2} f(z)\,dz = 0.$$

In the sequel we shall always suppose that a simple closed rectifiable curve is described in the positive or counter-clockwise sense, unless the contrary is explicitly stated.

It is very difficult to prove Cauchy's theorem in its most general form. In the next section we make the additional assumption that the derivative $f'(z)$ is continuous within and on C and follow the lines of Cauchy's second proof.[†] We then show that this additional assumption is not necessary when the contour is a polygon, and, finally, we indicate briefly how the extension to the general case may be carried out.

4.21. The elementary proof of Cauchy's theorem

We now prove the simplest and original form of Cauchy's theorem, that *if $f(z)$ is an analytic function whose derivative $f'(z)$ exists and is continuous at each point within and on the closed contour C, then*

$$\int_C f(z)\,dz = 0.$$

Let D be the closed domain which consists of all points within and on C. If we write $z = x+iy$, $f(z) = u+iv$, where x, y, u, v are real, we have, by § 4.13,

$$\int_C f(z)\,dz = \int_C (u\,dx - v\,dy) + i\int_C (v\,dx + u\,dy),$$

where, by $\int_C (P\,dx + Q\,dy)$, we mean the sum of the integrals of the form $\int (P\dot{x} + Q\dot{y})\,dt$ over all the regular arcs composing C.

We now transform each of these curvilinear integrals by means of Green's theorem,[‡] which states that if $P(x,y)$, $Q(x,y)$,

---

[†] *Comptes Rendus*, **23** (1846), 251–5. This proof is often called Riemann's proof; he gave it in his inaugural dissertation at Göttingen in 1851 (*Ges. Werke* (1876), 3–46).

Cauchy's first proof depended on the calculus of variations. It occurs in his 'Mémoire sur les intégrales définies, prises entre limites imaginaires' (Paris, 1825), which has been reprinted in *Bulletin des sci. math.* **7** (1874), 265–304, **8** (1875), 43–55, 148–59.

[‡] See Gibson, *Advanced Calculus* (London, 1931), 335–6, or Phillips, *Course of Analysis* (Cambridge, 1930), 290–1.

$\partial Q/\partial x$, $\partial P/\partial y$ are continuous functions of both variables in D, then

$$\int_C (P\,dx + Q\,dy) = \iint_D \left(\frac{\partial Q}{\partial x} - \frac{\partial P}{\partial y}\right) dx\,dy.$$

By hypothesis $f'(z)$ exists and is continuous in D. Since, however,

$$f'(z) = u_x + iv_x \equiv v_y - iu_y,$$

we are, in fact, assuming that u and v and their partial derivatives u_x, v_x, u_y, v_y are continuous functions of both variables x and y in D. The conditions of Green's theorem are thus satisfied.

Hence we see that

$$\int_C f(z)\,dz = -\iint_D \left(\frac{\partial v}{\partial x} + \frac{\partial u}{\partial y}\right) dx\,dy + i\iint \left(\frac{\partial u}{\partial x} - \frac{\partial v}{\partial y}\right) dx\,dy$$
$$= 0,$$

by the Cauchy-Riemann differential equations. This completes the proof of Cauchy's theorem.

4.22. The general form of Cauchy's theorem

Although the simple form of Cauchy's theorem which we have just proved suffices for many of the applications we have in view, it is desirable to consider whether the assumptions we have made are necessary for the truth of the theorem. The first step in this direction was taken by Goursat,† who showed that it is unnecessary to assume the continuity of $f'(z)$, and that Cauchy's theorem is true if it is only assumed that $f'(z)$ exists at each point within or on the simple closed rectifiable curve C. Actually the continuity of the derivative $f'(z)$ and, indeed, its differentiability are consequences of Cauchy's theorem.

More generally still, it can be shown that *if $f(z)$ is an analytic function, continuous within and on the simple closed rectifiable curve C, and if $f'(z)$ exists at each point within C, then*

$$\int_C f(z)\,dz = 0.$$

We shall now indicate briefly the lines of the proof of this general form of Cauchy's theorem.

† *Trans. American Math. Soc.* **1** (1900), 14–16. Goursat's proof will also be found in his *Cours d'Analyse*, **2** (1918), 74–8.

The first step is to show that, if $f(z)$ is an analytic function whose derivative $f'(z)$ exists at each point within and on a triangular contour C, the integral of $f(z)$ round C vanishes. Let us write

$$\left| \int_C f(z)\, dz \right| = h,$$

so that $h \geqslant 0$. The proof consists in showing that we are led to a contradiction if we assume that $h > 0$.

Let us suppose, then, that $h > 0$. If we join the middle points of the sides of C by straight lines, the domain within C is divided into four congruent triangles whose boundaries are $\gamma_1, \gamma_2, \gamma_3, \gamma_4$, say. Then

$$\int_C f(z)\, dz = \sum_{r=1}^{4} \int_{\gamma_r} f(z)\, dz,$$

since, on the right-hand side, we are integrating twice in opposite directions over each side of a triangle γ_r which is not part of a side of C, and the corresponding integrals cancel. Hence we have

$$h \leqslant \sum_{r=1}^{4} \left| \int_{\gamma_r} f(z)\, dz \right|,$$

so that the inequality

$$\left| \int_{\gamma_r} f(z)\, dz \right| \geqslant \tfrac{1}{4} h$$

must hold for at least one value of r; if it holds for more than one value of r, we take the least. In this way we obtain a triangular contour, C_1, say, of half the linear dimensions of C, with the property that

$$\left| \int_{C_1} f(z)\, dz \right| \geqslant \tfrac{1}{4} h.$$

We now treat C_1 in the same manner, and so on indefinitely. Proceeding thus, we obtain a sequence of triangles $C, C_1, C_2, ..., C_n, ...$, each of which is contained in and has half the linear dimensions of its predecessor, with the property that

$$\left| \int_{C_n} f(z)\, dz \right| \geqslant h/4^n.$$

By the example of § 2.2 there is precisely one point, α say, which lies within or on every triangle of this sequence. Moreover, by hypothesis, $f(z)$ is regular at α. Hence, given any positive number ϵ, we can find a neighbourhood of α, whose radius depends on ϵ, in which the inequality

$$|f(z)-f(\alpha)-(z-\alpha)f'(\alpha)| < \epsilon|z-\alpha|$$

holds. This neighbourhood of α contains all the triangles of the sequence for which $n > N$, where N is an integer depending on ϵ. It follows that, if l_n is the perimeter of the triangle C_n, the inequality

$$|f(z)-f(\alpha)-(z-\alpha)f'(\alpha)| < \epsilon l_n$$

is satisfied by the affix z of every point on C_n, provided that $n > N$.

We know, however, that[†]

$$\int_{C_n} dz = 0, \qquad \int_{C_n} z\, dz = 0,$$

from which it follows that

$$\int_{C_n} f(z)\, dz = \int_{C_n} \{f(z)-f(\alpha)-(z-\alpha)f'(\alpha)\}\, dz.$$

Hence, when $n > N$, we have, by § 4.14,

$$\left|\int_{C_n} f(z)\, dz\right| = \left|\int_{C_n} \{f(z)-f(\alpha)-(z-\alpha)f'(\alpha)\}\, dz\right|$$
$$< \epsilon l_n^2 = \epsilon l^2/4^n,$$

where l is the perimeter of C.

We have thus shown that, when $n > N$,

$$0 < h \leqslant 4^n \left|\int_{C_n} f(z)\, dz\right| < \epsilon l^2.$$

This is, however, impossible, since ϵ is arbitrary; the assumption that h is positive is thus untenable. But since $h \geqslant 0$, we must, therefore, have $h = 0$. This completes the proof [‡] of Cauchy's theorem for a triangle within and on which the integrand is regular.

The next step is to extend this result to the case of a polygonal contour. We shall make use of the fact that the interior of any closed polygon can be divided up into a finite number of

---

† See § 4.12, Ex. 1.
‡ The proof is due to E. H. Moore, *Trans. American Math. Soc.* **1** (1900), 499–506.

triangles. For, if the polygon is not convex, it can be divided up into convex polygons by producing the sides sufficiently, and any convex polygon can be divided into triangles by joining any interior point to the vertices.

Let us suppose that $f(z)$ is an analytic function regular within and on a closed polygon C. If C is now divided up into n triangles whose boundaries are $C_1, C_2, ..., C_n$, we obtain

$$\int_C f(z)\, dz = \sum_{r=1}^{n} \int_{C_r} f(z)\, dz,$$

since, on the right-hand side, we are integrating twice in opposite directions over each side of a triangle C_r which is not also part of a side of C, and the corresponding integrals cancel. But we have shown that the integral of $f(z)$ round each triangular contour C_r vanishes, and so

$$\int_C f(z)\, dz = 0.$$

We have now reached the really difficult stage in the proof of Cauchy's theorem in the general form enunciated at the beginning of this section. We are given that $f(z)$ is regular within the simple closed rectifiable curve C and continuous within and on C. These conditions imply that $\int_C f(z)\, dz$ exists; we have to show that it is zero.

It can be proved that, when any positive number ϵ is assigned, a closed polygon P can be constructed, each point of which lies within C and at a distance less than ϵ from C. The derivative $f'(z)$ exists at every point within or on P, so that the integral of $f(z)$ round P vanishes. The general form of Cauchy's theorem would, then, be completely proved if we could show that

$$\lim_{\epsilon \to 0} \int_P f(z)\, dz = \int_C f(z)\, dz.$$

The validity of this passage to the limit is immediately suggested by geometrical intuition. Nevertheless, it is one of the most difficult things to prove in the whole of the theory of functions of a complex variable. A proof has been given by Pollard which depends on 'some rather delicate theorems of de la Vallée Poussin, the development of which requires great care and unusual nicety of thought'. We shall, therefore, con-

tent ourselves by relying on geometrical intuition for the validity
of this passage to the limit, and refer the reader to the original
memoirs† for the proof.

4.3. The deformation of contours

The evaluation of the integral of an analytic function round
a closed contour, within which the function is not necessarily
regular, can often be simplified by noticing that *the value of the
contour integral of an analytic function is unaltered by deformation
of the contour, provided that the contour crosses no singularity of
the integrand during deformation.*

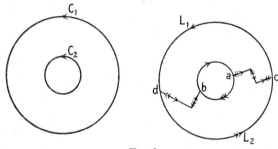

Fig. 1

For simplicity, we shall only consider a particular case of this
result, though the method of proof is quite general. We shall
show that *if C_1 and C_2 are two closed contours, C_2 lying completely inside C_1, then*

$$\int_{C_1} f(z)\, dz = \int_{C_2} f(z)\, dz,$$

*provided that $f(z)$ is continuous in the closed annulus and regular
in the open annulus bounded by C_1 and C_2.*

Let us take two points of affixes a and b on C_1 and two points
of affixes c and d on C_2. If we join a to c and b to d by two
polygonal arcs which have no point in common and which do
not cross C_1 or C_2, we form two closed contours L_1 and L_2, as
shown in the figure. Now $f(z)$ is continuous in the closed domain
and regular in the open domain bounded by L_1, and so its

† Pollard, *Proc. London Math. Soc.* (2) **21** (1923), 456–82; **28** (1928), 145–60.
See also Watson, *Complex Integration and Cauchy's Theorem* (Cambridge, 1914),
37–40.

integral round L_1 is zero; similarly for L_2. Hence

$$\int_{L_1} f(z)\,dz + \int_{L_2} f(z)\,dz = 0.$$

But L_1 and L_2 each contain the polygonal arc ac described twice in opposite senses, so that the two integrals along the arc ac cancel; similarly for the polygonal arc bd. Hence this last equation takes the form

$$\int_{C_1} f(z)\,dz - \int_{C_2} f(z)\,dz = 0,$$

when we take into consideration the conventional sense of description of the contour C_2.

4.31. Cauchy's integral formula

We now show that *if $f(z)$ is an analytic function, regular within a closed contour C and continuous within and on C, and if a is any point within C, then*

$$f(a) = \frac{1}{2\pi i} \int_C \frac{f(z)}{z-a}\,dz.$$

Since $f(z)$ is regular at a, we have

$$f(z) = f(a) + (z-a)f'(a) + (z-a)\eta,$$

where η is a function of z and a which tends to zero as $z \to a$. Hence, given any positive number ϵ, we can find a neighbourhood $|z-a| < \delta$ in which the inequality $|\eta| < \epsilon$ holds.

Now draw a circle γ with centre a and radius r, where r is less than δ and is also so small that γ lies entirely within C. Then, since $f(z)/(z-a)$ is regular in the annulus bounded by γ and C, we have, by the theorem of § 4.3,

$$\int_C \frac{f(z)}{z-a}\,dz = \int_\gamma \frac{f(z)}{z-a}\,dz$$

$$= f(a) \int_\gamma \frac{dz}{z-a} + f'(a) \int_\gamma dz + \int_\gamma \eta\,dz$$

$$= 2\pi i f(a) + \int_\gamma \eta\,dz.$$

From this we deduce that

$$\left| \int_C \frac{f(z)}{z-a}\, dz - 2\pi i\, f(a) \right| = \left| \int_\gamma \eta\, dz \right| < 2\pi r\epsilon,$$

since $|\eta| < \epsilon$ on γ. The expression on the right-hand side of this inequality tends to zero with r. The expression on the left-hand side is, however, quite independent of r and so must be identically zero.

This completes the proof of Cauchy's integral formula

$$f(a) = \frac{1}{2\pi i} \int_C \frac{f(z)}{z-a}\, dz,$$

which expresses the value of an analytic function at a point within a closed contour in terms of its values on the contour.

Example. Let C_1 and C_2 be two closed contours, C_2 lying completely within C_1, and let a be a point between C_1 and C_2. Show that

$$f(a) = \frac{1}{2\pi i} \int_{C_1} \frac{f(z)}{z-a}\, dz - \frac{1}{2\pi i} \int_{C_2} \frac{f(z)}{z-a}\, dz,$$

provided that $f(z)$ is continuous in the closed annulus and regular in the open annulus bounded by C_1 and C_2.

4.32. The derivatives of an analytic function

If it were known that the process of differentiating Cauchy's formula for $f(a)$ under the sign of integration is valid, we could deduce at once that

$$f'(a) = \frac{1}{2\pi i} \int_C \frac{f(z)}{(z-a)^2}\, dz.$$

We now show that this formula is true under the conditions of § 4.31.

Let us suppose that the shortest distance from a to the contour C is 2δ, so that the inequality $|z-a| \geqslant 2\delta$ is satisfied by the affix z of every point on C. If $|h| \leqslant \delta$, the point $a+h$ also lies within C at a distance not less than δ from C.

By Cauchy's integral formula, we have

$$\frac{f(a+h)-f(a)}{h} = \frac{1}{2\pi i} \int_C f(z)\left\{ \frac{1}{z-a-h} - \frac{1}{z-a} \right\} \frac{dz}{h}$$

$$= \frac{1}{2\pi i} \int_C \frac{f(z)}{(z-a-h)(z-a)}\, dz,$$

and so

$$\frac{f(a+h)-f(a)}{h} - \frac{1}{2\pi i} \int_C \frac{f(z)}{(z-a)^2} \, dz = \frac{h}{2\pi i} \int_C \frac{f(z)}{(z-a-h)(z-a)^2} \, dz.$$

Hence

$$f'(a) = \lim_{h \to 0} \frac{f(a+h)-f(a)}{h} = \frac{1}{2\pi i} \int_C \frac{f(z)}{(z-a)^2} \, dz,$$

provided that

$$\left| \int_C \frac{f(z)}{(z-a-h)(z-a)^2} \, dz \right|$$

is bounded as h tends to zero.

Now $f(z)$ is continuous on C, so that an inequality $|f(z)| \leqslant M$ is satisfied there. Hence

$$\left| \frac{f(z)}{(z-a-h)(z-a)^2} \right| \leqslant \frac{M}{4\delta^3}$$

when z is on C, and so

$$\left| \int_C \frac{f(z)}{(z-a-h)(z-a)^2} \, dz \right| \leqslant \frac{Ml}{4\delta^3}$$

where l is the length of C. This completes the proof of Cauchy's integral formula for $f'(a)$.

The result we have just proved has the very remarkable consequence that $f'(z)$ *is itself regular within* C. To prove this, we have to show that the derivative $f''(z)$ of the function $f'(z)$ exists at each point a within C.

Formal differentiation under the sign of integration gives

$$f''(a) = \frac{1}{\pi i} \int_C \frac{f(z)}{(z-a)^3} \, dz.$$

Accordingly we consider

$$\frac{f'(a+h)-f'(a)}{h} - \frac{1}{\pi i} \int_C \frac{f(z)}{(z-a)^3} \, dz$$

$$= \frac{1}{2\pi i} \int_C f(z) \left\{ \frac{1}{(z-a-h)^2} - \frac{1}{(z-a)^2} - \frac{2h}{(z-a)^3} \right\} \frac{dz}{h}$$

$$= \frac{h}{2\pi i} \int_C f(z) \frac{3(z-a)-2h}{(z-a-h)^2(z-a)^3} \, dz.$$

But it is easily seen by using the same type of argument as before that this last expression tends to zero with h. Hence

$$f''(a) = \lim_{h \to 0} \frac{f'(a+h)-f'(a)}{h}$$

exists and is given by

$$f''(a) = \frac{2!}{2\pi i} \int_C \frac{f(z)}{(z-a)^3}\, dz.$$

In a similar manner we can show that $f''(z)$ is regular within C, its derivative $f'''(z)$ being given by the formula

$$f'''(a) = \frac{3!}{2\pi i} \int_C \frac{f(z)}{(z-a)^4}\, dz,$$

when a is any point within C. And so on indefinitely. Hence *if $f(z)$ is an analytic function regular within a closed contour C and continuous within and on C, it possesses derivatives of all orders which are regular within C, the nth derivative being given by*

$$f^{(n)}(a) = \frac{n!}{2\pi i} \int_C \frac{f(z)}{(z-a)^{n+1}}\, dz.$$

Example. The function $f(z)$ is regular within a closed contour C. Show that, if $z = x+iy$, the functions $\log|f(z)|$, $\arg f(z)$, $\mathrm{Rl}\,f(z)$, $\mathrm{Im}\,f(z)$ all satisfy Laplace's equation

$$\frac{\partial^2 V}{\partial x^2} + \frac{\partial^2 V}{\partial y^2} = 0.$$

Prove also that
$$\left(\frac{\partial^2}{\partial x^2} + \frac{\partial^2}{\partial y^2}\right)|f|^2 = 4|f'|^2.$$

4.33. Cauchy's inequalities

Let $f(z)$ be an analytic function regular within a circle C of centre a and radius R. Then if the inequality $|f(z)| \leqslant M$ holds everywhere on C,

$$|f^{(n)}(a)| \leqslant \frac{Mn!}{R^n}.$$

We have proved that

$$f^{(n)}(a) = \frac{n!}{2\pi i} \int_C \frac{f(z)}{(z-a)^{n+1}}\, dz.$$

On C, $|f(z)/(z-a)^{n+1}| \leqslant M/R^{n+1}$, and the length of C is $2\pi R$. The result stated follows immediately by § 4.14.

Example. Prove that the modulus of an analytic function cannot have a true maximum at a point a if it is regular in a neighbourhood of a.

4.34. Liouville's theorem on integral functions

An analytic function which is regular in every finite region of the z-plane is called an *integral function*.

If $f(z)$ is an integral function which satisfies the inequality $|f(z)| \leqslant M$ for all values of z, M being a constant, then $f(z)$ is a constant.

This theorem† follows at once from Cauchy's inequality concerning the derivative of an analytic function. For, if a is any point of the z-plane, $f(z)$ is regular when $|z-a| \leqslant R$, no matter how large R may be, and satisfies there the inequality $|f(z)| \leqslant M$. Hence we have

$$|f'(a)| \leqslant \frac{M}{R}.$$

Making R tend to infinity, we find that $f'(a)$ is zero. Since, however, a is arbitrary, we have thus shown that the derivative of $f(z)$ vanishes everywhere. Hence $f(z)$ is a constant.

4.4. The converse of Cauchy's theorem

Let $f(z)$ be a one-valued function, continuous within a closed contour C. In order that the integral of $f(z)$ along any contour within C may depend only on the affixes of the end-points of that contour, it is both necessary and sufficient that $f(z)$ be an analytic function, regular within C.

The condition is evidently sufficient. For the difference between the integrals of $f(z)$ along two different contours, which lie within C and have the same end-points, is equal to the integral of $f(z)$ round a closed contour within C, and so vanishes.

To show that the condition is also necessary, we consider the integral of $f(z)$ along a path within C from a fixed point a to a variable point z. Since, by hypothesis, the value of this integral is independent of the path, it is a one-valued function of z; let us denote it by

$$F(z) = \int_a^z f(z)\, dz.$$

We shall show that $F(z)$ is an analytic function, regular within C.

† It was given by Liouville in lectures in 1847, but seems to be really due to Cauchy.

Let b be any point within C. If the shortest distance of b from C is 2δ, every point z for which $|z-b| \leqslant \delta$ certainly lies within C. Hence, if $|h| \leqslant \delta$,

$$F(b+h)-F(b) = \int_{b}^{b+h} f(z)\,dz,$$

where the path of integration is now taken to be a straight line. From this it follows that

$$\frac{F(b+h)-F(b)}{h}-f(b) = \frac{1}{h}\int_{b}^{b+h} \{f(z)-f(b)\}\,dz.$$

Now, by hypothesis, $f(z)$ is continuous at b. We can, therefore, assign arbitrarily a positive number ϵ, and then choose a positive number η, depending on ϵ, such that

$$|f(z)-f(b)| < \epsilon$$

when $|z-b| < \eta$. Hence we have, by § 4.14,

$$\left| \frac{F(b+h)-F(b)}{h}-f(b) \right| < \epsilon,$$

provided that $|h| < \eta$, and so $F'(b)$ exists and is equal to $f(b)$.

Since, however, b was any point within C, we have thus shown that $F(z)$ is regular inside C and that its derivative is $f(z)$. This, however, implies, by § 4.32, that $f(z)$ is itself regular within C. This completes the proof of the necessity of the condition.

The theorem we have just proved is due to Morera.† It is really a converse of Cauchy's theorem, and is more usually stated in the following form.

If $f(z)$ is continuous and one-valued within a closed contour C and if

$$\int_{\Gamma} f(z)\,dz = 0$$

for every closed contour Γ within C, then $f(z)$ is an analytic function, regular within C.

It should be observed that we have proved incidentally that *if $f(z)$ is regular within a closed contour C, the integral*

$$\int_{a}^{z} f(z)\,dz,$$

† *Rendiconti del R. Ist. Lombardo,* **19** (1886), 304–7.

taken along any contour within C, *is an analytic function, regular within* C, *and has derivative* $f(z)$. This is the fundamental theorem of the calculus of analytic functions; it asserts that the operations of integration and differentiation are inverse operations.

Example. Let $f(z)$, $g(z)$ be analytic functions, regular within a closed contour C. Show that

$$\int\limits_a^z f(z)g'(z)\, dz = f(z)g(z) - f(a)g(a) - \int\limits_a^z f'(z)g(z)\, dz,$$

when integration is along any contour within C.

4.5. Taylor's theorem

We saw in § 3.33 that the sum of a power series with non-zero radius of convergence is an analytic function, regular within the circle of convergence. We now prove the converse theorem, that *if* $f(z)$ *is an analytic function regular in a neighbourhood of* $z = a$, *it is expansible as a power series of the form* $\sum\limits_0^\infty a_n(z-a)^n$, *whose radius of convergence is not zero.*

By hypothesis, there exists a positive number R with the property that $f(z)$ is regular when $|z-a| < R$. Let R_1 be any positive number less than R, and let $R_2 = \frac{1}{2}(R+R_1)$, so that $0 < R_1 < R_2 < R$. Then $f(z)$ is certainly regular within and on the circle C whose equation is $|z-a| = R_2$.

Now let $a+h$ be any point of the region $|z-a| \leqslant R_1$. Then, as $a+h$ is within the circle C, we find, by using Cauchy's integral formula (§ 4.31), that

$$f(a+h) = \frac{1}{2\pi i} \int\limits_C \frac{f(z)}{z-a-h}\, dz$$

$$= \frac{1}{2\pi i} \int\limits_C f(z)\left\{\frac{1}{z-a} + \frac{h}{(z-a)^2} + \frac{h^2}{(z-a)^3} + \ldots + \right.$$

$$\left. + \frac{h^n}{(z-a)^{n+1}} + \frac{h^{n+1}}{(z-a)^{n+1}(z-a-h)}\right\}\, dz.$$

If we now use Cauchy's formula for the derivatives of an analytic function, we obtain

$$f(a+h) = f(a) + \sum_{r=1}^n f^{(r)}(a)\frac{h^r}{r!} + A_n,$$

where
$$A_n = \frac{h^{n+1}}{2\pi i} \int_C \frac{f(z)}{(z-a)^{n+1}(z-a-h)}\, dz.$$

But $|f(z)|$ is continuous on the circle C and so is bounded there. Hence there exists a positive number M such that $|f(z)| \leqslant M$ on C. Moreover, when $|z-a| = R_2$,
$$|z-a-h| \geqslant |\{|z-a|-|h|\}| \geqslant R_2-R_1.$$
Using the result of § 4.14, we find that
$$|A_n| \leqslant \frac{M|h|}{R_2-R_1}\left(\frac{|h|}{R_2}\right)^n.$$

Since, however, $|h| \leqslant R_1 < R_2$, it follows from this inequality that A_n tends to zero as n tends to infinity and therefore that
$$f(a+h) = f(a) + \sum_{n=1}^{\infty} f^{(n)}(a)\frac{h^n}{n!}.$$

It is, however, possible to prove rather more than the mere convergence of this power series. Since $|h| \leqslant R_1$, we have
$$|A_n| \leqslant \frac{MR_1}{R_2-R_1}\left(\frac{R_1}{R_2}\right)^n,$$

the expression on the right-hand side of the inequality being independent of h. Hence, given any positive number ϵ, we can choose an integer N, depending on ϵ but quite independent of h, such that $|A_n| < \epsilon$ when $n > N$. We express this property by saying that the power series converges uniformly† with respect to h when $|h| \leqslant R_1$.

We have now proved that *if $f(z)$ is an analytic function, regular in the neighbourhood $|z-a| < R$ of the point $z = a$, it can be expressed in that neighbourhood as a convergent power series of the form*
$$f(z) = f(a) + \sum_{n=1}^{\infty} f^{(n)}(a)\frac{(z-a)^n}{n!}.$$

This expansion is uniformly convergent when $|z-a| \leqslant R_1$, provided that $R_1 < R$. This result is known as Taylor's theorem concerning analytic functions of a complex variable.

---

† For an account of the theory of uniform convergence, see Chapter V.

Example 1. Prove that, when $|z| < 1$, the principal value of $(1+z)^\alpha$ is equal to

$$1 + \sum_{n=1}^{\infty} \frac{\alpha(\alpha-1)\ldots(\alpha-n+1)}{n!} z^n.$$

Example 2. Show that, when $|z| < 1$,

$$\log(1+z) = z - \frac{z^2}{2} + \frac{z^3}{3} - \ldots .$$

4.51. Zeros

If $f(z)$ is an analytic function which vanishes when $z = a$ and is regular in a neighbourhood $|z-a| < R$ of a, we say that a is a zero of $f(z)$. By Taylor's theorem we can expand $f(z)$ as a power series of the form

$$f(z) = \sum_{n=1}^{\infty} a_n(z-a)^n$$

which converges in the given neighbourhood of a and has no constant term. If a_m is the first non-zero coefficient in this expansion, we say that a is a zero of order m.

Let us suppose, then, that $f(z)$ has a zero of order m at a. We can therefore write

$$f(z) = (z-a)^m \sum_{n=0}^{\infty} a_{m+n}(z-a)^n = (z-a)^m\phi(z),$$

where $\phi(z)$ is regular when $|z-a| < R$ and does not vanish when $z = a$. We now show that there exists a neighbourhood of the point a which contains no other zero of $f(z)$.

For if $\phi(a) = 2c$, it follows from the continuity of $\phi(z)$ that there exists a region $|z-a| < \delta$ in which

$$|\phi(z)-\phi(a)| < |c|.$$

This implies that

$$|\phi(z)| \geqslant |\{\,|\phi(a)| - |\phi(z)-\phi(a)|\,\}| > |c|$$

when $|z-a| < \delta$, and so $\phi(z)$ certainly does not vanish there. Since $f(z) = (z-a)^m\phi(z)$, we have thus shown that the only point at which $f(z)$ vanishes in the region $|z-a| < \delta$ is the given zero $z = a$.

From this it follows that *if $f(z)$ is an analytic function regular in a domain D, and if $z_1, z_2, \ldots, z_n, \ldots$ is a sequence of zeros of $f(z)$ having as limiting point an interior point a of D, then $f(z)$ vanishes identically in D.*

For since $f(z)$ is a continuous function having zeros z_n as near a as we please, $f(a)$ must be zero. Moreover, as $f(z)$ is regular in the domain D, of which a is an interior point, we can expand $f(z)$ as a power series

$$f(z) = \sum_{n=1}^{\infty} a_n(z-a)^n,$$

converging in a certain neighbourhood of a. Either $f(z)$ is identically zero, or else there is a first coefficient, a_m say, in this power series which is not zero. But if the latter is the case, we have just seen that there is a neighbourhood of a which contains no zero other than a, and this is contrary to the hypothesis that a is a limiting point of the sequence of zeros $z_1, z_2,..., z_n,....$ Hence $f(z)$ is identically zero.

4.52. Laurent's theorem

Let us consider an analytic function $f(z)$ which is regular in the annulus $R < |z-a| < R'$ but not regular everywhere in $|z-a| < R'$. Although such a function cannot be expanded as a power series in $z-a$, it can be expressed, as we now show, as the sum of two series of the form

$$f(z) = \sum_0^{\infty} a_n(z-a)^n + \sum_1^{\infty} b_n(z-a)^{-n},$$

each series being convergent in the annulus.

Let R_1, R_1' be any two positive numbers such that $R < R_1 < R_1' < R'$ and let $R_2 = \frac{1}{2}(R+R_1)$, $R_2' = \frac{1}{2}(R'+R_1')$. Then $f(z)$ is certainly regular in the closed annulus bounded by the circles C, C' whose equations are $|z-a| = R_2$, $|z-a| = R_2'$ respectively.

Now let $a+h$ be any point of the annulus $R_1 \leqslant |z-a| \leqslant R_1'$. Then, as $a+h$ lies between the circles C and C', we have, by the example of § 4.31,

$$f(a+h) = \frac{1}{2\pi i} \int_{C'} \frac{f(z)}{z-a-h}\, dz - \frac{1}{2\pi i} \int_C \frac{f(z)}{z-a-h}\, dz.$$

Just as in the proof of Taylor's theorem, we easily show that

$$\frac{1}{2\pi i} \int_{C'} \frac{f(z)}{z-a-h}\, dz = \sum_0^{\infty} a_n h^n,$$

where
$$a_n = \frac{1}{2\pi i} \int_{C'} \frac{f(z)}{(z-a)^{n+1}} \, dz.$$

This series converges uniformly when $|h| \leqslant R_1'$. We cannot, however, write $f^{(n)}(a)/n!$ for a_n, since $f(z)$ is not regular everywhere within C'.

Similarly we have

$$-\frac{1}{2\pi i} \int_C \frac{f(z)}{z-a-h} \, dz$$

$$= \frac{1}{2\pi i} \int_C f(z) \left\{ \frac{1}{h} + \frac{(z-a)}{h^2} + \ldots + \frac{(z-a)^{n-1}}{h^n} - \frac{(z-a)^n}{h^n(z-a-h)} \right\} dz$$

$$= \sum_{r=1}^{n} \frac{b_r}{h^r} - B_n,$$

where
$$b_r = \frac{1}{2\pi i} \int_C f(z)(z-a)^{r-1} \, dz$$

and
$$B_n = \frac{1}{2\pi i} \int_C \frac{f(z)(z-a)^n}{h^n(z-a-h)} \, dz.$$

But if M denotes the greatest value, necessarily finite, of $|f(z)|$ on C, we have

$$|B_n| \leqslant \frac{M R_2}{|h|-R_2} \left(\frac{R_2}{|h|} \right)^n \leqslant \frac{M R_2}{R_1-R_2} \left(\frac{R_2}{R_1} \right)^n.$$

Thus B_n tends to zero as n tends to infinity, uniformly with respect to h when $|h| \geqslant R_1$, and so

$$-\frac{1}{2\pi i} \int_C \frac{f(z)}{z-a-h} \, dz = \sum_{n=1}^{\infty} \frac{b_n}{h^n},$$

the series being uniformly convergent when $|h| \geqslant R_1$. We have thus proved that

$$f(a+h) = \sum_0^{\infty} a_n h^n + \sum_1^{\infty} b_n h^{-n},$$

provided that $R_1 \leqslant h \leqslant R_1'$.

Changing the notation slightly, this result, which is known as *Laurent's theorem*,† can be expressed in the following form. *If $f(z)$ is an analytic function, regular in the open annulus*

---

† It was published by Laurent in *Comptes Rendus*, **17** (1843), 348–9.

$R < |z-a| < R'$, *it can be expressed there as a convergent series of the form*

$$f(z) = \sum_{-\infty}^{\infty} a_n(z-a)^n.$$

This expansion is uniformly convergent in the closed annulus $R_1 \leqslant |z-a| \leqslant R_1'$, provided that $R < R_1 < R_1' < R'$. The coefficients a_n are now given by the single formula

$$a_n = \frac{1}{2\pi i} \int_{\Gamma} \frac{f(z)}{(z-a)^{n+1}} \, dz,$$

where Γ denotes C when $n < 0$ and C' when $n \geqslant 0$. Since, however, the integrand is regular in the annulus $R < |z-a| < R'$, we may take Γ to be any circle $|z-a| = r$, where $R < r < R'$, no matter what value n has.

The real importance of Laurent's theorem rests in the fact that it is an existence theorem. It shows that an analytic function can be expanded, under certain circumstances, as a series of a given type, but it does not necessarily provide the simplest method of calculating the coefficients.

Finally, it should be observed that Laurent's theorem will not provide an expansion of the logarithm of z as a series of positive and negative powers of z. For $\text{Log}\, z$ is a many-valued function, whose principal value, $\log z$, is discontinuous along the negative half of the real axis and so is not regular in any annulus with centre at the origin.

Example 1. Show that

$$\cosh\!\left(z + \frac{1}{z}\right) = a_0 + \sum_{1}^{\infty} a_n\!\left(z^n + \frac{1}{z^n}\right),$$

where

$$a_n = \frac{1}{2\pi} \int_0^{2\pi} \cos n\theta \cosh(2\cos\theta) \, d\theta,$$

the series being uniformly convergent in any closed annulus with centre at the origin.

We have to expand the function $\cosh w$ where $w = z + z^{-1}$. Now $\cosh w$ is an integral function of w, whereas w is an analytic function of z whose only singular point is the origin. Hence $\cosh(z+z^{-1})$ is an analytic function of z regular in the annulus $R \leqslant |z| \leqslant R'$, no matter how small the positive number R may be or how large R' may be.

We can, therefore, apply Laurent's theorem to obtain

$$\cosh(z+z^{-1}) = \sum_{-\infty}^{\infty} a_n z^n,$$

where
$$a_n = \frac{1}{2\pi i} \int_{\Gamma} \frac{\cosh(z+z^{-1})}{z^{n+1}} \, dz,$$

the contour Γ being any circle $|z| = r$. If we take $r = 1$, then $z = e^{\theta i}$ on Γ, where θ varies from 0 to 2π. Hence we have

$$a_n = \frac{1}{2\pi} \int_0^{2\pi} \cosh(e^{\theta i} + e^{-\theta i}) e^{-n\theta i} \, d\theta$$

$$= \frac{1}{2\pi} \int_0^{2\pi} \cosh(2\cos\theta)\cos n\theta \, d\theta + \frac{i}{2\pi} \int_0^{2\pi} \cosh(2\cos\theta)\sin n\theta \, d\theta.$$

If we put $\theta = 2\pi - \phi$, we find that the last integral vanishes, and so

$$a_n = \frac{1}{2\pi} \int_0^{2\pi} \cos n\theta \cosh(2\cos\theta) \, d\theta.$$

But evidently $a_n = a_{-n}$, and therefore

$$\cosh(z+z^{-1}) = a_0 + \sum_1^{\infty} a_n(z^n + z^{-n}).$$

The uniform convergence of this series in every annulus with centre at the origin is an immediate consequence of Laurent's theorem.

Example 2. Find the Taylor or Laurent series which represent the function $1/\{(z^2+1)(z+2)\}$, (i) when $|z| < 1$, (ii) when $1 < |z| < 2$, (iii) when $|z| > 2$.

4.53. Isolated singularities of an analytic function

Let $f(z)$ be an analytic function with a singular point at $z = a$. If there exists a neighbourhood of the point a which contains no other singularity of $f(z)$, the point a is called an *isolated singularity* of the function.

If this is the case, there exists an annulus $r < |z-a| < R$ in which $f(z)$ is regular and can be represented by the Laurent series

$$f(z) = \sum_0^{\infty} a_n(z-a)^n + \sum_1^{\infty} b_n(z-a)^{-n}.$$

Since, however, we can make r as small as we please, this Laurent expansion actually holds when $0 < |z-a| < R$. The infinite series

$$\sum_1^{\infty} b_n(z-a)^{-n}$$

is called the *principal part* of $f(z)$ at the singular point $z = a$.

There are three cases to be considered. First of all, it may happen that all the coefficients b_n are zero. We then call $z = a$ a *removable singularity* of $f(z)$, since we can make $f(z)$ regular when $|z-a| < R$ by suitably defining its value at a. For if we write $F(z) = f(z)$ when $0 < |z-a| < R$ and $F(a) = a_0$, the function $F(z)$ has the Taylor expansion $\sum_0^\infty a_n(z-a)^n$ and so is regular when $|z-a| < R$. Singularities of this type are of little importance.

Secondly, the principal part of $f(z)$ at the isolated singularity may be a terminating series of powers of $1/(z-a)$. The singularity is then called a *pole*. If b_m is the last non-zero coefficient in the principal part, the pole is said to be of order m. Poles of orders 1, 2, 3,... are usually called simple, double, triple,... poles. The coefficient b_1 is called the *residue* of $f(z)$ at the pole a.

If $f(z)$ has a pole of order m at $z = a$, the Laurent series takes the form

$$f(z) = (z-a)^{-m}\{b_m + b_{m-1}(z-a) + b_{m-2}(z-a)^2 + ... +$$
$$+ b_1(z-a)^{m-1} + \sum_0^\infty a_n(z-a)^{m+n}\}$$
$$= (z-a)^{-m}\phi(z),$$

where $\phi(z)$ is regular when $|z-a| < R$, and $\phi(a)$, being equal to b_m, is not zero. We can therefore find† a neighbourhood $|z-a| < \delta$ of the pole in which

$$|f(z)| \geqslant \tfrac{1}{2}|b_m|.|z-a|^{-m}.$$

Hence, if $f(z)$ has a pole at a, $|f(z)|$ tends to infinity as z tends to a in any manner.

Moreover, if $f(z)$ has a pole of order m at a, $1/f(z)$ is regular and has a zero of order m there. For

$$1/f(z) = (z-a)^m/\phi(z),$$

where $\phi(z)$ is regular and does not vanish when $|z-a| < \delta$. Similarly we can show that the converse is also true, that if $F(z)$ has a zero of order m at a, $1/F(z)$ has a pole of order m there.

Finally, if the principal part of $f(z)$ at the isolated singularity a is not a terminating series but has an infinite number of non-zero coefficients, a is called an *isolated essential singularity*. In this case, a is evidently also a singularity of $1/f(z)$.

† See § 4.51.

Example 1. The function $f(z)$ has a simple pole at $z = a$. Show that the residue at this pole is $\lim_{z \to a} \{(z-a)f(z)\}$.

Since a is a simple pole, we have

$$f(z) = \frac{b_1}{z-a} + \psi(z),$$

where $\psi(z)$ is regular in a neighbourhood of $z = a$ and b_1 is the residue to be determined. Hence

$$(z-a)f(z) = b_1 + (z-a)\psi(z) \to b_1$$

as $z \to a$, since $\psi(z)$ is bounded near a.

Example 2. Show that the only singularities of $\cot \pi z/(z-a)^2$ are poles. Find the residues of the function at these poles.

If we write

$$\frac{\cot \pi z}{(z-a)^2} = \frac{\cos \pi z}{(z-a)^2 \sin \pi z},$$

we see that the function is the quotient of two integral functions, and so its only singularities are at the zeros of the denominator. Thus the function is regular save for poles at $z = a$ and at $z = 0, \pm 1, \pm 2, \dots$. If a is not an integer or zero, $z = a$ is usually a double pole and the rest all simple poles; but if a is an integer or zero, $z = a$ is a triple pole.

Let us consider first the pole $z = n$, when n is an integer or zero, and let us suppose that $n \neq a$. The residue at this pole is, by Ex. 1,

$$\lim_{z \to n} \frac{(z-n)\cot \pi z}{(z-a)^2} = \lim_{\zeta \to 0} \frac{\zeta \cot \pi(\zeta+n)}{(\zeta+n-a)^2}$$

$$= \lim_{\zeta \to 0} \frac{\zeta \cos \pi \zeta}{(\zeta+n-a)^2 \sin \pi \zeta} = \frac{1}{\pi(n-a)^2}.$$

When we determine the residue at $z = a$, we have to consider separately the cases when a is or is not an integer or zero. If a is an integer or zero, we obtain by writing $z - a = \zeta$

$$\frac{\cot \pi z}{(z-a)^2} = \frac{\cot \pi \zeta}{\zeta^2} = \frac{1}{\pi \zeta^3}(1 - \tfrac{1}{3}\pi^2 \zeta^2 + \tfrac{2}{45}\pi^4 \zeta^4 + \dots),$$

and so the residue is $-\tfrac{1}{3}\pi$. But when a is not an integer, we have

$$\frac{\cot \pi z}{(z-a)^2} = \frac{\cot \pi(a+\zeta)}{\zeta^2} = \frac{\cot \pi a}{\zeta^2} - \frac{\pi \csc^2 \pi a}{\zeta} + \pi^2 \csc^2 \pi a \cot \pi a + \dots,$$

so that the residue at a is now $-\pi \csc^2 \pi a$. If a is half an odd integer, $\cot \pi a$ is zero; and the pole at a is simple of residue $-\pi$.

Example 3. Determine the singularities of $z \csc z$, and find the residues at its poles.

Example 4. Find the residues of $z^4/(c^2+z^2)^4$ at its poles.

Example 5. Show that $e^{1/z}$ has an isolated essential singularity at the origin.

Example 6. Show that $\sin(1/z)$ has an isolated essential singularity at the origin, which is also the limiting point of the zeros of the function.

Example 7. $f(z)$ is an analytic function with an isolated singularity at $z = a$. Show that, if $f(z) = O(|z-a|^{-n})$ as $z \to a$, the singularity is a pole of order not exceeding n.

4.54. Limiting points of zeros or poles

We have already seen that if a is a limiting point of zeros of an analytic function $f(z)$, regular when $0 < |z-a| < R$, then $f(z)$ either vanishes identically or else has a singularity at a. In the latter case the singularity is isolated, but it is not a pole since $|f(z)|$ does not tend to infinity as z tends to a in any manner. Thus, apart from the trivial case when $f(z)$ is zero save at a, the function has an isolated essential singularity at the point a.

If, however, $f(z)$ is an analytic function whose only singularities in the region $0 < |z-a| < R$ are poles, infinite in number, having the point a as limiting point, a is a singularity; for $f(z)$ is unbounded in every neighbourhood of a. A singularity of this type is not a pole, since it is not an isolated singular point. We call it an essential singularity.

Example. Show that $\sec(1/z)$ has simple poles at the points $z = 1/\{(n+\tfrac{1}{2})\pi\}$, where n is an integer or zero, and an essential singularity at the origin. Prove also that the residue at $1/\{(n+\tfrac{1}{2})\pi\}$ is $(-1)^n/\{(n+\tfrac{1}{2})\pi\}^2$.

4.55. The behaviour of a function near an isolated essential singularity

We have seen that, if a is a pole of the function $f(z)$, then $|f(z)|$ increases indefinitely as z tends to a in any manner. On the other hand, the behaviour of a function near an isolated essential singularity is of a far more complicated character; in fact, *in every neighbourhood of an isolated essential singularity, there exists a point† at which the function differs by as little as we please from any previously assigned number.* This result is due to Weierstrass.‡

Let us consider, then, an analytic function $f(z)$ which has an isolated essential singularity at $z = a$. Let c be any number,

---

† Actually there are an infinite number of such points. For if z_1 be such a point in the neighbourhood $|z-a| < r$ of the essential singularity a, there must be another in $|z-a| < \tfrac{1}{2}|z_1-a|$, and so on indefinitely.

‡ *Abh. der Preuss. Akad. Wiss. zu Berlin* (*Math. Klasse*) 1876, 11. This is reprinted in Weierstrass's *Werke*, **2**, 77.

real or complex; we have to show that, given two positive numbers ϵ and r, no matter how small, we can find a point z_1 in the region $|z-a| < r$ at which $|f(z)-c| < \epsilon$.

If a is a limiting point of zeros of the function $f(z)-c$, the theorem is obviously true, since we have only to take z_1 to be any zero in the given neighbourhood of a. But if a is not a limiting point of zeros, the function $f(z)-c$ has no zeros in the given neighbourhood, provided that r is sufficiently small, and hence the function

$$g(z) = \frac{1}{f(z)-c}$$

is regular when $0 < |z-a| < r$. We have to show that there exists a point z_1 in this region at which $|g(z)| > 1/\epsilon$.

Let us suppose that, on the contrary, $|g(z)| \leqslant 1/\epsilon$ there. Then, if the principal part of $g(z)$ at a is $\sum\limits_1^\infty b_n(z-a)^{-n}$, we have

$$b_n = \frac{1}{2\pi i} \int\limits_{|z|=\rho} g(z)(z-a)^{n-1}\, dz,$$

where $0 < \rho < r$, and hence

$$|b_n| \leqslant \frac{\rho^n}{\epsilon}.$$

Since, however, b_n is independent of ρ, we find, by making ρ tend to zero, that b_n is zero for all values of n and hence that $g(z)$ is regular at a. This is impossible; for it would imply that $f(z)$ is regular at a or else has a pole there. The assumption that $|g(z)| \leqslant 1/\epsilon$ when $0 < |z-a| < r$ is, therefore, untenable.

We have thus shown that the inequality $|g(z)| > 1/\epsilon$ must be satisfied at one point at least in the given neighbourhood of a; this completes the proof of Weierstrass's theorem.

A more striking result still is Picard's† theorem, which states that, *in every neighbourhood of an isolated essential singularity, there exists a point at which the function actually attains any given value with at most one exception.* For example, $\sin 1/z$ and $e^{1/z}$ have isolated essential singularities at the origin; $\sin 1/z$ actually attains every value in $0 < |z| < r$, no matter how small r may be, whereas $e^{1/z}$ attains there every value except zero. The

† *Comptes Rendus*, **88** (1879), 1024–7; **89** (1879), 745–7.

proof of Picard's theorem is too difficult to be given at the present stage.

4.56. The point at infinity

The equation $z' = 1/z$ sets up a continuous one-to-one correspondence between the points of the complete z-plane and the points of the complete z'-plane. If z is at the point at infinity, z' is at the origin. Accordingly we shall say that a function $f(z)$ has a zero, a pole, or an essential singularity at infinity if the function $f(z^{-1})$ has a zero, a pole, or an essential singularity at the origin. For example, the functions $\sin 1/z$, $(z+1)^2$, and e^z have respectively a simple zero, a double pole, and an essential singularity at infinity.

It is important to notice that *if the only singularities of an analytic function, including possibly the point at infinity, are poles, the function is a rational function.*

For let $F(z)$ be such a function. It can have only a finite number of poles since a limiting point of poles is an essential singularity; let its poles be at $a_1, a_2,..., a_k, \infty$, of orders $n_1, n_2,..., n_k, m$ respectively. It follows that

$$G(z) = (z-a_1)^{n_1}(z-a_2)^{n_2}...(z-a_k)^{n_k}F(z)$$

is regular in every bounded domain, and so is an integral function. We can, therefore, expand $G(z)$ as a Taylor series

$$G(z) = \sum_0^\infty b_n z^n,$$

which converges for every finite value of z.

But $(z-a_1)^{n_1}(z-a_2)^{n_2}...(z-a_k)^{n_k}$ has a pole of order

$$N = n_1 + n_2 + ... + n_k$$

at infinity. Hence $G(z)$ also has a pole at infinity, its order being $N+m$. This, however, implies that the Taylor series for $G(z)$ terminates and is of the form

$$G(z) = \sum_0^{N+m} b_n z^n.$$

This gives $\qquad F(z) = \left\{ \sum_0^{N+m} b_n z^n \right\} \bigg/ \left\{ \prod_{r=1}^k (z-a_r)^{n_r} \right\},$

and so $F(z)$ is a rational function.

4.6. Analytical continuation

Let $f_1(z)$ be a regular analytic function defined in a domain D_1. We shall now show that it is sometimes possible to continue this function analytically. By this we mean that it is sometimes possible to find an analytic function $F(z)$ which is equal to $f_1(z)$ at each point of D_1 but is regular in a more extensive domain.

Let D_2 be another domain which has in common with D_1 a set of points forming a domain Δ. If there exists a function $f_2(z)$, regular in D_2, which is equal to $f_1(z)$ at a set of points having a limiting point ζ belonging to Δ, the analytical continuation of $f_1(z)$ is possible.

In the first place, the functions $f_1(z)$ and $f_2(z)$ are equal at every point of Δ. For $f_1(z)-f_2(z)$ is regular in Δ and has a set of zeros with ζ as limiting point; since ζ is a point of Δ, this implies that $f_1(z)-f_2(z)$ vanishes everywhere in Δ.

If we now write $F(z) = f_1(z)$ when z is in D_1 and $F(z) = f_2(z)$ when z is in D_2, the function $F(z)$ so defined is evidently an analytic function, regular in the domain† D_1+D_2; the function $f_1(z)$ has, therefore, been continued analytically into D_2. Moreover this analytical continuation is unique. For if $g(z)$ is another function, regular in D_2, which is equal to $f_1(z)$ at a set of points having a point of Δ as limiting point, $g(z)$ is equal to $f_1(z)$ at every point of Δ and hence is also equal to $f_2(z)$ there; a repetition of the previous argument then shows that $f_2(z)$ and $g(z)$ are equal everywhere in D_2.

When $f_2(z)$ has been found in this way, it may be possible to continue $f_2(z)$ analytically into a domain D_3 which overlaps D_2. If this is so, there is a function $f_3(z)$, regular in D_3, which is equal to $f_2(z)$ in the common part of D_2 and D_3. If D_3 overlaps D_1, we should expect that the analytical continuation of $f_3(z)$ into D_1 would be the original function $f_1(z)$. If D_1, D_2, and D_3 are circles having a domain Δ' in common, this conjecture is, in fact, true. For in Δ' we have $f_1(z) = f_2(z) = f_3(z)$, and this implies that $f_1(z) = f_3(z)$ in the common part of D_3 and D_1. But if D_1, D_2, and D_3 have no domain in common, it is not necessarily the case that the analytical continuation of $f_3(z)$ into D_1 is $f_1(z)$. For example, let us denote the domains $|z-1| < \rho$, $|z-\omega| < \rho$,

† By D_1+D_2 we mean the set of points which belong to D_1 or to D_2 or to both. Since D_1 and D_2 are domains, D_1+D_2 is also a domain.

$|z-\omega^2| < \rho$, where $\omega = e^{2\pi i/3}$ and $\frac{1}{2}\sqrt{3} < \rho < 1$, by D_1, D_2, D_3 respectively; any two of these domains have in common an area bounded by two circular arcs, but there is no point common to all three. The function $z^{\frac{1}{2}}$ is regular in D_1; if we continue it analytically into D_2, from D_2 into D_3, and, finally, from D_3 into D_1, the function obtained in this way is not $z^{\frac{1}{2}}$ but $-z^{\frac{1}{2}}$.

4.61. The general definition of an analytic function

Let $f(z)$ be an analytic function defined only in a certain domain where it is regular. Let us suppose that it is possible to continue this function analytically outside the given domain. If we form all the continuations of the function, then all the continuations of these continuations, and so on in every possible way, the complete analytic function $f(z)$ is defined as consisting of the original function and all the continuations so obtained. The complete analytic function defined in this way is, of course, not necessarily a one-valued function.

If $f(z)$ is not an integral function, there will be certain exceptional points which do not lie in any of the domains into which the function has been continued. These exceptional points are called the singularities of the complete analytic function. It is evident that the singular points of a one-valued analytic function are also singularities in this wider sense.

It may happen that, in this process of continuation, we ultimately reach a closed curve across which it is impossible to continue the function. Such a closed curve is called a *natural boundary* of the complete analytic function. An example of a function with a natural boundary will be found in § 4.62, Ex. 2.

4.62. Analytical continuation by power series

We shall now consider very briefly the problem of continuing analytically a function $f(z)$ defined initially as the sum of a power series $\sum_{0}^{\infty} a_n(z-z_0)^n$ whose circle of convergence C_0 has a finite non-zero radius.

The first thing to observe is that, when the continuation has been carried out, there must be at least one singularity of the complete analytic function on the circle of convergence C_0. For if there were not, we could construct, by analytical continuation, an analytic function which is equal to $f(z)$ within C_0 but is regular in a larger concentric circle C_0'. The expansion of this function as a Taylor series in powers of $z-z_0$ would then converge everywhere within C_0'; this is, however, impossible since the series would necessarily be the original series, whose circle of convergence is C_0.

In order to carry out the continuation, we take any fixed point z_1 within C_0, and calculate the values of $f(z)$ and its successive derivatives at that point from the given power series by repeated term-by-term differentiation. We then form the Taylor series

$$\sum_0^\infty f^{(n)}(z_1)\frac{(z-z_1)^n}{n!},$$

whose circle of convergence is C_1, say.

Let Γ_1 denote the circle with centre z_1 which touches C_0 internally. By Taylor's theorem, this new power series is certainly convergent within Γ_1 and has sum $f(z)$ there. The radius of C_1 cannot, therefore, be less than that of Γ_1. There are now three possibilities:

(i) C_1 may have a larger radius than Γ_1. In this case C_1 lies partly outside C_0, and the new power series provides an analytical continuation of $f(z)$. We can then take a point z_2 within C_1 and outside C_0, and repeat the process.

(ii) C_0 may be a natural boundary of $f(z)$. In this case we cannot continue $f(z)$ outside C_0, and the circle C_1 touches C_0 internally, no matter what point z_1 within C_0 was chosen.

(iii) C_1 may touch C_0 internally even when C_0 is not a natural boundary of $f(z)$. The point of contact of C_0 and C_1 is a singularity of the complete analytic function obtained by the analytical continuation of the original power series. For there is necessarily one singularity on C_1 and this cannot be within C_0.

We see, then, that if C_0 is not a natural boundary of the function $f(z) = \sum a_n(z-z_0)^n$, this process of forming new power series provides a simple means of continuing the function analytically.† It is, therefore, theoretically possible to deduce all the properties of the complete analytic function from the properties of the coefficients a_n of the Taylor series which defines

---

† For further information on the theory of analytical continuation by power series, see, for example, Goursat, *Cours d'Analyse*, **2** (1918), 235–62.

the function initially. This interesting but extremely difficult problem is, however, beyond the scope of the present book.†

Example 1. Show that the function
$$f(z) = 1+z+z^2+\ldots+z^n+\ldots$$
can be continued analytically outside its circle of convergence.

The circle of convergence C_0 of this power series has the equation $|z| = 1$. Within C_0 the sum of the series is $(1-z)^{-1}$. But this function is an analytic function, regular in any domain which does not contain the point $z = 1$, and so provides the required analytical continuation of $f(z)$.

It is, however, instructive to carry out the continuation by means of power series. If a is any point within C_0, it is easily seen that the power series expressing $f(z)$ in powers of $z-a$ is

$$\sum_{n=0}^{\infty} \frac{(z-a)^n}{(1-a)^{n+1}}.$$

The circle of convergence C_1 of this new power series is $|z-a| = |1-a|$.

Now if $0 < a < 1$, C_1 touches C_0 at $z = 1$, which is, therefore, a singularity of the complete analytic function defined initially by the given power series. If, however, a is not real and positive, we have $|1-a| > 1-|a|$, so that C_1 crosses C_0; in this case the new power series provides an analytical continuation of $f(z)$ outside C_0.

Example 2. Show that the circle of convergence of the power series
$$f(z) = 1+z+z^2+z^4+z^8+\ldots$$
is a natural boundary.

The circle of convergence C_0 of the power series is $|z| = 1$. If the point $e^{\alpha i}$ on C_0 is not a singularity of $f(z)$, then $f(re^{\alpha i})$ must tend to a finite limit as the real number r increases and tends to unity.‡

Let us consider, then, the behaviour of $f(z)$ as z moves up to C_0 along the radius through the point of affix $e^{2p\pi i/2^q}$, where p and q are integers. Now we can express $f(z)$ in the form

$$f(z) = 1+z+z^2+\ldots+z^{2^q}+ \sum_{n=q+1}^{\infty} z^{2^n}$$
$$= f_1(z)+f_2(z),$$

say. Since $f_1(re^{2p\pi i/2^q})$ is a polynomial in r of degree 2^q, it tends to a unique limit as $r \to 1$. But

$$f_2(re^{2p\pi i/2^q}) = \sum_{n=q+1}^{\infty} r^{2^n}e^{2^{1+n-q}p\pi i} = \sum_{n=q+1}^{\infty} r^{2^n},$$

† An interesting account of recent researches on this problem is given by Hadamard and Mandelbrojt, *La Série de Taylor* (Collection 'Scientia'; 1926). See also Dienes, *The Taylor Series* (Oxford, 1931), Chapter X.

‡ It is not, however, the case that, if $f(re^{\alpha i})$ tends to a finite limit, then $e^{\alpha i}$ is not a singularity of $f(z)$. For example, the binomial expansion of $(1-z)^{\frac{1}{2}}$ converges when $|z| \leqslant 1$, and $(1-r)^{\frac{1}{2}}$ tends to zero as $r \to 1$. Yet $z = 1$ is a singularity (a branch-point) of $(1-z)^{\frac{1}{2}}$.

which tends to infinity as $r \to 1$. Accordingly the point of affix $e^{2p\pi i/2^q}$ on C_0 is a singularity of $f(z)$.

But any arc of C_0, no matter how small its length, contains a point whose affix is of the form $e^{2p\pi i/2^q}$, where p and q are integers. There are, therefore, points whose affix is of this form within every circle which crosses C_0, so that it is impossible to continue $f(z)$ analytically outside its circle of convergence.

REFERENCES

Complex integration and Cauchy's theorem:

E. GOURSAT, *Cours d'Analyse*, **2** (Paris, 1918), Chap. XIV.

S. POLLARD, *Proc. London Math. Soc.* (2), **21** (1923), 456–82; **28** (1928), 145–60.

G. N. WATSON, *Complex Integration and Cauchy's Theorem* (Cambridge Math. Tract, 1914).

Analytical continuation:

E. GOURSAT, loc. cit., Chap. XVI.

J. HADAMARD and S. MANDELBROJT, *La Série de Taylor* (Collection 'Scientia'; Paris, 1926).

MISCELLANEOUS EXAMPLES

1. The function $f(z)$ is regular when $|z-a| < R$. Show that, if $0 < r < R$, then

$$f'(a) = \frac{1}{\pi r} \int_0^{2\pi} F(\theta) e^{-\theta i} \, d\theta,$$

where $F(\theta)$ denotes the real part of $f(a+re^{\theta i})$.

2. The function $f(z)$ is regular when $|z| < R'$. Prove that, if

$$|a| < R < R',$$

then

$$f(a) = \frac{1}{2\pi i} \int_C \frac{R^2 - a\bar{a}}{(z-a)(R^2 - z\bar{a})} f(z) \, dz,$$

where C is the circle $|z| = R$. Deduce Poisson's formula, that, if $0 < r < R$,

$$f(re^{\theta i}) = \frac{1}{2\pi} \int_0^{2\pi} \frac{R^2 - r^2}{R^2 - 2Rr\cos(\theta-\phi) + r^2} f(Re^{\phi i}) \, d\phi.$$

3. When $|z| \leqslant R$, the function $f(z)$ is regular and satisfies the inequality $|f(z)| \geqslant 1$. Show, by applying Poisson's formula to $\log f(z)$, that, if $|z| \leqslant kR$ where $k < 1$, then

$$|f(z)| \leqslant |f(0)|^{\frac{1+k}{1-k}}.$$

4. The function $f(z)$ is regular when $|z| < R$ and has the Taylor expansion $\sum_0^\infty a_n z^n$. Show that, if $r < R$,

$$\frac{1}{2\pi} \int_0^{2\pi} |f(re^{\theta i})|^2 \, d\theta = \sum_0^\infty |a_n|^2 r^{2n}.$$

Hence prove that, if $|f(z)| \leqslant M$ when $|z| < R$,

$$\sum_0^\infty |a_n|^2 R^{2n} \leqslant M^2.$$

5. Deduce Cauchy's inequalities from Ex. 4, and show that, in the notation of § 4.33, $\quad |f^{(n)}(a)| = n!\,M/R^n$
if and only if $f(z) = Me^{\alpha i}(z-a)^n/R^n$, where α is a real constant.

6. The integral function $f(z)$ satisfies everywhere the inequality $|f(z)| \leqslant A|z|^k$, where A and k are positive constants. Prove that $f(z)$ is a polynomial of degree not exceeding k.

7. Show that the branch of the function $(1-2\mu z+z^2)^{-1/2}$ which is equal to $+1$ when $z = 0$, is regular when $|z|$ is less than the smaller of $|\mu \pm \sqrt{(\mu^2-1)}|$, and so can be represented by a Taylor series

$$1 + \sum_{n=1}^\infty P_n(\mu)z^n.$$

Prove that the coefficients in this expansion are given by

$$P_n(\mu) = \frac{1}{2\pi i} \int_C \frac{(1-2\mu z+z^2)^{-1/2}}{z^{n+1}} \, dz$$

where C is a closed contour surrounding the origin but not enclosing either of the points $\mu \pm \sqrt{(\mu^2-1)}$.

8. Prove that the function $\exp\{\frac12 u(z-z^{-1})\}$ is regular save at the origin and can be expanded as a Laurent series

$$\sum_{-\infty}^\infty z^n J_n(u),$$

where $\quad J_n(u) = (-1)^n J_{-n}(u) = \dfrac{1}{2\pi} \displaystyle\int_0^{2\pi} \cos(n\theta - u\sin\theta)\, d\theta.$

9. The function $f(z)$ is regular when $|z| > R$ and $|f(z)|$ is bounded as $|z| \to \infty$. Prove that $f(z)$ can be expanded as a series of the form $\sum_0^\infty a_n z^{-n}$, convergent when $|z| > R$.

10. The function $f(z)$ is regular in the strip $-\alpha < \operatorname{Im} z < \alpha$, where α is positive. Prove by using Laurent's theorem that, if $f(z)$ is periodic, of period 2π, it can be expanded in the form

$$f(z) = \sum_{-\infty}^\infty c_n e^{inz},$$

where
$$c_n = \frac{1}{2\pi} \int_0^{2\pi} f(z) e^{-inz}\, dz,$$

the series being uniformly convergent in the strip $-\alpha+\delta \leqslant \operatorname{Im} z \leqslant \alpha-\delta$ for every positive value of δ $(< \alpha)$.

Deduce that†

$$f(z) = \tfrac{1}{2}a_0 + \sum_{n=1}^{\infty} (a_n \cos nz + b_n \sin nz),$$

where
$$a_n = \frac{1}{\pi} \int_0^{2\pi} f(z) \cos nz\, dz, \qquad b_n = \frac{1}{\pi} \int_0^{2\pi} f(z) \sin nz\, dz.$$

11. Each of the functions

    (i) $\cot z$,   (ii) $\operatorname{cosec}^2 z \log(1-z)$,   (iii) $z/(\sin z - \tan z)$

has a pole at the origin. Find its order and residue in each case.

12. Show that the circle $|z| = 1$ is a natural boundary of each of the functions

    (i) $\displaystyle\sum_0^{\infty} z^{n!}$,   (ii) $\displaystyle\sum_0^{\infty} \frac{2^{-n}}{z - e^{2\sqrt{2}n\pi i}}.$

13. Show that the sum of the series

$$\frac{a-cz}{1-z} + (a-c)\left\{ \frac{z}{z^2-1} + \frac{z^2}{z^4-1} + \frac{z^4}{z^8-1} + \dots \right\}$$

is a when $|z| < 1$, but is c when $|z| > 1$. Why is this?

14. Prove that the sum of the series

$$\sum_1^{\infty} \frac{z^n}{(1+z^n)(1+z^{n+1})}$$

is $z/(1-z^2)$ when $|z| < 1$, but is $1/(z^2-1)$ when $|z| > 1$.

15. The function $f(z)$ is regular within and on the circle C whose equation is $|z| = R$, save for simple poles $b_1, b_2, \dots, b_n$ within C. Moreover, $f(z)$ does not vanish on C, but has simple zeros $a_1, a_2, \dots, a_m$ within C. Prove that the function

$$F(z) = f(z) \prod_{s=1}^{m} \left\{ \frac{R^2 - \bar{a}_s z}{R(z-a_s)} \right\} \prod_{s=1}^{n} \left\{ \frac{R(z-b_s)}{R^2 - \bar{b}_s z} \right\}$$

is regular and non-zero within and on C, and also that $|F(z)| = |f(z)|$ on C.

---

† This result is Fourier's theorem for analytic functions of a complex variable. A detailed account of the conditions under which Fourier's theorem for functions of a real variable is valid will be found in Hobson's *Functions of a Real Variable*, **2** (1926).

By applying Poisson's formula to $\log F(z)$, show that, if $z = re^{\theta i}$ where $r < R$, then

$$\log|f(z)| = \sum_{s=1}^{m} \log\left|\frac{R(z-a_s)}{R^2-\bar{a}_s z}\right| - \sum_{s=1}^{n} \log\left|\frac{R(z-b_s)}{R^2-\bar{b}_s z}\right| +$$

$$+\frac{1}{2\pi}\int_0^{2\pi} \log|f(Re^{\phi i})|\frac{R^2-r^2}{R^2-2Rr\cos(\theta-\phi)+r^2}\,d\phi.$$

Deduce that

$$\int_0^{2\pi} \log|f(Re^{\phi i})|\,d\phi = 2\pi\log\frac{|b_1 b_2 \dots b_n|R^{m-n}}{|a_1 a_2 \dots a_m|} + 2\pi\log|f(0)|,$$

provided that the origin is not a zero or pole of $f(z)$.

How would these results be modified if $f(z)$ possessed multiple poles or multiple zeros within C? (JENSEN.†)

† J. L. W. V. Jensen, *Acta Math.* **22** (1899), 359–64.

CHAPTER V

UNIFORM CONVERGENCE

5.1. The limiting function of a sequence of functions

LET $s_0(z)$, $s_1(z)$, $s_2(z)$,... be a sequence of one-valued functions, each defined in a bounded closed domain D. At present we do not assume that these functions are differentiable or even continuous in D; they are merely functions of the complex variable z in the most general sense.

It may happen that, when ζ is a point of D, the sequence of complex numbers $s_0(\zeta)$, $s_1(\zeta)$, $s_2(\zeta)$,... tends to a definite finite limit. We then say that the sequence of functions is convergent at ζ. If the sequence converges at each point of D, it is said to be convergent in D, and the limiting function $s(z)$ of the sequence is defined at each point of D by the equation

$$s(z) = \lim_{n \to \infty} s_n(z).$$

This means that, given any point ζ of D and any positive number ϵ, no matter how small, we can find an integer N such that $|s(\zeta) - s_n(\zeta)| < \epsilon$ when $n \geqslant N$. The integer N, which is made definite by being taken as small as possible, will depend, in general, not only on ϵ but also on the particular point ζ under consideration; we denote this fact by writing $N = N(\epsilon, \zeta)$.

In this way we have associated with the convergent sequence a function $N(\epsilon, z)$ which is defined at each point of D and which only takes positive integral values. In general, this function will not be bounded in D. But when $N(\epsilon, z)$ is bounded, we say that the sequence is *uniformly convergent* in the domain D.

The uniform convergence of the sequence implies, therefore, that there exists an integer $M = M(\epsilon)$, depending on ϵ alone, such that $N(\epsilon, z) \leqslant M(\epsilon)$ at each point z of D. In other words, the sequence of functions $s_0(z)$, $s_1(z)$,... converges uniformly in the domain D to the limiting function $s(z)$ if, given a positive number ϵ, no matter how small, we can find an integer M, depending on ϵ alone, such that the inequality $|s(z) - s_n(z)| < \epsilon$ holds at each point z of D provided only that $n \geqslant M$.

The idea of uniform convergence is of great importance in

analysis; for, as we shall see, it often enables us to deduce properties of the limiting function of a sequence from the common properties of the members of the sequence.

5.11. The principle of uniform convergence

The definition which we have just given of the uniform convergence of a sequence presupposes that the limiting function of the sequence is known. Before we proceed to discuss the properties of uniformly convergent sequences, it is desirable to express the condition for uniform convergence in a form which does not involve the actual determination of the limiting function. This is provided by the following principle of uniform convergence, analogous to the principle of convergence for sequences of numbers. *The necessary and sufficient condition for the uniform convergence of the sequence of functions* $s_0(z)$, $s_1(z)$, $s_2(z)$... *in the bounded closed domain D is that, corresponding to any positive number ϵ, there should exist an integer $m(\epsilon)$, depending on ϵ alone, such that the inequality*

$$|s_{m+p}(z) - s_m(z)| < \epsilon$$

holds at each point z of D for every positive integer p.

In the first place, the condition is necessary. For if the sequence converges uniformly to $s(z)$, we have, in the notation of § 5.1,

$$|s(z) - s_n(z)| < \tfrac{1}{2}\epsilon$$

at each point z of D provided that $n \geqslant M(\tfrac{1}{2}\epsilon)$. Hence, if $m = M(\tfrac{1}{2}\epsilon)$ and p is any positive integer,

$$\begin{aligned}
|s_{m+p}(z) - s_m(z)| &= |\{s(z) - s_m(z)\} - \{s(z) - s_{m+p}(z)\}| \\
&\leqslant |s(z) - s_m(z)| + |s(z) - s_{m+p}(z)| \\
&< \epsilon
\end{aligned}$$

at each point z of D.

The condition is also sufficient. For if it is satisfied, the sequence converges, in virtue of the principle of convergence, to a limiting function $s(z)$. If we make p tend to infinity in the inequality

$$|s_{m+p}(z) - s_m(z)| < \epsilon,$$

we find that

$$|s(z) - s_m(z)| \leqslant \epsilon.$$

But since $|s_n(z) - s_m(z)| < \epsilon$ at each point of D provided that

$n > m$, this inequality gives

$$|s(z)-s_n(z)| = |\{s(z)-s_m(z)\}+\{s_m(z)-s_n(z)\}|$$
$$\leqslant |s(z)-s_m(z)|+|s_m(z)-s_n(z)|$$
$$< 2\epsilon,$$

when $n > m$. Hence the sequence converges uniformly to $s(z)$.

5.12. Uniformly convergent sequences of continuous functions

At first sight we should expect that the limiting function of a convergent sequence of continuous functions would itself be continuous. This is, however, not the case. For example, the sequence of functions 1, z^2, z^4, z^6,... converges at each point within and on the ellipse $x^2+2y^2 = 1$, yet the limiting function of the sequence has the value 1 at the points $z = \pm 1$, but is zero at every other point within or on the ellipse. It can, however, be proved that *if $s_0(z)$, $s_1(z)$, $s_2(z)$,... is a convergent sequence of functions, each continuous in a bounded closed domain D, a sufficient condition for the continuity in D of the limiting function $s(z)$ of the sequence is that the convergence be uniform.*

For if the sequence is uniformly convergent, then, given any positive number ϵ, we can find an integer M, depending on ϵ alone, such that the inequality

$$|s(z)-s_n(z)| < \epsilon$$

holds at each point z of D, provided only that $n \geqslant M$. Hence, if z_1 and z_2 are any two points of D,

$$|s(z_1)-s(z_2)| = |\{s(z_1)-s_M(z_1)\}+\{s_M(z_1)-s_M(z_2)\}+\{s_M(z_2)-s(z_2)\}|$$
$$\leqslant |s(z_1)-s_M(z_1)|+|s(z_2)-s_M(z_2)|+|s_M(z_1)-s_M(z_2)|$$
$$< 2\epsilon+|s_M(z_1)-s_M(z_2)|.$$

But $s_M(z)$ is a continuous function, and so is also uniformly continuous. We can therefore find a positive number δ, depending only on ϵ, such that the inequality

$$|s_M(z)-s_M(z')| < \epsilon$$

holds for each pair of points z, z' of D for which $|z-z'| < \delta$. Hence, if $|z_1-z_2| < \delta$, we have

$$|s(z_1)-s(z_2)| < 3\epsilon;$$

this proves the theorem.

From this we shall deduce that *if $s_0(z)$, $s_1(z)$, $s_2(z)$,... is a sequence of continuous functions which converges uniformly to $s(z)$ in a bounded closed domain D, and if L is a contour lying in D, then*

$$\lim_{n\to\infty} \int_L s_n(z)\, dz = \int_L s(z)\, dz.$$

The function $s(z)$ has been shown to be continuous in D and so is certainly integrable along L. Now, given any positive number ϵ, we can, by hypothesis, find an integer M, depending on ϵ alone, such that, when $n \geqslant M$, the inequality $|s(z) - s_n(z)| < \epsilon$ holds everywhere in D and, in particular, on L. Hence, if l be the length of L, we have

$$\left| \int_L s(z)\, dz - \int_L s_n(z)\, dz \right| = \left| \int_L \{s(z) - s_n(z)\}\, dz \right| < \epsilon l.$$

Since, however, ϵ can be as small as we please, this shows that

$$\lim_{n\to\infty} \int_L s_n(z)\, dz = \int_L s(z)\, dz.$$

5.13. Uniformly convergent sequences of analytic functions

Let us suppose that the sequence of functions $s_0(z)$, $s_1(z)$, $s_2(z)$,... *converges uniformly to $s(z)$ in every closed domain D within a closed contour C, and that each member of the sequence is an analytic function regular within C. Then $s(z)$ is also regular within C and the sequence $s_n'(z)$ converges uniformly to $s'(z)$ in D.*

We know that the limiting function $s(z)$ is continuous within C; we shall prove that it is also regular there by means of Morera's theorem (§ 4.4).

Let L be any contour, not necessarily closed, lying entirely within C. Since each member of the sequence is a regular analytic function, $\int_L s_n(z)\, dz$ depends only on the affixes of the end-points of L.

But since L lies within C, it lies in a closed domain in which the sequence of functions converges uniformly, and so

$$\lim_{n\to\infty} \int_L s_n(z)\, dz = \int_L s(z)\, dz.$$

The value of $\int_L s(z)\, dz$ depends, therefore, only on the affixes of the end-points of L. Hence, by Morera's theorem, $s(z)$ is regular within C.

It remains to show that $s_n'(z)$ converges uniformly to $s'(z)$ in any closed domain D within C. We construct a closed contour Γ which lies within C and yet is definitely outside D; let δ be the shortest distance between Γ and D. Now let a be any point of D; then, by Cauchy's integral for the derivative of an analytic function,

$$s'(a)-s_n'(a) = \frac{1}{2\pi i}\int_\Gamma \frac{s(z)-s_n(z)}{(z-a)^2}\,dz.$$

But, by hypothesis, $s_n(z)$ converges uniformly to $s(z)$ within and on Γ. Hence, when we are given any positive number ϵ, we can find an integer M, depending on ϵ alone, such that $|s(z)-s_n(z)| < \epsilon$ when z is any point within or on Γ, provided that $n \geqslant M$. By the result of § 4.14, it follows that, when $n \geqslant M$,

$$|s'(a)-s_n'(a)| < \frac{\epsilon l}{2\pi\delta^2},$$

where l is the length of Γ. The expression on the right-hand side of this inequality is independent of a, and therefore $s_n'(z)$ converges uniformly in D to the limiting function $s'(z)$.

A repetition of the same argument shows that $s_n''(z)$ converges uniformly in every closed domain within C to $s''(z)$, and so on indefinitely.

5.2. Uniformly convergent series

Let each term of the infinite series $\sum_0^\infty u_n(z)$ be a one-valued function of z, defined in a bounded closed domain D. We associate with this series the sequence of partial sums $s_0(z)$, $s_1(z)$, $s_2(z)$,... where

$$s_n(z) = u_0(z)+u_1(z)+u_2(z)+...+u_n(z).$$

If this sequence is convergent in D and has the limiting function $s(z)$, we say that the series converges in D and that its sum is $s(z)$. If, further, $s_n(z)$ tends to its limiting function uniformly in D, the infinite series is said to be uniformly convergent in the bounded closed domain D.

If each term of the infinite series $\sum_0^\infty u_n(z)$ is continuous in a bounded closed domain D, and if the series converges uniformly *in D, then the sum of the series $s(z)$ is also continuous in D. Moreover, if L is any contour in D,*

$$\int_L s(z)\,dz = \sum_{n=0}^{\infty} \int_L u_n(z)\,dz.$$

This important result is obtained immediately by applying the theorems of § 5.12 to the sequence of partial sums of the infinite series.

Similarly, we deduce from § 5.13 that *if each term of the infinite series $\sum_0^{\infty} u_n(z)$ is an analytic function, regular within a closed contour C, and if the infinite series converges uniformly in every closed domain D within C, then the sum of the series $s(z)$ is also an analytic function, regular within C. Moreover,*

$$s'(z) = \sum_0^{\infty} u_n'(z),$$

the latter series being uniformly convergent in D. This result is sometimes called Weierstrass's[†] double-series theorem, since his proof of it depended on expressing each term as a power series and rearranging the double series so formed.

It should be observed that we can apply Weierstrass's theorem to the series $\sum_0^{\infty} u_n'(z)$, to obtain

$$s''(z) = \sum_0^{\infty} u_n''(z),$$

and so on indefinitely. In other words, a uniformly convergent series of regular analytic functions can be differentiated term by term as often as we please.

5.21. Weierstrass's M-test

One of the simplest sufficient conditions for the uniform convergence of a series is Weierstrass's M-test, which runs as follows. *The infinite series $\sum u_n(z)$ converges uniformly and absolutely in a bounded closed domain D if each term satisfies there an inequality $|u_n(z)| \leqslant M_n$, where M_n is independent of z and $\sum M_n$ is convergent.*

† *Monatsberichte der Preuss. Akad. Wiss.* (1880), 719–43. This paper is reprinted in Weierstrass's *Werke*, **2**, 201–30. See also Bromwich, *Infinite Series* (1926), 266–7, or Knopp, *Theory and Application of Infinite Series* (1928), 430–3.

The series is evidently absolutely convergent in D. To prove that it is also uniformly convergent in D, we observe that, if $s_n(z)$ is the nth partial sum of the series, then

$$|s_{m+p}(z)-s_m(z)| = \left| \sum_{m+1}^{m+p} u_n(z) \right| \leqslant \sum_{m+1}^{m+p} |u_n(z)|$$

$$\leqslant \sum_{m+1}^{m+p} M_n < \sum_{m+1}^{\infty} M_n,$$

for every positive integral value of p. Now $\sum M_n$ is convergent; hence, given any positive number ϵ, we can choose m so that

$$\sum_{m+1}^{\infty} M_n < \epsilon.$$

With this value of m, which depends only on ϵ, we have

$$|s_{m+p}(z)-s_m(z)| < \epsilon$$

where z denotes any point of D and p is any positive integer. The required result now follows by the principle of uniform convergence.

Example 1. The radius of convergence of the power series $\sum_0^{\infty} a_n z^n$ is R. Show that the series converges uniformly and absolutely when $|z| \leqslant R'$, provided that $R' < R$. Deduce that the sum of the series is an analytic function regular within its circle of convergence.

Example 2. Show that the series $\sum_1^{\infty} n^{-z}$ converges absolutely and uniformly in any bounded closed domain in which $\mathrm{Rl}\, z > 1$.

5.22. Further tests for the uniform convergence of an infinite series†

The series $\sum a_n(z) v_n(z)$ is uniformly convergent in a bounded closed domain D if

    (i) *the partial sums of the series $\sum a_n(z)$ are uniformly bounded in D,*

    (ii) *$\sum \{v_n(z)-v_{n+1}(z)\}$ is uniformly and absolutely convergent in D, and*

    (iii) *$v_n(z)$ tends to zero uniformly in D.*

---

† The tests of this section are similar to those of Abel and Dirichlet for the ordinary convergence of real series. They were first published by Hardy, *Proc. London Math. Soc.* (2), **4** (1907), 247–65.

Let us write

$$s_n(z) = a_0(z) + a_1(z) + \ldots + a_n(z),$$
$$S_n(z) = a_0(z)v_0(z) + a_1(z)v_1(z) + \ldots + a_n(z)v_n(z).$$

The first condition implies that there exists a positive constant K, such that the inequality $|s_n(z)| < K$ holds when z is any point of D and n is any positive integer.

As in § 2.43, we obtain by partial summation

$$S_{n+p}(z) - S_n(z)$$
$$= -s_n(z)v_{n+1}(z) + \sum_{r=n+1}^{n+p-1} s_r(z)\{v_r(z) - v_{r+1}(z)\} + s_{n+p}(z)v_{n+p}(z),$$

and therefore

$$|S_{n+p}(z) - S_n(z)| \leqslant K\{|v_{n+1}(z)| + \sum_{n+1}^{n+p-1} |v_r(z) - v_{r+1}(z)| + |v_{n+p}(z)|\}$$
$$< K\{|v_{n+1}(z)| + |v_{n+p}(z)| + \sum_{n+1}^{\infty} |v_r(z) - v_{r+1}(z)|\}$$

when z denotes any point of D and p is any positive integer.

The second condition states that the series $\sum |v_n(z) - v_{n+1}(z)|$ converges uniformly in D. Hence, given any positive number ϵ, we can find an integer N_1, depending only on ϵ, such that

$$\sum_{n+1}^{\infty} |v_r(z) - v_{r+1}(z)| < \tfrac{1}{3}\epsilon/K$$

when z is any point of D and $n \geqslant N_1$.

Moreover, since $v_n(z)$ tends to zero uniformly in D, we can find another integer N_2, depending only on ϵ, such that $|v_n(z)| < \tfrac{1}{3}\epsilon/K$ when $n \geqslant N_2$ and z is any point of D. Combining these results, we find that, if m is the greater of N_1 and N_2,

$$|S_{m+p}(z) - S_m(z)| < \epsilon,$$

for every positive integral value of p. Hence, by the principle of uniform convergence, the sequence of functions $S_0(z)$, $S_1(z)$, $S_2(z),\ldots$ converges uniformly in D. This completes the proof.

In a similar manner it can be proved† that *the series $\sum a_n(z)v_n(z)$ is uniformly convergent in a bounded closed domain D if*

(i) *the series $\sum a_n(z)$ converges uniformly in D,*

---

† See § 2.43, Ex. Compare the corresponding discussion of the uniform convergence of integrals in § 5.52.

(ii) *the series* $\sum |v_n(z) - v_{n+1}(z)|$ *is convergent and has a sum which is bounded in D, and*

(iii) *the function* $v_0(z)$ *is bounded in D.*

Example 1. The power series $\sum\limits_0^\infty a_n z^n$, whose radius of convergence is unity, converges at the point $z = 1$. Show that the series converges uniformly in the domain $|1-z| \leqslant \cos\delta$, $|\arg(1-z)| \leqslant \delta$, if $0 < \delta < \tfrac{1}{2}\pi$. Deduce that

$$\sum_0^\infty a_n z^n \to \sum_0^\infty a_n$$

as $z \to 1$ along any path within the circle of convergence which does not touch that circle.

We apply the second test of § 5.22, with $a_n(z) = a_n$, $v_n(z) = z^n$. Since $\sum a_n$ is convergent and a_n does not depend on z, the first condition is satisfied. The third condition is also satisfied since $v_0(z) = 1$.

When $|z| < 1$, we have

$$\sum |v_n(z) - v_{n+1}(z)| = |1-z| \sum |z|^n = \frac{|1-z|}{1-|z|}.$$

Now the domain defined by the inequalities $|1-z| \leqslant \cos\delta$, $|\arg(1-z)| \leqslant \delta$, is a sector of the circle with centre at $z = 1$ and radius $\cos\delta$. If $0 < \delta < \tfrac{1}{2}\pi$, each point of the sector, save $z = 1$, lies within the circle of convergence of the given power series. In this sector we have $1-z = \rho e^{i\phi}$, where $0 \leqslant \rho \leqslant \cos\delta$ and $-\delta \leqslant \phi \leqslant \delta$. Hence

$$|z|^2 = 1 - 2\rho\cos\phi + \rho^2 \leqslant 1 - 2\rho\cos\delta + \rho^2$$
$$\leqslant 1 - 2\rho\cos\delta + \rho\cos\delta \leqslant 1 - \rho\cos\delta + \tfrac{1}{4}\rho^2\cos^2\delta,$$

and so $|z| \leqslant 1 - \tfrac{1}{2}\rho\cos\delta.$

It follows, therefore, that at each point of the sector, save $z = 1$,

$$\sum |v_n(z) - v_{n+1}(z)| \leqslant \frac{\rho}{\tfrac{1}{2}\rho\cos\delta} = 2\sec\delta.$$

This inequality is also satisfied at $z = 1$, since each term of the series $\sum |v_n(z) - v_{n+1}(z)|$ vanishes there. The second condition of the test is thus also satisfied, and the proof of the first part of the problem is completed.

By § 5.12, the sum of the series $\sum a_n z^n$ is continuous in the sector under consideration. Hence

$$\sum a_n z^n \to \sum a_n$$

as $z \to 1$ along any path in the sector. This conclusion also holds when $z \to 1$ along any path within $|z| = 1$ which does not touch the circle of convergence; for, by choosing δ sufficiently near to $\tfrac{1}{2}\pi$, we can ensure that such a path lies in the given sector.

More generally, if the radius of convergence of the power series $\sum a_n z^n$ is finite and non-zero, and if the series converges at the point z_0 on the circle of convergence, then

$$\sum a_n z^n \to \sum a_n z_0^n$$

as $z \to z_0$ along any path which does not touch the circle of convergence. For the series $\sum a_n z_0^n z^n$ has radius of convergence unity and converges at the point $z = 1$. This result is *Abel's theorem on the continuity of power series.*

Example 2. Give an example to show that if the power series $\sum a_n z^n$ has a finite non-zero radius of convergence, and if the sum of the series tends to a finite limit as $z \to z_0$ on the circle of convergence along a path which does not touch that circle, it is not necessarily the case that $\sum a_n z_0^n$ converges.†

Example 3. Riemann's Zeta-function is defined by the equation $\zeta(z) = \sum_{1}^{\infty} n^{-z}$, when $\mathrm{Rl}\,z > 1$. Show that the analytical continuation of this function into the region where $\mathrm{Rl}\,z > 0$ is given by

$$(1 - 2^{1-z})\zeta(z) = 1^{-z} - 2^{-z} + 3^{-z} - 4^{-z} + \dots.$$

Hence show that the only singularity of $\zeta(z)$ in the right-hand half of the z-plane is a simple pole of residue 1 at the point $z = 1$.

We have seen (§ 5.21, Ex. 2) that the series defining $\zeta(z)$ converges uniformly and absolutely in any bounded closed domain to the right of the line $\mathrm{Rl}\,z = 1$. Hence, by § 5.13, $\zeta(z)$ is an analytic function, regular when $\mathrm{Rl}\,z > 1$.

Now, when $\mathrm{Rl}\,z > 1$,

$$(1 - 2^{1-z})\zeta(z) = \sum_{1}^{\infty} n^{-z}(1 - 2^{1-z}) = \sum_{1}^{\infty} n^{-z} - 2\sum_{1}^{\infty}(2n)^{-z}$$

$$= 1^{-z} - 2^{-z} + 3^{-z} - \dots,$$

the reordering of the terms of the series being valid by absolute convergence. We now show that the latter series converges uniformly in any bounded closed domain D in which $\mathrm{Rl}\,z \geqslant \delta$, provided that δ is positive. We use the first test of § 5.22, with

$$a_n(z) = (-1)^n, \qquad v_n(z) = (n+1)^{-z}.$$

The partial sums of $\sum a_n$ are alternately 1 and 0, so that condition (i) is satisfied. Condition (iii) is also satisfied, for

$$|v_n(z)| = (n+1)^{-\mathrm{Rl}\,z} \leqslant (n+1)^{-\delta},$$

and so $v_n(z)$ certainly tends to zero uniformly in D.

To show that condition (ii) also holds, we use the formula

$$v_n(z) - v_{n+1}(z) = (n+1)^{-z} - (n+2)^{-z} = z \int_{n+1}^{n+2} t^{-z-1}\, dt.$$

† For an account of the conditions under which the converse of Abel's theorem is true, see, for example, Landau, *Darstellung und Begründung einiger neuerer Ergebnisse der Funktionentheorie* (Berlin, 1929), 52–67.

This gives

$$|v_n(z)-v_{n+1}(z)| \leqslant |z| \int_{n+1}^{n+2} |t^{-z-1}|\, dt \leqslant |z| \int_{n+1}^{n+2} t^{-\delta-1}\, dt$$
$$< |z|.(n+1)^{-\delta-1}.$$

Since z is bounded in D, it follows by Weierstrass's M-test that $\sum \{v_n(z)-v_{n+1}(z)\}$ converges uniformly and absolutely there.

We have thus shown that the series

$$\eta(z) = 1^{-z}-2^{-z}+3^{-z}-4^{-z}+\dots$$

converges uniformly in any bounded closed domain in which $\mathrm{Rl}\,z > 0$. Hence $\eta(z)$ is an analytic function, regular when $\mathrm{Rl}\,z > 0$. But when $\mathrm{Rl}\,z > 1$, we have

$$\eta(z) = (1-2^{1-z})\zeta(z).$$

Accordingly this equation provides the analytical continuation of $\zeta(z)$ into the region $0 < \mathrm{Rl}\,z \leqslant 1$.

Now the function $1-2^{1-z}$ has simple zeros at the points given by

$$(1-z)\log 2 = 2p\pi i,$$

where p is any integer or zero. The equation $\zeta(z) = \eta(z)/(1-2^{1-z})$ shows that a point of this set is a simple pole of $\zeta(z)$, provided that $\eta(z)$ does not vanish there, and also shows that $\zeta(z)$ has no other singularities in the right-hand half of the z-plane.

The point $z = 1$ is a simple pole of $\zeta(z)$, since $\eta(1) = \log 2$. The residue there is

$$\lim_{z \to 1} \frac{(z-1)\eta(z)}{1-2^{1-z}} = \frac{\eta(1)}{\log 2} = 1.$$

But no other zero of $1-2^{1-z}$ is a pole of $\zeta(z)$. To show this, we use the equation

$$\eta_1(z) = (1-3^{1-z})\zeta(z),$$

where

$$\eta_1(z) = 1^{-z}+2^{-z}-2.3^{-z}+4^{-z}+5^{-z}-2.6^{-z}+\dots,$$

which the reader will easily prove. The function $\eta_1(z)$ is evidently an analytic function, regular when $\mathrm{Rl}\,z > 0$. Hence the poles of $\zeta(z)$ in the right-hand half of the z-plane are the points of the set

$$(1-z)\log 3 = 2q\pi i,$$

where q is any integer or zero, at which $\eta_1(z)$ does not vanish.

If $\zeta(z)$ possessed a pole other than $z = 1$ in the right-hand half of the z-plane, this would imply the existence of integers p and q such that

$$\frac{\log 3}{\log 2} = \frac{p}{q},$$

which is impossible. Hence $\zeta(z)$ has only one pole in $\mathrm{Rl}\,z > 0$.

5.3. Infinite products

The symbol

$$(1+a_1)(1+a_2)(1+a_3)\dots(1+a_n)\dots,$$

which involves the multiplication of an infinite number of complex numbers, has, in itself, no meaning. In order to assign

a meaning to the value of such an infinite product, we form the
sequence of partial products p_1, p_2, p_3,..., where

$$p_n = \prod_{r=1}^{n} (1+a_r).$$

If p_n tends to a finite non-zero limit p as n tends to infinity,
we say that the infinite product is convergent, and we write

$$p = \prod_{r=1}^{\infty} (1+a_r).$$

If, however, p_n tends to zero or does not tend to any finite
limit, we say that the infinite product is divergent.

In order that the infinite product may converge it is necessary that no factor should vanish; for if $1+a_m = 0$, then $p_n = 0$
when $n \geqslant m$. We shall suppose this condition is always satisfied. It is also necessary† that $a_n \to 0$ as $n \to \infty$, since

$$p_n = p_{n-1} + a_n p_{n-1}.$$

We shall now show that *the necessary and sufficient condition
for the convergence of the infinite product $\prod (1+a_n)$ is the convergence of the series $\sum \log(1+a_n)$, where each logarithm has its
principal value.*

Let us write $$s_n = \sum_{r=1}^{n} \log(1+a_r).$$

We then have $p_n = \exp(s_n)$. But since the exponential function
is continuous, $s_n \to s$ implies that $p_n \to e^s$. This proves the
sufficiency of the condition.

Now $$s_n = \log p_n + 2q_n \pi i,$$

where q_n is an integer. Since the principal value of the logarithm
of a product is not necessarily the sum of the principal values
of the logarithms of its factors, q_n is not necessarily zero. We
show that q_n is, however, constant for all sufficiently large values
of n; from this the necessity of the given condition will follow
immediately.

Let us write α_n and β_n for the principal values of the arguments of $1+a_n$ and p_n respectively. If the infinite product is
convergent, $\alpha_n \to 0$ and $\beta_n \to \beta$, say, as $n \to \infty$. The integer q_n
is then given by

$$\alpha_1 + \alpha_2 + \ldots + \alpha_n = \beta_n + 2q_n \pi.$$

† The example of the infinite product $\prod (1+1/n)$, for which $p_n = (n+1)$,
shows that this condition is not sufficient.

Hence we have

$$2(q_{n+1}-q_n)\pi = \alpha_{n+1}-(\beta_{n+1}-\beta_n) \to 0$$

as $n \to \infty$. But since q_n is an integer, this implies that $q_n = q$ for all sufficiently large values of n.

Therefore, if p_n tends to the finite non-zero limit p as $n \to \infty$, it follows that

$$s_n \to \log p + 2q\pi i,$$

and so the condition is also necessary.

5.31. Absolutely convergent infinite products

The infinite product $\prod (1+a_n)$ is said to be absolutely convergent if the series $\sum \log(1+a_n)$ is absolutely convergent. Evidently an absolutely convergent infinite product is convergent and its value is not altered when its factors are deranged. *The necessary and sufficient condition for the absolute convergence of the infinite product $\prod (1+a_n)$ is the absolute convergence of the series $\sum a_n$.*

For since $a_n \to 0$ as $n \to \infty$, we can find an integer N such that $|a_n| \leqslant \frac{1}{2}$ when $n \geqslant N$. Hence we have, when $n \geqslant N$,

$$\left| 1-\frac{\log(1+a_n)}{a_n} \right| = \left| \frac{a_n}{2}-\frac{a_n^2}{3}+\frac{a_n^3}{4}-... \right|$$

$$\leqslant \tfrac{1}{2}\{|a_n|+|a_n|^2+|a_n|^3+...\} \leqslant \tfrac{1}{2}$$

and so $$\tfrac{1}{2}|a_n| \leqslant |\log(1+a_n)| \leqslant \tfrac{3}{2}|a_n|.$$

This shows that the series $\sum \log(1+a_n)$ converges absolutely if and only if the series $\sum |a_n|$ is convergent, and the required result follows at once.

5.32. Uniformly convergent infinite products

Let $u_1(z), u_2(z), u_3(z),...$ be a sequence of one-valued functions, defined in a bounded closed domain D, such that the infinite product $\prod \{1+u_n(z)\}$ converges at each point of D. If the sequence of partial products

$$f_n(z) = \prod_{r=1}^{n} \{1+u_r(z)\}$$

converges uniformly in D, we say that the infinite product converges uniformly in D.

The simplest test for the uniform convergence of an infinite product is the M-test, which states that *the infinite product $\prod \{1+u_n(z)\}$ converges uniformly and absolutely in the bounded closed domain D if each function $u_n(z)$ satisfies there an inequality $|u_n(z)| \leqslant M_n$, where M_n is independent of z and $\sum M_n$ is convergent.*

The absolute convergence of this product is a consequence of § 5.31.

Let us write $P_n = \prod_1^n (1+M_r)$. Then since $\sum M_r$ is convergent, P_n tends to a finite limit as $n \to \infty$.

Now when $n > m$, we have

$$|f_n(z)-f_m(z)| = |f_m(z)| . \left| \prod_{m+1}^n \{1+u_r(z)\} - 1 \right|.$$

But if we multiply out $\prod_{m+1}^n \{1+u_r(z)\} - 1$, we obtain an expression of the form

$$\sum u_r(z) + \sum u_r(z)u_s(z) + \sum u_r(z)u_s(z)u_t(z) + \ldots +$$
$$+ u_{m+1}(z)u_{m+2}(z)\ldots u_n(z),$$

whose absolute value does not exceed

$$\sum M_r + \sum M_r M_s + \sum M_r M_s M_t + \ldots + M_{m+1}M_{m+2}\ldots M_n$$
$$= \prod_{m+1}^n (1+M_r) - 1.$$

Hence we have

$$|f_n(z)-f_m(z)| \leqslant \prod_{r=1}^m (1+M_r) \left\{ \prod_{m+1}^n (1+M_r) - 1 \right\} = P_n - P_m.$$

But since P_n tends to a limit, we can assign arbitrarily a positive number ϵ, and then choose m so that $0 < P_n - P_m < \epsilon$ when $n > m$. This gives

$$|f_n(z)-f_m(z)| < \epsilon$$

when $n > m$ and z is any point of D. Since m depends only on ϵ, the sequence of functions $f_1(z)$, $f_2(z)$, $f_3(z),\ldots$ converges uniformly. The test is thus established.

Finally, it follows immediately from § 5.13 that *if the infinite product $\prod \{1+u_n(z)\}$ converges uniformly to $f(z)$ in every closed domain within a closed contour C, and if each factor of the product is an analytic function, regular within C, then $f(z)$ is also regular within C.*

Example. Discuss the convergence of the infinite products

(i) $\left(1-\dfrac{z^2}{1^2}\right)\left(1-\dfrac{z^2}{2^2}\right)\left(1-\dfrac{z^2}{3^2}\right)...,$

(ii) $\left(1-\dfrac{z}{1}\right)\left(1+\dfrac{z}{1}\right)\left(1-\dfrac{z}{2}\right)\left(1+\dfrac{z}{2}\right)...,$

(iii) $\left\{\left(1-\dfrac{z}{1}\right)e^z\right\}\left\{\left(1+\dfrac{z}{1}\right)e^{-z}\right\}\left\{\left(1-\dfrac{z}{2}\right)e^{z/2}\right\}\left\{\left(1+\dfrac{z}{2}\right)e^{-z/2}\right\}...,$

in any bounded closed domain D which contains none of the points $\pm 1, \pm 2,....$.

There exists a constant R such that $|z| \leqslant R$ when z lies in D. Since $|z^2/n^2| \leqslant R^2/n^2$ and $\sum R^2/n^2$ is convergent, the product (i) converges uniformly and absolutely in D, by the M-test. If $F(z)$ is the value of the product, it is an analytic function,† regular in D.

On the other hand, the product (ii) does not converge absolutely in D, since the series $R(1+1+\tfrac{1}{2}+\tfrac{1}{2}+\tfrac{1}{3}+\tfrac{1}{3}+...)$ is divergent. Let us write $F_n(z), f_n(z)$ for the nth partial products of (i) and (ii) respectively. Then we have

$$f_{2n}(z) = F_n(z), \qquad f_{2n+1}(z) = \left(1-\frac{z}{n+1}\right)F_n(z),$$

and so the sequences $f_1(z), f_3(z), f_5(z),...$ and $f_2(z), f_4(z), f_6(z),...$ both converge uniformly to $F(z)$. Hence the infinite product (ii) converges uniformly in D to $F(z)$.

To discuss the third product we write

$$\left(1-\frac{z}{n}\right)e^{z/n} = 1-u_n(z),$$

where

$$u_n(z) = \sum_{r=2}^{\infty} \frac{(r-1)}{r!}\left(\frac{z}{n}\right)^r.$$

Then

$$|u_n(z)| \leqslant \sum_{r=2}^{\infty} \frac{1}{(r-2)!}\left(\frac{R}{n}\right)^r = \left(\frac{R}{n}\right)^2 e^{R/n} \leqslant e\left(\frac{R}{n}\right)^2,$$

when $n > R$. Similarly we have

$$\left(1+\frac{z}{n}\right)e^{-z/n} = 1-v_n(z),$$

where $|v_n(z)| \leqslant e(R/n)^2$ when z is any point of D and $n > R$. The M-test shows that the product (iii) converges uniformly and absolutely in D.

Finally, since the partial product of (iii) of order $2n$ is equal to $F_n(z)$, the third product also converges to $F(z)$.

5.4. Functions depending on a parameter

Let $f(z, \alpha)$ be a one-valued function of the two complex variables z and α, defined when z lies in a bounded closed

† It is well known that $F(z) = \sin \pi z/(\pi z)$. See § 6.83, Ex.

domain D and α lies in the circle $|\alpha-\alpha_0| < \rho$. If $f(z,\alpha)$ tends to a finite limit as $\alpha \to \alpha_0$ when z is any point of D, the limiting function $F(z)$ has a definite finite value at each point of D.

Let us suppose that this is the case. Then, given any positive number ϵ, we can find a positive number $\delta(\epsilon,z)$, depending on ϵ and on z, such that $|f(z,\alpha)-F(z)| < \epsilon$ when $|\alpha-\alpha_0| < \delta$.

We choose δ as large as possible.† Then $\delta(\epsilon,z)$ is a one-valued positive function of z defined everywhere in D. If there exists a positive number $\Delta(\epsilon)$, independent of z, such that $\delta(\epsilon,z) \geqslant \Delta(\epsilon)$ at each point z of D, we say that $f(z,\alpha)$ tends uniformly in D to the limiting function $F(z)$ as $\alpha \to \alpha_0$.

By the appropriate modification of the analysis of § 5.12, we can show that *if $f(z,\alpha)$ is a continuous function of z in the bounded closed domain D for each value of α in $|\alpha-\alpha_0| < \rho$, and if $f(z,\alpha) \to F(z)$ uniformly as $\alpha \to \alpha_0$, then $F(z)$ is continuous in D. Moreover, if L is any contour lying in D,*

$$\lim_{\alpha \to \alpha_0} \int_L f(z,\alpha)\, dz = \int_L F(z)\, dz.$$

Again, by an argument similar to that of § 5.13, we find that *if, for every value of α in $|\alpha-\alpha_0| < \rho$, the function $f(z,\alpha)$ is an analytic function of z, regular within a closed contour C, and if $f(z,\alpha) \to F(z)$ uniformly in every closed domain D within C, then $F(z)$ is regular within C and*

$$\frac{\partial f(z,\alpha)}{\partial z} \to F'(z)$$

uniformly in D.

5.5. Analytic functions defined by definite integrals

Let $F(z,t)$ be a one-valued function of the complex variable $z = x+iy$ and the real variable t defined when z lies within a closed contour C and $a \leqslant t \leqslant b$. Let us write

$$F(z,t) = \phi(x,y,t)+i\psi(x,y,t),$$

where ϕ and ψ are real functions of the three real variables

---

† The existence of a largest δ is readily proved by means of Dedekind's section of the real numbers.

x, y, t. If ϕ and ψ are continuous functions of position in the corresponding region of the three-dimensional space in which (x, y, t) are rectangular cartesian coordinates, we say that $F(z, t)$ is a continuous function of both variables z and t.

We shall now show that *if $F(z, t)$ is a continuous function of both variables when z lies within a closed contour C and $a \leqslant t \leqslant b$, and if, for each such value of t, $F(z, t)$ is an analytic function, regular within C, the function*

$$f(z) = \int_a^b F(z, t)\, dt$$

is also regular within C and its derivatives of all orders may be found by differentiating under the sign of integration.

To prove this, we divide the range of integration into n equal parts by points

$$a = t_0 < t_1 < t_2 < \ldots < t_{n-1} < t_n = b$$

and consider the behaviour of

$$f_n(z) = \sum_{r=1}^{n} F(z, t_r)(t_r - t_{r-1})$$

as $n \to \infty$. Since $F(z, t)$ is a continuous function of t,

$$f_n(z) \to \int_a^b F(z, t)\, dt = f(z)$$

as $n \to \infty$, for each value of z under consideration.

We now show that $f_n(z)$ tends to its limiting function $f(z)$ uniformly in every closed domain D within C. Since $F(z, t)$ is a continuous function of both variables when z lies in D and $a \leqslant t \leqslant b$, it is uniformly continuous there. Hence, given any positive number ϵ, we can find an integer m, depending only on ϵ, such that the inequality

$$|F(z, t) - F(z, t')| < \epsilon$$

holds when z is any point of D provided that $|t' - t| \leqslant (b-a)/m$. But, since

$$f_n(z) - f(z) = \sum_{r=1}^{n} \int_{t_{r-1}}^{t_r} \{F(z, t_r) - F(z, t)\}\, dt,$$

we have

$$|f_n(z)-f(z)| \leqslant \sum_{r=1}^{n} \int_{t_{r-1}}^{t_r} |F(z,t_r)-F(z,t)|\, dt < (b-a)\epsilon$$

provided that $n \geqslant m$, and so the sequence is uniformly convergent.

By the theorem of § 5.13, it follows that $f(z)$ is an analytic function, regular within C, and also that $f'_n(z) \to f'(z)$ uniformly in D. But since

$$f'_n(z) = \sum_{r=1}^{n} \frac{\partial F(z,t_r)}{\partial z}(t_r - t_{r-1}),$$

this implies that

$$f'(z) = \int_{a}^{b} \frac{\partial F(z,t)}{\partial z}\, dt.$$

The derivatives of higher orders may be discussed in the same manner. This completes the proof of the theorem.

Example. Show that the equation

$$\int_{0}^{2\pi} \frac{dt}{1+z\sin t} = \frac{2\pi}{\sqrt{(1-z^2)}}$$

holds everywhere in the z-plane, supposed cut along the real axis from $-\infty$ to -1 and from $+1$ to $+\infty$, provided that the branch of $\sqrt{(1-z^2)}$ which reduces to $+1$ at the origin is taken.

The integrand is a continuous function of both variables, save when $z = -\operatorname{cosec} t$. Now as t varies from 0 to π, this point moves along the real axis from $-\infty$ to -1 and then back to $-\infty$; as t increases from π to 2π, it moves along the real axis from $+\infty$ to $+1$ and then back to $+\infty$. Thus the integrand is a continuous function of both variables when t is real and z lies in the cut z-plane; moreover, for each such value of t, it is an analytic function whose only singularity is a pole lying on one or other of the cuts. Hence, by § 5.5, the value of the integral is an analytic function, regular in the cut plane.

We can, however, show by elementary methods that, when $-1 < z < 1$, the value of the integral is $2\pi/\sqrt{(1-z^2)}$, the positive square root being taken. But the branch of $2\pi/\sqrt{(1-z^2)}$ which is positive when $-1 < z < 1$ is an analytic function, regular in the cut plane.

We have thus shown that the expressions on each side of the equation

$$\int_{0}^{2\pi} \frac{dt}{1+z\sin t} = \frac{2\pi}{\sqrt{(1-z^2)}}$$

are regular in the same cut plane and are equal when $-1 < z < 1$. By analytical continuation, this equation holds everywhere in the cut plane.

5.51. Functions defined by infinite integrals†

Let the function $F(z,t)$ satisfy the following conditions:

(i) *it is a continuous function of both variables when z lies within the closed contour C and $a \leqslant t \leqslant T$, for every finite value of T;*

(ii) *for each such value of t, it is an analytic function of z, regular within C;*

(iii) *the integral*

$$f(z) = \int_a^\infty F(z,t)\, dt$$

is convergent when z lies within C and uniformly convergent when z lies in any closed domain D within C.

Then $f(z)$ is an analytic function of z, regular within C, whose derivatives of all orders may be found by differentiating under the sign of integration.

The third condition means that, as the real positive number T tends to infinity,

$$\int_a^T F(z,t)\, dt$$

tends to $f(z)$ when z is any point within C and that the convergence is uniform when z lies in D.

Let us consider, then, the behaviour of

$$f_n(z) = \int_a^n F(z,t)\, dt$$

as the integer n tends to infinity. By § 5.5, $f_n(z)$ is regular within C and satisfies all the conditions of the theorem of § 5.13. Hence $f(z)$ is regular within C, and $f_n'(z)$ converges uniformly to $f'(z)$ in D. But

$$f_n'(z) = \frac{d}{dz}\int_a^n F(z,t)\, dt = \int_a^n \frac{\partial F(z,t)}{\partial z}\, dt,$$

and so

$$f'(z) = \int_a^\infty \frac{\partial F(z,t)}{\partial z}\, dt.$$

This completes the proof of the theorem.

† It is assumed that the reader is acquainted with the theory of the convergence of infinite integrals, as given, for example, by Hardy, *Pure Mathematics* (1921), Chap. VIII.

5.52. Tests for the uniform convergence of infinite integrals

The simplest test for the uniform convergence of an infinite integral is the analogue of Weierstrass's M-test (§ 5.21), and runs as follows. *Let $F(z,t)$ be a continuous function of t when z lies in a bounded closed domain D and $t \geqslant a$, satisfying at each point of D the inequality*

$$|F(z,t)| \leqslant M(t),$$

where $M(t)$ is a positive function, independent of z. Then, if $\int_a^\infty M(t)\,dt$ converges, the integral $\int_a^\infty F(z,t)\,dt$ is uniformly and absolutely convergent in D.

Since $F(z,t)$ is a continuous function of t, $\int_a^T F(z,t)\,dt$ exists for every value of T ($> a$) and for each point z in D. By hypothesis, $\int_a^\infty M(t)\,dt$ converges; we can, therefore, assign arbitrarily a positive number ϵ, and then choose T, independently of z, so that

$$\int_T^\infty M(t)\,dt < \epsilon.$$

But if $T' > T$, we have

$$\left| \int_T^{T'} F(z,t)\,dt \right| \leqslant \int_T^{T'} |F(z,t)|\,dt \leqslant \int_T^\infty M(t)\,dt < \epsilon.$$

Hence $\int_a^\infty F(z,t)\,dt$ converges absolutely and uniformly when z lies in D.

To discuss the uniform convergence of integrals which do not converge absolutely, the following tests, similar to those of § 5.22 for series, are frequently of service. *Let $u(z,t)$ and $\partial v(z,t)/\partial t$ be continuous functions of t when z lies in a bounded closed domain D and $t \geqslant a$. Then the integral $\int_a^\infty u(z,t)\,v(z,t)\,dt$ is uniformly convergent in D if either of the following sets of conditions is satisfied:*

I. (i) $\left| \int_a^T u(z,t)\,dt \right| \leqslant K$, *where K is independent of z and T,*

(ii) $\displaystyle\int_a^\infty \frac{\partial v(z,t)}{\partial t}\, dt$ *is uniformly and absolutely convergent in* D,

  and

(iii) $v(z,t) \to 0$ *as* $t \to \infty$ *uniformly with respect to* z.

II. (i) $\displaystyle\int_a^\infty u(z,t)\, dt$ *is uniformly convergent in* D,

  (ii) $\displaystyle\int_a^\infty \left| \frac{\partial v(z,t)}{\partial t} \right| dt$ *converges and is a bounded function of* z,

  and

(iii) $v(z,a)$ *is a bounded function of* z *in* D.

For brevity, we shall only prove this theorem under conditions II. The proof under conditions I follows very similar lines.

The operation of partial summation on which the proof of the corresponding tests for series depended is replaced here by integration by parts. Let us write

$$U(z,t) = \int_a^t u(z,t)\, dt.$$

Then, if $T' > T$, we have

$$\int_T^{T'} u(z,t)\, v(z,t)\, dt = \{U(z,T') - U(z,T)\} v(z,T') -$$

$$- \int_T^{T'} \{U(z,t) - U(z,T)\} \frac{\partial v(z,t)}{\partial t}\, dt.$$

Now, by condition II (i), we can assign arbitrarily a positive number ϵ and then choose T, independently of z, such that the inequality $|U(z,t) - U(z,T)| < \epsilon$ holds when $t \geqslant T$ and z is any point of D. Hence

$$\left| \int_T^{T'} u(z,t)\, v(z,t)\, dt \right| \leqslant \epsilon \left\{ |v(z,T')| + \int_T^{T'} \left| \frac{\partial v(z,t)}{\partial t} \right| dt \right\}$$

$$= \epsilon \left\{ \left| v(z,a) + \int_a^{T'} \frac{\partial v(z,t)}{\partial t}\, dt \right| + \int_T^{T'} \left| \frac{\partial v(z,t)}{\partial t} \right| dt \right\}$$

$$\leqslant \epsilon \left\{ |v(z,a)| + 2 \int_a^{T'} \left| \frac{\partial v(z,t)}{\partial t} \right| dt \right\}$$

$$\leqslant \epsilon \left\{ |v(z,a)| + 2 \int_a^\infty \left| \frac{\partial v(z,t)}{\partial t} \right| dt \right\} < K\epsilon,$$

where, by II (ii) and II (iii), the finite positive number K is independent of z, T, T'. This, however, shows that

$$\int_a^\infty u(z,t)v(z,t)\, dt$$

converges uniformly in D.

Example 1. Show that

$$\int_0^\infty e^{-zt^2}\, dt = \frac{1}{2}\sqrt{\left(\frac{\pi}{z}\right)}$$

when $\mathrm{Rl}\, z > 0$, provided that the branch of $\sqrt{z}$ which is positive on the real axis is taken.

Let D be any bounded closed domain which contains part of the real axis and lies entirely to the right of the imaginary axis, so that the inequality $\mathrm{Rl}\, z \geqslant \delta$, where $\delta > 0$, is satisfied at each point z of D. Now, if $z = x + iy$, $$|e^{-zt^2}| = e^{-xt^2} \leqslant e^{-\delta t^2},$$ and $\int_0^\infty e^{-\delta t^2}\, dt$ is convergent. Hence, by the M-test, the given integral converges uniformly and absolutely in D, and its value is an analytic function of z, regular in D.

When z is real and positive, we can evaluate the integral by the substitution $zt^2 = u^2$, which gives

$$\int_0^\infty e^{-zt^2}\, dt = \frac{1}{\sqrt{z}} \int_0^\infty e^{-u^2}\, du = \frac{1}{2}\sqrt{\left(\frac{\pi}{z}\right)},$$

the square root being positive. Hence the expressions on each side of the equation

$$\int_0^\infty e^{-zt^2}\, dt = \frac{1}{2}\sqrt{\left(\frac{\pi}{z}\right)}$$

are analytic functions of z, regular in D, which are equal on the positive part of the real axis, provided that we take that branch of the square root which is positive when $z > 0$. It follows, by the principle of analytical continuation, that the equation still subsists everywhere in D.

4111   I

Example 2. Show that the result of Ex. 1 holds when $\mathrm{Rl}\, z \geqslant 0$, provided that $z \neq 0$. Deduce the value of $\int_0^\infty \cos t^2\, dt$.

We prove, first of all, that, if $a > 0$, $\int_a^\infty e^{-zt^2}\, dt$ converges uniformly when $r \leqslant |z| \leqslant R$, $|\arg z| \leqslant \tfrac{1}{2}\pi$, no matter how small the positive number r may be. The M-test is obviously inapplicable here, since $|e^{-zt^2}| = 1$ when $\mathrm{Rl}\, z = 0$.

Now if δ is any positive number less than r, we have seen that the integral converges uniformly when $\mathrm{Rl}\, z \geqslant \delta$, $|z| \leqslant R$. Accordingly it suffices to demonstrate its uniform convergence in the two rectangles defined by $0 \leqslant \mathrm{Rl}\, z \leqslant \delta$, $\rho \leqslant |\mathrm{Im}\, z| \leqslant R$, where $\rho = \sqrt{(r^2 - \delta^2)} > 0$. This we do by writing the integral in the form

$$\int_a^\infty e^{-xt^2} e^{-iyt^2}\, dt,$$

where $z = x + iy$, and then applying the second test of § 5.52, with

$$u(z,t) = te^{-iyt^2}, \qquad v(z,t) = e^{-xt^2}/t.$$

Now, when $0 \leqslant x \leqslant \delta$, $\rho \leqslant |y| \leqslant R$, we have

$$\left| \int_a^T u(z,t)\, dt \right| = \left| \frac{1}{2iy}(e^{-iya^2} - e^{-iyT^2}) \right| \leqslant \frac{1}{\rho},$$

so that condition I(i) is satisfied. Again I(ii) also holds; for $\partial v/\partial t$ is of constant sign and

$$\int_a^T \frac{\partial v(z,t)}{\partial t}\, dt = \frac{e^{-xT^2}}{T} - \frac{e^{-xa^2}}{a} \to -\frac{e^{-xa^2}}{a}$$

as $T \to \infty$, uniformly with respect to z. Finally, since $|v(z,t)| \leqslant 1/t$, condition I(iii) is satisfied, and so $\int_a^\infty e^{-zt^2}\, dt$ converges uniformly.

We have thus shown that $\int_0^\infty e^{-zt^2}\, dt$ converges uniformly† when $r \leqslant |z| \leqslant R$ and $|\arg z| \leqslant \tfrac{1}{2}\pi$, and so represents a regular analytic function. But in the part of this domain for which $\mathrm{Rl}\, z \geqslant \delta$, the value of the integral is $\tfrac{1}{2}\sqrt{(\pi/z)}$. Hence, by analytical continuation, this is the value of the integral when $\mathrm{Rl}\, z \geqslant 0$, provided that $z \neq 0$.

Putting $z = e^{\theta i}$, we have

$$\int_0^\infty \exp(-e^{\theta i}t^2)\, dt = \tfrac{1}{2}\sqrt{\pi}\, e^{-\frac{1}{2}\theta i}.$$

---

† Actually we proved this result with a as lower limit. This, obviously, does not affect the result but considerably simplifies its proof. It should be observed that the integral diverges when $z = 0$ and also when $\mathrm{Rl}\, z < 0$.

In particular,
$$\int_0^\infty e^{-it^2}\, dt = \tfrac{1}{2}\sqrt{\pi}\, e^{-\pi i/4},$$

and so
$$\int_0^\infty \cos t^2\, dt = \int_0^\infty \sin t^2\, dt = \sqrt{\frac{\pi}{8}}.$$

REFERENCE

T. J. I'A BROMWICH, *Infinite Series* (London, 1926), Chaps. VII, X and Appendix III.

MISCELLANEOUS EXAMPLES

1. Show that the series $\sum_0^\infty z e^{-nz}$ converges absolutely but not uniformly in the sector $|z| \leqslant R$, $|\arg z| \leqslant \delta$, where $0 < \delta < \tfrac{1}{2}\pi$. Is the convergence uniform when $r \leqslant |z| \leqslant R$, $|\arg z| \leqslant \delta$?

2. Prove that the sum of the series†
$$\frac{1}{z} + \sum_{n=-\infty}^{\infty}{}' \left(\frac{1}{z-n} + \frac{1}{n}\right)$$

is an analytic function whose only singularities are simple poles at the points $z = 0,\ \pm 1,\ \pm 2,\dots$.

3. Show that, if $\sum_1^\infty a_n$ is convergent, the series $\sum a_n n^{-z}$ converges when $\mathrm{Rl}\, z > 0$, but is not necessarily convergent when $\mathrm{Rl}\, z = 0$. Prove also that the convergence is uniform in any bounded closed domain for which $\mathrm{Rl}\, z \geqslant \delta$ where $\delta > 0$.

4. The series $\sum a_n(z^2 - 1^2)(z^2 - 2^2)\dots(z^2 - n^2)$ is known to converge for a non-integral value of z. Show that it converges uniformly in any bounded closed domain.

5. Discuss the convergence of the following infinite products:

(i) $\displaystyle\prod_1^\infty \left(n \sin\frac{z}{n}\right),$

(ii) $\displaystyle\prod_1^\infty \left\{\frac{n-z}{n+z} e^{2z/n}\right\},$

(iii) $\displaystyle\prod_1^\infty \left\{\left(1+\frac{1}{n}\right)^z \left(1-\frac{z}{n}\right)\right\},$

(iv) $\displaystyle\prod_0^\infty (1+z^{2^n}).$

Show also that, when $|z| < 1$, the value of the product (iv) is $1/(1-z)$.

6. If $\int_0^\infty \phi(t)\, dt$ converges, show that $\int_0^\infty e^{-zt}\phi(t)\, dt$ is uniformly convergent when $|z| \leqslant R$, $|\arg z| \leqslant \delta$, if $0 < \delta < \tfrac{1}{2}\pi$.

† The accent indicates that the term corresponding to $n = 0$ is omitted.

7. Show that $\int_{-\infty}^{\infty} e^{-t^2+2zt}\, dt$ is uniformly and absolutely convergent in any bounded closed domain and that its value is $\sqrt{\pi}\, e^{z^2}$. Deduce that

$$\int_{-\infty}^{\infty} e^{-t^2} \cos 2ty\, dt = \sqrt{\pi}\, e^{-y^2}.$$

8. The function $F(z, t)$ satisfies the conditions of § 5.5 save that it does not tend to a finite limit as $t \to a$, but

$$\int_{a}^{b} F(z, t)\, dt = \lim_{\delta \to 0} \int_{a+\delta}^{b} F(z, t)\, dt \qquad (\delta > 0)$$

exists. Show that if this limit is approached uniformly when z lies in any bounded closed domain within C, the function

$$f(z) = \int_{a}^{b} F(z, t)\, dt$$

is an analytic function, regular within C, whose derivatives may be calculated by differentiation under the sign of integration.

9. Show that†
$$\int_{0}^{\infty} t^{z-1} \cos t\, dt, \qquad \int_{0}^{\infty} t^{z-1} \sin t\, dt$$

represent analytic functions of z which are regular when $0 < \mathrm{Rl}\, z < 1$ and $-1 < \mathrm{Rl}\, z < 1$ respectively.

10. Prove that the equation

$$\Gamma(z) = \int_{0}^{\infty} e^{-t} t^{z-1}\, dt$$

defines an analytic function of z, regular when $\mathrm{Rl}\, z > 0$, which satisfies the difference equation $\Gamma(z+1) = z\Gamma(z)$.

$$\dagger \text{ Consider } \int_{0}^{1} \text{ and } \int_{1}^{\infty} \text{ separately.}$$

CHAPTER VI

THE CALCULUS OF RESIDUES

6.1. Cauchy's theorem of residues

Let $f(z)$ be continuous within and on a closed contour C and regular, save for a finite number of poles, within C. Then

$$\int_C f(z)\, dz = 2\pi i \times (\text{sum of residues of } f(z) \text{ at its poles within } C).$$

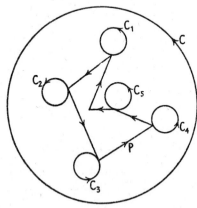

Fig. 2

If we denote by $z_1, z_2, ..., z_n$ the poles of $f(z)$ within C, we can evidently draw a set of circles C_r, of radius ϵ and centre z_r, which do not intersect and all lie within C, provided that ϵ is sufficiently small. Then $f(z)$ is regular in the domain bounded externally by C and internally by the circles C_r. We can, there-fore, deform C continuously without crossing a singularity of $f(z)$ until it consists of the circles C_r joined together by a poly-gon P, as shown in the figure. We then have

$$\int_C f(z)\, dz = \int_P f(z)\, dz + \sum_{r=1}^{n} \int_{C_r} f(z)\, dz = \sum_{r=1}^{n} \int_{C_r} f(z)\, dz,$$

the integral round the polygon P vanishing since $f(z)$ is regular within and on P.

Let z_r be a pole of order m, say, so that

$$f(z) = \phi(z) + \sum_{s=1}^{m} \frac{a_s}{(z-z_r)^s},$$

where $\phi(z)$ is regular within and on C_r. Then

$$\int_{C_r} f(z)\, dz = \sum_{s=1}^{m} \int_{C_r} \frac{a_s}{(z-z_r)^s}\, dz.$$

Now on C_r, $z = z_r + \epsilon e^{\theta i}$ where θ varies from 0 to 2π. Making this substitution we find that

$$\int_{C_r} f(z)\, dz = \sum_{s=1}^{m} a_s \epsilon^{1-s} \int_{0}^{2\pi} e^{(1-s)\theta i}\, i\, d\theta = 2\pi i a_1$$

$$= 2\pi i \times (\text{residue of } f(z) \text{ at } z_r).$$

From this it follows that

$$\int_{C} f(z)\, dz = \sum_{r=1}^{n} \int_{C_r} f(z)\, dz$$

$$= 2\pi i \times \sum_{r=1}^{n} (\text{residue of } f(z) \text{ at } z_r).$$

This completes the proof of Cauchy's theorem of residues.

6.2. The number of zeros of an analytic function

An important deduction from Cauchy's theorem of residues is a formula for the number of zeros of an analytic function within a given closed contour. Let $f(z)$ be regular within and on a closed contour C, save for poles b_1, b_2,..., b_n, none of which lie on C. Moreover, let $f(z)$ not vanish on C but have zeros a_1, a_2,..., a_m within C. Then, by the theorem of residues,

$$\frac{1}{2\pi i} \int_{C} \frac{f'(z)}{f(z)}\, dz$$

is equal to the sum of the residues of $f'(z)/f(z)$ at its singularities within C.

Now the only possible singularities of this function are the poles and zeros of $f(z)$. If a is a zero of order r, we have

$$f(z) = (z-a)^r \phi(z)$$

where $\phi(z)$ is regular and non-zero in a certain neighbourhood of a. This gives

$$\frac{f'(z)}{f(z)} = \frac{r}{z-a} + \frac{\phi'(z)}{\phi(z)}.$$

But since $\phi'(z)/\phi(z)$ is regular in the neighbourhood of a, the function $f'(z)/f(z)$ has a simple pole of residue r at $z = a$. Similarly, if $z = b$ is a pole of order s of the function $f(z)$, then $f'(z)/f(z)$ has a simple pole of residue $-s$ at $z = b$.

If, therefore, the order of the zero at $z = a_p$ is r_p and the order of the pole at $z = b_p$ is s_p, we have shown that

$$\frac{1}{2\pi i}\int_C \frac{f'(z)}{f(z)}\,dz = \sum_{p=1}^m r_p - \sum_{p=1}^n s_p.$$

This result takes a particularly simple form if we agree to regard each zero of order r as equivalent to r simple zeros and each pole of order s as equivalent to s simple poles; for, with this convention,

$$\frac{1}{2\pi i}\int_C \frac{f'(z)}{f(z)}\,dz$$

is equal to the excess of the number of zeros of $f(z)$ within C over the number of poles there.

If we actually carry out the integration, we find that this excess is equal to

$$\frac{1}{2\pi i}[\log f(z)]_C = \frac{1}{2\pi i}[\log|f(z)| + i\arg f(z)]_C = \frac{1}{2\pi}[\arg f(z)]_C,$$

since $\log|f(z)|$ returns to its original value when we go once round C. Hence *the excess of the number of zeros over the number of poles of $f(z)$ within C is $(1/2\pi)$ times the increase in $\arg f(z)$ as z goes once round C.* This result is sometimes called *the principle of the argument.*

Example 1. If $g(z)$ is regular within and on C and $f(z)$ satisfies the conditions of § 6.2, show that

$$\frac{1}{2\pi i}\int_C \frac{f'(z)}{f(z)}g(z)\,dz = \sum_{p=1}^m r_p\,g(a_p) - \sum_{p=1}^n s_p\,g(b_p).$$

Example 2. If $f(z)$ is regular within and on C and does not vanish on C, show that the sum of the affixes of the zeros of $f(z)$ within C is

$$\frac{1}{2\pi i}\int_C \frac{zf'(z)}{f(z)}\,dz,$$

the affix of a multiple zero being repeated according to its order.

6.21. Rouché's theorem

Rouché† has proved that, *if $f(z)$ and $g(z)$ are two functions regular within and on a closed contour C, on which $f(z)$ does not*

† *Journal de l'École Pol.* **39** (1862), 217.

vanish and also $|g(z)| < |f(z)|$, *then* $f(z)$ *and* $f(z)+g(z)$ *have the same number of zeros within* C.

For let $f(z)$ and $f(z)+g(z)$ have respectively m and n zeros within C, multiple zeros being counted according to their order. Then the function

$$F(z) = 1 + \frac{g(z)}{f(z)}$$

has n zeros and m poles within C, and is regular and never zero on C. By the principle of the argument, $2\pi(n-m)$ is equal to the increase in the argument of $F(z)$ as z goes round C.

But, when z is on C, we have

$$\mathrm{Rl}\{F(z)\} = 1 + \mathrm{Rl}\left\{\frac{g(z)}{f(z)}\right\}$$

$$\geqslant 1 - \left|\frac{g(z)}{f(z)}\right| > 0.$$

Hence as z goes round C, $F(z)$ describes a closed path entirely to the right of the imaginary axis, so that its argument returns to its original value; and this proves Rouché's theorem.

In particular, if we take

$$f(z) = a_0 z^m, \qquad g(z) = a_1 z^{m-1} + a_2 z^{m-2} + \ldots + a_m,$$

we have

$$\left|\frac{g(z)}{f(z)}\right| = \frac{1}{|a_0 z|}\left|a_1 + \frac{a_2}{z} + \ldots + \frac{a_m}{z^{m-1}}\right|,$$

which can be made as small as we please by taking $|z|$ sufficiently large. Hence there exists a circle $|z| = R$ on which $f(z)$ does not vanish and also $|g(z)| < |f(z)|$. But $f(z)$ has one zero of order m within this circle; therefore, by Rouché's theorem, the polynomial $a_0 z^m + a_1 z^{m-1} + \ldots + a_m$ has precisely m zeros within the circle $|z| = R$ for all sufficiently large values of R. If these zeros are $z_1, z_2, \ldots, z_m$, multiple zeros being repeated according to their order, the function

$$\frac{a_0 z^m + a_1 z^{m-1} + \ldots + a_m}{(z-z_1)(z-z_2)\ldots(z-z_m)}$$

is an integral function which tends to a_0 as $|z| \to \infty$, and so has the value a_0 for all values of z, by Liouville's theorem. Hence

$$a_0 z^m + a_1 z^{m-1} + \ldots + a_m = a_0(z-z_1)(z-z_2)\ldots(z-z_m).$$

We have thus proved the fundamental theorem of the algebra

of complex numbers, that *a polynomial of degree m has m zeros and can be expressed as a product of m linear factors.*

Example 1. Prove that a rational function takes any given value p times where p is the number of its poles, including the point at infinity, a pole of order s being counted s times.

Example 2. Each function of the sequence $f_0(z)$, $f_1(z)$, $f_2(z)$,.... is regular in the closed domain D bounded by a closed contour C. The sequence converges uniformly to $f(z)$ in D. Show that, if $f(z)$ does not vanish on C, then $f(z)$ and the functions $f_n(z)$, for all sufficiently large values of n, all have the same number of zeros within C.

Prove also that a zero of $f(z)$ is either a zero of $f_n(z)$ for all sufficiently large values of n or else is a limiting point of the set of zeros of the functions of the sequence. (HURWITZ.[†])

6.22. Inverse functions

Let $f(z)$ be an analytic function, regular in a neighbourhood of the point z_0, at which it takes the value w_0. The necessary and sufficient condition that the equation $f(z) = w$ should have a unique solution $z = F(w)$, regular in a neighbourhood of w_0, is that $f'(z_0)$ should not vanish.

The condition is obviously necessary. For if $F(w)$ were regular in a neighbourhood of w_0, $F'(w_0)$ would be finite; since, however, $F'(w_0) = 1/f'(z_0)$, $f'(z_0)$ cannot be zero.

The proof of the sufficiency of the condition is much more difficult; the one given below is due to Landau.[‡] We shall suppose that z_0 and w_0 are both zero; for, if they were not, we could make the transformation $z' = z - z_0$, $w' = w - w_0$. By hypothesis, $f(z)$ is regular when $|z| \leqslant R$, and so can be expressed there as a convergent Taylor series

$$f(z) = a_1 z + a_2 z^2 + ...,$$

where
$$|f'(0)| = |a_1| = a > 0.$$

Now if z_1 and z_2 are any two points of the region $|z| \leqslant \lambda R$ where $\lambda < 1$, we have

$$\left| \frac{f(z_1) - f(z_2)}{z_1 - z_2} \right| = \left| a_1 + \sum_2^\infty a_n(z_1^{n-1} + z_1^{n-2} z_2 + ... + z_2^{n-1}) \right|$$

$$\geqslant a - \sum_2^\infty n |a_n| \lambda^{n-1} R^{n-1}.$$

† *Math. Annalen*, **33** (1889), 246–66.
‡ *Berlin Sitzungsberichte* (1904), 1118–33; (1926), 467–74. *Math. Zeitschrift*, **30** (1929), 616–17.

Hence if λ is so small that

$$\sum_2^\infty n|a_n|\lambda^{n-1}R^{n-1} < a,$$

the equation $w = f(z)$ can have at most one root in $|z| \leqslant \lambda R$. Moreover, if such a root exists, it is not a multiple root; for

$$|f'(z)| = \left|a_1 + \sum_2^\infty na_n z^{n-1}\right| \geqslant a - \sum_2^\infty n|a_n|\lambda^{n-1}R^{n-1} > 0.$$

But, by hypothesis, $f(z)$ is regular in $|z| \leqslant R$ and so satisfies there an inequality $|f(z)| \leqslant M$, where M is a finite constant. Hence, by Cauchy's inequalities, we have

$$a \leqslant M/R, \qquad |a_n| \leqslant M/R^n,$$

and therefore

$$\sum_2^\infty n|a_n|\lambda^{n-1}R^{n-1} \leqslant \sum_2^\infty \frac{M}{R} n\lambda^{n-1} = \frac{M\lambda(2-\lambda)}{R(1-\lambda)^2} < \frac{2M\lambda}{R(1-\lambda)^2}.$$

If we now take $\lambda = \frac{1}{4}Ra/M$, so that $\lambda \leqslant \frac{1}{4}$, we easily find that

$$\sum_2^\infty n|a_n|\lambda^{n-1}R^{n-1} < 8a/9.$$

Hence the equation $w = f(z)$ has at most one simple root in the region $|z| \leqslant \frac{1}{4}R^2a/M$.

This, of course, implies that $f(z)$ has but one zero when $|z| \leqslant \frac{1}{4}R^2a/M$, namely the known simple zero at the origin. We deduce from this, by the aid of Rouché's theorem, that $f(z)-w$ has precisely one simple zero in the same region, provided that w is not too large.

Now when $|z| = \frac{1}{4}R^2a/M$, we have

$$|f(z)| \geqslant |a_1 z| - \sum_2^\infty |a_n z^n|$$

$$\geqslant a|z| - M \sum_2^\infty |z/R|^n$$

$$= \frac{R^2a^2}{4M} - M \sum_2^\infty \left(\frac{Ra}{4M}\right)^n$$

$$= \frac{R^2a^2}{4M}\left\{1 - \frac{M}{4M-Ra}\right\} \geqslant \frac{R^2a^2}{4M}\{1-\tfrac{1}{3}\} = \frac{R^2a^2}{6M},$$

by making use of the fact that $Ra \leqslant M$. We now see, by using Rouché's theorem, that $f(z)-w$ has just as many zeros as $f(z)$

in the region $|z| \leqslant \frac{1}{4} R^2 a/M$, provided that $|w| < \frac{1}{6} R^2 a^2/M$. In other words, it has precisely one simple zero there; let us denote this zero by $F(w)$.

Finally, by § 6.2, Ex. 2, we can obtain an explicit formula for $F(w)$, namely

$$F(w) = \frac{1}{2\pi i} \int_C \frac{zf'(z)}{f(z)-w}\, dz,$$

where C denotes the circle $|z| = \frac{1}{4} R^2 a/M$. On the contour C,

$$z = \tfrac{1}{4} R^2 a e^{it}/M,$$

where t varies from 0 to 2π, and so the integrand is a continuous function of t and w. Hence, by § 5.5, $F(w)$ is an analytic function of w, regular when $|w| < \frac{1}{6} R^2 a^2/M$. This completes the proof of the sufficiency of the condition.

It should be observed that we have not proved that $\frac{1}{6} R^2 a^2/M$ is the radius of convergence of the Taylor series for $F(w)$ in powers of w. All we know is that the radius of convergence is not less than $\frac{1}{6} R^2 a^2/M$.

Example. The function $f(z)$ is regular in a neighbourhood of the point z_0, at which it takes the value w_0. Show that, if the first $p-1$ derivatives of $f(z)$ vanish at z_0, the equation $f(z) = w$ has a solution

$$z - z_0 = \sum_1^\infty b_n (w-w_0)^{n/p},$$

where the series of powers of $(w-w_0)^{1/p}$ converges in a neighbourhood of w_0. Deduce that z is a p-valued function of w, having a branch-point at w_0.

6.23. Lagrange's formula for the reversion of series

We have just seen that, if

$$f(z) = w_0 + a_1(z-z_0) + a_2(z-z_0)^2 + \dots \qquad (a_1 \neq 0)$$

is regular near z_0, there is a unique function

$$F(w) = z_0 + b_1(w-w_0) + b_2(w-w_0)^2 + \dots,$$

regular near w_0, such that $z = F(w)$ is the solution of the equation $w = f(z)$. It is possible to obtain the coefficients b_n by substituting in the equation $w - w_0 = \sum_1^\infty a_n(z-z_0)^n$ the power series for $z - z_0$, and equating coefficients. A more elegant method can, however, be obtained by means of Cauchy's theorem, as we shall now show.

In the notation of § 6.22, we have

$$F(w) = \frac{1}{2\pi i} \int_C \frac{zf'(z)}{f(z)-w}\,dz,$$

where C is the circle $|z-z_0| = \frac{1}{4}R^2a/M$. From this it follows, by integration by parts, that

$$F'(w) = \frac{1}{2\pi i} \int_C \frac{zf'(z)}{\{f(z)-w\}^2}\,dz = -\frac{1}{2\pi i} \int_C z\frac{d}{dz}\{f(z)-w\}^{-1}\,dz$$

$$= \frac{1}{2\pi i} \int_C \frac{dz}{f(z)-w},$$

and so

$$F'(w) = \frac{1}{2\pi i} \int_C \left[1 + \sum_{n=1}^{\infty} \left\{\frac{w-w_0}{f(z)-w_0}\right\}^n\right] \frac{dz}{f(z)-w_0}.$$

We have, however, shown that

$$|f(z)-w_0| \geqslant \frac{1}{6}R^2a^2/M$$

when z lies on the contour C. Hence if

$$|w-w_0| \leqslant \frac{1}{6}\lambda R^2a^2/M,$$

where $0 < \lambda < 1$, the infinite series under the sign of integration in the formula for $F'(w)$ converges uniformly with respect to z and so can be integrated term by term. This gives

$$F'(w) = \sum_{n=1}^{\infty} nb_n(w-w_0)^{n-1},$$

where

$$nb_n = \frac{1}{2\pi i} \int_C \frac{dz}{\{f(z)-w_0\}^n}.$$

Since $f(z)-w_0$ has a simple zero at z_0 and vanishes nowhere else within or on C, the coefficient nb_n is evidently the residue of $\{f(z)-w_0\}^{-n}$ at the point z_0. A simple method of finding b_n is to proceed as follows. If we write

$$f(z)-w_0 = \frac{z-z_0}{\phi(z)},$$

$\phi(z)$ is regular within and on C, and therefore

$$nb_n = \frac{1}{2\pi i} \int_C \frac{\{\phi(z)\}^n}{(z-z_0)^n}\,dz = \frac{1}{(n-1)!}\left[\frac{d^{n-1}}{dz^{n-1}}\{\phi(z)\}^n\right]_{z=z_0}.$$

If we substitute this value of b_n in the series for $F'(w)$, we find that *if $f(z)$ is regular in a neighbourhood of z_0 and if $f(z_0) = w_0$, $f'(z_0) \neq 0$, then the equation*

$$f(z) = w$$

has a unique solution, regular in a neighbourhood of w_0, of the form

$$z = z_0 + \sum_{n=1}^{\infty} \frac{(w-w_0)^n}{n!} \left[\frac{d^{n-1}}{dz^{n-1}} \{\phi(z)\}^n \right]_{z=z_0},$$

where
$$f(z) - w_0 = (z - z_0)/\phi(z).$$

This is Lagrange's formula† for the reversion of a power series. It is a particular case of the following more general expansion

$$\psi(z) = \psi(z_0) + \sum_{n=1}^{\infty} \frac{(w-w_0)^n}{n!} \left[\frac{d^{n-1}}{dz^{n-1}} (\psi'(z)\{\phi(z)\}^n) \right]_{z=z_0},$$

which is also due to Lagrange. The proof of this is left to the reader.

6.3. The evaluation of definite integrals

The rest of this chapter is devoted to one of the first applications which Cauchy made of his residue theorem—the evaluation of definite integrals. The method to be adopted in any particular case should be clear after a consideration of the typical examples discussed below.

It should, however, be observed that a definite integral which can be evaluated by Cauchy's method of residues can always be evaluated by other means, though generally not so simply. On the other hand, quite simple definite integrals exist which cannot be evaluated by Cauchy's method, $\int_0^{\infty} e^{-x^2}\, dx$ being a case in point.

We discuss here three main types of definite integral, namely

$$\int_0^{2\pi} f(\cos\theta, \sin\theta)\, d\theta, \qquad \int_{-\infty}^{\infty} f(x)\, dx, \qquad \int_0^{\infty} x^{a-1} f(x)\, dx.$$

We also show how the values of certain integrals, usually determined by a complex change of variable, can be easily found by means of Cauchy's theorem.

† *Mémoires de l'Acad. Roy. des Sci.* (*Berlin*) **24** (1768), 251.

6.4. The evaluation of $\int\limits_0^{2\pi} f(\cos\theta, \sin\theta)\, d\theta$

If $f(\cos\theta, \sin\theta)$ is a rational function of the two variables $\cos\theta$ and $\sin\theta$ which is finite on the range of integration, we make the transformation $z = e^{\theta i}$. The integral becomes

$$\int\limits_C g(z)\, dz,$$

where $g(z)$ is a rational function of z, finite on the circle C whose equation is $|z| = 1$. The labour of evaluating the residues of $g(z)$ may often be considerably lightened by preliminary manipulation of the integral, before introducing the complex variable z.

Example 1. Evaluate $\int\limits_0^\pi \dfrac{a\, d\phi}{a^2 + \sin^2\phi}$, where a is positive.

If we denote the required value of the integral by I, we know that

$$I = \frac{1}{2}\int\limits_0^{2\pi} \frac{a\, d\phi}{a^2 + \sin^2\phi},$$

since the integrand is periodic, of period π. We may now evaluate the integral by the method of contour integration by making the substitution $z = e^{\phi i}$. This, however, leads to an integrand containing a polynomial of degree 4 in the denominator, so that the work would be rather laborious.

A simpler method is to write

$$I \equiv \int\limits_0^\pi \frac{a\, d\phi}{a^2 + \sin^2\phi} = \int\limits_0^\pi \frac{2a\, d\phi}{1 + 2a^2 - \cos 2\phi} = \int\limits_0^{2\pi} \frac{a\, d\theta}{1 + 2a^2 - \cos\theta},$$

and then to put $z = e^{\theta i}$. In this way we find that

$$I = \int\limits_C \frac{2ai}{z^2 - 2z(1 + 2a^2) + 1}\, dz,$$

where C denotes the circle $|z| = 1$.

The integrand has simple poles at the points $1 + 2a^2 + 2a\sqrt{(1+a^2)}$ and $(1 + 2a^2) - 2a\sqrt{(1+a^2)}$. If we take the positive square root, the former point lies outside C, the latter within C; moreover, the residue at the pole within C is

$$\frac{1}{2i\sqrt{(1+a^2)}}.$$

From this it follows, by Cauchy's theorem of residues, that

$$I = \pi/\sqrt{(1+a^2)}.$$

Example 2. Evaluate $\int_0^{2\pi} e^{\cos\theta}\cos(n\theta-\sin\theta)\,d\theta$, where n is a positive integer.

Consider

$$I = \int_0^{2\pi} e^{\cos\theta}\{\cos(n\theta-\sin\theta)-i\sin(n\theta-\sin\theta)\}\,d\theta$$

$$= \int_0^{2\pi} e^{\cos\theta+i\sin\theta-n\theta i}\,d\theta$$

$$= \frac{1}{i}\int_C e^z z^{-n-1}\,dz.$$

The origin is a pole of order $n+1$ of the function $e^z z^{-n-1}$, and the residue there is $1/n!$. Since the integrand has no other singularity, $I = 2\pi/n!$. Equating real and imaginary parts, we have

$$\int_0^{2\pi} e^{\cos\theta}\cos(n\theta-\sin\theta)\,d\theta = \frac{2\pi}{n!},$$

$$\int_0^{2\pi} e^{\cos\theta}\sin(n\theta-\sin\theta)\,d\theta = 0.$$

6.5. The evaluation of $\int_{-\infty}^{\infty} f(x)\,dx$

If the function $f(z)$ is regular in the half-plane $\operatorname{Im} z \geqslant 0$ save possibly for certain poles which do not lie on the real axis, we can evaluate

$$\int_{-\infty}^{\infty} f(x)\,dx$$

by considering the integral of $f(z)$ round a closed contour, consisting of the real axis from $-R$ to R and a semicircle in the upper half of the z-plane on this segment as diameter, provided that the integral round the semicircle tends to a limit as $R \to \infty$.

The simplest case occurs when the integrand is $O(|z|^{-k})$ for large values of $|z|$. Since the length of the semicircular part of the contour is πR, the integral along it is $O(R^{1-k})$ when R is large, and this will certainly tend to zero as $R \to \infty$, provided that $k > 1$. When, however, the integrand is not of the order of $|z|^{-k}$, where $k > 1$, a more delicate type of argument is needed to determine the limit of the integral round the semicircle.

It will be observed that this method gives

$$\lim_{R \to \infty} \int_{-R}^{R} f(x)\, dx.$$

If

$$\int_{-\infty}^{\infty} f(x)\, dx$$

exists in the ordinary sense,† it is necessarily equal to this limit. It may, however, happen that the limit exists, even though the integral does not. In this case we call the limit the *Cauchy principal value* of $\int_{-\infty}^{\infty} f(x)\, dx$, and write

$$\lim_{R \to \infty} \int_{-R}^{R} f(x)\, dx = P \int_{-\infty}^{\infty} f(x)\, dx.$$

Finally, it should be noticed that there is no special merit in a semicircle. All we need is a curve joining the points $\pm R$ which tends to the point at infinity as $R \to \infty$. For some purposes, the rectangle with vertices $\pm R$, $\pm R + iR$ is more convenient.

Example 1. Evaluate

$$\int_{-\infty}^{\infty} \frac{x^2 - x + 2}{x^4 + 10x^2 + 9}\, dx.$$

We consider

$$I = \int_{\Gamma} \frac{z^2 - z + 2}{z^4 + 10z^2 + 9}\, dz,$$

where Γ is the contour consisting of the real axis from $-R$ to R and the semicircle in the upper half-plane on this segment as diameter. The integrand has simple poles at the points $\pm i$, $\pm 3i$; when $R > 3$, the poles i and $3i$, which have residues $-(1+i)/16$ and $(3-7i)/48$ respectively, lie within Γ. Hence, by Cauchy's theorem of residues,

$$I = 5\pi/12.$$

† The integral exists in the ordinary sense when

$$\int_{0}^{\infty} f(x)\, dx, \qquad \int_{-\infty}^{0} f(x)\, dx$$

converge separately; that is, when

$$\int_{-R}^{S} f(x)\, dx$$

tends to a limit as R and S tend to infinity independently.

Now, when $|z|$ is large, the integrand is $O(|z|^{-2})$; we should, therefore, expect that the integral round the semicircle would be $O(1/R)$ when R is large, and so would tend to zero as $R \to \infty$. To put this argument in a rigorous form, we write $z = Re^{\theta i}$ when z lies on the semicircle, to obtain

$$I = \int_{-R}^{R} \frac{x^2 - x + 2}{x^4 + 10x^2 + 9} \, dx + J,$$

where

$$J = \int_{0}^{\pi} \frac{R^3 e^{3\theta i} - R^2 e^{2\theta i} + 2Re^{\theta i}}{(R^2 e^{2\theta i} + 1)(R^2 e^{2\theta i} + 9)} \, i \, d\theta.$$

Remembering the important inequality†

$$\left| \frac{1}{a-b} \right| \leqslant \left| \frac{1}{|a| - |b|} \right|,$$

we find that the modulus of the integrand does not exceed

$$\frac{R^3 + R^2 + 2R}{(R^2 - 1)(R^2 - 9)}$$

when $R > 3$. Hence

$$|J| \leqslant \frac{\pi(R^3 + R^2 + 2R)}{(R^2 - 1)(R^2 - 9)},$$

so that $J \to 0$ as $R \to \infty$.

We have thus proved that

$$\lim_{R \to \infty} \int_{-R}^{R} \frac{x^2 - x + 2}{x^4 + 10x^2 + 9} \, dx = \frac{5\pi}{12}.$$

But, since the integrand behaves like $1/x^2$ for large values of x,

$$\int_{-\infty}^{\infty} \frac{x^2 - x + 2}{x^4 + 10x^2 + 9} \, dx$$

exists in the ordinary sense and has, therefore, the value $5\pi/12$.

Example 2. Evaluate $\displaystyle\int_{-\infty}^{\infty} \frac{\cos x}{x^2 + a^2} \, dx$, where $a > 0$.

Let us consider

$$I = \int_{\Gamma} \frac{e^{iz}}{z^2 + a^2} \, dz$$

taken round the contour of Ex. 1. When $R > a$, there is only one pole of the integrand within Γ, namely a simple pole at ai of residue $e^{-a}/(2ai)$; hence

$$I = \pi e^{-a}/a.$$

† See § 1.32.

Now, when $z = x+iy$ and $y \geqslant 0$, we have

$$|e^{iz}| = |e^{ix-y}| = e^{-y} \leqslant 1,$$

so that e^{iz} is bounded in the upper half-plane. We should, therefore, expect that the integral round the curved part of Γ would be $O(1/R)$, when R is large, and so would tend to zero as $R \to \infty$. To prove this, we write $z = Re^{\theta i}$ when z lies on the semicircle to obtain

$$I = \int_{-R}^{R} \frac{e^{ix}}{x^2+a^2}\, dx + J,$$

where

$$J = \int_{0}^{\pi} iRe^{\theta i}\, \frac{e^{iR\cos\theta - R\sin\theta}}{R^2 e^{2\theta i}+a^2}\, d\theta.$$

From this it follows that

$$|J| \leqslant \int_{0}^{\pi} \frac{R}{R^2-a^2}\, e^{-R\sin\theta}\, d\theta < \frac{\pi R}{R^2-a^2}$$

so that $J \to 0$ as $R \to \infty$.

We have thus proved that the integral

$$\int_{-\infty}^{\infty} \frac{e^{ix}}{x^2+a^2}\, dx,$$

which obviously exists in the ordinary sense, has the value $\pi e^{-a}/a$. If we now equate real and imaginary parts, we find that

$$\int_{-\infty}^{\infty} \frac{\cos x}{x^2+a^2}\, dx = \frac{\pi e^{-a}}{a}, \qquad \int_{-\infty}^{\infty} \frac{\sin x}{x^2+a^2}\, dx = 0.$$

Example 3. Evaluate $\displaystyle\int_{0}^{\infty} \frac{x\sin x}{x^2+a^2}\, dx$, when a is positive.

We shall find the value of this definite integral by considering the contour integral

$$I = \int_{\Gamma} \frac{ze^{iz}}{z^2+a^2}\, dz.$$

Here Γ denotes a closed contour consisting of the segment of the real axis from $-R$ to R and a curve σ in the upper half-plane which joins the ends of this segment and tends to the point at infinity as $R \to \infty$. Evidently, for sufficiently large values of R, there is no singularity of the integrand on Γ and one singularity, namely the simple pole ai, within Γ. By Cauchy's theorem of residues, it follows that

$$I = \pi i e^{-a}$$

for all sufficiently large values of R.

We can also express I in the form

$$I = \int_{-R}^{R} \frac{x e^{ix}}{x^2 + a^2} \, dx + J,$$

where

$$J = \int_{\sigma} \frac{z e^{iz}}{z^2 + a^2} \, dz.$$

To determine the value of the given definite integral, it is necessary to consider the behaviour of J as R is increased indefinitely.

Now when $\operatorname{Im} z \geqslant 0$ and $|z|$ is large, the integrand is $O(|z|^{-1})$. It follows that, if σ is a semicircle, J is bounded as $R \to \infty$. To see whether J actually tends to a limit, a more delicate type of argument is needed.

One method of doing this is to keep the semicircular contour σ and apply Jordan's inequality; this is explained in § 6.52, below. A more elementary method is to use a rectangular contour Γ with vertices $\pm R$, $\pm R + Ri$. In this case σ consists of three sides of this rectangle, and we easily find that

$$J = \int_{0}^{R} \frac{(R + iy) e^{iR - y}}{(R + iy)^2 + a^2} i \, dy - \int_{-R}^{R} \frac{(x + iR) e^{ix - R}}{(x + iR)^2 + a^2} \, dx -$$

$$- \int_{0}^{R} \frac{(-R + iy) e^{-iR - y}}{(-R + iy)^2 + a^2} i \, dy$$

$$= J_1 - J_2 - J_3,$$

say. We then have

$$|J_1| \leqslant \int_{0}^{R} \frac{\sqrt{(R^2 + y^2)} e^{-y}}{R^2 + y^2 - a^2} \, dy \leqslant \frac{R\sqrt{2}}{R^2 - a^2} \int_{0}^{R} e^{-y} \, dy$$

$$= \frac{R\sqrt{2}}{R^2 - a^2} (1 - e^{-R})$$

so that $J_1 \to 0$ as $R \to \infty$; similarly $J_3 \to 0$. Again

$$|J_2| \leqslant \int_{-R}^{R} \frac{\sqrt{(x^2 + R^2)} e^{-R}}{x^2 + R^2 - a^2} \, dx \leqslant \frac{R\sqrt{2}}{R^2 - a^2} e^{-R} \int_{-R}^{R} dx$$

$$= \frac{R^2 \sqrt{8}}{R^2 - a^2} e^{-R},$$

and so $J_2 \to 0$ as $R \to \infty$. Adding these results, we find that J tends to zero as R is increased indefinitely.

Another simple method of obtaining the limit of J is to keep the semicircular contour σ and integrate by parts.† This gives

$$\int_\sigma \frac{ze^{iz}}{z^2+a^2}\,dz = -\left[\frac{ize^{iz}}{z^2+a^2}\right]_{-R}^R + \int_\sigma \frac{(a^2-z^2)ie^{iz}}{(z^2+a^2)^2}\,dz,$$

and the two terms on the right-hand side of this equation clearly tend to zero as $R \to \infty$.

We have thus shown that

$$\lim_{R\to\infty}\int_{-R}^R \frac{xe^{ix}}{x^2+a^2}\,dx = \pi i e^{-a}.$$

This, however, implies that

$$\int_{-\infty}^\infty \frac{xe^{ix}}{x^2+a^2}\,dx = \pi i e^{-a},$$

the existence of this infinite integral in the ordinary sense being an easy consequence of Dirichlet's test.‡ Equating real and imaginary parts we obtain

$$\int_{-\infty}^\infty \frac{x\cos x}{x^2+a^2}\,dx = 0, \qquad \int_{-\infty}^\infty \frac{x\sin x}{x^2+a^2}\,dx = \pi e^{-a}.$$

From this it follows that

$$\int_0^\infty \frac{x\sin x}{x^2+a^2}\,dx = \tfrac{1}{2}\pi e^{-a},$$

when a is positive.

Example 4. Prove that

$$\int_{-\infty}^\infty \frac{x^2\,dx}{(x^2+a^2)^3} = \frac{\pi}{8a^3},$$

provided that $\mathrm{Rl}\,a$ is positive. What is the value of this integral when $\mathrm{Rl}\,a$ is negative?

Example 5. Show that

$$\int_{-\infty}^\infty \frac{dx}{(x^2+a^2)^2(x^2+b^2)} = \frac{\pi(2a+b)}{2a^3b(a+b)^2}$$

when the real parts of a and b are positive.

† I owe this remark to Mr. W. L. Ferrar.
‡ See Bromwich, *Infinite Series* (1926), 477. This test is essentially the second test of § 5.52, above, under conditions I with the references to uniformity omitted.

Example 6. $f(z)$ is an analytic function whose only singularities in the upper half-plane are poles, finite in number, and which has no singularity on the real axis. Show that, if $Rf(Re^{\theta i})$ tends to zero as $R \to \infty$, uniformly with respect to θ when $0 \leqslant \theta \leqslant \pi$, then the principal value of $\int_{-\infty}^{\infty} f(x)\, dx$ is equal to $2\pi i$ times the sum of the residues of $f(z)$ at its poles in the upper half-plane.

6.51. Cauchy's definition of an improper integral

The ordinary definition of the integral of a function $f(x)$ of the real variable x over a finite interval $a \leqslant x \leqslant b$ presupposes that $f(x)$ has a definite finite value at each point of the interval. We shall now explain how Cauchy extended this definition to cover cases when $f(x)$ is infinite at a finite number of points of the interval.

It suffices to consider the case when there is only one point c at which $f(x)$ becomes infinite. If c is not an end-point of the interval, we take two small positive numbers ϵ and η and consider the expression

$$\int_a^{c-\epsilon} f(x)\, dx + \int_{c+\eta}^b f(x)\, dx.$$

If this expression exists and tends to a unique limit as ϵ and η tend to zero independently, we say that the improper integral of $f(x)$ over the interval exists, its value being defined by

$$\int_a^b f(x)\, dx = \lim_{\epsilon \to +0} \int_a^{c-\epsilon} f(x)\, dx + \lim_{\eta \to +0} \int_{c+\eta}^b f(x)\, dx.$$

If, however, the expression does not tend to a limit as ϵ and η tend to zero independently, it may still happen that

$$\lim_{\epsilon \to +0} \left\{ \int_a^{c-\epsilon} f(x)\, dx + \int_{c+\epsilon}^b f(x)\, dx \right\}$$

exists. When this is the case, we call this limit the *Cauchy principal value* of the improper integral and denote it by

$$P \int_a^b f(x)\, dx.$$

Finally, if $f(x)$ becomes infinite at an end-point, a say, of the range of integration, we say that $f(x)$ is integrable over $a \leqslant x \leqslant b$ if

$$\lim_{\epsilon \to +0} \int_{a+\epsilon}^{b} f(x)\, dx$$

exists.

When we attempt to determine the value or principal value of an improper integral by means of Cauchy's theorem of residues, we have the difficulty that the integrand has a singularity c on the contour of integration. We avoid this difficulty by modifying the contour in the following way: we delete from the area within the contour the portion which also lies within a small circle $|z-c| = \epsilon$ and then integrate round the boundary of the remaining region. This process is called *indenting* the contour.

The integral round the indented contour is calculated by the theorem of residues and then the radius of each indentation is made to tend to zero. This process gives the Cauchy principal value of the improper integral, and the question of the existence of the improper integral in the ordinary sense requires further investigation. The details of this method will become obvious from a consideration of the following examples.

Example 1. Prove that, if $a > 0$,

$$P\int_{-\infty}^{\infty} \frac{\cos x}{a^2 - x^2}\, dx = \frac{\pi \sin a}{a}.$$

We consider

$$I = \int_{\Gamma} \frac{e^{iz}}{a^2 - z^2}\, dz,$$

where the closed contour Γ consists of the real axis from $-R$ to R and a semicircle in the upper half of the z-plane on this segment as diameter. Since the integrand has poles at $z = \pm a$, which lie on this contour, we modify Γ by making an indentation of radius ϵ at a and another of radius η at $-a$. The integrand is now regular within and on Γ, and so I is zero.

Evaluating the various parts of the integral I, we obtain

$$0 = \int_{0}^{\pi} \frac{e^{iR\cos\theta - R\sin\theta}}{a^2 - R^2 e^{2\theta i}}\, iRe^{\theta i}\, d\theta + J_1 + J_2 + \int_{-R}^{-a-\eta} + \int_{-a+\eta}^{a-\epsilon} + \int_{a+\epsilon}^{R} \frac{e^{ix}}{a^2 - x^2}\, dx,$$

where J_1 and J_2 denote the integrals round the indentations at a and $-a$ respectively.

The modulus of the first term on the right-hand side of this equation is less than $\pi R/(R^2-a^2)$ and so this term tends to zero as $R \to \infty$. To evaluate J_1, we observe that, on the indentation at a, $z = a+\epsilon e^{\theta i}$ where θ decreases from π to 0. Hence

$$J_1 = \int\limits_{\pi}^{0} \exp(ia+i\epsilon e^{\theta i}) \frac{\epsilon i e^{\theta i}\,d\theta}{-2a\epsilon e^{\theta i}-\epsilon^2 e^{2\theta i}}$$

$$= \int\limits_{0}^{\pi} \exp(ia+i\epsilon e^{\theta i}) \frac{i\,d\theta}{2a+\epsilon e^{\theta i}}$$

$$\to \frac{\pi i e^{ia}}{2a}$$

as ϵ tends to zero.† Similarly, J_2 tends to $-\tfrac{1}{2}\pi i e^{-ia}/a$ as η tends to zero.

Making $R \to \infty$, $\epsilon \to 0$, $\eta \to 0$, we find that

$$P \int\limits_{-\infty}^{\infty} \frac{e^{ix}}{a^2-x^2}\,dx = -\frac{\pi i}{2a}(e^{ia}-e^{-ia}) = \frac{\pi \sin a}{a},$$

where, so far, the integral is a principal value with respect to the infinite limits and also with respect to the singularities at $\pm a$. But since the integrand behaves like $1/x^2$ for large real values of x, the integral is an ordinary infinite integral as regards the limits. If, however, we write $x = a+\xi$, we find that the integrand behaves like a constant multiple of $1/\xi$ when ξ is small. Thus the integral exists only as a Cauchy principal value with respect to the pole a; a similar remark applies to $-a$.

Finally, equating real and imaginary parts, we obtain

$$P \int\limits_{-\infty}^{\infty} \frac{\cos x}{a^2-x^2}\,dx = \frac{\pi}{a}\sin a, \qquad P \int\limits_{-\infty}^{\infty} \frac{\sin x}{a^2-x^2}\,dx = 0.$$

Example 2. The function $f(z)$ has a simple pole of residue r at a point c on a simple closed contour Γ. If Γ be indented at c, show that the integral of $f(z)$ round the indentation tends to $-r\alpha i$ as the radius of the indentation tends to zero, α being the internal angle between the two parts of Γ meeting at c.

Example 3. By integrating e^{iz}/z round the rectangle with vertices at $\pm R$, $\pm R+Ri$ indented at the origin, prove that

$$\int\limits_{-\infty}^{\infty} \frac{\sin x}{x}\,dx = \pi.$$

Example 4. Obtain the result of Ex. 3 by using an indented semi-circular contour.

† Evidently J_1 has, as *limit*, $-\pi i$ times the residue of the integrand at a. See Ex. 2, below.

6.52. Jordan's inequality

Since $\cos\theta$ decreases steadily as θ increases from 0 to $\frac{1}{2}\pi$, the mean ordinate of the graph of $y = \cos x$ over the range $0 \leqslant x \leqslant \theta$ also decreases steadily. But this mean ordinate is

$$\frac{1}{\theta} \int_0^\theta \cos x \, dx = \frac{\sin\theta}{\theta}.$$

We have therefore proved that, when $0 \leqslant \theta \leqslant \frac{1}{2}\pi$,

$$\frac{2}{\pi} \leqslant \frac{\sin\theta}{\theta} \leqslant 1,$$

that is, that $\qquad \dfrac{2\theta}{\pi} \leqslant \sin\theta \leqslant \theta.$

This is known as *Jordan's inequality*.†

The importance of Jordan's inequality lies in the fact that it enables us to evaluate integrals of the type exemplified by § 6.5, Ex. 3, without having to use a rectangular contour or integration by parts.

Example 1. Evaluate $\displaystyle\int_{-\infty}^{\infty} \frac{x\sin x}{x^2+a^2}\, dx,$ where $a > 0$.

We have already proved that

$$\int_{-R}^{R} \frac{xe^{ix}}{x^2+a^2}\, dx + \int_0^\pi \frac{e^{iR\cos\theta - R\sin\theta}}{R^2 e^{2\theta i} + a^2}\, iR^2 e^{2\theta i}\, d\theta = \pi i e^{-a}.$$

Now the absolute value of the second integral on the left-hand side does not exceed

$$\frac{R^2}{R^2 - a^2} \int_0^\pi e^{-R\sin\theta}\, d\theta = \frac{2R^2}{R^2 - a^2} \int_0^{\frac{1}{2}\pi} e^{-R\sin\theta}\, d\theta$$

$$\leqslant \frac{2R^2}{R^2 - a^2} \int_0^{\frac{1}{2}\pi} e^{-2R\theta/\pi}\, d\theta, \quad \text{by Jordan's inequality,}$$

$$= \frac{\pi R}{R^2 - a^2}\{1 - e^{-R}\} < \frac{\pi R}{R^2 - a^2},$$

† *Cours d'Analyse*, **2** (1894), 286.

which tends to zero as $R \to \infty$. We have thus proved that

$$\lim_{R \to \infty} \int_{-R}^{R} \frac{xe^{ix}}{x^2+a^2}\, dx = \pi i e^{-a},$$

from which the value of the given integral follows at once.

Example 2. Evaluate $\int_{-\infty}^{\infty} \frac{\sin x}{x}\, dx$, by the aid of Jordan's inequality.

Example 3. Prove *Jordan's lemma*, that, if σ denotes the semicircle $|z| = R$ in the upper half-plane and if $m > 0$, then

$$\lim_{R \to \infty} \int_{\sigma} e^{miz} f(z)\, dz = 0,$$

provided that, as $R \to \infty$, $f(Re^{\theta i}) \to 0$ uniformly with respect to θ when $0 \leqslant \theta \leqslant \pi$.

6.6. Evaluation of integrals of the form $\int_0^{\infty} x^{a-1} f(x)\, dx$, where a is a real constant

Let $f(x)$ be a rational function which has either no poles or else only simple poles on the positive part of the real axis. Then if $x^a f(x) \to 0$ as $x \to 0$ and also as $x \to \infty$, $\int_0^{\infty} x^{a-1} f(x)\, dx$ converges at the upper and lower limits of integration and possesses a Cauchy principal value with respect to each singularity on the range of integration.

There are three main methods of evaluating such integrals.

First method. If we make the substitution $t = e^x$, we find that

$$\int_0^{\infty} t^{a-1} f(t)\, dt = \int_{-\infty}^{\infty} e^{ax} f(e^x)\, dx.$$

The latter integral may be evaluated by considering

$$\int_{\Gamma} e^{az} f(e^z)\, dz,$$

where Γ consists of the segment of the real axis† from $-R$ to R, and the semicircle in the upper half-plane on this segment as diameter.

But if α is a pole of $f(z)$, the function $f(e^z)$ has a pole at each

† Indented if necessary.

point $z = \log \alpha + 2n\pi i$, where n is any integer. The contour integral is thus expressed as a sum of an infinite series of residues, which often diverges.†

This difficulty is overcome by observing that, since $f(e^z)$ is a rational function of e^z,

$$e^{a(z+2\pi i)}f(e^{z+2\pi i}) = e^{2a\pi i}e^{az}f(e^z);$$

that is, the values of the integrand on the real axis differ from those on the line $\operatorname{Im} z = 2\pi$ only in the factor $e^{2a\pi i}$.

We consider, therefore,

$$\int_\Gamma e^{az}f(e^z)\, dz,$$

where Γ is the rectangle with vertices $R, R+2\pi i, -S+2\pi i, -S$ and then make the positive numbers R, S tend to infinity.

Second method. The function $z^{a-1}f(-z)$ has, in general, a branch-point at the origin. If z^{a-1} is taken to be real and positive on the positive part of the real axis, the branch of $z^{a-1}f(-z)$ so defined is regular, save for poles, in the whole z-plane cut along the negative part of the real axis.

If, then, Γ consists of the real axis from $-R$ to R indented at the origin (and elsewhere, if necessary) and the semicircle in the upper half-plane on this segment as diameter, we can evaluate

$$\int_\Gamma z^{a-1}f(-z)\, dz$$

by Cauchy's theorem of residues. But the contribution of the real axis to this contour integral is

$$\int_\epsilon^R x^{a-1}f(-x)\, dx + \int_R^\epsilon (re^{\pi i})^{a-1}f(-re^{\pi i})e^{\pi i}\, dr$$

$$= \int_\epsilon^R x^{a-1}f(-x)\, dx - e^{a\pi i}\int_\epsilon^R r^{a-1}f(r)\, dr$$

since $\arg z$ has increased to π when z reaches the negative part of the real axis in going round Γ. The value of the given integral is then obtained by equating imaginary parts.

---

† It may, however, be summable by one of the conventional methods of summation of divergent series.

Third method. If Γ denotes the contour† formed by the circles $|z| = R$, $|z| = \epsilon$, joined together along the upper and lower sides of the cut along the negative part of the real axis, we may evaluate

$$\int_{\Gamma} z^{a-1} f(-z)\, dz,$$

where z^{a-1} has its principal value, by Cauchy's theorem of residues, since the integrand is regular, save for poles, within and on Γ. The contributions of the two sides of the cut are

$$\int_{R}^{\epsilon} e^{a\pi i} r^{a-1} f(r)\, dr + \int_{\epsilon}^{R} e^{-a\pi i} r^{a-1} f(r)\, dr = -2i \sin a\pi \int_{\epsilon}^{R} r^{a-1} f(r)\, dr,$$

since $\arg z$ is equal to $\pm\pi i$ on the cut. The value of the required integral now follows at once. It should be observed that the contour in the third method may be derived from that of the first by the substitution $e^z = -\zeta$.

These three methods are illustrated in the following examples.

Example 1. Evaluate $\displaystyle\int_{0}^{\infty} \frac{t^{a-1}}{1+t}\, dt$, where $0 < a < 1$.

First method. If we put $t = e^x$, we have

$$\int_{0}^{\infty} \frac{t^{a-1}}{1+t}\, dt = \int_{-\infty}^{\infty} \frac{e^{ax}}{e^x+1}\, dx.$$

We consider therefore $\qquad I = \displaystyle\int_{\Gamma} \frac{e^{az}}{e^z+1}\, dz,$

where Γ is the rectangle with vertices at R, $R+2\pi i$, $-S+2\pi i$, $-S$ where R and S are positive. The integrand has but one singularity within Γ, a simple pole at $z = \pi i$; the residue is

$$\lim_{z\to\pi i} \frac{e^{az}(z-\pi i)}{e^z+1} = e^{a\pi i} \lim_{z\to\pi i} \frac{z-\pi i}{e^z+1} = -e^{a\pi i},$$

and so $I = -2\pi i e^{a\pi i}$.

But we may write

$$I = (1-e^{2a\pi i}) \int_{-S}^{R} \frac{e^{ax}}{e^x+1}\, dx + \int_{0}^{2\pi} \frac{e^{aR+iay}}{e^{R+iy}+1} i\, dy - \int_{0}^{2\pi} \frac{e^{-aS+iay}}{e^{-S+iy}+1} i\, dy.$$

† Cf. Fig. 4 on p. 141.

Now
$$\left| \int_0^{2\pi} \frac{e^{aR+iy}}{e^{R+iy}+1} i \, dy \right| \leqslant \frac{2\pi e^{aR}}{e^R-1},$$

which tends to zero as $R \to \infty$, since $a < 1$; moreover

$$\left| \int_0^{2\pi} \frac{e^{-aS+iy}}{e^{-S+iy}+1} i \, dy \right| \leqslant \frac{2\pi e^{-aS}}{1-e^{-S}},$$

which tends to zero as $S \to \infty$, since $a > 0$. Hence we have

$$-2\pi i e^{a\pi i} = (1-e^{2a\pi i}) \int_{-\infty}^{\infty} \frac{e^{ax}}{e^x+1} dx,$$

so that
$$\int_0^{\infty} \frac{t^{a-1}}{1+t} dt = \int_{-\infty}^{\infty} \frac{e^{ax}}{e^x+1} dx = \frac{\pi}{\sin a\pi}.$$

It should be observed that, by the principle of analytical continuation, this equation also holds when $0 < \mathrm{Rl}\, a < 1$, since the expressions on each side of the equation are analytic functions of a, regular in this strip.

Second method. We consider the value of the contour integral

$$I = \int_{\Gamma} \frac{z^{a-1}}{1-z} dz,$$

where z^{a-1} has its principal value and Γ is the contour of Fig. 3, the radii of the indentations at 0 and 1 being ϵ and η respectively. Since the integrand is regular within and on Γ, I is zero.

This contour integral can be written in the form

$$I = \int_{\epsilon}^{1-\eta} \frac{x^{a-1}}{1-x} dx + J + \int_{1+\eta}^{R} \frac{x^{a-1}}{1-x} dx +$$

$$+ \int_0^{\pi} \frac{iR^a e^{a\theta i}}{1-Re^{\theta i}} d\theta + \int_R^{\epsilon} \frac{e^{a\pi i} r^{a-1}}{1+r} dr + \int_{\pi}^0 \frac{i\epsilon^a e^{a\theta i}}{1-\epsilon e^{\theta i}} d\theta,$$

where J denotes the integral round the indentation at $z = 1$. Now

$$\left| \int_0^{\pi} \frac{iR^a e^{a\theta i}}{1-Re^{\theta i}} d\theta \right| \leqslant \frac{\pi R^a}{R-1},$$

which tends to zero as $R \to \infty$, since $a < 1$. Again, since $a > 0$, we have

$$\left| \int_{\pi}^0 \frac{i\epsilon^a e^{a\theta i}}{1-\epsilon e^{\theta i}} d\theta \right| \leqslant \frac{\pi \epsilon^a}{1-\epsilon} \to 0$$

as $\epsilon \to 0$. Also, by applying the result of § 6.51, Ex. 2, we find that the limit of J as $\eta \to 0$ is πi.

Hence, if we make $R \to \infty$, $\epsilon \to 0$, $\eta \to 0$, we obtain

$$P \int_0^\infty \frac{x^{a-1}}{1-x}\,dx - e^{a\pi i} \int_0^\infty \frac{x^{a-1}}{1+x}\,dx + \pi i = 0,$$

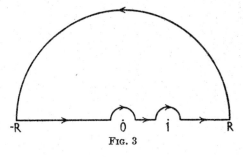

Fig. 3

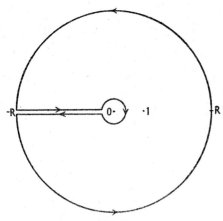

Fig. 4

the first integral being a Cauchy principal value with respect to the singularity $x = 1$. Equating real and imaginary parts in this formula, we find that

$$\sin a\pi \int_0^\infty \frac{x^{a-1}}{1+x}\,dx = \pi$$

as before, and also that

$$P \int_0^\infty \frac{x^{a-1}}{1-x}\,dx = \cos a\pi \int_0^\infty \frac{x^{a-1}}{1+x}\,dx = \pi \cot a\pi.$$

It should be observed that the second method gives us the values of two definite integrals at once.

Third method. If Γ is the contour of Fig. 4, we have

$$\int_{\Gamma} \frac{z^{a-1}}{1-z} dz = -2\pi i$$

when z^{a-1} has its principal value. Evaluating this contour integral, we obtain

$$-2\pi i = \int_{-\pi}^{\pi} \frac{iR^a e^{a\theta i}}{1-Re^{\theta i}} d\theta + \int_{R}^{\epsilon} \frac{r^{a-1}e^{a\pi i}}{1+r} dr + \int_{\pi}^{-\pi} \frac{i\epsilon^a e^{a\theta i}}{1-\epsilon e^{\theta i}} d\theta + \int_{\epsilon}^{R} \frac{r^{a-1}e^{-a\pi i}}{1+r} dr,$$

in which the second and fourth terms arise from integrating along the upper and lower sides of the cut. If we now make $R \to \infty$ and $\epsilon \to 0$, we evidently arrive at the same result as before.

6.7. Complex transformations of definite integrals

When a given definite integral has been evaluated, it is often possible to deduce formally the values of certain related integrals by means of a complex change of variable. Cauchy's theorem of residues provides a simple means of proving the validity of this formal process. We shall illustrate this by considering two transformations of the well-known integral

$$\int_{-\infty}^{\infty} e^{-x^2} dx = \sqrt{\pi}.$$

In the first place, let us consider

$$I = \int_{\Gamma} e^{-z^2} dz,$$

Γ being the rectangle whose vertices are $\pm R$, $\pm R + ib$, where b is real. Since the integrand is regular within and on Γ, I is zero. Hence we have

$$\int_{-R}^{R} e^{-x^2} dx + \int_{0}^{b} e^{-(R+iy)^2} i\, dy = \int_{-R}^{R} e^{-(x+ib)^2} dx + \int_{0}^{b} e^{-(R-iy)^2} i\, dy.$$

But since

$$\left| \int_{0}^{b} e^{-(R\pm iy)^2} i\, dy \right| \leqslant \int_{0}^{|b|} e^{-R^2+y^2}\, dy < |b| e^{-R^2+b^2}$$

which tends to zero as $R \to \infty$, this equation gives

$$\int_{-\infty}^{\infty} e^{-x^2+b^2}(\cos 2bx - i \sin 2bx)\, dx = \int_{-\infty}^{\infty} e^{-x^2}\, dx = \sqrt{\pi}.$$

Thus, equating real and imaginary parts, we obtain

$$\int_{-\infty}^{\infty} e^{-x^2}\cos 2bx\, dx = \sqrt{\pi}\, e^{-b^2},$$

$$\int_{-\infty}^{\infty} e^{-x^2}\sin 2bx\, dx = 0.$$

Secondly, let us take the same integrand in the case when Γ is the sector of the circle $|z| = R$, bounded by radii $\arg z = 0$ and $\arg z = \alpha$, where $-\tfrac{1}{4}\pi \leqslant \alpha \leqslant \tfrac{1}{4}\pi$. As before, I vanishes, and so

$$\int_{0}^{R} e^{-x^2}\, dx + \int_{0}^{\alpha} e^{-R^2\cos 2\theta - iR^2\sin 2\theta}\, iRe^{\theta i}\, d\theta$$
$$= \int_{0}^{R} e^{-r^2\cos 2\alpha - ir^2\sin 2\alpha}\, e^{\alpha i}\, dr.$$

Now

$$\left| \int_{0}^{\alpha} e^{-R^2\cos 2\theta - iR^2\sin 2\theta}\, iRe^{\theta i}\, d\theta \right| \leqslant R \int_{0}^{|\alpha|} e^{-R^2\cos 2\theta}\, d\theta$$
$$\leqslant R \int_{0}^{\pi/4} e^{-R^2\cos 2\theta}\, d\theta = \tfrac{1}{2}R \int_{0}^{\frac{1}{2}\pi} e^{-R^2\sin \phi}\, d\phi$$
$$< \frac{\pi}{4R}, \quad \text{by Jordan's inequality.}$$

Hence, making $R \to \infty$, we deduce that

$$\int_{0}^{\infty} e^{-r^2\cos 2\alpha - ir^2\sin 2\alpha}\, dr = e^{-\alpha i} \int_{0}^{\infty} e^{-x^2}\, dx = \tfrac{1}{2}e^{-\alpha i}\sqrt{\pi},$$

and so

$$\int_{0}^{\infty} e^{-r^2\cos 2\alpha}\cos(r^2\sin 2\alpha)\, dr = \tfrac{1}{2}\sqrt{\pi}\cos \alpha,$$

$$\int_{0}^{\infty} e^{-r^2\cos 2\alpha}\sin(r^2\sin 2\alpha)\, dr = \tfrac{1}{2}\sqrt{\pi}\sin \alpha,$$

provided that $-\tfrac{1}{4}\pi \leqslant \alpha \leqslant \tfrac{1}{4}\pi$.

6.8. Cauchy's expansion of a function as a series of rational functions

One of Cauchy's most important applications of his theorem of residues is concerned with the expansion, under suitable conditions, of an analytic function as a series of partial fractions.

Let us suppose that

  (i) *the function $f(z)$ is regular, save for poles, in any finite region of the z-plane;*

  (ii) *there exists an increasing sequence of positive numbers R_n such that $R_n \to \infty$ as $n \to \infty$, and such that the circle C_n, whose equation is $|z| = R_n$, passes through no pole of $f(z)$, for any value of n;*

  (iii) *the upper bound of $|f(z)|$ on C_n is itself bounded as $n \to \infty$;*

  (iv) *$|f(R_n e^{\theta i})| \to 0$ as $n \to \infty$, uniformly with respect to θ in $0 \leqslant \theta \leqslant 2\pi$, or, more generally, in every portion of this interval which does not include one of a finite number of exceptional values of θ.*

Then, if ζ is not a pole of $f(z)$, we have

$$f(\zeta) = \lim_{n \to \infty} S_n(\zeta),$$

where $S_n(\zeta)$ is the sum of the residues of $f(z)/(\zeta - z)$ at the poles of $f(z)$ within C_n.

That this theorem does provide the required representation of $f(\zeta)$ in partial fractions is easily seen. For if α is a pole of $f(z)$ with principal part $\sum_1^m b_r(z-\alpha)^{-r}$, the contribution of α to the sum $S_n(\zeta)$ is $\sum_1^m b_r(\zeta-\alpha)^{-r}$.

Let us now suppose that ζ is any point of a bounded closed domain D which lies in $|z| \leqslant R$ and contains no poles of $f(z)$. Then since $R_n \to \infty$ with n, we can choose an integer N such that $R_N > R$; the point ζ lies, therefore, within all the circles C_n for which $n \geqslant N$. Since the singularities of $f(z)/(\zeta-z)$ are ζ and the poles of $f(z)$, we have, by the theorem of residues,

$$\frac{1}{2\pi i} \int_{C_n} \frac{f(z)}{\zeta - z}\, dz = S_n(\zeta) - f(\zeta),$$

† *Exercices de Math.* (Paris, 1827); reprinted in *Œuvres de Cauchy* (IIᵉ série), **7**, 324–44.

provided that $n \geqslant N$. It remains to show that the integral on the left-hand side of this equation tends to zero as $n \to \infty$.

For simplicity, we shall suppose that there is only one exceptional value of θ, α say; the method of proof is, however, applicable in the general case. By hypothesis (iii), there exists a positive number M, independent of n, such that $|f(z)| < M$ when z lies on C_n; moreover, by (iv), if δ is any positive number, the upper bound ϵ_n of $|f(R_n e^{\theta i})|$ when $\alpha+\delta \leqslant \theta \leqslant 2\pi+\alpha-\delta$ tends to zero as $n \to \infty$. It follows that, when $n \geqslant N$,

$$\left| \int_{C_n} \frac{f(z)}{\zeta-z}\, dz \right| \leqslant \frac{R_n}{R_n-R} \int_0^{2\pi} |f(R_n e^{\theta i})|\, d\theta$$

$$\leqslant \frac{R_n}{R_n-R} \left\{ \int_{\alpha-\delta}^{\alpha+\delta} M\, d\theta + \int_{\alpha+\delta}^{2\pi+\alpha-\delta} \epsilon_n\, d\theta \right\}$$

$$\leqslant \frac{R_n}{R_n-R} (2M\delta + 2\pi\epsilon_n),$$

and so

$$\lim_{n\to\infty} \left| \int_{C_n} \frac{f(z)}{\zeta-z}\, dz \right| \leqslant 2M\delta.$$

But as δ is quite arbitrary, this implies that

$$\lim_{n\to\infty} \int_{C_n} \frac{f(z)}{\zeta-z}\, dz = 0.$$

It should be observed that we have shown incidentally that $S_n(\zeta)$ converges uniformly to $f(\zeta)$ when ζ lies in the domain D.

By this theorem the function $f(\zeta)$ is expressed as a series of the form

$$S_1(\zeta) + \sum_{n=1}^{\infty} \{ S_{n+1}(\zeta) - S_n(\zeta) \},$$

which converges uniformly in any bounded closed domain which contains no poles of $f(z)$. But $S_{n+1}(\zeta) - S_n(\zeta)$ is the sum of the residues of $f(z)/(\zeta-z)$ at the poles of $f(z)$ between C_n and C_{n+1}. We have, therefore, expressed $f(\zeta)$ as a series of partial fractions which converges uniformly, provided that the terms are suitably bracketed.

6.81. The expansion of $\operatorname{cosec} z$ as a series of partial fractions

As an application of the theorem of the previous section, we consider the expansion of $\operatorname{cosec} z$ as a series of partial fractions. This function has simple poles at the points 0, $\pm\pi$, $\pm 2\pi,...$, so that the circle C_n, whose equation is $|z| = (n+\tfrac{1}{2})\pi$, does not pass through a pole of $\operatorname{cosec} z$ for any value of the integer n. In order to apply the theorem, we must consider the behaviour of $\operatorname{cosec} z$ on this circle.

Let us draw, with each pole as centre, a circle of radius ϵ, where ϵ is less than $\tfrac{1}{2}\pi$. We shall show that $\operatorname{cosec} z$ is bounded† in the region T exterior to all these circles.

In the first place, if $z = x+iy$, we have

$$|\operatorname{cosec} z| = \frac{2}{|e^{ix-y}-e^{-ix+y}|} \leqslant \frac{2}{|\{e^{-y}-e^{y}\}|} = \operatorname{cosech} |y|$$

so that the inequality $|\operatorname{cosec} z| \leqslant \operatorname{cosech} a$ holds in the part of T outside the strip $|\operatorname{Im} z| \leqslant a$. On the other hand, $|\operatorname{cosec} z|$ is obviously bounded in the portion of T within the rectangle with vertices $\pm\tfrac{3}{2}\pi\pm ai$, and therefore, by periodicity, is bounded in the part of T for which $|\operatorname{Im} z| \leqslant a$. Combining these two results, we find that an inequality $|\operatorname{cosec} z| \leqslant M$ holds everywhere in T, the constant M being obviously dependent on ϵ. As the points on the circle C_n are all at a distance not less than $\tfrac{1}{2}\pi-\epsilon$ from the circles defining T, this inequality also holds everywhere on C_n, independently of the value of n.

Again, when $z = (n+\tfrac{1}{2})\pi e^{\theta i}$, we have

$$|\operatorname{cosec} z| \leqslant \operatorname{cosech} |(n+\tfrac{1}{2})\pi \sin\theta| \leqslant \operatorname{cosech}\{(n+\tfrac{1}{2})\pi \sin\delta\},$$

provided that $\delta \leqslant \theta \leqslant \pi-\delta$ or $\pi+\delta \leqslant \theta \leqslant 2\pi-\delta$, where δ is any small positive number. It follows that, as $n \to \infty$, $|\operatorname{cosec} z|$ tends to zero uniformly with respect to θ in the two given angles.

All the conditions of the theorem of § 6.8 are thus satisfied.

---

† The method of proof is taken from the footnote on p. 32 of Lindelöf's Borel tract, *Le Calcul des Résidus* (Paris, 1905).

A similar result can be proved in the same manner for each of the functions $\sec z$, $\tan z$, $\cot z$, $e^{az}/(e^z-1)$ $(0 \leqslant a \leqslant 1)$, in the regions obtained by excluding their poles by small circles.

Hence, if ζ is not a pole of $\operatorname{cosec} z$,

$$\operatorname{cosec} \zeta = \lim_{n \to \infty} \sum_{-n}^{n} (\text{residue of } \operatorname{cosec} z/(\zeta-z) \text{ at } z = m\pi)$$

$$= \lim_{n \to \infty} \sum_{-n}^{n} \frac{(-1)^m}{\zeta - m\pi}$$

$$= \frac{1}{\zeta} + \sum_{1}^{\infty} \frac{2(-1)^m \zeta}{\zeta^2 - m^2 \pi^2}.$$

By Weierstrass's M-test, this series converges uniformly and absolutely when ζ lies in any bounded part of T, and so may be integrated term by term. This gives

$$\log \tan \tfrac{1}{2}\zeta = \log A + \log \tfrac{1}{2}\zeta + \sum_{m=1}^{\infty} (-1)^m \log\left(1 - \frac{\zeta^2}{m^2\pi^2}\right),$$

or $$\tan \tfrac{1}{2}\zeta = \tfrac{1}{2}A\zeta \prod_{m=1}^{\infty} \left\{\frac{1 - \zeta^2/(4m^2\pi^2)}{1 - \zeta^2/\{(2m-1)^2\pi^2\}}\right\}.$$

Since $\tan \tfrac{1}{2}\zeta/(\tfrac{1}{2}\zeta) \to 1$ as $\zeta \to 0$, the constant of integration A is unity. Hence, if we write $\zeta = 2z$, we have

$$\frac{\tan z}{z} = \prod_{m=1}^{\infty} \left(1 - \frac{z^2}{m^2\pi^2}\right) \Big/ \prod_{m=1}^{\infty} \left(1 - \frac{4z^2}{(2m-1)^2\pi^2}\right),$$

which represents $\tan z$ as a quotient of two infinite products, each of which is an integral function.†

6.82. An extension of the theorem of § 6.8

Cauchy also showed how the theorem of § 6.8 may be used when the function $f(z)$ satisfies conditions (i), (ii), and (iii) but not condition (iv). In this case the function

$$F(z) = \frac{f(z)}{z}$$

is considered; it obviously satisfies conditions (i) and (ii). But on C_n, $z = R_n e^{\theta i}$, and so

$$|F(z)| = \frac{|f(z)|}{R_n} \leqslant \frac{M}{R_n};$$

hence, as $n \to \infty$, $F(R_n e^{\theta i})$ tends to zero uniformly with respect to θ in $0 \leqslant \theta \leqslant 2\pi$. The function $F(z)$ satisfies, therefore, all

† Cf. the results of Exx. 35, 36 at the end of this chapter.

the conditions of § 6.8, and we conclude that

$$\frac{f(z)}{z} = \lim_{n \to \infty} \left\{ \text{sum of residues of } \frac{f(t)}{t(z-t)} \text{ at poles of } \frac{f(t)}{t} \text{ within } C_n \right\}$$

A particularly important case of this arises when $f(z)$ is regular at the origin and has only simple poles. If we suppose that the poles $a_1, a_2, a_3, \ldots$, of residues $b_1, b_2, b_3, \ldots$ respectively, are arranged in order of increasing distance from the origin, so that $0 < |a_1| \leqslant |a_2| \leqslant |a_3| \leqslant \ldots$, we easily find that the residue at a_r of $f(t)/(zt - t^2)$ is

$$\frac{b_r}{a_r(z-a_r)} = \frac{b_r}{z}\left(\frac{1}{z-a_r} + \frac{1}{a_r}\right),$$

whilst the residue at the origin is $f(0)/z$. The partial fraction formula for $f(z)/z$ now becomes

$$\frac{f(z)}{z} = \frac{f(0)}{z} + \sum_{r=1}^{\infty} \frac{b_r}{a_r(z-a_r)},$$

and so, finally,†

$$f(z) = f(0) + \sum_{r=1}^{\infty} b_r\left(\frac{1}{z-a_r} + \frac{1}{a_r}\right).$$

More generally, if the condition (iii) of § 6.8 is replaced by the boundedness, as $n \to \infty$, of the upper bound on C_n of $|z^{-p}f(z)|$, where p is a positive integer, the function $f(z)/z^{p+1}$ satisfies all the conditions of § 6.8, and the representation of $f(z)$ as an infinite series of partial fractions follows immediately.

6.83. The representation of an integral function as an infinite product

Let $F(z)$ be an integral function which does not vanish at the origin but has simple zeros $z_1, z_2, z_3, \ldots$, arranged in order of increasing modulus. As these zeros can have no limiting point of finite affix, $|z_n| \to \infty$ as $n \to \infty$.

If we write $F(z) = (z-z_r)\Phi(z)$, then $\Phi(z)$ is regular and non zero in a certain neighbourhood of z_r. Hence we have

$$\frac{F'(z)}{F(z)} = \frac{1}{z-z_r} + \frac{\Phi'(z)}{\Phi(z)},$$

† This series converges uniformly in any bounded closed domain which contains none of the poles of $f(z)$, provided that the terms are arranged in groups corresponding to poles of equal modulus.

and so the only singularities of $F'(z)/F(z)$ are simple poles of residue 1 at the points z_r.

Let us now suppose that $F'(z)/F(z)$ satisfies the conditions of § 6.8. It follows that

$$\frac{F'(z)}{F(z)} = \sum_{n=1}^{\infty} \frac{1}{z-z_n},$$

the series being uniformly convergent in any bounded closed domain which contains none of the zeros of $F(z)$, provided that the terms are suitably bracketed. If we now integrate term by term, we find that

$$\log F(z) = \log F(0) + \sum_{n=1}^{\infty} \log\left(1-\frac{z}{z_n}\right).$$

Hence
$$F(z) = F(0) \prod_{1}^{\infty} \left(1-\frac{z}{z_n}\right),$$

the infinite product being uniformly convergent in any bounded closed domain which contains none of the zeros of $F(z)$.

If, however, $F'(z)/F(z)$ satisfies only conditions (i), (ii), (iii) of § 6.8, it follows by § 6.82, that

$$\frac{F'(z)}{F(z)} = \frac{F'(0)}{F(0)} + \sum_{n=1}^{\infty} \left(\frac{1}{z-z_n}+\frac{1}{z_n}\right),$$

and so

$$\log F(z) = A + \frac{F'(0)}{F(0)}z + \sum_{n=1}^{\infty} \left\{\log\left(1-\frac{z}{z_n}\right)+\frac{z}{z_n}\right\},$$

where A is a constant of integration, whose value is easily seen to be $\log F(0)$. Finally, taking the exponentials of the expressions on each side of this equation, we deduce that

$$F(z) = F(0)e^{zF'(0)/F(0)} \prod_{n=1}^{\infty} \left\{\left(1-\frac{z}{z_n}\right)e^{z/z_n}\right\}.$$

Example. Prove that $\sin \pi z = \pi z \prod_{1}^{\infty} \left(1-\frac{z^2}{n^2}\right).$

Let us consider the integral function

$$F(z) = \sum_{0}^{\infty} (-1)^n \frac{(\pi z)^{2n}}{(2n+1)!}$$

which is equal to $(\sin \pi z)/(\pi z)$ when $z \neq 0$ and to 1 when $z = 0$. It has simple zeros at $z = \pm 1, \pm 2, \pm 3, \ldots$. Moreover, its logarithmic derivative

$$\frac{F'(z)}{F(z)} = \pi \cot \pi z - \frac{1}{z}$$

satisfies all the conditions of § 6.8. Hence

$$\frac{F'(z)}{F(z)} = \lim_{m \to \infty} \sum_1^m \left\{ \frac{1}{z-n} + \frac{1}{z+n} \right\} = \sum_1^\infty \frac{2z}{z^2 - n^2}.$$

Integrating, we obtain immediately

$$F(z) = \prod_1^\infty \left(1 - \frac{z^2}{n^2} \right).$$

We cannot, however, write†

$$F(z) = \prod_{-\infty}^{\infty}{}' \left(1 - \frac{z}{n} \right),$$

since this infinite product diverges.

Again, by § 6.82, we have‡

$$\frac{F'(z)}{F(z)} = \lim_{m \to \infty} \left[\sum_{n=1}^m \left(\frac{1}{z-n} + \frac{1}{n} \right) + \sum_{n=1}^m \left(\frac{1}{z+n} - \frac{1}{n} \right) \right]$$

$$= \sum_1^\infty \left(\frac{1}{z-n} + \frac{1}{n} \right) + \sum_1^\infty \left(\frac{1}{z+n} - \frac{1}{n} \right),$$

each of these series being uniformly and absolutely convergent in any bounded closed domain which contains none of the zeros of $F(z)$. From this it follows at once that

$$F(z) = \prod_1^\infty \left\{ \left(1 - \frac{z}{n} \right) e^{z/n} \right\} \prod_1^\infty \left\{ \left(1 + \frac{z}{n} \right) e^{-z/n} \right\},$$

and so

$$\sin \pi z = \pi z \prod_{-\infty}^{\infty}{}' \left\{ \left(1 - \frac{z}{n} \right) e^{z/n} \right\},$$

the latter product being absolutely convergent.

REFERENCES

E. Lindelöf, *Le Calcul des Résidus* (Borel tract; Paris, 1905).

G. N. Watson, *Complex Integration and Cauchy's Theorem* (Cambridge, 1914).

† The accent indicates that the term corresponding to $n = 0$ is omitted.

‡ $F'(0)/F(0) = \lim_{z \to 0} \left\{ \pi \cot \pi z - \frac{1}{z} \right\} = 0.$

MISCELLANEOUS EXAMPLES

1. If the function $f(z)$ is regular within and on the level curve $|f(z)| = M$, show that z_0 is a double point of this curve if and only if it is a zero of $f'(z)$.

2. If C is a simple closed level curve of the function $f(z)$ which is regular within and on C, show that $f(z)$ has at least one zero within C. Prove also that, if $f(z)$ has m zeros within C, $f'(z)$ has $m-1$. (MAC-DONALD.†)

3. Show that, if $k > 1$, the equation

$$z^n e^{k-z} = 1$$

has n roots in $|z| < 1$.

4. The function $f(z)$ is regular in $|z| \leqslant 1$ where it has only one zero a, whose modulus is less than 1. Show that, if $|b| < 1$, the function

$$f(z)\left[1 - \frac{1-\bar{a}z}{z-a}\frac{b-a}{1-\bar{a}b}\{1 + \epsilon(z-b)^2\}\right]$$

has exactly one zero in $|z| \leqslant 1$, provided that the constant ϵ be sufficiently small. (Cambridge, 1932.)

5. Express as a series of powers of w the solution of

$$w = \frac{2(z-\mu)}{z^2-1},$$

which reduces to μ when $w = 0$. Hence prove that

$$(1 - 2\mu w + w^2)^{-1/2} = \sum_0^\infty w^n P_n(\mu),$$

where

$$P_n(\mu) = \frac{1}{2^n n!}\frac{d^n(\mu^2-1)^n}{d\mu^n}.$$

6. Show that the solution of the equation

$$z = a + we^z$$

which reduces to a when $w = 0$ is

$$z = a + we^a + \frac{w^2}{2!}2e^{2a} + \ldots + \frac{w^n}{n!}n^{n-1}e^{na} + \ldots,$$

the expansion being valid when

$$|w| < e^{-1-\mathrm{Rl}\,a}.$$

† *Proc. London Math. Soc.* (1), **29** (1898), 576. See also Watson, ibid. (2), **15** (1916), 227–42.

7. Show that, if $|a| < 1$,

$$\int_0^{2\pi} \frac{d\theta}{1+a^2-2a\cos\theta} = \frac{2\pi}{1-a^2},$$

and deduce the value of the integral when $|a| > 1$.

8. Show that, when $\mathrm{Rl}\,a > 0$,

$$\int_0^{\pi} \tan(\theta+ai)\,d\theta = \pi i.$$

9. Show that, if m be real and $-1 < a < 1$,

$$\int_0^{2\pi} \frac{e^{m\cos\theta}}{1+a^2-2a\sin\theta}\{\cos(m\sin\theta)-a\sin(m\sin\theta+\theta)\}\,d\theta = 2\pi\cos ma,$$

$$\int_0^{2\pi} \frac{e^{m\cos\theta}}{1+a^2-2a\sin\theta}\{\sin(m\sin\theta)+a\cos(m\sin\theta+\theta)\}\,d\theta = 2\pi\sin ma.$$

(Edinburgh, 1931.)

10. By using Cauchy's formula for the derivative of $\sin\alpha$ or otherwise, prove that

$$\int_0^{2\pi} \{\cos\theta\sin(\alpha+\cos\theta)\cosh(\sin\theta)+\sin\theta\cos(\alpha+\cos\theta)\sinh(\sin\theta)\}\,d\theta$$

$$= 2\pi\cos\alpha.$$

(Edinburgh, 1930.)

11. Prove that

$$\int_{-\infty}^{\infty} \frac{\cos x\,dx}{(x^2+a^2)(x^2+b^2)} = \frac{\pi}{a^2-b^2}\left(\frac{e^{-b}}{b}-\frac{e^{-a}}{a}\right)$$

when the real parts of a and b are positive and a is not equal to b. Show also that

$$\int_{-\infty}^{\infty} \frac{\cos x\,dx}{(x^2+a^2)^2} = \frac{\pi(1+a)}{2a^3e^a}$$

when the real part of a is positive.

12. Show that the Cauchy principal value of

$$\int_{-\infty}^{\infty} \frac{e^{ipx}}{(x-\xi)(x-\eta)}\,dx,$$

where ξ, η, and p are real, is $\lambda\pi i(e^{ip\xi}-e^{ip\eta})/(\xi-\eta)$, the value of λ being

1, 0, or -1 according as p is greater than, equal to, or less than zero.

Deduce that

$$\int_{-\infty}^{\infty} \frac{\sin m(x-\xi)}{(x-\xi)} \frac{\sin n(x-\eta)}{(x-\eta)}\, dx = \pi\, \frac{\sin m(\xi-\eta)}{(\xi-\eta)}$$

when $n \geqslant m > 0$.

13. Prove that $\displaystyle\int_0^{\infty} \frac{\sin \pi x}{x(1-x^2)}\, dx = \pi.$ (Math. Trip., 1919.)

14. Show that $\displaystyle\int_{-\infty}^{\infty} \frac{\cos px - \cos qx}{x^2}\, dx = -\pi(p-q)$

when p and q are positive.

15. Prove that the residue of the function $e^{niz}/(z^2 - 2z\cos\alpha + 1)^2$, $(n > 0,\ 0 < \alpha < \pi)$, at the pole which lies in the upper half-plane is $-i\lambda e^{ni\cos\alpha}$, where

$$\lambda = \frac{e^{-n\sin\alpha}(n\sin\alpha + 1)}{4\sin^3\alpha}.$$

Hence show that

$$\int_0^{\infty} \frac{x(x^2+1)\sin nx\, dx}{(x^4 - 2x^2\cos 2\alpha + 1)^2} = \frac{\pi\lambda\sin(n\cos\alpha)}{4\cos\alpha}.$$

(Edinburgh, 1930.)

16. Prove that

$$\int_0^{\infty} e^{\cos x}\sin(\sin x)\frac{dx}{x} = \tfrac{1}{2}\pi(e-1).$$ (CAUCHY.)

17. By integrating round the rectangle with vertices $c \pm iR$, $-S \pm iR$, where c, R, and S are positive, prove that, when $\alpha \geqslant 0$,

$$\int_{c-\infty i}^{c+\infty i} e^{\alpha z}\frac{dz}{z^2} = 2\pi i\alpha,$$

the path of integration being a straight line parallel to the imaginary axis.

Show also that the integral is zero when $\alpha < 0$.

18. Show that, if $\mathrm{Rl}\,\alpha > 0$, $|\mathrm{Im}\,\alpha| < \pi$,

$$\int_{c-\infty i}^{c+\infty i} \frac{e^{\alpha z}}{\sin \pi z}\, dz = \frac{2i}{1+e^{-\alpha}},$$

the path of integration being the straight line $\mathrm{Rl}\,z = c$, where $0 < c < 1$.

19. By integrating $e^{i\alpha z^2}\operatorname{cosech} \pi z$ round the rectangle with vertices $\pm R \pm \tfrac{1}{2}i$, show that, if $0 < \alpha \leqslant \pi$,

$$\int_0^\infty \cos(\alpha x^2)\frac{\cosh \alpha x}{\cosh \pi x}\,dx = \tfrac{1}{2}\cos \tfrac{1}{4}\alpha,$$

$$\int_0^\infty \sin(\alpha x^2)\frac{\cosh \alpha x}{\cosh \pi x}\,dx = \tfrac{1}{2}\sin \tfrac{1}{4}\alpha.$$

(Math. Trip., 1932.)

20. Show that, if $-1 < a < 1$ and $0 < \alpha < \pi$,

$$\int_0^\infty \frac{x^a\,dx}{1+2x\cos\alpha+x^2} = \frac{\pi \sin a\alpha}{\sin a\pi \sin \alpha}.$$

21. Prove that, if $0 < a < 3$, $b > 0$, $c > 0$,

$$\int_0^\infty x^{a-1}\sin(\tfrac{1}{2}\pi a - bx)\frac{dx}{x^2+c^2} = \tfrac{1}{2}\pi c^{a-2}e^{-bc},$$

$$P\int_0^\infty x^{a-1}\sin(\tfrac{1}{2}\pi a - bx)\frac{dx}{c^2-x^2} = \tfrac{1}{2}\pi c^{a-2}\cos(\tfrac{1}{2}\pi a - bc).$$

(Cauchy.)

22. Prove that, if $0 < \alpha < \beta$ and $0 < a < 2$,

$$\int_\alpha^\beta \left(\frac{\beta-t}{t-\alpha}\right)^{a-1}\frac{dt}{t} = \frac{\pi}{\sin a\pi}\left\{1-\left(\frac{\beta}{\alpha}\right)^{a-1}\right\}.$$

23. By making the transformation $t = e^u$, show that

$$\int_0^\infty (\log t)^2\,\frac{dt}{1+t^2} = \tfrac{1}{8}\pi^3.$$

24. $f(z)$ is a rational function with no poles on the real axis and is such that $zf(z)$ tends to zero as $z \to \infty$ and also as $z \to 0$. By integrating $\log z f(-z)$ round an appropriate contour, prove that

$$\int_0^\infty \log x \,\{f(x)+f(-x)\}\,dx + \pi i\int_0^\infty f(x)\,dx$$

is equal to $2\pi i$ times the sum of the residues of $\log z f(-z)$ at its poles in the upper half-plane.† How is this result to be modified when there are simple poles on the real axis?

† This result is of particular value when $f(z)$ is an odd function, as it enables us to evaluate $\int_0^\infty f(x)\,dx$, whereas the method of § 6.5 fails.

25. Show that

$$\int_0^\infty \frac{\log x}{(1+x^2)^2}\, dx = -\tfrac14\pi, \qquad \int_0^\infty \frac{dx}{(1+x^2)^2} = \tfrac14\pi.$$

26. Find the theorem corresponding to that of Ex. 24, obtained by integrating $(\log z)^2 f(-z)$ round the same contour.

Hence evaluate the integral of Ex. 23.

27. By integrating $z/(1-ae^{-iz})$ round the rectangle with vertices at $\pm\pi$, $\pm\pi+iR$, prove that, if $a \geqslant 1$,

$$\int_0^\pi \frac{ax\sin x}{1-2a\cos x+a^2}\, dx = \pi\log(1+a^{-1}).$$

What is the value of this integral when $0 < a < 1$? (CAUCHY.)

28. Integrate $\log\sin z$ round the rectangle with vertices at $0, \pi, \pi+iR, iR$, indented at 0 and π, and so prove that

$$\int_0^\pi \log\sin x \, dx = -\pi\log 2.$$

29. By integrating $e^{az}/(e^{-2iz}-1)$ round a suitable contour, prove that

$$\int_0^\infty \frac{\sin ay}{e^{2y}-1}\, dy = \tfrac14\pi\coth\tfrac12\pi a - \tfrac12 a.$$

30. Prove that, if $-\pi < a < \pi$,

$$\int_{-\infty}^\infty \frac{\sinh ax}{\sinh \pi x}\, dx = \tan\tfrac12 a.$$

31. The Gamma function is defined by

$$\Gamma(a) = \int_0^\infty x^{a-1}e^{-x}\, dx$$

when $a > 0$. Integrate $z^{a-1}e^{-z}$ round a sector, indented at the origin, and so prove that, if $a > 0$ and $-\tfrac12\pi < \alpha < \tfrac12\pi$,

$$\int_0^\infty x^{a-1}e^{-x\cos\alpha}\, \frac{\cos}{\sin}(x\sin\alpha)\, dx = \Gamma(a)\frac{\cos}{\sin}(a\alpha).$$

Show that this formula still holds when $\alpha = \pm\tfrac12\pi$ if $0 < a < 1$.

32. Integrate the principal value of $z^{a-1}e^z$ round the contour of Fig. 5, and so prove that, if $0 < a < 1$ and $c > 0$,

$$\int_{-\infty}^{\infty} e^{iy}(c+iy)^{a-1}\, dy = 2e^{-c}\sin a\pi\, \Gamma(a).$$

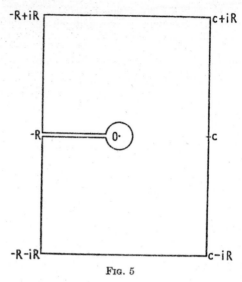

FIG. 5

Deduce that

$$\int_0^{\tfrac{1}{2}\pi} \cos\{\tan\theta - (1-a)\theta\}\sec^{1+a}\theta\, d\theta = e^{-1}\sin a\pi\, \Gamma(a).$$

(CAUCHY.)

33. By integrating the branch of $z^{-p}(c+a-z)^{-q}$ which is real when $0 < z < c+a$, round the contour of Fig. 5, prove that, if $c > 0$, $a > 0$ and $p < 1 < p+q$, then

$$\int_{-\infty}^{\infty} \frac{dy}{(c+iy)^p(a-iy)^q} = 2\sin p\pi \int_0^{\infty} \frac{dr}{r^p(c+a+r)^q}.$$

(CAUCHY.)

34. Prove that $\sec z = 4\pi \sum_0^{\infty} (-1)^n(2n+1)/\{(2n+1)^2\pi^2 - 4z^2\}$.

35. Show that, if h is not an integer or zero,

$$\sin\pi(z+h) = e^{\pi z\cot\pi h}\sin\pi h \prod_{-\infty}^{\infty} \left\{\left(1 + \frac{z}{n+h}\right)e^{-z/(n+h)}\right\}.$$

36. Prove that $\tan z = 8z \sum_{0}^{\infty} 1/\{(2n+1)^2\pi^2 - 4z^2\}$.

Deduce that $\qquad \cos z = \prod_{0}^{\infty}\left(1 - \frac{z^2}{(n+\frac{1}{2})^2\pi^2}\right)$.

37. Show that, if $0 < a < 1$,

$$\frac{e^{az}}{e^z - 1} = \frac{1}{z} + \sum_{n=1}^{\infty}\frac{2z\cos 2n\pi a - 4n\pi\sin 2n\pi a}{z^2 + 4n^2\pi^2}.$$

38. Prove that

$$\frac{1}{\cosh z - \cos z} = \frac{1}{z^2} + \pi z^2 \sum_{n=1}^{\infty}\frac{(-1)^n n \operatorname{cosech} n\pi}{(n\pi)^4 + \frac{1}{4}z^4}.$$

39. Prove that, if $-\pi < \alpha < \pi$,

$$\frac{\sin \alpha z}{\sin \pi z} = \frac{2}{\pi}\sum_{n=1}^{\infty}(-1)^n\frac{n\sin n\alpha}{z^2 - n^2},$$

$$\frac{\cos \alpha z}{\sin \pi z} = \frac{1}{\pi z} + \frac{2z}{\pi}\sum_{n=1}^{\infty}(-1)^n\frac{\cos n\alpha}{z^2 - n^2}.$$

40. Prove that, if b is not an integer,

$$\frac{\sin \pi z}{z} = \frac{\sin \pi b \sin \pi(z-b)}{\pi}\sum_{n=-\infty}^{\infty}\frac{1}{(z-b-n)(b+n)}.$$

41. A function $f(z)$ is regular for all finite values of z and satisfies the inequality $|f(z)\operatorname{cosec} \pi z| < M$ on the circles $|z| = n+\frac{1}{2}$, where n is an integer and M is independent of n. Show that

$$f(z) = \frac{\sin \pi z}{\pi}\left[f'(0) + \frac{f(0)}{z} + \sum_{1}^{\infty}(-1)^n\left\{f(n)\left(\frac{1}{z-n} + \frac{1}{n}\right) + f(-n)\left(\frac{1}{z+n} - \frac{1}{n}\right)\right\}\right].$$

$F(z)$ is an integral function such that $\{F(z)\}^k$ can be expanded in a series of the above form for every positive integral value of k. Show that, if $|F(n)| < K$ when $n = 0, \pm 1, \pm 2,...$, K being independent of n, then $F(z)$ is a constant.   (Cambridge, 1933.)

42. $f(z)$ is a periodic analytic function of period π whose only singularities in the strip $0 < \mathrm{Rl}\, z \leqslant \pi$ are simple poles $a_1, a_2,..., a_n$, of residue $c_1, c_2,..., c_n$ respectively. Show that, if $f(x+iy) \to l$ as $y \to +\infty$ and $\to l'$ as $y \to -\infty$, uniformly with respect to x, then

$$l'-l = 2i\sum_{1}^{n}c_r.$$

By applying this result to the function $f(z)\cot(z-z_0)$, where z_0 is not a pole of $f(z)$, prove that

$$f(z) = \tfrac{1}{2}(l+l') + \sum_{1}^{n}c_r\cot(z-a_r).$$

CHAPTER VII

INTEGRAL FUNCTIONS

7.1. The factorization of integral functions

THE most important property of a polynomial is that it can be expressed uniquely as a product of linear factors of the form

$$Az^p\left(1-\frac{z}{z_1}\right)\left(1-\frac{z}{z_2}\right)\cdots\left(1-\frac{z}{z_n}\right),$$

where A is a constant, p a positive integer or zero, and $z_1, z_2, ..., z_n$ the points, other than the origin, at which the polynomial vanishes, multiple zeros being repeated in the set according to their order. Conversely, if the zeros are given, the polynomial is determined apart from an arbitrary constant multiplier.

Now a polynomial is an integral function of a very simple type, its singularity at infinity being a pole. We naturally ask whether it is possible to exhibit in a similar manner the way in which any integral function depends on its zeros. It has been shown in § 6.83 that such a factorization is possible under certain circumstances.

There are, however, two rather serious difficulties to be considered. The first is that if an integral function has an infinite number of zeros $z_1, z_2, ..., z_n, ...$, say, it is not necessarily the case that the infinite product $\prod_{1}^{\infty} (1-z/z_n)$ converges, much less that the value of the product is independent of the order of its factors. For example, the function $(\sin \pi z)/(\pi z)$ has zeros ± 1, $\pm 2, \pm 3, ...$; but the infinite product†

$$\prod_{-\infty}^{\infty}{}' \left(1-\frac{z}{n}\right),$$

defined as the limit of

$$\prod_{-M}^{N}{}' \left(1-\frac{z}{n}\right)$$

as M and N tend to infinity independently, diverges. This product can, however, be made to converge by grouping its factors

† Here and in the sequel, the accent indicates that the infinite term, given by $n = 0$, is to be omitted.

suitably, but, even so, the value of the product then depends on the mode of grouping.†

It was shown by Weierstrass that the appropriate method of expressing $(\sin \pi z)/(\pi z)$ as a convergent infinite product whose value does not depend on the order of its factors is

$$\frac{\sin \pi z}{\pi z} = \prod_{-\infty}^{\infty}{}' \left\{ \left(1 - \frac{z}{n}\right) e^{z/n} \right\}.$$

Evidently it will not suffice, in the solution of our problem, to consider only simple factors of the form $(1 - z/z_n)$.

A second difficulty is due to the fact that there exist integral functions which never vanish, e^z being a simple instance of this. It follows that a knowledge of the zeros of an integral function cannot determine the function save for an arbitrary constant multiplier; the multiplier is now an integral function with no zeros.

The most general integral function with no zeros is of the form $e^{g(z)}$, where $g(z)$ is itself an integral function. For if $f(z)$ is an integral function which never vanishes, the function

$$F(z) = f'(z)/f(z)$$

is also an integral function. Integrating the expressions on each side of this equation along any path from z_0 to z, we find that

$$\log f(z) = \log f(z_0) + \int_{z_0}^{z} F(z)\, dz.$$

But as the expression on the right-hand side of this equation is an integral function, the result stated is now established.

Example 1. Prove that

$$\pi z \left(1 + \frac{z}{1}\right)\left(1 + \frac{z}{2}\right)\left(1 - \frac{z}{1}\right)\left(1 + \frac{z}{3}\right)\left(1 + \frac{z}{4}\right)\left(1 - \frac{z}{2}\right)\ldots = e^{z \log 2} \sin \pi z.$$

We have

$$\pi z \left(1 + \frac{z}{1}\right)\left(1 + \frac{z}{2}\right)\left(1 - \frac{z}{1}\right)\ldots\left(1 + \frac{z}{2n-1}\right)\left(1 + \frac{z}{2n}\right)\left(1 - \frac{z}{n}\right)$$

$$= \pi z \prod_{1}^{2n} \left(1 + \frac{z}{r}\right) \prod_{1}^{n} \left(1 - \frac{z}{r}\right)$$

$$= \pi z e^{z\left(1 + \frac{1}{2} + \frac{1}{3} + \ldots + \frac{1}{2n}\right)} \prod_{1}^{2n} \left\{ \left(1 + \frac{z}{r}\right) e^{-z/r} \right\} e^{-z\left(1 + \frac{1}{2} + \frac{1}{3} + \ldots + \frac{1}{n}\right)} \prod_{1}^{n} \left\{ \left(1 - \frac{z}{r}\right) e^{z/r} \right\}$$

† See the examples at the end of this section.

$$= \pi z e^{z\left(1-\frac{1}{2}+\frac{1}{3}-\frac{1}{4}+\dots+\frac{1}{2n-1}-\frac{1}{2n}\right)} \prod_{-n}^{2n}{}' \left\{\left(1+\frac{z}{r}\right)e^{-z/r}\right\}$$

$$\to \pi z e^{z\log 2} \prod_{-\infty}^{\infty}{}' \left\{\left(1+\frac{z}{r}\right)e^{-z/r}\right\}$$

as $n \to \infty$. The required result now follows by Weierstrass's formula for $\sin \pi z$.

Example 2. Prove that

$$\pi z\left(1+\frac{z}{1}\right)\left(1+\frac{z}{2}\right)\left(1+\frac{z}{3}\right)\left(1-\frac{z}{1}\right)\left(1+\frac{z}{4}\right)\left(1+\frac{z}{5}\right)\left(1+\frac{z}{6}\right)\left(1-\frac{z}{2}\right)\dots = e^{z\log 3}\sin \pi z.$$

7.2. The construction of an integral function with given zeros

If $f(z)$ is an integral function with only a finite number of zeros, $z_1, z_2, \dots, z_n$, say, the function

$$f(z)/\{(z-z_1)(z-z_2)\dots(z-z_n)$$

is an integral function with no zeros; hence

$$f(z) = (z-z_1)(z-z_2)\dots(z-z_n)e^{g(z)}$$

where $g(z)$ is an integral function.

If, however, an integral function has an infinite number of zeros, the set of zeros cannot have a limiting point in any finite region of the plane, since such a limiting point would be a singularity of the function. The only limiting point of the set is, therefore, the point at infinity.

We now prove Weierstrass's theorem,† that *if $z_1, z_2, \dots, z_n, \dots$ be any sequence of numbers whose only limiting point is the point at infinity, it is possible to construct an integral function which vanishes at each of the points z_n and nowhere else.* The construction involves the use of Weierstrass's primary factors

$$E(z, 0) = 1-z; \quad E(z, p) = (1-z)e^{z+z^2/2+\dots+z^p/p} \quad (p > 0).$$

Each primary factor is an integral function which has but one zero, a simple zero at $z = 1$.

Now when $|z| < 1$, we have

$$E(z, p) = \exp\left\{\log(1-z)+z+\frac{z^2}{2}+\dots+\frac{z^p}{p}\right\}$$

$$= \exp\left\{-\frac{z^{p+1}}{p+1}-\frac{z^{p+2}}{p+2}-\dots\right\},$$

† *Abh. der Preuss. Akad. Wiss. zu Berlin* (Math. Klasse) (1876), 11–60; reprinted in Weierstrass's *Werke*, **2**, 77–124.

and so
$$\log E(z,p) = -\frac{z^{p+1}}{p+1} - \frac{z^{p+2}}{p+2} - \ldots.$$

From this it follows that, when $|z| \leqslant \frac{1}{2}$,

$$|\log E(z,p)| \leqslant \frac{|z|^{p+1}}{p+1}(1+\tfrac{1}{2}+\tfrac{1}{4}+\ldots) \leqslant 2|z|^{p+1}.$$

We may suppose that the origin is not a zero of the integral function to be constructed; for if we require a function which vanishes at the origin, we need only multiply the function $G(z)$ determined below by an appropriate power of z. Let the given zeros $z_1, z_2,\ldots$ be arranged in order of non-decreasing modulus, multiple zeros being supposed to be repeated in the set according to their order. Then, since $r_n = |z_n|$ increases indefinitely with n, we can always find a sequence of positive integers $p_1, p_2,\ldots,$ $p_n,\ldots$ such that the series

$$\sum_1^\infty \left(\frac{r}{r_n}\right)^{p_n}$$

converges for all positive values of r. In fact, it suffices to take $p_n = n$, since for any given value of r the inequality $r/r_n < \frac{1}{2}$ holds for all sufficiently large values of n.

We next assign arbitrarily a positive number R and then choose the integer N such that $r_N \leqslant 2R < r_{N+1}$. Hence, when $n > N$ and $|z| \leqslant R$, we have

$$\left|\frac{z}{z_n}\right| \leqslant \frac{R}{r_n} < \frac{R}{r_{N+1}} < \frac{1}{2},$$

and so
$$\left|\log E\left(\frac{z}{z_n}, p_n-1\right)\right| \leqslant 2\left(\frac{R}{r_n}\right)^{p_n}.$$

It follows, by Weierstrass's M-test, that the series

$$\sum_1^\infty \log E\left(\frac{z}{z_n}, p_n-1\right)$$

converges absolutely and uniformly when $|z| \leqslant R$. This implies that the infinite product

$$\prod_{n=1}^\infty E\left(\frac{z}{z_n}, p_n-1\right)$$

converges uniformly and absolutely in the circle $|z| \leqslant R$, no matter how large R may be, and so represents an integral function $G(z)$.

With the same value of R, we choose another integer M such that $r_M \leqslant R < r_{M+1}$. Then all the functions of the sequence

$$\prod_{n=1}^{m} E\left(\frac{z}{z_n}, p_n - 1\right) \qquad (m = M+1, M+2, ...),$$

vanish at the points $z_1, z_2, ..., z_M$ and nowhere else in $|z| \leqslant R$. Hence, by Hurwitz's theorem (§ 6.21, Ex. 2), the only zeros of $G(z)$ in $|z| \leqslant R$ are $z_1, z_2, ..., z_M$. But since R is arbitrary, this means that the only zeros of $G(z)$ are the points of the sequence $z_1, z_2, ...$. This completes the proof of the theorem.

Since there are many possible sequences p_n, the function $G(z)$ is not uniquely determined. But when such a sequence has been fixed, the most general integral function with the given zeros is $G(z) e^{H(z)}$, where $H(z)$ is an integral function.

7.3. The principle of the maximum modulus

Let $f(z)$ be an analytic function, continuous within and on a closed contour C and regular within C. Let M be the upper bound of $|f(z)|$ on C. Then the inequality $|f(z)| \leqslant M$ holds everywhere within C. Moreover, $|f(z)| = M$ at a point within C if and only if $f(z)$ is a constant. The following proof of this result, which is known as the principle of the maximum modulus, is due to Landau.

If n is any positive integer and a any point within C, we have

$$\{f(a)\}^n = \frac{1}{2\pi i} \int_C \{f(z)\}^n \frac{dz}{z-a}$$

by Cauchy's integral formula. If a is at a distance δ from C, this equation gives

$$|f(a)|^n \leqslant \frac{M^n l}{2\pi\delta}$$

where l is the length of C. Hence

$$|f(a)| \leqslant M\left(\frac{l}{2\pi\delta}\right)^{1/n}.$$

The expression on the left-hand side of this inequality is

independent of n, so that, making n tend to infinity, we obtain
$$|f(a)| \leqslant M,$$
the first result of the theorem.

Again
$$n f'(a)\{f(a)\}^{n-1} = \frac{1}{2\pi i} \int_C \{f(z)\}^n \frac{dz}{(z-a)^2},$$

and so
$$n|f'(a)|\,|f(a)|^{n-1} \leqslant \frac{M^n l}{2\pi \delta^2}.$$

Now if there exists a point a within C such that $|f(a)| = M$, this inequality gives
$$|f'(a)| \leqslant \frac{Ml}{2\pi \delta^2 n};$$

making $n \to \infty$ we obtain $f'(a) = 0$. Similarly we can show that if $|f(a)| = M$, all the derivatives of $f(z)$ vanish at $z = a$. By Taylor's theorem it follows that $f(z)$ is constant in a neighbourhood of a and hence, by analytical continuation, is constant everywhere within and on C. This completes the proof of the theorem.

It should be observed that the principle of the maximum modulus holds also when $f(z)$ is continuous in the closed annulus and regular in the open annulus bounded by two non-intersecting closed contours C_1 and C_2. For if a is any point of the open annulus, we have
$$\{f(a)\}^n = \frac{1}{2\pi i} \int_{C_1} \{f(z)\}^n \frac{dz}{z-a} - \frac{1}{2\pi i} \int_{C_2} \{f(z)\}^n \frac{dz}{z-a},$$

and the proof follows the same lines as before, M being now. the upper bound of $|f(z)|$ on C_1 and C_2.

7.31. The maximum modulus of an integral function

If $f(z)$ is an integral function, its modulus is continuous on the circle $|z| = r$ and so actually attains its upper bound $M(r)$ on that circle. *M(r) is a steadily increasing unbounded function.* For, by the principle of the maximum modulus, we have
$$|f(r_1 e^{\theta i})| < M(r_2)$$
where $r_1 < r_2$, and hence
$$M(r_1) < M(r_2),$$

save in the trivial case when $f(z)$ is a constant. Moreover, $M(r)$ cannot be bounded; for if it were, $f(z)$ would be a constant, by Liouville's theorem. Thus $M(r)$ increases indefinitely with r.

We can, however, prove very much more than this; in fact, $\eta = \log M(e^{\xi})$ *is a continuous function of ξ, whose graph is convex downwards.* To prove this, we consider the behaviour of $z^{\alpha}f(z)$ in the annulus $r_1 \leqslant |z| \leqslant r_2$, where α is a real constant to be fixed later.

The function $z^{\alpha}f(z)$ is not, in general, one-valued. But if we cut the annulus along the negative part of the real axis, we obtain a domain in which the principal branch of this function is regular. The maximum modulus of this branch in the cut annulus is attained on the boundary of the domain.

Now since α is real, all the branches of $z^{\alpha}f(z)$ have the same modulus. If we consider a branch of this function which is regular in the part of the annulus for which $\frac{1}{2}\pi \leqslant \arg z \leqslant \frac{3}{2}\pi$, we see at once that the principal value cannot attain its maximum modulus on the cut, and so must attain it on one of the boundary circles of the annulus. We have thus shown that, when $r_1 \leqslant |z| \leqslant r_2$,

$$|z^{\alpha}f(z)| \leqslant \max\{r_1^{\alpha}M(r_1),\, r_2^{\alpha}M(r_2)\}.$$

Using an obvious notation, we deduce at once that

$$r^{\alpha}M(r) \leqslant \max\{r_1^{\alpha}M_1,\, r_2^{\alpha}M_2\}$$

when $r_1 \leqslant r \leqslant r_2$.

We now choose α so that $r_1^{\alpha}M_1 = r_2^{\alpha}M_2$; thus

$$\alpha = -\frac{\log(M_2/M_1)}{\log(r_2/r_1)}.$$

We then have $r^{\alpha}M(r) \leqslant r_1^{\alpha}M_1$, and so

$$\{M(r)\}^{\log(r_2/r_1)} \leqslant \left(\frac{r}{r_1}\right)^{\log(M_2/M_1)} M_1^{\log(r_2/r_1)} = \left(\frac{M_2}{M_1}\right)^{\log(r/r_1)} M_1^{\log(r_2/r_1)},$$

or, finally, $\qquad \{M(r)\}^{\log(r_2/r_1)} \leqslant M_1^{\log(r_2/r)} M_2^{\log(r/r_1)}.$

The result contained in this inequality is known as *Hadamard's three-circles theorem.*†

† *Bulletin de la Soc. math. de France,* **24** (1896), 186. The result obviously holds not only for integral functions, but also for any function which is regular in an annulus.

Since $M_1 \leqslant M(r)$, we may write this inequality in the form

$$1 \leqslant \left\{\frac{M(r)}{M_1}\right\}^{\log(r_2/r_1)} \leqslant \left\{\frac{M_2}{M_1}\right\}^{\log(r/r_1)},$$

from which it follows that $M(r) \to M_1$ as $r \to r_1+0$. Similarly we may show that $M(r) \to M_2$ as $r \to r_2-0$. Since, however, r_1 and r_2 are arbitrary, this implies that $M(r)$ is a continuous function of r.

Finally, if we write $\eta(\xi) = \log M(e^\xi)$, we find that, when $\xi_1 \leqslant \xi \leqslant \xi_2$,

$$(\xi_2-\xi_1)\eta(\xi) \leqslant (\xi_2-\xi)\eta(\xi_1)+(\xi-\xi_1)\eta(\xi_2),$$

so that the graph of $\eta = \log M(e^\xi)$ is convex downwards. We express this property by saying that $\log M(r)$ is a convex function† of $\log r$.

Example. $M(r)$ is the maximum modulus of the integral function $f(z)$ on $|z| = r$, and λ is a constant between 0 and 1. Show that $M(\lambda r)/M(r)$ decreases steadily as r increases, and that

$$\lim_{r\to\infty} M(\lambda r)/M(r) = 0,$$

save when $f(z)$ is a polynomial. What is the limit of the quotient in this case?

7.4. The order of an integral function

An integral function is said to be of finite order if there exists a real number k, independent of r, such that its maximum modulus $M(r)$ on the circle $|z| = r$ satisfies the inequality

$$\log M(r) < r^k$$

for all sufficiently large values of r. If there exists no such number k, the function is said to be of infinite order.

If $f(z)$ is of finite order, the constant k occurring in the inequality

$$\log M(r) < r^k$$

must be positive. For if it were zero or negative, $M(r)$ would be bounded and so $f(z)$ would be a constant, by Liouville's theorem. Moreover, if the inequality holds for one value of k, it evidently holds for all greater values of k.

† For an account of the properties of convex functions, see J. L. W. V. Jensen, *Acta Math.* **30** (1906), 175, or Hardy, Littlewood, and Pólya, *Inequalities* (Cambridge, 1934), 70–8, 91–6.

By means of a Dedekind section of the real numbers, we can determine a number ρ with the property that, for a given integral function $f(z)$ of finite order, the inequality

$$\log M(r) < r^k$$

holds for all sufficiently large values of r when $k > \rho$ but not when $k < \rho$. This number ρ is called the order of $f(z)$. The definition implies that, when $k < \rho$, the inequality

$$\log M(r) > r^k$$

holds for a sequence of values of r which increase indefinitely. In other words,

$$\rho = \varlimsup_{r \to \infty} \frac{\log\log M(r)}{\log r}.$$

When $f(z)$ is of infinite order, we have

$$\varlimsup_{r \to \infty} \frac{\log\log M(r)}{\log r} = +\infty.$$

Many of the elementary functions of analysis are integral functions of finite order. For example, a polynomial is of order zero; e^z, $\sin z$, and $\cos z$ are of order 1; $\cos \sqrt{z}$ is of order $\frac{1}{2}$. On the other hand, e^{e^z} is of infinite order.

Example. $f(z)$ is an integral function of finite order ρ. $M^1(r)$ is the maximum modulus of $f'(z)$ on $|z| = r$. Prove that, if $R > r$,

$$\frac{M(r) - |f(0)|}{r} \leqslant M^1(r) \leqslant \frac{M(R)}{R - r}.$$

Deduce that $f'(z)$ is also of order ρ.

7.41. Integral functions of finite order with no zeros

We shall now show that $e^{H(z)}$ *is an integral function of finite order with no zeros if and only if $H(z)$ is a polynomial.* We have already seen that $e^{H(z)}$ is an integral function with no zeros if and only if $H(z)$ is an integral function; moreover, if $H(z)$ is a polynomial of degree k, $e^{H(z)}$ is obviously of finite order k.

To complete the proof of the theorem, it only remains to show that *if the real part of an integral function $H(z)$ satisfies the inequality*

$$\mathrm{Rl}\, H(z) < r^{\rho+\epsilon}$$

for every positive value of ϵ and all sufficiently large values of r, $H(z)$ is a polynomial of degree not exceeding ρ. This analogue of Liouville's theorem is due to Hadamard.†

† *Journal de Math.* (4) **9** (1893), 186–7.

By Taylor's theorem, we have

$$H(z) = a_0 + a_1 z + a_2 z^2 + \ldots$$

where

$$a_n = \frac{1}{2\pi i} \int_C H(z) \frac{dz}{z^{n+1}},$$

C being the circle $|z| = r$. Now, when $n > 0$,

$$\int_C \overline{H(z)} \frac{dz}{z^{n+1}} = \int_C \sum_{m=0}^{\infty} \bar{a}_m \bar{z}^m \frac{dz}{z^{n+1}}$$

$$= \sum_{m=0}^{\infty} \int_0^{2\pi} \bar{a}_m r^{m-n} e^{-(m+n)\theta i} i \, d\theta$$

$$= 0,$$

the term-by-term integration being valid since the series $\sum \bar{a}_m \bar{z}^m$ converges uniformly. By addition, it follows that

$$a_n = \frac{1}{\pi i} \int_C \operatorname{Rl} H(z) \frac{dz}{z^{n+1}} = \frac{1}{\pi} \int_0^{2\pi} \operatorname{Rl} H(re^{\theta i}) \frac{d\theta}{r^n e^{n\theta i}}.$$

Hence we have

$$|a_n| r^n \leqslant \frac{1}{\pi} \int_0^{2\pi} |\operatorname{Rl} H(re^{\theta i})| \, d\theta.$$

On the other hand

$$a_0 = \frac{1}{2\pi i} \int_C H(z) \frac{dz}{z} = \frac{1}{2\pi} \int_0^{2\pi} H(re^{\theta i}) \, d\theta,$$

and so

$$\operatorname{Rl} a_0 = \frac{1}{2\pi} \int_0^{2\pi} \operatorname{Rl} H(re^{\theta i}) \, d\theta.$$

Hence we see that

$$2 \operatorname{Rl} a_0 + |a_n| r^n \leqslant \frac{1}{\pi} \int_0^{2\pi} \{|\operatorname{Rl} H| + \operatorname{Rl} H\} \, d\theta.$$

But the integrand is equal to $2 \operatorname{Rl} H$ or 0 according as $\operatorname{Rl} H >$ or $\leqslant 0$. Since $\operatorname{Rl} H < r^{\rho+\epsilon}$, we have, therefore,

$$2 \operatorname{Rl} a_0 + |a_n| r^n < 4 r^{\rho+\epsilon}$$

for every positive value of ϵ and all sufficiently large values of r.

If we now write this inequality in the form

$$|a_n| < 4 r^{\rho+\epsilon-n} - 2 \operatorname{Rl} a_0 r^{-n}$$

and then make $r \to \infty$, we see that $a_n = 0$ when $n > \rho$, and so $H(z)$ is a polynomial of degree not exceeding ρ. This completes the proof of the theorem.

Example. Prove that, if $f(z)$ is an integral function of finite order, it attains any assigned value, with at most one exception, infinitely often. Show also that, if the order is a fraction, there is no exceptional value.†

7.42. Jensen's inequality

Let $f(z)$ be an integral function which does not vanish at the origin. Let its zeros, arranged in order of increasing modulus, be $z_1, z_2, z_3, \ldots$, multiple zeros being repeated. Then if

$$|z_N| < R \leqslant |z_{N+1}|,$$

we have

$$R^N |f(0)| \leqslant M(R) |z_1 z_2 \ldots z_N|.$$

For the function

$$F(z) = f(z) \prod_{n=1}^{N} \frac{R^2 - z \bar{z}_n}{R(z - z_n)}$$

is also an integral function, and $|F(z)| = |f(z)|$ when $|z| = R$. Hence when $|z| \leqslant R$, we have, by the principle of the maximum modulus,

$$|F(z)| \leqslant M(R)$$

where $M(R)$ is the maximum modulus of $f(z)$ on $|z| = R$. Putting $z = 0$, we find that

$$\frac{R^N |f(0)|}{|z_1 z_2 \ldots z_N|} \leqslant M(R),$$

as stated above. This result‡ is known as Jensen's inequality.§

Let us now denote by $n(r)$ the number of zeros of $f(z)$ in $|z| \leqslant r$; evidently $n(r)$ is a non-decreasing function of r which is constant in any interval which does not contain the modulus of a zero of $f(z)$. Then

$$\log \frac{R^N}{|z_1 z_2 \ldots z_N|} = \sum_{n=1}^{N} \int_{|z_n|}^{R} \frac{dx}{x} = \int_{0}^{R} \frac{n(x)}{x}\, dx.$$

† The result contained in this example is a particular case of Picard's theorem, to which reference was made in § 4.55.

‡ The inequality evidently also holds if $f(z)$ is not an integral function, but is regular when $|z| \leqslant R$. See also p. 90, Ex. 15, for a more general result.

§ *Acta Math.* **22** (1899), 359–64.

Accordingly Jensen's inequality can be written in the form

$$\int_0^R \frac{n(x)}{x}\, dx \leqslant \log M(R) - \log |f(0)|.$$

From this we deduce that *if $f(z)$ is an integral function of finite order ρ, then $n(r) = O(r^{\rho+\epsilon})$ for every positive value of ϵ and all sufficiently large values of r.*

For if we put $R = 2r$, we have

$$\int_0^{2r} \frac{n(x)}{x}\, dx \leqslant \log M(2r) - \log |f(0)| < Ar^{\rho+\epsilon}$$

for every positive value of ϵ and all sufficiently large values of r, A being a finite constant independent of r. But since $n(x)$ is a non-decreasing function, we have

$$n(r)\log 2 \leqslant \int_r^{2r} \frac{n(x)}{x}\, dx \leqslant \int_0^{2r} \frac{n(x)}{x}\, dx < Ar^{\rho+\epsilon},$$

and so $n(r) = O(r^{\rho+\epsilon})$.

7.43. The exponent of convergence of the zeros of $f(z)$

Let $f(z)$ be an integral function with zeros $z_1, z_2, \ldots$ arranged in order of increasing modulus. We associate with this sequence of zeros a number ρ_1 defined by the equation

$$\rho_1 = \varlimsup_{n \to \infty} \frac{\log n}{\log r_n},$$

where $r_n = |z_n|$. This number ρ_1 is called the *exponent of convergence* of the zeros of $f(z)$, since it has the following important property. *If ρ_1 is finite, the series $\sum r_n^{-\tau}$ converges when $\tau > \rho_1$ and diverges when $\tau < \rho_1$; but if ρ_1 is infinite, the series diverges for every real value of τ.*

For if ρ_1 is finite and $\tau > \rho_1$, the inequality

$$\frac{\log n}{\log r_n} < \tfrac{1}{2}(\tau + \rho_1)$$

holds for all sufficiently large values of n, and so

$$r_n^\tau > n^{1+p},$$

where $p = (\tau - \rho_1)/(\tau + \rho_1) > 0$. Hence $\sum r_n^{-\tau}$ converges when $\tau > \rho_1$.

On the other hand, if ρ_1 is finite and $\tau < \rho_1$, or if ρ_1 is infinite and τ has any real value, there exists a sequence of integers for which $r_n^\tau < n$. Let N be such a value of n and let m be the least integer greater than $\tfrac{1}{2}N$. Then since r_n increases with n, we have

$$\sum_{N-m}^{N} r_n^{-\tau} > \frac{m}{r_N^\tau} > \frac{m}{N} > \frac{1}{2}.$$

But as there are values of N as large as we please, this implies that $\sum r_n^{-\tau}$ diverges.

If ρ_1 is finite, the series $\sum r_n^{-\rho_1}$ may be either convergent or divergent. For example, if $r_n = n$, we have $\rho_1 = 1$ and $\sum n^{-1}$ diverges; but if $r_n = n(\log n)^2$, we again have $\rho_1 = 1$, but in this case the series converges.

Finally, *if $f(z)$ is an integral function of finite order ρ, ρ_1 is finite and does not exceed ρ.* For, by § 7.42,

$$\rho_1 = \overline{\lim_{n\to\infty}} \frac{\log n}{\log r_n} = \overline{\lim_{r\to\infty}} \frac{\log n(r)}{\log r} \leqslant \overline{\lim_{r\to\infty}} \frac{\log(Ar^{\rho+\epsilon})}{\log r} = \rho + \epsilon,$$

for every positive value of ϵ, and so $\rho_1 \leqslant \rho$.

Example. Show that the series $\sum r_n^{-\tau}$ and the integral $\int_0^\infty n(x)x^{-1-\tau}\,dx$ converge or diverge together.

7.5. Canonical products

If $f(z)$ is an integral function of finite order ρ with an infinite number of zeros $z_1, z_2, \ldots$, there exists a least integer p such that the series $\sum r_n^{-1-p}$ is convergent. If ρ_1 is not an integer, p is the greatest integer less than ρ_1; if ρ_1 is an integer, p may be either ρ_1 or $\rho_1 - 1$. But, in any case, $\rho_1 - 1 \leqslant p \leqslant \rho_1 \leqslant \rho$.

By § 7.2, the infinite product

$$G(z) = \prod_{n=1}^{\infty} E\!\left(\frac{z}{z_n}, p\right)$$

converges uniformly and absolutely in any finite region of the plane, and represents an integral function which vanishes if and only if z is a zero of $f(z)$. We call it the *canonical product* formed with the zeros of $f(z)$; the integer p is called its *genus*.

7.51. Borel's theorems on canonical products

Borel[†] has proved two fundamental theorems on canonical products which we shall deduce from the following lemma.[‡]

If $G(z)$ is a canonical product of genus p with zeros $z_1, z_2,...,$ and if N is a positive integer such that $|z_N| \leqslant 2|z| < |z_{N+1}|$, then

$$\log \prod_1^N \left| 1 - \frac{z}{z_n} \right| - I \leqslant \log |G(z)| \leqslant I$$

where I is equal to

$$\sum_1^N \log \left(1 + \left| \frac{z}{z_n} \right| \right) + 2 \sum_{N+1}^\infty \left| \frac{z}{z_n} \right| \qquad (p = 0),$$

or
$$A \sum_1^N \left| \frac{z}{z_n} \right|^p + 2 \sum_{N+1}^\infty \left| \frac{z}{z_n} \right|^{p+1} \qquad (p > 0),$$

A being independent of z.

The canonical product is

$$G(z) = \prod_1^N E\left(\frac{z}{z_n}, p \right) \prod_{N+1}^\infty E\left(\frac{z}{z_n}, p \right) = \Pi_1 \Pi_2$$

say. We shall denote $|z|$, $|z_n|$, $|z/z_n|$ by r, r_n, u_n respectively.

In Π_2, we have $u_n < \frac{1}{2}$ and so

$$|\log |\Pi_2|| \leqslant |\log \Pi_2| \leqslant \sum_{N+1}^\infty \left| \log E\left(\frac{z}{z_n}, p \right) \right| \leqslant 2 \sum_{N+1}^\infty u_n^{p+1},$$

by the inequality of § 7.2.

To obtain inequalities satisfied by Π_1 we have to consider separately the cases $p > 0$ and $p = 0$. Now when $p > 0$ and $|z| \geqslant \frac{1}{2}$, we have

$$|E(z,p)| \leqslant (1 + |z|) \exp\left(|z| + \tfrac{1}{2}|z|^2 + ... + \frac{1}{p}|z|^p \right),$$

and so

$$\log |E(z,p)| \leqslant \log(1 + |z|) + |z| + \tfrac{1}{2}|z|^2 + ... + \frac{1}{p}|z|^p \leqslant A|z|^p$$

† *Acta Math.* **20** (1897), 357–96.

‡ The proof of this lemma is a modification of that of Valiron, *Integral Functions* (Toulouse, 1923), 53–8.

where A is independent of z; similarly

$$\log |E(z,p)| \geqslant \log|1-z| - |z| - \tfrac{1}{2}|z|^2 - \ldots - \frac{1}{p}|z|^p$$

$$\geqslant \log|1-z| - A|z|^p.$$

Since $u_n \geqslant \tfrac{1}{2}$ in Π_1, we deduce from these inequalities that

$$\sum_1^N \log\left|1 - \frac{z}{z_n}\right| - A\sum_1^N u_n^p \leqslant \log|\Pi_1| \leqslant A\sum_1^N u_n^p,$$

when $p > 0$. If we combine this with the other inequality

$$-2\sum_{N+1}^\infty u_n^{p+1} \leqslant \log|\Pi_2| \leqslant 2\sum_{N+1}^\infty u_n^{p+1},$$

the result stated in the lemma for $p > 0$ follows at once.

When $p = 0$, we have

$$\log|G(z)| = \log|\Pi_1| + \log|\Pi_2|$$

$$\leqslant \sum_1^N \log\left|1 - \frac{z}{z_n}\right| + 2\sum_{N+1}^\infty u_n$$

$$\leqslant \sum_1^N \log(1+u_n) + 2\sum_{N+1}^\infty u_n = I,$$

and also

$$\log|G(z)| \geqslant \sum_1^N \log\left|1 - \frac{z}{z_n}\right| - 2\sum_{N+1}^\infty u_n$$

$$= \sum_1^N \log\left|1 - \frac{z}{z_n}\right| + \sum_1^N \log(1+u_n) - I$$

$$\geqslant \sum_1^N \log\left|1 - \frac{z}{z_n}\right| - I.$$

This completes the proof of the lemma.

We shall now prove the first of Borel's theorems, that *the order of a canonical product is equal to the exponent of convergence of its zeros.*

Let μ be a number such that $p < \mu \leqslant p+1$ and also such that $\sum r_n^{-\mu}$ is convergent. Then, when $p > 0$, we have

$$I = A\sum_1^N u_n^\mu u_n^{p-\mu} + 2\sum_{N+1}^\infty u_n^\mu u_n^{p+1-\mu}$$

$$\leqslant 2^{\mu-p} A\sum_1^N u_n^\mu + 2^{\mu-p}\sum_{N+1}^\infty u_n^\mu,$$

since $u_n \geqslant \frac{1}{2}$ when $n \leqslant N$, and $u_n < \frac{1}{2}$ when $n > N$. This gives

$$I \leqslant 2^{\mu-p} r^\mu \Big\{ A \sum_1^N r_n^{-\mu} + \sum_{N+1}^\infty r_n^{-\mu} \Big\} = O(r^\mu).$$

A similar proof can be given when $p = 0$ and leads to the same result.

Let the exponent of convergence of the zeros of $G(z)$ be ρ_1. It follows from the lemma that, when $\mu > \rho_1$, the inequality

$$|G(z)| < e^{r^\mu}$$

holds for all sufficiently large values of r, and so the order ρ of $G(z)$ cannot exceed μ. Since μ is any number greater than ρ_1, this implies that $\rho \leqslant \rho_1$. We have, however, already proved that $\rho_1 \leqslant \rho$ for any integral function. Hence, for a canonical product, $\rho_1 = \rho$.

From this theorem, in conjunction with the lemma, we deduce that, *given a canonical product $G(z)$ of order ρ and an arbitrary positive number ϵ, there exists an infinite number of circles of arbitrarily large radius on each of which holds the inequality*

$$|G(z)| > e^{-|z|^{\rho+\epsilon}}.$$

This theorem sets a lower bound to the minimum value, $m(r)$ say, of $|G(z)|$ on $|z| = r$.

Since $m(r)$ vanishes whenever r is the modulus of a zero of $G(z)$, we cannot expect that $m(r)$ will behave quite as simply as $M(r)$. To overcome this difficulty, we describe a circle $|z - z_n| = r_n^{-h}$ about each zero z_n for which $r_n = |z_n| > 1$, h being any real number greater than ρ. Since $\sum r_n^{-h}$ is convergent, these circles do not cover the whole plane, and so there exists an infinite number of circles $|z| = r$ of arbitrarily large radius which do not intersect any of the small circles having zeros of $G(z)$ as centre. It will, therefore, suffice to prove that the inequality in question holds for all sufficiently large values of $|z|$, provided that z lies outside all these small circles.

The proof of the theorem depends on the inequality

$$\log |G(z)| \geqslant \log \prod_1^N \Big| 1 - \frac{z}{z_n} \Big| - I$$

established in the lemma. As we have shown,

$$I < r^{\rho+\frac{1}{2}\epsilon}$$

for all sufficiently large values of r.

It will be recalled that the integer N was defined by the inequality $r_N \leqslant 2r < r_{N+1}$. Now when $r_n \leqslant 1$, we have $|1-z/z_n| > 1$ provided that $r > 2$, and so

$$\log \prod_{r_n \leqslant 1} \left| 1 - \frac{z}{z_n} \right| > 0.$$

But when $1 < r_n \leqslant 2r$ and z lies outside all the small circles, we have

$$\left| 1 - \frac{z}{z_n} \right| = \frac{|z - z_n|}{r_n} \geqslant \frac{1}{r_n^{1+h}} \geqslant \frac{1}{(2r)^{1+h}}.$$

Hence $\log \prod_{1 < r_n \leqslant 2r} \left| 1 - \frac{z}{z_n} \right| \geqslant -N(1+h)\log 2r.$

We have, however, shown in § 7.42 that, for all sufficiently large values of r, $N < Ar^{\rho + \frac{1}{2}\epsilon}.$

Combining these results, we find that

$$\log \prod_{1}^{N} \left| 1 - \frac{z}{z_n} \right| > -A(1+h)\log(2r)r^{\rho + \frac{1}{2}\epsilon}.$$

It follows that, when z lies outside all the small circles and r is sufficiently large,

$$\log |G(z)| > -r^{\rho + \frac{1}{2}\epsilon}\{1 + (A+h)\log(2r)\} > -r^{\rho + \epsilon}.$$

This result is due to Borel.

7.6. Hadamard's factorization theorem

If $f(z)$ is an integral function of finite order ρ which has zeros $z_1, z_2, \ldots$ and does not vanish at the origin, it can be factorized in the form $$f(z) = G(z)e^{H(z)},$$

where $G(z)$ is the canonical product formed with the zeros of $f(z)$ and $H(z)$ is a polynomial of degree not exceeding ρ.

It has already been proved that such a factorization is possible, $H(z)$ being an integral function. It remains to show that $H(z)$ is a polynomial.

Let ρ_1 be the exponent of convergence of the zeros of $f(z)$. Then the canonical product $G(z)$ is of order ρ_1, and ρ_1 does not exceed ρ. If ϵ denotes an arbitrary positive number, there exists, as we have just seen, an infinite number of circles $|z| = r$ of arbitrarily large radius on which the inequality

$$|G(z)| > e^{-r^{\rho_1 + \epsilon}}$$

is satisfied. But since $f(z)$ is of order ρ, the inequality

$$|f(z)| < e^{r^{\rho + \epsilon}}$$

holds for all sufficiently large values of r.

From these two inequalities it follows that

$$|e^{H(z)}| = \left| \frac{f(z)}{G(z)} \right| < e^{r^{\rho + \epsilon} + r^{\rho_1 + \epsilon}} \leqslant e^{2r^{\rho + \epsilon}}$$

for a certain set of arbitrarily large values of r. Hence, by the principle of maximum modulus,

$$|e^{H(z)}| < e^{2r^{\rho + \epsilon}}$$

for all sufficiently large values of r, and so $e^{H(z)}$ is an integral function which does not vanish and whose order does not exceed ρ. By § 7.41, $H(z)$ is a polynomial whose degree does not exceed ρ. This completes the proof of Hadamard's factorization theorem.

If $G(z)$ is of genus p and $H(z)$ of degree q, the greater of the integers p and q is called the genus of $f(z)$. Since $p \leqslant \rho$ and $q \leqslant \rho$, the genus of an integral function does not exceed its order. It can be shown that, when ρ is not an integer, the genus is the greatest integer less than ρ. But when ρ is an integer, the genus is either ρ or $\rho - 1$, the actual determination in any particular case being sometimes difficult.

7.7. The Taylor coefficients of an integral function of finite order

The necessary and sufficient condition for

$$f(z) = \sum_0^\infty a_n z^n$$

to be an integral function of finite order is that

$$\lim_{n \to \infty} \frac{\log(1/|a_n|)}{n \log n} > 0.$$

The condition is necessary. For suppose that $f(z)$ is of finite order ρ. Then, when $k > \rho$, the inequality

$$M(r) < e^{r^k}$$

is satisfied by the maximum modulus of $f(z)$ for all sufficiently large values of r. Hence we have, by Cauchy's inequality,

$$|a_n| < e^{r^k}r^{-n}.$$

The expression on the right-hand side of this inequality has a maximum value $(ek/n)^{n/k}$, attained when $r^k = n/k$, and so

$$|a_n| < \left(\frac{ek}{n}\right)^{n/k}.$$

From this it follows that

$$\varliminf \frac{\log(1/|a_n|)}{n \log n} \geqslant \frac{1}{k} > 0,$$

so that the condition is necessary.

It remains to show that, if

$$\mu = \varliminf \frac{\log(1/|a_n|)}{n \log n}$$

is positive, $f(z)$ is an integral function of finite order. We consider separately the two cases, (i) μ finite, (ii) μ infinite.

Let us suppose that μ is finite. The definition of μ implies that, if ϵ is an arbitrary positive number less than μ, there exists an integer N such that the inequality

$$\log(1/|a_n|) > (\mu-\epsilon)n \log n$$

holds whenever $n > N$. This inequality may be written

$$|a_n| < n^{-(\mu-\epsilon)n}.$$

But since $\mu-\epsilon$ is positive, this implies that $|a_n|^{1/n}$ tends to zero as $n \to \infty$ and hence that $f(z)$ is an integral function.

Now, when $r > 1$, we have

$$|f(z)| \leqslant \sum_0^N |a_n|r^n + \sum_{N+1}^\infty |a_n|r^n < Ar^N + \sum_{N+1}^\infty \left(\frac{r}{n^{\mu-\epsilon}}\right)^n$$

where A is a constant. Let us choose an integer M such that

$$M^{\mu-\epsilon} \leqslant 2r < (M+1)^{\mu-\epsilon}.$$

If r is sufficiently large, M will be greater than N. When $N+1 \leqslant n \leqslant M$, we have

$$r^n \leqslant r^M \leqslant \exp\{(2r)^{1/(\mu-\epsilon)}\log r\}$$

and so

$$\sum_{N+1}^{M} \left(\frac{r}{n^{\mu-\epsilon}}\right)^n \leqslant \exp\{(2r)^{1/(\mu-\epsilon)}\log r\} \sum_{N+1}^{M} n^{-(\mu-\epsilon)n}$$

$$< \exp\{(2r)^{1/(\mu-\epsilon)}\log r\} \sum_{1}^{\infty} n^{-(\mu-\epsilon)n}$$

$$= B\exp\{(2r)^{1/(\mu-\epsilon)}\log r\}$$

where B is independent of r. Also

$$\sum_{M+1}^{\infty} \left(\frac{r}{n^{\mu-\epsilon}}\right)^n < \sum_{M+1}^{\infty} \left(\frac{r}{(M+1)^{\mu-\epsilon}}\right)^n < \sum_{M+1}^{\infty} \frac{1}{2^n} < 1.$$

Combining these inequalities, we find that

$$|f(z)| < Ar^N + B\exp\{(2r)^{1/(\mu-\epsilon)}\log r\} + 1,$$

from which it follows that

$$M(r) < \exp\{2(2r)^{1/(\mu-\epsilon)}\log r\}$$

for all sufficiently large values of r. Let us now denote the order of $f(z)$ by ρ. Then we have

$$\rho = \varlimsup_{r\to\infty} \frac{\log\log M(r)}{\log r} \leqslant \varlimsup \frac{\log 2 + \log(2r)^{1/(\mu-\epsilon)} + \log\log r}{\log r},$$

and so

$$\rho \leqslant 1/(\mu-\epsilon).$$

Again, it also follows from the definition of μ that there exists an infinite number of positive integers n such that

$$\log(1/|a_n|) < (\mu+\epsilon)n\log n,$$

or

$$|a_n| > n^{-(\mu+\epsilon)n}.$$

Using Cauchy's inequality we find that, for each such value of n,

$$M(r) \geqslant |a_n|r^n > \left(\frac{r}{n^{\mu+\epsilon}}\right)^n.$$

If we take $r = 2n^{\mu+\epsilon}$, we now have

$$M(r) > 2^n = \exp\{(\tfrac{1}{2}r)^{1/(\mu+\epsilon)}\log 2\}$$

for certain arbitrarily large values of r. This, however, implies that $\rho \geqslant 1/(\mu+\epsilon)$.

We have thus shown that the order ρ of $f(z)$ satisfies the inequality

$$\frac{1}{\mu+\epsilon} \leqslant \rho \leqslant \frac{1}{\mu-\epsilon}$$

for all positive values of ϵ less than μ. Making ϵ tend to zero, we find that $f(z)$ is of finite order $1/\mu$.

4111   N

To deal with the case when μ is infinite, we observe that the inequality

$$\log(1/|a_n|) > Kn\log n$$

holds for any given positive value of K and all sufficiently large values of n. A repetition of the first part of the previous argument shows that $f(z)$ is an integral function of order not exceeding $1/K$. Since K can be as large as we please, the order of $f(z)$ must be zero. This completes the proof of the theorem.

It should be observed that we have proved incidentally that

$$\varlimsup_{n\to\infty} \frac{n\log n}{\log(1/|a_n|)}$$

is the order of the integral function $f(z)$.

REFERENCES

E. Borel, *Leçons sur les fonctions entières* (Paris, 1900).

R. Nevanlinna, *Le Théorème de Picard-Borel* (Paris, 1929).

E. C. Titchmarsh, *The Theory of Functions* (Oxford, 1932), Chap. VIII.

G. Valiron, *Lectures on the General Theory of Integral Functions* (Toulouse, 1923).

   See also G. Pólya and G. Szegö, *Aufgaben und Lehrsätze aus der Analysis* (Berlin, 1925), **2**, IV. Abschn., Kap. 1.

MISCELLANEOUS EXAMPLES

1. Prove that, if $|a| > 1$, the integral function

$$\prod_1^\infty \left(1 - \frac{z}{a^n}\right)$$

is of order zero.

2. Show that, if $\alpha > 1$, the integral function

$$\prod_1^\infty \left(1 - \frac{z}{n^\alpha}\right)$$

is of order $1/\alpha$.

3. Prove that,[†] if

$$\varlimsup \frac{\log|a_n/a_{n+1}|}{\log n} = \kappa > 0,$$

the function $\sum_0^\infty a_n z^n$ is an integral function of order not exceeding $1/\kappa$. Show also that the order is $1/\kappa$ if

$$\lim \frac{\log|a_n/a_{n+1}|}{\log n} = \kappa > 0.$$

[†] Use Stirling's approximation to the Gamma function, that when x is large and positive,
$$\Gamma(1+x) = e^{-x}x^x\sqrt{(2\pi x)}\{1+o(1)\}.$$

4. Determine the orders of the following integral functions:

(i) $\cos \sqrt{z}$;

(ii) $\displaystyle\sum_0^\infty \frac{z^n}{(n!)^\alpha}$ $(\alpha > 0)$;

(iii) $\displaystyle\sum_0^\infty \frac{z^n}{\Gamma(1+\alpha n)}$ $(\alpha > 0)$;

(iv) $z^{-\frac{1}{2}\nu} J_\nu(\sqrt{z}) = \displaystyle\sum_0^\infty \frac{(-z)^n}{2^{\nu+2n} n! \, \Gamma(\nu+n+1)}$.

5. $f(z)$ is an integral function of finite order ρ. Show that, corresponding to any positive number ϵ, there exists an infinite number of circles $|z| = r$ of arbitrarily large radius on which the lower bound $m(r)$ of $|f(z)|$ satisfies the inequality

$$m(r) > e^{-r^{\rho+\epsilon}}.$$

6. Prove that, if the order of an integral function is not an integer or zero, it is equal to the exponent of convergence of its zeros. Deduce that such a function has an infinite number of zeros.

7. By means of Hadamard's factorization theorem prove that, if h is not an integer or zero,

$$\sin \pi(z+h) = e^{\pi z \cot \pi h} \sin \pi h \prod_{-\infty}^{\infty} \left\{ \left(1 + \frac{z}{n+h}\right) e^{-z/(n+h)} \right\},$$

and also that $\sin \pi z = \pi z \displaystyle\prod_{-\infty}^{\infty}{}' \left\{ \left(1 + \frac{z}{n}\right) e^{-z/n} \right\}.$

CHAPTER VIII

CONFORMAL REPRESENTATION

8.1. Isogonal mapping

LET us suppose that the functions $u(x,y)$ and $v(x,y)$ are continuous and possess continuous partial derivatives of the first order at each point of a domain S in a plane in which x and y are rectangular Cartesian coordinates. The equations $u = u(x,y)$, $v = v(x,y)$ set up a correspondence between the points of S and the points of a set Σ in the (u,v)-plane. The set Σ is evidently a domain and is called a *map* of S. Moreover, since the partial derivatives of the first order of u and v are continuous, a curve in S which has a continuously turning tangent is mapped on a curve with the same property in Σ. The correspondence between the two domains is not, however, necessarily a one-to-one correspondence.

A simple example of this is given by taking $u = x^2$, $v = y^2$. The domain $x^2+y^2 \leqslant 1$ is mapped on the triangle bounded by $u = 0$, $v = 0$, $u+v = 1$, but there are four points of the circle corresponding to each point of the triangle.

A method of mapping S on Σ is said to be *isogonal* if it is a one-to-one transformation which turns any two intersecting curves of S into two curves of Σ which cut at the same angle. In order that the correspondence may conserve angle in the sense just defined, it is both necessary and sufficient that the involution of orthogonal directions at each point of S be transformed into the involution of orthogonal directions at the corresponding point of Σ. This is equivalent to saying that the isotropic directions at each point of S transform into the isotropic directions at the corresponding point of Σ, and conversely.

Now the differential equation of the isotropic directions in the (x,y)-plane is
$$(dx)^2+(dy)^2 = 0.$$

Hence
$$(du)^2+(dv)^2 = h^2\{(dx)^2+(dy)^2\}$$

where h depends only on x and y and is not zero.

To determine the properties of the functions u and v for which this equation holds, we make the substitution
$$du = u_x dx + u_y dy, \qquad dv = v_x dx + v_y dy,$$

where suffixes denote partial differentiation, and then equate coefficients. It follows that the functions u and v satisfy the partial differential equations

$$u_x^2+v_x^2 = h^2, \qquad u_y^2+v_y^2 = h^2, \qquad u_x u_y+v_x v_y = 0.$$

If we satisfy the first two equations by putting

$$u_x = h\cos\alpha, \quad v_x = h\sin\alpha, \quad u_y = h\cos\beta, \quad v_y = h\sin\beta,$$

we find that the third equation is also satisfied if $\alpha-\beta = \pm\tfrac{1}{2}\pi$.

Hence, if the correspondence $u = u(x,y)$, $v = v(x,y)$ is one-to-one, it is also isogonal if and only if, at each point of S, the four first-order partial derivatives satisfy one of the following sets of equations:

$$\text{(a)}\ u_x = v_y, \quad u_y = -v_x, \qquad \text{(b)}\ u_x = -v_y, \quad u_y = v_x,$$

and do not vanish simultaneously

The equations (a) are, however, the well-known Cauchy-Riemann differential equations. In virtue of the initial restrictions on u and v, the conditions (a) and (b) are, therefore, equivalent to

$$\text{(a')}\ u+iv = f(x+iy), \qquad \text{(b')}\ u-iv = f(x+iy),$$

where $f(x+iy)$ is an analytic function, regular in S. Moreover, since $|f'(x+iy)|^2 = u_x^2+v_x^2$, the derivative $f'(x+iy)$ vanishes nowhere in S. In other words, the only isogonal transformations of a domain S of the z-plane into a domain Σ of the w-plane are of the form $w = f(z)$ or $\bar{w} = f(z)$, where $f(z)$ is an analytic function whose derivative is finite and non-zero at each point of S. Actually it suffices to consider only isogonal transformations of the former type, since the transformation $\bar{w} = f(z)$ is equivalent to $w = f(z)$ followed by a reflection in the real axis of the w-plane.

Now if $f(z)$ is an analytic function, regular in a neighbourhood of the point z_0 at which $f'(z)$ does not vanish, we know, by the inverse-function theorem (§ 6.22), that the equation $w = f(z)$ sets up a one-to-one correspondence between a certain neighbourhood of z_0 in which $f'(z)$ does not vanish and the region within a certain closed contour within which the point $w_0 = f(z_0)$ lies. Thus the neighbourhood of z_0 is mapped isogonally on the region within the closed contour.

It must not, however, be supposed that, if $f'(z)$ is finite and non-zero at each point of a domain S, then $w = f(z)$ necessarily maps S isogonally on a domain Σ of the w-plane. For, although a neighbourhood of each point of S is mapped isogonally, it is not necessarily the case that the mapping of the whole of S is a one-to-one correspondence. For example, the function z^2 has a derivative $2z$ which is finite and non-zero when $1 \leqslant |z| \leqslant 2$, $-\frac{3}{4}\pi \leqslant \arg z \leqslant \frac{3}{4}\pi$; yet $w = z^2$ maps this domain on an overlapping region $1 \leqslant |w| \leqslant 4$, $-\frac{3}{2}\pi \leqslant \arg w \leqslant \frac{3}{2}\pi$, and so the transformation is not one-to-one.

Example. Show that $w = z/(1-z)^2$ maps $|z| < 1$ isogonally on the whole w-plane, supposed cut along the real axis from $-\infty$ to $-\frac{1}{4}$.

8.11. Conformal mapping

Let us suppose that $w = f(z)$, where $f(z)$ is an analytic function, maps a domain S of the z-plane isogonally on a certain domain Σ of the w-plane. If C is a regular arc $z = x(t) + iy(t)$ in S, the equation of its map is

$$w = f\{x(t) + iy(t)\},$$

so that C is mapped on a regular arc Γ, say.

Let us now denote by ϕ and ψ respectively the angles which the tangents to C and Γ at the points of the same parameter t make with the real axis. Then we have

$$\phi = \tan^{-1}\frac{\dot{y}}{\dot{x}} = \arg\{\dot{x}(t) + i\dot{y}(t)\}$$

and

$$\psi = \arg\left[\frac{d}{dt}f\{x(t) + iy(t)\}\right] = \arg[f'(z)\{\dot{x}(t) + i\dot{y}(t)\}]$$

$$= \phi + \arg f'(z).$$

Thus $\psi - \phi$ is equal to $\arg f'(z)$ and so depends only on the affix of the point z and not on the particular curve through that point. This, however, implies that the transformation conserves not only the magnitude of the angle of intersection of two curves but also the sense of the angle.

But since the transformation $\bar{w} = f(z)$ is equivalent to $w = f(z)$ followed by a reflection in the real axis of the w-plane, this transformation conserves the magnitude of the angle of intersection of two curves but reverses its sense.

A *conformal transformation* is defined to be an isogonal transformation which conserves the sense of an angle as well as its magnitude. It follows that the only conformal transformations of a domain of the z-plane into a domain of the w-plane are of the form $w = f(z)$, where $f(z)$ is an analytic function.

Returning now to the regular arc C and its map Γ, let us denote by s and σ the lengths of C and Γ respectively up to the point of parameter t. Then we have

$$\frac{ds}{dt} = \sqrt{(\dot{x}^2 + \dot{y}^2)} = |\dot{x}(t) + i\dot{y}(t)|$$

and

$$\frac{d\sigma}{dt} = \left| \frac{d}{dt} f\{x(t) + iy(t)\} \right| = |f'(z)\{\dot{x}(t) + i\dot{y}(t)\}|;$$

hence we see that

$$\frac{d\sigma}{dt} = |f'(z)| \frac{ds}{dt}.$$

We have thus shown that the conformal transformation $w = f(z)$ maps a small neighbourhood of a point z_0 on a neighbourhood of the corresponding point w_0, which, correct to the first order, is obtained by a magnification in the ratio $|f'(z_0)| : 1$ and a rotation through the angle $\arg f'(z_0)$.

Example 1. The domain S of the z-plane is mapped conformally on the domain Σ of the w-plane by $w = f(z)$. Show that the curves in Σ corresponding to $x =$ constant and $y =$ constant form two orthogonal families. Verify that this is the case when (i) $w = \cosh z$, (ii) $w = z^2$. Explain the apparent contradiction in (ii) when $x = 0$ and $y = 0$.

Example 2. Prove that, in the notation of Ex. 1, the area of Σ is

$$\iint_S |f'(z)|^2 \, dx \, dy.$$

Example 3. The function $w = f(z)$ maps $|z| < R$ conformally on a domain of area A. Prove that $A \geqslant \pi |f'(0)|^2 R^2$.

Example 4. Prove that the quadrant $|z| \leqslant 1$, $0 \leqslant \arg z \leqslant \tfrac{1}{2}\pi$ is mapped conformally on a domain Σ in the w-plane by $w = 4/(z+1)^2$. Find Σ and determine the length of its boundary.

The derivative of the function $4/(z+1)^2$ is finite and non-zero at each point of the quadrant. Accordingly $w = 4/(z+1)^2$ maps the quadrant conformally on a domain Σ provided that w does not take any value twice in the quadrant. Now if

$$4/(z+1)^2 = 4/(z_1+1)^2,$$

then either $z = z_1$ or $z = -z_1 - 2$. But if z_1 is a point of the quadrant, $-z_1 - 2$ certainly is not. Hence $w = 4/(z+1)^2$ maps the quadrant conformally on a domain Σ in the w-plane.

The boundary of Σ is evidently a closed contour Γ. But since w is infinite only when $z = -1$, the quadrant is mapped on the domain within Γ.

When z moves along the real axis from 0 to 1, w moves along the real axis from 4 to 1, and so the length of this part of Γ is 3.

When z moves from 1 to i along an arc of $|z| = 1$, we have $z = e^{2it}$, where t increases from 0 to $\tfrac{1}{4}\pi$. Then w moves from 1 to $-2i$ along the arc whose parametric equation is $w = \sec^2 t\, e^{-2it}$. From this we deduce that $|w| = 2 - \mathrm{Rl}\, w$, so that the path is an arc of the parabola with focus at the origin and directrix $\mathrm{Rl}\, w = 2$. The length of this part of Γ is

$$\int_0^{\pi/4} \left| \frac{dw}{dt} \right| dt = \int_0^{\pi/4} 2 \sec^3 t\, dt = \sqrt{2} + \log(1 + \sqrt{2}).$$

Finally when z moves along the imaginary axis from i to 0, w goes from $-2i$ to 4. If we write $z = -i \tan t$, where t increases from $-\tfrac{1}{4}\pi$ to 0, we find that the parametric equation of this portion of Γ is $w = 4 \cos^2 t\, e^{2it}$. This curve is, however, the inverse of the parabola $w = \sec^2 t\, e^{-2it}$ with respect to the circle $|w| = 2$, and so is a cardioid with cusp at the origin. The length of this portion of Γ is

$$\int_{-\pi/4}^{0} \left| \frac{dw}{dt} \right| dt = \int_{-\pi/4}^{0} 8 \cos t\, dt = 4\sqrt{2}.$$

Combining these results, we see that the length of Γ is

$$3 + 5\sqrt{2} + \log(1 + \sqrt{2}).$$

8.12. Simple functions

If $w = f(z)$ maps a domain S conformally on a certain domain Σ of the w-plane, we say that $f(z)$ is *simple*† in S. The characteristic property of such a function is that it takes no value more than once in S. The general theory of simple functions is too difficult to be included in the present book.‡ It is, however, quite easy to show that *if $f(z)$ is regular within and on a closed contour C and takes no value more than once on C, then $f(z)$ is simple within and on C.*

The relation $w = f(z)$ evidently sets up a continuous one-to-one correspondence between the points of C and the points of a

---

† The French and German words are *univalente* and *schlicht* respectively.

‡ For an account of the very interesting recent work on this subject, see, for example, L. Bieberbach, *Lehrbuch der Funktionentheorie*, **2** (1927), 82–94; P. Dienes, *The Taylor Series* (1931), Chap. VIII; E. Landau, *Darstellung und Begründung einiger neuerer Ergebnisse der Funktionentheorie* (1929), 107–14.

closed contour Γ. If w_0 is any point of the w-plane which does not lie on Γ, the number of zeros of $f(z)-w_0$ within C is

$$m = \frac{1}{2\pi i} \int_C \frac{f'(z)}{f(z)-w_0}\, dz = \frac{1}{2\pi i} \int_\Gamma \frac{dw}{w-w_0},$$

the direction of integration round Γ being that which corresponds to the positive sense of description of C.

If w_0 lies outside Γ, then $m = 0$, and so no point within C is mapped on a point outside Γ. But when w_0 lies within C, we have $m = \pm 1$. Since m cannot be negative,† the equation $f(z) = w_0$ has precisely one root within C when w_0 lies within Γ.

To complete the proof of the theorem it only remains to show that $f(z)$ cannot take a value w_1 on Γ at any point z_1 within C. If this were the case, a neighbourhood of z_1 would be mapped conformally on a neighbourhood of w_1; this is impossible since the neighbourhood of w_1 contains points outside Γ.

8.2. Riemann's theorem on conformal mapping

The fundamental problem in the theory of conformal mapping is concerned with the possibility of transforming conformally a given domain S of the z-plane into any given domain Σ of the w-plane. Actually it suffices to consider whether it is possible to map conformally any given domain on the interior of a circle. For if $\zeta = f(z)$ maps S on $|\zeta| < 1$ and $w = g(\zeta)$ maps Σ on $|\zeta| < 1$, then the equation $w = g\{f(z)\}$ provides a conformal transformation of S into Σ.

It is not, however, possible to map a completely arbitrary domain on the interior of a circle; there must be some restriction on the nature of the boundary. For example, we cannot map a domain whose boundary consists of a single point conformally on $|\zeta| < 1$; for if the domain had a single boundary point, which we may take to be the point at infinity,‡ the mapping function $\zeta = f(z)$ would be an integral function which satisfied everywhere the inequality $|f(z)| < 1$ and so, by Liouville's theorem, would be a constant. Thus, in order that a domain

---

† This implies that the sense of description of Γ is the positive one.

‡ If $z = a$ is the boundary point, it can be transformed into the point at infinity by $z_1 = 1/(z-a)$.

may be mapped conformally on a circle, it must possess more than one boundary point.

The simplest case occurs when the boundary is a simple closed Jordan curve. It can be shown that *if S is the open domain bounded by a simple closed Jordan curve C, there exists a unique analytic function f(z), regular in S, such that w = f(z) maps S conformally on |w| < 1 and also transforms a point z = a within C into the origin and a given direction at z = a into the positive direction of the real axis.* This theorem was first stated by Riemann in his inaugural dissertation† at Göttingen in 1851, but his proof, which depended on the Calculus of Variations, was shown by Weierstrass to be incomplete.

Whilst it is difficult to give a rigorous proof of this theorem, its truth will become obvious to the reader who is content to rely on physical intuition. Let us suppose that such a function does exist and consider what properties it must have.

In the first place, $f(z)/(z-a)$ is regular and non-zero in S and so is of the form $e^{\phi(z)}$ where $\phi(z)$ is regular within C. Thus

$$f(z) = (z-a)e^{\phi(z)}.$$

Moreover, since $|f(z)| = 1$ on C, the function $\phi(z)$ satisfies there the condition

$$\log|z-a| + \mathrm{Rl}\,\phi(z) = 0.$$

Now the real part of an analytic function satisfies Laplace's equation

$$\frac{\partial^2 V}{\partial x^2} + \frac{\partial^2 V}{\partial y^2} = 0,$$

where $z = x+iy$. If, therefore, it could be shown that there exists a unique real solution of Laplace's equation, V say, which vanishes on C and is finite within C save at the point $z = a$, in whose neighbourhood it behaves like $\log|z-a|$, the real part of $\phi(z)$ would be given by the equation

$$V = \log|z-a| + \mathrm{Rl}\,\phi(z).$$

The Cauchy-Riemann differential equations would then enable us to find the imaginary part of $\phi(z)$, save for an additive constant.

A physical argument renders intuitive the existence of such

† See Riemann's *Ges. Werke* (1876), 3–43.

a solution of Laplace's equation. For consider an earthed cylindrical conductor of infinite length whose cross-section is the curve C. Then V is uniquely determined as being the electrostatic potential within this cylinder due to a line-charge of density $-\frac{1}{2}$, which is parallel to the axis of the cylinder and passes through the point of affix a. Unfortunately, however, it is just as difficult to give a rigorous proof of the existence and uniqueness of the electrostatic potential† as it is to prove Riemann's theorem on conformal representation.

If the reader is prepared to accept this argument from physical intuition, it is easy to complete the 'proof' of Riemann's theorem. It only remains to choose the arbitrary additive constant occurring in the imaginary part of $\phi(z)$ so as to make the given direction at $z = a$ correspond to the real axis in the w-plane. We shall not attempt to give here an adequate proof of Riemann's theorem, which can be found in various easily accessible works.‡

8.3. Homographic transformations

We shall now consider whether it is possible to map conformally the complete z-plane, apart from a finite number of exceptional points, on the complete w-plane. If it is possible, it will be effected by a relation $w = f(z)$, where $f(z)$ is an analytic function which has only a finite number of singularities.

The function $f(z)$ cannot possess an isolated essential singularity; for, by Weierstrass's theorem (§ 4.55), a function approaches as near as we please to any assigned value in every neighbourhood of an essential singularity, and this is clearly inadmissible here. The only singularities of $f(z)$ are, therefore, poles, of which the point at infinity may be one, and so $f(z)$ is a rational function (§ 4.56).

But, by § 6.21, Ex. 1, a rational function takes any assigned value p times, where p is the number of its poles. Hence the function $f(z)$ has but one singularity, a simple pole, since a conformal transformation is one-to-one. If the singular point is at

† See O. D. Kellogg, *Foundations of Potential Theory* (Berlin, 1929).

‡ See, for example, C. Carathéodory, *Conformal Representation* (Cambridge, 1932), Chap. V; L. R. Ford, *Automorphic Functions* (New York, 1929), Chap. VIII; G. Julia, *Leçons sur la représentation conforme* (Paris, 1931), Chap. III.

a finite distance, the transformation is of the form

$$w = (az+b)/(cz+d),$$

where a, b, c, and d are constants such that $ad-bc \neq 0$; but if the singularity is at infinity, then

$$w = Az+B,$$

where A ($\neq 0$) and B are constants. In either case the transformation is homographic.†

8.31. Homographic transformations which leave the unit circle invariant

Homographic transformations which map the circle $|z| = 1$ on $|w| = 1$ are of particular importance in the theory of functions. The transformation $w = (az+b)/(cz+d)$ will be of this type if

$$\left| \frac{az+b}{cz+d} \right| = 1$$

whenever $|z| = 1$; using conjugate complex numbers, we require that

$$(az+b)(\bar{a}\bar{z}+\bar{b}) = (cz+d)(\bar{c}\bar{z}+\bar{d}).$$

The constants a, b, c, and d must, therefore, satisfy the equations

$$a\bar{a}+b\bar{b} = c\bar{c}+d\bar{d}, \qquad a\bar{b} = c\bar{d},$$

as well as the inequality $ad \neq bc$.

Now, if a is not zero, the second equation gives $\bar{b} = c\bar{d}/a$ and hence $b = \bar{c}d/\bar{a}$. Substituting these values in the first equation, we find that

$$(a\bar{a}-c\bar{c})(a\bar{a}-d\bar{d}) = 0,$$

and so $|a| = |c|$ or $|a| = |d|$.

When $|a| = |c|$, we can write $c = ae^{\gamma i}$, where γ is real. Substituting this in the equation $a\bar{b} = c\bar{d}$, we deduce that $d = be^{\gamma i}$. Hence, when $|a| = |c|$, the transformation degenerates into $w = e^{-\gamma i}$, which is not a homographic transformation.

To deal with the case $|a| = |d|$, we write $d = \bar{a}e^{-\delta i}$, where δ is real. We easily find that $c = \bar{b}e^{-\delta i}$, so that the transforma-

---

† For an account of the elementary properties of homographic transformations, see G. H. Hardy, *Pure Mathematics* (Cambridge, 1921), 94–6. Some of these properties are given in examples 6, 7, 8, 9 at the end of Chapter I of the present book.

tion is of the form

$$w = e^{\delta i}\frac{az+b}{\bar{a}+\bar{b}z}, \qquad\qquad (A)$$

where $|a| \neq |b|$. A similar investigation shows that this formula also holds when $a = 0$, the transformation then taking the particularly simple form $w = e^{\alpha i}/z$, where α is real.

When w and z are connected by the homographic transformation (A), it can be shown without difficulty that

$$(1-w\bar{w})|a+b\bar{z}|^2 = (1-z\bar{z})(a\bar{a}-b\bar{b}).$$

Hence when $|z| < 1$, we have $|w| < 1$ or $|w| > 1$ according as $|a| > |b|$ or $|a| < |b|$. Thus the homographic transformation (A) maps $|z| \leqslant 1$ conformally on $|w| \leqslant 1$ only if $|a| > |b|$. In § 8.33 we show that no other conformal transformation has this property.

8.32. Schwarz's lemma

The proof of the result stated at the end of the previous section depends on the following lemma due to Schwarz.† *If $f(z)$ is regular in $|z| < R$, where it satisfies the inequality $|f(z)| \leqslant M$, and if $f(0) = 0$, then the inequality $|f(z)| \leqslant M|z|/R$ holds whenever $|z| < R$. Moreover, equality can occur only when $f(z) = Mze^{\alpha i}/R$, where α is a real constant.*

It follows from the data of the lemma that $f(z)$ is expansible as a power series $a_1 z + a_2 z^2 + ...$, whose radius of convergence is not less than R. The function $\phi(z) = f(z)/z$ is, therefore, regular when $|z| < R$.

Let a be any number whose modulus is less than R. If we choose r so that $|a| < r < R$, then, by the principle of the maximum modulus, the function $\phi(z)$ attains its maximum modulus in $|z| \leqslant r$ at some point on the circle $|z| = r$. Hence we have

$$|\phi(a)| \leqslant \max_{|z|=r}\left|\frac{f(z)}{z}\right| = \frac{1}{r}\max |f(z)|$$

and so
$$|\phi(a)| \leqslant M/r.$$

This last inequality holds no matter how near r is to R, and $\phi(a)$ is independent of r. Making $r \to R$, we deduce that $|\phi(a)| \leqslant M/R$, the first result of the lemma.

† H. A. Schwarz (1869), *Ges. Math. Abhandlungen*, **2**, 109–10.

If there exists a number a of modulus less than R, such that $|\phi(a)| = M/R$, we know that $\phi(z)$ is a constant of modulus M/R. Hence we have $f(z) = Mze^{\alpha i}/R$, where α is a real constant. This completes the proof of the lemma.

Example. Prove that, if $f(z)$ satisfies the conditions of Schwarz's lemma, $|f'(0)| \leqslant M/R$. Show also that equality occurs only when $f(z) = Mze^{\alpha i}/R$, where α is a real constant.

8.33. Riemann's theorem for a circle

Let us suppose that $w = f(z)$ maps $|z| \leqslant 1$ conformally on $|w| \leqslant 1$ and turns the interior point $z = c$ into the origin. We shall now show that such a transformation is necessarily homographic.

We know that $\zeta = (z-c)/(1-\bar{c}z)$ maps $|z| \leqslant 1$ conformally on $|w| \leqslant 1$ and transforms $z = c$ into the origin. Eliminating z, we obtain a transformation $w = \phi(\zeta)$ which maps $|\zeta| \leqslant 1$ on $|w| \leqslant 1$ and conserves the origin. This function $\phi(\zeta)$ satisfies all the conditions of Schwarz's lemma, and so

$$|w| \leqslant |\zeta|$$

when $|\zeta| \leqslant 1$.

But we can also write this transformation in the form $\zeta = \Phi(w)$, where $\Phi(w)$ again satisfies the conditions of Schwarz's lemma. Hence we have

$$|\zeta| \leqslant |w|$$

when $|w| \leqslant 1$. Combining these two inequalities, we find that

$$|\zeta| \leqslant |w| \leqslant |\zeta|$$

when $|\zeta| \leqslant 1$, and so $|w| = |\zeta|$. The second part of Schwarz's lemma now gives $w = \zeta e^{\alpha i}$, where α is a real constant. Thus the transformation $w = f(z)$ is of the form

$$w = e^{\alpha i}\frac{z-c}{1-\bar{c}z},$$

and so is homographic.

If, in addition, we require that the direction $\arg(z-c) = \beta$ at c is to be transformed into the positive direction of the real axis, we must take $\alpha = -\beta$.

We can now show that there is a unique function $w = f(z)$ which maps $|z-a| \leqslant R$ conformally on $|w| \leqslant 1$ and also transforms an interior point $z = c$ into the origin and a given direction at c into the positive direction of the real axis. For the transformation $z' = (z-a)/R$ maps $|z-a| \leqslant R$ on $|z'| \leqslant 1$, transforms $z = c$ into an interior point $z' = c'$, and leaves the prescribed direction unaltered. We have only to apply a homographic transformation to get the result stated. This completes the proof of Riemann's theorem for a circle.

Example. Show that the region $|z-a| \leqslant R$ is mapped conformally on $|w| \leqslant 1$ by

$$w = \frac{R(z-c)}{R^2-(z-a)(\bar{c}-\bar{a})}e^{\alpha i},$$

where α is real and $z = c$ is the point which is transformed into the origin.

8.34. The conformal representation of a half-plane on a circle

We shall now consider the problem of mapping the half-plane $\operatorname{Im} z > 0$ conformally on $|w| < 1$ and simultaneously transforming a given point c of that half-plane into the origin $w = 0$. By choosing R sufficiently large, we can make c lie within the circle $|z-iR| = R$. As R tends to infinity, the interior of this circle increases until it fills up the whole half-plane.

Now the transformation

$$w = \frac{Re^{\alpha i}(z-c)}{R^2-(z-iR)(\bar{c}+iR)}$$

maps $|z-iR| \leqslant R$ conformally on $|w| \leqslant 1$ and turns $z = c$ into $w = 0$. If we write this transformation in the form

$$w = \frac{ie^{\alpha i}(z-c)}{(1-i\bar{c}/R)z-\bar{c}}$$

and then make $R \to \infty$, we find that

$$w = \lambda\frac{z-c}{z-\bar{c}},$$

where $|\lambda| = 1$, maps the half-plane $\operatorname{Im} z > 0$ conformally on $|w| < 1$ and turns $z = c$ into $w = 0$.

It should be observed that, by suitably choosing λ, we can make any prescribed direction at $z = c$ correspond to the positive direction of the real axis at $w = 0$. Making the appropriate changes in the argument of § 8.33, we easily show that

Riemann's theorem on conformal representation is also true for a half-plane.

Finally, by making a preliminary translation and rotation, any half-plane can be mapped conformally on the interior of a circle.

Example 1. Show that $\operatorname{Im} z > 0$ is mapped conformally on $\operatorname{Im} w > 0$ by $w = (az+b)/(cz+d)$, provided that a, b, c, and d are real and $ad-bc > 0$. What happens if $ad-bc < 0$?

Example 2. Show that $w = (1-z)/(1+z)$ maps $|z| < 1$ conformally on $\operatorname{Rl} w > 0$. Determine the curves in the w-plane which correspond to $|z| = r$ and to $\arg z = \alpha$.

8.4. Schwarz's principle of symmetry

Let Γ be a closed contour consisting of a segment AB of the real axis and a curve in the upper half-plane joining the ends of that segment. Let $f(z)$ be an analytic function which is regular within Γ and continuous within and on Γ, and which also takes real values on AB. We shall now show that we can continue $f(z)$ analytically across AB by means of the equation $f(z) = \overline{f(\bar{z})}$. This result is known as Schwarz's principle of symmetry.[†]

If we reflect Γ in the real axis, we obtain a closed contour Γ_1 consisting of the segment AB and a curve in the lower half-plane. We define the function $\phi(z)$ by the equation $\phi(z) = f(z)$ when z is within or on Γ, and by $\phi(z) = \overline{f(\bar{z})}$ when z is within or on Γ_1. By hypothesis, $\phi(z)$ is regular within Γ. It is also regular within Γ_1; for when z and $z+h$ lie within Γ_1, $\bar{z}$ and $\bar{z}+\bar{h}$ lie within Γ and so

$$\lim_{h \to 0} \frac{\phi(z+h)-\phi(z)}{h} = \lim_{h \to 0} \frac{\overline{f(\bar{z}+\bar{h})}-\overline{f(\bar{z})}}{h}$$

$$= \lim_{h \to 0} \overline{\left[\frac{f(\bar{z}+\bar{h})-f(\bar{z})}{\bar{h}} \right]} = \overline{f'(\bar{z})}.$$

If we denote by C the closed contour formed by the curved parts of Γ and Γ_1, $\phi(z)$ is evidently continuous within and on C. Hence, by § 5.5, the function

$$F(z) = \frac{1}{2\pi i} \int_C \frac{\phi(t)}{t-z} \, dt$$

† *Journal für Math.* **70** (1869), 106–7.

is regular within C. But, when z lies within Γ, we have

$$F(z) = \frac{1}{2\pi i} \int_{\Gamma} \frac{\phi(t)}{t-z}\, dt + \frac{1}{2\pi i} \int_{\Gamma_1} \frac{\phi(t)}{t-z}\, dt;$$

the value of the first integral is $\phi(z)$ and the second integral vanishes. Hence we see that $F(z) = \phi(z)$ when z lies within Γ, and, similarly, also when z lies within Γ_1. Finally, by continuity, it follows that this equation holds also when z is an interior point of the segment AB, but not necessarily when z is an endpoint of that segment.

We have thus shown that the function $\phi(z)$ is regular within C. Since it is equal to $f(z)$ within Γ, it provides the required analytical continuation of $f(z)$ across AB. This completes the proof of the principle of symmetry.

Example 1. Γ is a closed contour consisting of an arc AB of the circle $|z| = 1$ and a curve within that circle joining A to B. The function $f(z)$ is regular within Γ and continuous within and on Γ. By mapping the arc AB on a segment of the real axis, prove that, if $f(z)$ is real on AB, it can be continued analytically across AB by means of the relation $f(z) = \overline{f(1/\bar{z})}$.

Example 2. The function $f(z)$ satisfies the conditions of Ex. 1, save that it now takes values of modulus 1 on the arc AB. Show that the analytical continuation of $f(z)$ across AB is given by $f(z) = 1/\overline{f(1/\bar{z})}$.

Example 3. Show that, if $0 < \alpha < 1$, the angular region

$$-\alpha\pi < \arg z < \alpha\pi$$

is mapped conformally on the right-hand half-plane by $w = z^{1/(2\alpha)}$.

8.5. The conformal representation of a polygon on a half-plane

Let us suppose that the relation $w = f(z)$ enables us to map the domain within a closed polygon Γ in the z-plane conformally on the region $\operatorname{Im} w > 0$. We propose to investigate the properties of this function $f(z)$. Actually it turns out to be more convenient to consider, not $f(z)$, but the inverse function $z = F(w)$.

Now the function $F(w)$ is regular and $F'(w)$ does not vanish when $\operatorname{Im} w > 0$. From this it follows that

$$\frac{d}{dw} \log F'(w) = \frac{F''(w)}{F'(w)}$$

is regular in the upper half-plane. We next show that this is also true at any point on the line $\mathrm{Im}\, w = 0$ which does not correspond to a vertex of Γ.

Let L be a side of Γ making an angle θ with the real axis. Then if b is any point of L which is not a vertex of Γ, $(z-b)e^{-\theta i}$ is real on L. Hence if $w = \beta$ is the point corresponding to $z = b$, the function $\{F(w)-b\}e^{-\theta i}$ is real and continuous on the segment Λ of the real axis corresponding to L, and is regular when $\mathrm{Im}\, w > 0$. By Schwarz's principle of symmetry, this function can be continued analytically across Λ; it is, therefore, regular in a neighbourhood of β and can be expressed as a Taylor series of the form

$$\{F(w)-b\}e^{-\theta i} = \sum_{r=1}^{\infty} a_r (w-\beta)^r,$$

where the coefficients a_r are real. Now if the first non-zero coefficient in this expansion were a_p, this would imply that the two segments into which L is divided by the point b intersect at an angle π/p. Hence a_1 is not zero, and so $d\log F'(w)/dw$ is regular in a neighbourhood of β and is real when w is real.

When the point corresponding to $z = b$ is the point at infinity,[†] we have similarly

$$\{F(w)-b\}e^{-\theta i} = \sum_{r=1}^{\infty} c_r w^{-r},$$

where the coefficients c_r are real and $c_1 \neq 0$. This gives

$$\frac{F''(w)}{F'(w)} = -\frac{2}{w} + \sum_{r=2}^{\infty} \frac{c_r'}{w^r}.$$

Hence in this case $d\log F'(w)/dw$ is regular in a neighbourhood of the point at infinity and is real when w is real.

Next, let us suppose that L and L' are consecutive sides of Γ intersecting in the vertex z' where Γ has an angle $\alpha\pi$. The function $F(w)$ cannot be regular in a neighbourhood of the point w' corresponding to $z = z'$, since an angle $\alpha\pi$ at z' is mapped on an angle π at w'. But since $\mathrm{ar\dot{g}}\{(z'-z)e^{-\theta i}\}$ is equal to zero and $\alpha\pi$ on L and L' respectively, the function $[\{z'-F(w)\}e^{-\theta i}]^{1/\alpha}$ is real and continuous on the segment of the real axis corresponding to the consecutive sides L and L'. Moreover, this

† In this case Λ consists of two segments of the real axis, each of infinite length.

function is regular when $\operatorname{Im} w > 0$, since $F(w) - z'$ is regular and does not vanish there. Applying the same argument as before, we see that

$$[\{z' - F(w)\}e^{-\theta i}]^{1/\alpha}$$

is regular in a neighbourhood of w' and can be expressed as a Taylor series of the form

$$[\{z' - F(w)\}e^{-\theta i}]^{1/\alpha} = \sum_{r=1}^{\infty} b_r(w - w')^r,$$

where the coefficients b_r are real and b_1 is not zero. But this gives

$$F(w) = z' + e^{\theta i}(w - w')^\alpha \sum_{r=0}^{\infty} b_r'(w - w')^r,$$

where b_0' is not zero. Hence we have

$$F'(w) = (w - w')^{\alpha-1} \Phi(w),$$

where $\Phi(w)$ is regular and does not vanish in a neighbourhood of w', and so

$$\frac{d}{dw} \log F'(w) = \frac{\alpha - 1}{w - w'} + \frac{\Phi'(w)}{\Phi(w)}.$$

Hence if w' corresponds to a point at which Γ has an angle $\alpha\pi$, the function $d \log F'(w)/dw$ has there a simple pole of residue $\alpha - 1$.

In a similar manner the reader will readily show that, if the point at infinity corresponds to a vertex of Γ of angle $\alpha\pi$, then

$$\frac{d}{dw} \log F'(w) = -\frac{\alpha+1}{w} + \sum_2^{\infty} \frac{d_r}{w^r}.$$

Now suppose that the points $a, b, c, ..., l$ (all of finite affix) lie on the real axis of the w-plane and correspond to the vertices of Γ, and let

$$\alpha\pi, \ \beta\pi, \ \gamma\pi, ..., \ \lambda\pi$$

be the corresponding angles of Γ. Then the function

$$d \log F'(w)/dw$$

must satisfy the following conditions:

(i) It is regular when $\operatorname{Im} w \geqslant 0$ save for simple poles of residue $\alpha - 1, \ \beta - 1, \ \gamma - 1, ..., \ \lambda - 1$ at the points $a, b, c, .., l$ respectively.

(ii) It is real when w is real.

(iii) It possesses an expansion of the form

$$\frac{d}{dw}\log F'(w) = -\frac{2}{w} + \sum_{r=2}^{\infty} \frac{c_r'}{w^r}$$

valid in a neighbourhood of the point at infinity.

Since the function is regular when $\operatorname{Im} w > 0$ and real when $\operatorname{Im} w = 0$, we can continue it analytically across the real axis by Schwarz's principle of symmetry, and we find that the only singularities of the function in the complete w-plane are the prescribed poles on the real axis. Hence, by § 4.56, the function is a rational function and so is of the form

$$\frac{d}{dw}\log F'(w) = \frac{\alpha-1}{w-a} + \frac{\beta-1}{w-b} + \ldots + \frac{\lambda-1}{w-l} + \Phi(w)$$

where $\Phi(w)$ is a polynomial.

Now when $|w|$ is large, we have

$$\frac{d}{dw}\log F'(w) = \Phi(w) + \sum_{r=1}^{\infty} \frac{c_r'}{w^r}$$

where $c_1' = (\alpha-1)+(\beta-1)+(\gamma-1)+\ldots+(\lambda-1).$

But since $\alpha\pi$, $\beta\pi$, $\gamma\pi$,..., $\lambda\pi$ are the internal angles of a closed polygon, $(1-\alpha)\pi+(1-\beta)\pi+\ldots+(1-\lambda)\pi = 2\pi$

and so $c_1' = -2$. Hence in order to satisfy condition (iii), $\Phi(w)$ must be identically zero.

We have thus shown that the mapping function $F(w)$ satisfies the differential equation

$$\frac{d}{dw}\log F'(w) = \frac{\alpha-1}{w-a} + \frac{\beta-1}{w-b} + \ldots + \frac{\lambda-1}{w-l}.$$

Integrating this equation, we deduce that

$$F(w) = A \int (w-a)^{\alpha-1}(w-b)^{\beta-1}\ldots(w-l)^{\lambda-1}\,dw + B,$$

where A and B are constants of integration. The integrand is not one-valued in the complete w-plane, but has branch-points $a, b, c,\ldots, l$ on the real axis. But if we take a definite branch of the integrand and suppose that the path of integration never passes below a branch-point, $F(w)$ is regular when $\operatorname{Im} w \geqslant 0$, save at the points corresponding to the vertices of Γ.

It remains to show that the constants $A, B, a, b,\ldots, l$ can be suitably determined. Now, with any set of real numbers a, b, c,..., l in the correct order, the relation $z = F(w)$ maps the line $\mathrm{Im}\, w = 0$ on a closed polygon Γ', not necessarily simple, whose angles are the same as those of Γ. But, in order to construct a polygon similar to a given polygon of n sides, it does not suffice to make corresponding angles equal; there are $n-3$ other conditions to be satisfied. We can, therefore, choose three of the numbers a, b, c,..., l arbitrarily and then choose the rest to make Γ' similar to Γ. This done, the scale, orientation, and position of Γ' are determined by $|A|$, $\arg A$, and B respectively. We can therefore choose A and B to make Γ' coincide with Γ.

Let us denote by C the closed contour in the w-plane which consists of the segment of the real axis from $-R$ to R, indented at the points a, b, c,..., l, and the semicircle in the upper half-plane on this segment as diameter. The function

$$z = A \int (w-a)^{\alpha-1}(w-b)^{\beta-1}...(w-l)^{\lambda-1}\, dw + B$$

is regular within and on C. Moreover, when w goes round C, z describes the polygon Γ, indented at the vertices and also at the point corresponding to $w = \infty$. It follows, by § 8.12, that the region within C is mapped conformally on the region within Γ. If we now make R tend to infinity and the radius of each indentation of C tend to zero, we find that *the region* $\mathrm{Im}\, w > 0$ *is mapped conformally on the interior of the closed polygon* Γ *of angles* $\alpha\pi$, $\beta\pi$,..., $\lambda\pi$, *by the relation*

$$z = A \int (w-a)^{\alpha-1}(w-b)^{\beta-1}...(w-l)^{\lambda-1}\, dw + B,$$

provided that the constants are suitably determined. This result was discovered independently by Schwarz[†] and Christoffel.[‡]

It is often convenient to suppose that a is the point at infinity. In this case, condition (iii) has to be modified; we now require that the expansion

$$\frac{d}{dw} \log F'(w) = -\frac{\alpha+1}{w} + \sum_{2}^{\infty} \frac{d_r}{w^r}$$

† *Journal für Math.* **70** (1869), 105–20.
‡ *Annali di Math.* (2) **1** (1867), 95–103; **4** (1871), 1–9.

should hold near the point at infinity. Making this change, the reader will readily prove that

$$F(w) = A \int (w-b)^{\beta-1}(w-c)^{\gamma-1}...(w-l)^{\lambda-1} \, dw + B.$$

8.51. Examples of the use of the Schwarz-Christoffel formula

The region within a triangle ABC, of angles $\alpha\pi$, $\beta\pi$, $\gamma\pi$ where $\alpha+\beta+\gamma = 1$, is mapped conformally on the upper half of the w-plane by taking

$$z = D \int (w-a)^{\alpha-1}(w-b)^{\beta-1}(w-c)^{\gamma-1} \, dw + E.$$

The constants a, b, c can be chosen arbitrarily, and D and E are then fixed by the scale, orientation, and position of the triangle. In particular, if we take b at infinity, the relation connecting w and z becomes

$$z = D \int (w-a)^{\alpha-1}(w-c)^{\gamma-1} \, dw + E.$$

The only non-degenerate triangles for which this integral can be simply evaluated† are the equilateral triangle, the right-angled isosceles triangle, and the right-angled triangle with one angle $\frac{1}{3}\pi$. In each of these cases w is an elliptic function of z.

There are, however, certain interesting degenerate triangles for which the integral can be easily evaluated. These are discussed below.

(i) Let us keep A and C and the direction of AB fixed and make γ tend to 1. The triangle becomes the region between two straight lines intersecting at A at an angle $\alpha\pi$. Taking $a = 0$, the relation connecting w and z becomes

$$z = Fw^{\alpha} + E.$$

The reader will easily verify that this relation enables us to map the angle $0 < \arg\{(z-E)/F\} < \alpha\pi$ conformally on $\operatorname{Im} w > 0$.

(ii) Let us keep A and C fixed and make β tend to zero. The triangle becomes the region between two parallel lines on one side of a transversal; the corresponding relation between w and z is

$$z = D \int (w-a)^{\alpha-1}(w-c)^{\gamma-1} \, dw + E,$$

where $\alpha+\gamma = 1$.

The simplest case occurs when the transversal cuts the parallel lines at right angles, so that $\alpha = \gamma = \frac{1}{2}$. Taking $c = -1$, $a = 1$, we then have

$$z = D \int \frac{dw}{\sqrt{(w^2-1)}} + E = D\cosh^{-1}w + E.$$

To verify that this is the case, we take $D = 1$, $E = 0$, so that $w = \cosh z$. Writing $z = x+iy$, $w = u+iv$, we find that

$$u = \cosh x \cos y, \qquad v = \sinh x \sin y.$$

† See Love, *American Journal of Math.* **11** (1889), 158–71.

Keeping the positive number x fixed, let y vary from 0 to π. Then w evidently moves round the upper half of the ellipse

$$\frac{u^2}{\cosh^2 x} + \frac{v^2}{\sinh^2 x} = 1.$$

Moreover, as x increases from 0 to ∞, this arc of the ellipse sweeps out the upper half of the w-plane. Thus $w = \cosh z$ maps the half-strip $\mathrm{Rl}\, z > 0, 0 < \mathrm{Im}\, z < \pi$ conformally on $\mathrm{Im}\, w > 0$. The discussion of the correspondence of the boundaries of the two regions is simple and is left to the reader.

(iii) Let us keep C and the direction AB fixed, and then make α and β tend to zero and γ tend to 1. In this way the triangle degenerates into the strip between two parallel lines, which is mapped conformally on the upper half of the w-plane by taking

$$z = D \int (w-a)^{-1}\, dw + E.$$

As a verification, let us consider the case when $D = 1$, $E = 0$, $a = 0$, so that $w = e^z$. If $\mathrm{Rl}\, z$ is kept fixed and $\mathrm{Im}\, z$ increases from 0 to π, w moves round the upper half of the circle $|w| = e^{\mathrm{Rl}\, z}$. Moreover, as $\mathrm{Rl}\, z$ increases from $-\infty$ to ∞, this circular arc sweeps out the upper half of the w-plane. Thus $w = e^z$ maps the strip $0 < \mathrm{Im}\, z < \pi$ conformally on $\mathrm{Im}\, w > 0$.

8.52. The conformal representation of a rectangle on a half-plane

The theorem of Schwarz and Christoffel shows that it is possible to map the interior of a rectangle conformally on the upper half of the w-plane by a transformation of the form

$$z = D \int [(w-a)(w-b)(w-c)(w-d)]^{-1/2}\, dw + E.$$

We shall now consider the particular transformation of this type

$$z = \int_0^w [(1-w^2)(1-k^2 w^2)]^{-1/2}\, dw,$$

where $0 < k < 1$.

This integral is an elliptic integral and its value cannot be expressed in terms of the elementary functions of analysis. At the present stage we cannot discuss the transformation by expressing w explicitly in terms of z, as this involves a knowledge of the theory of elliptic functions.

Let us suppose that the integrand is positive on the real axis when $-1 < w < 1$, and that it is defined elsewhere on the real axis by continuation along a path in the upper half-plane. It is easily seen that the integrand is equal to $i[(w^2-1)(1-k^2 w^2)]^{-1/2}$ when $1 < w < 1/k$, and is equal to $-[(w^2-1)(k^2 w^2-1)]^{-1/2}$ when $w > 1/k$. We now consider how z

behaves when w describes the complete boundary of the positive quadrant of $|w| \leqslant R$, where $R > 1/k$.

As w moves along the real axis from 0 to 1, z moves along the real axis from 0 to K, where

$$K = \int_0^1 [(1-w^2)(1-k^2w^2)]^{-1/2} \, dw.$$

This integral converges, and so K is finite and positive.

When $1 \leqslant w \leqslant 1/k$, the corresponding path of z is given by

$$z = \int_0^1 [(1-w^2)(1-k^2w^2)]^{-1/2} \, dw + i \int_1^w [(w^2-1)(1-k^2w^2)]^{-1/2} \, dw.$$

The first integral is equal to K, whilst the second is real and increases from 0 to K' as w increases from 1 to $1/k$, where

$$K' = \int_1^{1/k} [(w^2-1)(1-k^2w^2)]^{-1/2} \, dw.$$

The number K' is evidently finite. Thus as w moves along the real axis from 1 to $1/k$, z moves along the line $\mathrm{Rl}\, z = K$ from K to $K+iK'$.

When $w > 1/k$, the path of z is given by

$$z = K+iK' - \int_{1/k}^w [(w^2-1)(k^2w^2-1)]^{-1/2} \, dw.$$

But if we write $kw = 1/t$ in this integral, we find that

$$\int_{1/k}^w [(w^2-1)(k^2w^2-1)]^{-1/2} \, dw = \int_{1/kw}^1 [(1-t^2)(1-k^2t^2)]^{-1/2} \, dt$$

$$= K - \int_0^{1/kw} [(1-t^2)(1-k^2t^2)]^{-1/2} \, dt,$$

and so $$z = iK' + \int_0^{1/kw} [(1-t^2)(1-k^2t^2)]^{-1/2} \, dt. \tag{A}$$

Hence as w moves along the real axis from $1/k$ to R, z moves along the line $\mathrm{Im}\, z = K'$ from $K+iK'$ to the point of affix

$$iK' + \int_0^{1/kR} [(1-t^2)(1-k^2t^2)]^{-1/2} \, dt.$$

By analytical continuation, the formula (A) holds everywhere in $|w| > 1/k$. Hence z is regular there and can be represented by a convergent series of inverse powers of w; in fact, if we expand the integrand and integrate term by term, we obtain

$$z = iK' + \frac{1}{kw} - \frac{(1+k^2)}{6k^3w^3} + \dots.$$

This shows that $\qquad z - iK' = \dfrac{1}{kw}\left\{1 + O\left(\dfrac{1}{|w|^2}\right)\right\}$

when $|w|$ is large, and so the path of z, as w moves from R to iR, lies within a circle of centre iK' whose radius tends to zero as $R \to \infty$. Moreover, the argument of $z - iK'$ decreases by $\tfrac{1}{2}\pi$ in moving along this path.

Finally when $w = iv$ where v is positive, we have

$$z = i\int_0^v [(1+v^2)(1+k^2v^2)]^{-1/2}\,dv.$$

Since this integral is real and positive and decreases as v decreases, z moves along the imaginary axis from the point near iK' to the origin as w moves along the imaginary axis from iR to 0. We have thus shown that, as w moves round the complete boundary of the positive quadrant of $|w| \leqslant R$, z moves round the rectangle with vertices 0, K, $K+iK'$, iK', indented at iK', and that the radius of the indentation tends to zero as $R \to \infty$. From this it follows, by § 8.12, that the region $0 < \arg w < \tfrac{1}{2}\pi$ is mapped conformally on the interior of this rectangle.

Now z is purely imaginary when $\mathrm{Rl}\,w = 0$. By using Schwarz's principle of symmetry, we find that the region $\tfrac{1}{2}\pi < \arg w < \pi$ is mapped conformally on the interior of the rectangle with vertices 0, iK', $-K+iK'$, $-K$. Combining these two results, we see that the relation

$$z = \int_0^w [(1-w^2)(1-k^2w^2)]^{-1/2}\,dw$$

enables us to map the interior of the rectangle with vertices K, $K+iK'$, $-K+iK'$, $-K$ conformally on the upper half of the w-plane.

REFERENCES

The theory of conformal representation:

C. CARATHÉODORY, *Conformal Representation* (Cambridge Math. Tract, 1932).

A. R. FORSYTH, *Theory of Functions* (Cambridge, 1918), Chaps. XIX, XX.

G. JULIA, *Leçons sur la représentation conforme* (Paris, 1931).

G. JULIA, *Principes géométriques d'analyse*, **1** (Paris, 1930), **2** (Paris, 1932).

The application of conformal representation to physical problems:

H. BATEMAN, *Partial Differential Equations of Mathematical Physics* (Cambridge, 1932), Chap. IV.

A. R. FORSYTH, loc. cit., 639–52.

H. LAMB, *Hydrodynamics* (Cambridge, 1916), Chap. IV.

M. WALKER, *Conjugate Functions for Engineers* (Oxford, 1933).

MISCELLANEOUS EXAMPLES

1. Show that stereographic projection maps the surface of a sphere conformally on a plane.

2. Prove that it is possible to map a surface of revolution conformally on a plane in such a manner that the meridians and parallels on the surface correspond to lines parallel to the axes of coordinates.

Show that, in the case of the sphere

$$X = R\sin\theta\cos\phi, \qquad Y = R\sin\theta\sin\phi, \qquad Z = R\cos\theta,$$

where $0 \leqslant \theta \leqslant \pi$, $0 \leqslant \phi < 2\pi$, a conformal mapping of this type is provided by Mercator's projection $x = \phi$, $y = \log\tan\frac{1}{2}\theta$.

3. Prove that, when $w = \tanh z$, the curves corresponding to lines parallel to the real and imaginary axes in the z-plane form two families of coaxal circles.

Show that this relation maps the strip $0 < \operatorname{Im} z < \frac{1}{2}\pi$ conformally on the upper half of the w-plane.

4. Prove that $w = \cos z$ maps the strip $0 < \operatorname{Rl} z < \pi$ conformally on the whole w-plane, supposed cut along the real axis from $-\infty$ to -1 and from $+1$ to $+\infty$.

5. The circles $|z-1| = \sqrt{2}$, $|z+1| = \sqrt{2}$ divide the z-plane into four domains, of which one contains the origin; show that this domain is mapped conformally on $|w| < 1$ by $w = 2z/(1-z^2)$.

(Math. Tripos, 1932.)

6. Find a function $w = f(z)$ which maps $|z| < 1$ conformally on the exterior of the parabola $v^2 = -4u$, where $w = u+iv$, with $z = 0$ corresponding to $w = 3$ and the positive directions of the real axes at these points corresponding to one another. (Math. Tripos, 1932.)

7. Prove that, if $a > b > 0$, the equation

$$(a+b)z^2 - 2wz + (a-b) = 0$$

provides a conformal map of the annulus $\sqrt{\{(a-b)/(a+b)\}} < |z| < 1$ on the interior of the ellipse $x^2/a^2 + y^2/b^2 = 1$, cut along the real axis between its foci.

Discuss the representation in the w-plane of the curves $|z| = r$, $\arg z = \alpha$, and, in particular, the behaviour of the transformation at points on the boundary of the annulus.

8. Prove that
$$w = \frac{(1+z^3)^2 - i(1-z^3)^2}{(1+z^3)^2 + i(1-z^3)^2}$$

maps the region $|z| < 1$, $0 < \arg z < \frac{1}{3}\pi$ conformally on $|w| < 1$. Discuss the correspondence between the boundaries of the two regions.

(Edinburgh, 1932.)

9. A domain S containing the circle $|z| = 1$ is mapped conformally on a region Σ by $w = f(z)$, the circle being transformed into a curve Γ. Show that the curvature of Γ is

$$[1+\mathrm{Rl}\{zf''(z)/f'(z)\}] \div |f'(z)|.$$

10. Show that
$$z = \int_0^w [w(1-w^2)]^{-1/2}\, dw$$

maps the upper half of the w-plane conformally on the interior of a square of side $\int_0^{\frac{1}{2}\pi} \surd(\operatorname{cosec}\theta)\, d\theta$.

11. Prove that
$$z = \int_0^w (1-w^4)^{-1/2}\, dw$$

maps $|w| < 1$ conformally on the interior of a square of diagonal $2\int_0^1 (1-w^4)^{-1/2}\, dw$.

12. Show that the region outside a square in the z-plane can be mapped conformally on $|w| < 1$ by

$$z = \int_{w_0}^w \frac{(1-w^4)^{1/2}}{w^2}\, dw.$$

13. The function $f(z)$ is regular in $|z| < R$, where it satisfies the inequality $|f(z)| \leqslant M$; moreover, $f(0) = c$. By applying Schwarz's lemma to the function
$$F(z) = \frac{M\{f(z)-c\}}{M^2-\bar{c}f(z)},$$

prove that
$$\frac{M-|f(z)|}{R-\rho} \geqslant \frac{M(M-|c|)}{MR+\rho|c|}$$

when $|z| \leqslant \rho < R$. (CARATHÉODORY.)

14. Show that, if $h > 0$, the relation $\pi iw = 2h\log z$ maps the half-plane $\mathrm{Rl}\,z > 0$ conformally on the strip $-h < \mathrm{Rl}\,w < h$. Deduce that

$$\pi iw = 2h\log\frac{1+z}{1-z}$$

maps $|z| < 1$ conformally on $-h < \mathrm{Rl}\,w < h$.

15. The function $f(z)$ is regular in $|z| < R$, where its real part satisfies an inequality $|\mathrm{Rl}\,f(z)| \leqslant h$; moreover, $f(0) = 0$. Show that the inequality
$$|\mathrm{Im}\,f(z)| \leqslant \frac{2h}{\pi}\log\frac{R+|z|}{R-|z|}$$

holds when $|z| < R$. (CARATHÉODORY.)

16. The function $f(z)$ is regular in $|z| < R$, where its real part is never negative; moreover, $f(0) = 1$. By considering the function

$$F(z) = \frac{1-f(z)}{1+f(z)},$$

show that the inequalities

$$\frac{R-|z|}{R+|z|} \leqslant |f(z)| \leqslant \frac{R+|z|}{R-|z|},$$

$$|\operatorname{Im} f(z)| \leqslant \frac{2R|z|}{R^2-|z|^2}$$

hold when $|z| < R$. (LINDELÖF.)

CHAPTER IX

THE GAMMA FUNCTION

9.1. The definition of $\Gamma(z)$

THE problem of finding a function of a real variable x which is continuous when x is positive and reduces to $x!$ when x is a positive integer, was first solved by Euler† in 1729, when he showed that the limiting function‡ $\Pi(x)$ of the sequence

$$\Pi(x,n) = \frac{n!\,n^x}{(x+1)(x+2)...(x+n)} \qquad (n = 1,2,3,...)$$

has the desired property. To prove this we observe that, when x is a positive integer and $n > x$,

$$\Pi(x,n) = \frac{n!\,x!}{(n+x)!}\,n^x = \frac{x!\,n^x}{(n+1)(n+2)...(n+x)}$$

$$= x!\Big/\Big\{\Big(1+\frac{1}{n}\Big)\Big(1+\frac{2}{n}\Big)...\Big(1+\frac{x}{n}\Big)\Big\}$$

$$\to x!$$

as $n \to \infty$.

Euler also gave a definite integral formula for this function $\Pi(x)$, which is most simply obtained by considering the expression

$$\int_0^1 (1-\tau)^{n-1}\tau^x\,d\tau,$$

which is now called an Eulerian integral of the first kind. When n is a positive integer and $x > -1$, it is easily shown, by integration by parts, that the value of this integral is $\Pi(x,n)/n^{x+1}$. Writing $t = n\tau$, we deduce that

$$\Pi(x,n) = \int_0^n \Big(1-\frac{t}{n}\Big)^{n-1} t^x\,dt,$$

from which it follows (cf. § 9.21) that

$$\Pi(x) = \int_0^\infty e^{-t}t^x\,dt.$$

† He announced his discoveries in two letters addressed to Goldbach. These are printed in *Correspondance mathématique et physique de quelques célèbres géomètres du XVIIIème siècle* (Saint-Pétersbourg, 1843), **1**, 1–18.

‡ This notation is due to Gauss.

This infinite integral is called the Eulerian integral of the second kind.

In the present chapter we consider the properties of the Gamma function† of a complex variable, defined by the Eulerian integral of the second kind

$$\Gamma(z) = \int_0^\infty e^{-t}t^{z-1} \, dt$$

whenever this integral converges (it being understood that t^{z-1} has its principal value), and defined by analytical continuation elsewhere.

Example. Show that $\Gamma(n) = (n-1)!$ when n is a positive integer.

9.11. The analytical character of $\Gamma(z)$

To discuss the convergence of the integral defining $\Gamma(z)$, it is most convenient to write

$$\Gamma(z) = \Phi(z) + \Psi(z),$$

where $\quad \Phi(z) = \int_0^1 e^{-t}t^{z-1} \, dt, \qquad \Psi(z) = \int_1^\infty e^{-t}t^{z-1} \, dt.$

We consider the function $\Psi(z)$ first.

Let us suppose that z lies in a quite arbitrary bounded closed domain. Then there exists a constant Δ such that $\mathrm{Rl}\,z \leqslant \Delta$ when z lies in this domain, and so

$$|t^{z-1}| = t^{\mathrm{Rl}\,z-1} \leqslant t^{\Delta-1}$$

when $t \geqslant 1$. But since $e^{-\frac{1}{2}t}t^{\Delta-1}$ tends to zero as $t \to +\infty$, there exists a constant C, depending on Δ, such that $t^{\Delta-1} \leqslant Ce^{\frac{1}{2}t}$ when $t \geqslant 1$. Hence we have

$$|e^{-t}t^{z-1}| \leqslant Ce^{-\frac{1}{2}t}$$

when z lies in the given domain, and so, by the M-test (§ 5.52), the integral defining $\Psi(z)$ is uniformly and absolutely convergent. It follows, by § 5.51, that $\Psi(z)$ is an analytic function, regular in every bounded closed domain, and so is an integral function.

---

† The notation $\Gamma(z)$ is due to Legendre. For some purposes it is still found more convenient to use the older notation of Gauss and write $\Pi(z-1)$ for the function denoted here by $\Gamma(z)$.

To deal with the integral for $\Phi(z)$, it is simplest to make the transformation $t = 1/u$, which gives

$$\Phi(z) = \int\limits_1^\infty e^{-1/u} u^{-z-1}\, du.$$

This integral obviously does not converge when $\mathrm{Rl}\, z \leqslant 0$. It is, however, uniformly and absolutely convergent in any bounded closed domain which lies definitely to the right of the imaginary axis. For in such a domain an inequality $\mathrm{Rl}\, z \geqslant \delta$, where $\delta > 0$, is satisfied, and hence

$$|e^{-1/u} u^{-z-1}| \leqslant u^{-\delta-1}$$

when $u \geqslant 1$. The result stated follows immediately by the M-test, and implies that $\Phi(z)$ is an analytic function, regular when $\mathrm{Rl}\, z > 0$.

We have thus shown that $\Gamma(z)$ is the sum of an integral function $\Psi(z)$ and an analytic function $\Phi(z)$ which is regular to the right of the imaginary axis. We next show how to continue $\Phi(z)$ analytically across the imaginary axis. If in the formula

$$\Phi(z) = \int\limits_0^1 e^{-t} t^{z-1}\, dt$$

we replace e^{-t} by its Taylor series and then integrate term by term, as we obviously may when $\mathrm{Rl}\, z > 0$, we find that

$$\Phi(z) = \sum_0^\infty \frac{(-1)^n}{n!\,(z+n)}.$$

But this series is uniformly and absolutely convergent in any closed domain which contains none of the points $0, -1, -2, \ldots$, and so provides the analytical continuation of $\Phi(z)$.

The Gamma function is therefore of the form

$$\Gamma(z) = \Psi(z) + \sum_0^\infty \frac{(-1)^n}{n!\,(z+n)},$$

where $\Psi(z)$ is an integral function. The only singularities of $\Gamma(z)$ are thus simple poles at the points $0, -1, -2, \ldots$, the residue at $z = -n$ being $(-1)^n/n!$.

9.2. Tannery's theorem

In order to prove the identity of the Gamma function and Euler's limit (§ 9.1), we need the following lemma, which is the analogue of a well-known theorem concerning series, due to Tannery.†

If

$$\lim_{n \to \infty} f(t, n) = g(t), \qquad \lim_{n \to \infty} \lambda_n = +\infty,$$

then

$$\lim_{n \to \infty} \int_a^{\lambda_n} f(t, n)\, dt = \int_a^{\infty} g(t)\, dt,$$

provided that $f(t, n)$ tends to its limit $g(t)$ uniformly in any fixed interval, and provided also that there exists a positive function $M(t)$ such that $|f(t, n)| \leqslant M(t)$ for all values of n and t, and also such that $\int_a^{\infty} M(t)\, dt$ is convergent.

Let τ be any number greater than a. Then if n is chosen large enough to make $\lambda_n > \tau$, we have

$$\left| \int_a^{\lambda_n} f(t, n)\, dt - \int_a^{\infty} g(t)\, dt \right|$$

$$= \left| \int_a^{\tau} (f - g)\, dt + \int_{\tau}^{\lambda_n} f\, dt - \int_{\tau}^{\infty} g\, dt \right|$$

$$\leqslant \left| \int_a^{\tau} \{f(t, n) - g(t)\}\, dt \right| + \int_{\tau}^{\lambda_n} |f(t, n)|\, dt + \int_{\tau}^{\infty} |g(t)|\, dt.$$

But since $|f(t, n)| \leqslant M(t)$ for all values of n, we also have $|g(t)| \leqslant M(t)$. This gives

$$\left| \int_a^{\lambda_n} f(t, n)\, dt - \int_a^{\infty} g(t)\, dt \right|$$

$$\leqslant \left| \int_a^{\tau} \{f(t, n) - g(t)\}\, dt \right| + 2 \int_{\tau}^{\infty} M(t)\, dt.$$

Now $f(t, n)$ converges uniformly to $g(t)$ in the fixed interval $a \leqslant t \leqslant \tau$, and so the first term on the right-hand side of this inequality tends to zero. Hence we have

$$\overline{\lim_{n \to \infty}} \left| \int_a^{\lambda_n} f(t, n)\, dt - \int_a^{\infty} g(t)\, dt \right| \leqslant 2 \int_{\tau}^{\infty} M(t)\, dt.$$

† See Bromwich, *Infinite Series* (2nd edition), §§ 49, 172.

Since the integral $\int\limits_a^\infty M(t)\,dt$ converges, we can make the expression on the right-hand side of this inequality as small as we please by making τ sufficiently large. But as the expression on the left-hand side of the inequality does not involve τ, this implies that

$$\lim_{n\to\infty}\left|\int\limits_a^{\lambda_n} f(t,n)\,dt - \int\limits_a^\infty g(t)\,dt\right| = 0,$$

and so the lemma is proved.

Example. Let $F(n) = \sum\limits_{r=0}^{p} v_r(n)$, where p tends steadily to infinity with n. Then if $v_r(n) \to w_r$ as $n \to \infty$ for each fixed value of r, prove that

$$\lim_{n\to\infty} F(n) = \sum_{r=0}^{\infty} w_r,$$

provided that $|v_r(n)| \leqslant M_r$, where M_r is independent of n and $\sum M_r$ converges. (TANNERY.)

9.21. Euler's limit formula for $\Gamma(z)$

We shall now show that, if

$$\Gamma(z,n) = \frac{n!\,n^z}{z(z+1)(z+2)...(z+n)} \quad (n=1,2,3,...),$$

then $\Gamma(z,n)$ tends to $\Gamma(z)$ as $n \to \infty$, the convergence being uniform in any bounded closed domain D which contains none of the singularities of $\Gamma(z)$. The proof falls into two parts.

In the first place, we have

$$\Gamma(z,n) = \left(\frac{n}{n+1}\right)^z \frac{1}{z} \prod_{r=1}^{n} \left\{\left(1+\frac{1}{r}\right)^z\left(1+\frac{z}{r}\right)^{-1}\right\}.$$

But since

$$\left(1+\frac{1}{r}\right)^z\left(1+\frac{z}{r}\right)^{-1} = 1+\frac{z(z-1)}{2r^2}+O\left(\frac{1}{r^3}\right)$$

when r is large, the infinite product

$$\frac{1}{z} \prod_{r=1}^{\infty} \left\{\left(1+\frac{1}{r}\right)^z\left(1+\frac{z}{r}\right)^{-1}\right\}$$

converges uniformly and absolutely in D to an analytic function $F(z)$, say. This, however, implies that $\Gamma(z,n)$ tends uniformly to $F(z)$ in D. It only remains to show that $F(z)$ is identical with

4111   P

$\Gamma(z)$; moreover, by the theory of analytical continuation, it suffices to prove this when† $\mathrm{Rl}\, z > 1$.

Now if n is a positive integer and $\mathrm{Rl}\, z > 1$, it is easily shown by integration by parts that

$$\Gamma(z, n) = n^z \int_0^1 (1-\tau)^n \tau^{z-1}\, d\tau = \int_0^n \left(1-\frac{t}{n}\right)^n t^{z-1}\, dt.$$

It will follow that

$$\Gamma(z, n) \to \int_0^\infty e^{-t} t^{z-1}\, dt = \Gamma(z),$$

provided that we can show that the conditions of Tannery's theorem are satisfied.

From the equation

$$e^{-t} - \left(1-\frac{t}{n}\right)^n = e^{-t} \int_0^t e^v \left(1-\frac{v}{n}\right)^{n-1} \frac{v}{n}\, dv,$$

it follows that, when $0 \leqslant t \leqslant n$,

$$0 \leqslant e^{-t} - \left(1-\frac{t}{n}\right)^n \leqslant \int_0^t \frac{v}{n}\, dv = \frac{t^2}{2n}.$$

Hence, if x denotes the real part of z,

$$\left| e^{-t} t^{z-1} - \left(1-\frac{t}{n}\right)^n t^{z-1} \right| = t^{x-1}\left\{ e^{-t} - \left(1-\frac{t}{n}\right)^n \right\} \leqslant \frac{t^{x+1}}{2n},$$

and so

$$\left(1-\frac{t}{n}\right)^n t^{z-1} \to e^{-t} t^{z-1}$$

as $n \to \infty$, uniformly with respect to t in any fixed interval. The first condition of Tannery's theorem is thus satisfied.

Again, we also have

$$\left| \left(1-\frac{t}{n}\right)^n t^{z-1} \right| = \left(1-\frac{t}{n}\right)^n t^{x-1} \leqslant e^{-t} t^{x-1}.$$

But since $x > 1$, $\int_0^\infty e^{-t} t^{x-1}\, dt$ converges and the second condition of Tannery's theorem is satisfied. This completes the proof of Euler's limit formula for $\Gamma(z)$.

---

† We take $\mathrm{Rl}\, z > 1$ instead of $\mathrm{Rl}\, z > 0$ to avoid difficulties at the lower limit of integration.

It should be observed that we have shown incidentally that

$$\Gamma(z) = \frac{1}{z} \prod_{m=1}^{\infty} \left\{ \left(1+\frac{1}{m}\right)^z \left(1+\frac{z}{m}\right)^{-1} \right\}.$$

This formula is also due to Euler.

Example. Show, by using Hurwitz's theorem (§ 6.21, Ex. 2), that $\Gamma(z)$ never vanishes.

9.22. Two important identities

We shall now deduce from Euler's limit formula the two important identities

$$\Gamma(z+1) = z\,\Gamma(z)$$

and

$$\Gamma(z)\Gamma(1-z) = \pi \operatorname{cosec} \pi z.$$

To prove the first identity, we observe that

$$\begin{aligned}
\Gamma(z+1) &= \lim_{n\to\infty} \frac{n!\,n^{z+1}}{(z+1)(z+2)...(z+n+1)} \\
&= z\lim_{n\to\infty} \frac{n!\,n^z}{z(z+1)(z+2)...(z+n)}\,\frac{n}{z+n+1} \\
&= z\,\Gamma(z).
\end{aligned}$$

From this it follows immediately that, when n is a positive integer,

$$\Gamma(n) = (n-1)!\,\Gamma(1) = (n-1)!$$

Again, we also have

$$\begin{aligned}
\Gamma(z)\Gamma(1-z) &= \lim_{n\to\infty} \frac{n!\,n^z}{z(z+1)...(z+n)} \lim_{m\to\infty} \frac{m!\,m^{1-z}}{(1-z)(2-z)...(m+1-z)} \\
&= \lim_{n\to\infty} \frac{n!\,n!\,n}{z(1^2-z^2)(2^2-z^2)...(n^2-z^2)(n+1-z)} \\
&= \lim_{n\to\infty} \left\{ z\left(1-\frac{z^2}{1^2}\right)\left(1-\frac{z^2}{2^2}\right)...\left(1-\frac{z^2}{n^2}\right)\left(1+\frac{1-z}{n}\right) \right\}^{-1} \\
&= 1 \Big/ \left\{ z \prod_{1}^{\infty} \left(1-\frac{z^2}{n^2}\right) \right\}.
\end{aligned}$$

Hence, by the example of § 6.83,

$$\Gamma(z)\Gamma(1-z) = \pi \operatorname{cosec} \pi z.$$

Example 1. Prove that $\Gamma(\tfrac{1}{2}) = \sqrt{\pi}$.

Example 2. Show that

$$(2n)! = 2^{2n}n!\,\Gamma(n+\tfrac{1}{2})/\sqrt{\pi}.$$

Example 3. Show that, if x is real,

$$|\Gamma(ix)| = \sqrt{\left(\frac{\pi}{x \sinh \pi x}\right)}.$$

Example 4. Prove that $\Gamma(z, n) = n^z \Gamma(n+1)\Gamma(z)/\Gamma(n+z+1)$. Deduce that $n^z \Gamma(n)/\Gamma(n+z) \to 1$ as $n \to \infty$.

Example 5. If $\psi(z)$ denotes the derivative of $\log \Gamma(z)$, show that

$$\psi(1-z) - \psi(z) = \pi \cot \pi z.$$

9.23. Legendre's duplication formula

It was shown by Legendre that $\Gamma(2z)$ can be simply expressed in terms of $\Gamma(z)$ and $\Gamma(z+\tfrac{1}{2})$. To prove this result, we observe that, by § 9.22, Ex. 2,

$$\Gamma(2z, 2n) = \frac{(2n)! \, (2n)^{2z}}{2z(2z+1)(2z+2)...(2z+2n)}$$

$$= \frac{2^{2z-1} n^{2z} n! \, \Gamma(n+\tfrac{1}{2})}{\sqrt{\pi} \, z(z+1)(z+2)...(z+n)(z+\tfrac{1}{2})(z+\tfrac{3}{2})...(z+n-\tfrac{1}{2})}$$

$$= \frac{2^{2z-1}}{\sqrt{\pi}} \, \Gamma(z, n)\Gamma(z+\tfrac{1}{2}, n) \frac{\Gamma(n+\tfrac{1}{2})}{n^{\tfrac{1}{2}}\Gamma(n)} \frac{z+\tfrac{1}{2}+n}{n}.$$

If we now make $n \to \infty$ and use the result of § 9.22, Ex. 4, we find that
$$\pi^{\tfrac{1}{2}}\Gamma(2z) = 2^{2z-1}\Gamma(z)\Gamma(z+\tfrac{1}{2}).$$

This is Legendre's duplication formula.

9.3. The Eulerian integral of the first kind

The Beta function $B(p, q)$ is a function of two complex variables p and q, defined by the Eulerian integral of the first kind

$$B(p, q) = \int_0^1 t^{p-1}(1-t)^{q-1} \, dt$$

whenever this integral converges, it being understood that

$$t^{p-1} = e^{(p-1)\log t}, \qquad (1-t)^{q-1} = e^{(q-1)\log(1-t)}$$

where the logarithms have their principal values. This equation defines $B(p, q)$ when the real parts of p and q are positive. For other values of the variables, the Beta function is defined by analytical continuation.

As we have just seen, there is a close connexion between the

Eulerian integral of the first kind and the Gamma function. We shall now exhibit this connexion more fully by showing that

$$B(p,q) = \frac{\Gamma(p)\Gamma(q)}{\Gamma(p+q)}.$$

For simplicity of proof, we assume temporarily that the real parts of p and q exceed unity.

Let us denote by S_R the square bounded by the lines $x = 0$, $x = R$, $y = 0$, $y = R$. We then have

$$\Gamma(p)\Gamma(q) = \int_0^\infty e^{-x}x^{p-1}\,dx \times \int_0^\infty e^{-y}y^{q-1}\,dy$$

$$= \lim_{R\to\infty} \int_0^R dx \int_0^R dy\; e^{-x-y}x^{p-1}y^{q-1}$$

$$= \lim_{R\to\infty} \iint_{S_R} e^{-x-y}x^{p-1}y^{q-1}\,dxdy,$$

the double integral being equal to the repeated integral since the integrand is a continuous function of both variables. We next show that

$$\Gamma(p)\Gamma(q) = \lim_{R\to\infty} \iint_{T_R} e^{-x-y}x^{p-1}y^{q-1}\,dxdy,$$

where T_R denotes the triangle bounded by the axes and the line $x+y = R$.

For, if we call the integrand $f(x,y)$, we have

$$\left| \iint_{S_R} f(x,y)\,dxdy - \iint_{T_R} f(x,y)\,dxdy \right|$$

$$= \left| \iint_{S_R-T_R} f(x,y)\,dxdy \right|$$

$$\leqslant \iint_{S_R-T_R} |f(x,y)|\,dxdy$$

$$< \iint_{S_R} |f|\,dxdy - \iint_{S_{R/2}} |f|\,dxdy.$$

But this last expression tends to zero as $R \to \infty$, since

$$\iint_{S_R} |f|\,dxdy = \iint_{S_R} e^{-x-y}x^{\mathrm{Rl}\,p-1}y^{\mathrm{Rl}\,q-1}\,dxdy \to \Gamma(\mathrm{Rl}\,p)\Gamma(\mathrm{Rl}\,q).$$

Hence $$\Gamma(p)\Gamma(q) = \lim_{R\to\infty} \iint\limits_{T_R} e^{-x-y}x^{p-1}y^{q-1}\,dx\,dy.$$

If in this last equation we now make the substitution $x+y = \xi$, $y = \xi\eta$, we obtain

$$\Gamma(p)\Gamma(q) = \lim_{R\to\infty} \int_0^R e^{-\xi}\xi^{p+q-1}\,d\xi \times \int_0^1 \eta^{q-1}(1-\eta)^{p-1}\,d\eta$$

$$= \int_0^\infty e^{-\xi}\xi^{p+q-1}\,d\xi \times \int_0^1 t^{p-1}(1-t)^{q-1}\,dt$$

$$= \Gamma(p+q)\mathrm{B}(p,q).$$

This proves the theorem when the real parts of p and q exceed unity. The result still holds, however, whenever the integral defining $\mathrm{B}(p,q)$ converges, that is, when the real parts of p and q are positive. For the expressions on each side of the equation are regular analytic functions of each variable.

We have thus proved that

$$\mathrm{B}(p,q) = \frac{\Gamma(p)\Gamma(q)}{\Gamma(p+q)}$$

when the real parts of p and q are positive. For other values of p and q, this equation is to be regarded as the definition of the Beta function.

An important generalization of the Eulerian integral of the first kind is due to Pochhammer,† who showed that, with this general definition of the Beta function,

$$\int_C z^{p-1}(1-z)^{q-1}\,dz = -4e^{(p+q)\pi i}\sin\pi p \sin\pi q\,\mathrm{B}(p,q),$$

where C denotes a rather complicated contour encircling each of the points 0 and 1 twice in opposite directions. For the details of this we refer the reader to Pochhammer's original memoir.

9.4. Euler's constant

We now show that the numbers

$$u_n = 1 + \frac{1}{2} + \frac{1}{3} + \ldots + \frac{1}{n} - \log n \quad (n = 1, 2, 3, \ldots)$$

† *Math. Annalen*, **35** (1890), 495. See also Whittaker and Watson, *Modern Analysis* (1920), 256–7.

form a convergent sequence whose limit γ lies between 0 and 1. This constant γ, which is approximately equal to 0·5772, is of great importance in the theory of the Gamma function and is usually known as Euler's constant.

To prove this, we observe, in the first place, that the sequence is a steadily decreasing one. For

$$u_{n+1}-u_n = \frac{1}{n+1}-\log(n+1)+\log n = \frac{1}{n+1}+\log\left(1-\frac{1}{n+1}\right) < 0.$$

On the other hand, since $1/t$ decreases as t increases,

$$1+\frac{1}{2}+\frac{1}{3}+...+\frac{1}{n-1} > \int_1^n \frac{dt}{t} > \frac{1}{2}+\frac{1}{3}+\frac{1}{4}+...+\frac{1}{n},$$

from which it follows that

$$\frac{1}{n} < u_n < 1.$$

The sequence is, therefore, bounded and steadily decreasing, and so tends to a limit γ. Moreover, by the last inequality, γ must lie between 0 and 1.

9.41. The canonical product for $1/\Gamma(z)$

We have already seen that $\Gamma(z)$ is an analytic function which has no zeros and has simple poles at the points $0, -1, -2,...$. From this it follows that $1/\Gamma(z)$ is an integral function with simple zeros at the points $0, -1, -2,...$. We now exhibit the property more clearly by proving that

$$\frac{1}{\Gamma(z)} = ze^{\gamma z} \prod_{r=1}^{\infty} \left\{\left(1+\frac{z}{r}\right)e^{-z/r}\right\},$$

so that $1/\Gamma(z)$ is an integral function of order 1. This formula is due to Schlömilch[†] and F. W. Newman.[‡]

To prove this, we start with the equation

$$\frac{1}{\Gamma(z,n)} = \frac{z(z+1)(z+2)...(z+n)}{n!\,n^z}$$

[†] *Archiv der Math. und Phys.* **4** (1844), 171.
[‡] *Cambridge and Dublin Math. Journal*, **3** (1848), 57–60.

in the notation of § 9.21. Hence we have

$$\frac{1}{\Gamma(z,n)} = z\left(1+\frac{z}{1}\right)\left(1+\frac{z}{2}\right)...\left(1+\frac{z}{n}\right)e^{-z\log n}$$

$$= z\exp\left\{z\left(1+\frac{1}{2}+\frac{1}{3}+...+\frac{1}{n}-\log n\right)\right\}\prod_{r=1}^{n}\left\{\left(1+\frac{z}{r}\right)e^{-z/r}\right\}$$

$$\rightarrow ze^{\gamma z}\prod_{r=1}^{\infty}\left\{\left(1+\frac{z}{r}\right)e^{-z/r}\right\}$$

as $n \rightarrow \infty$, by the result of § 9.3. Since $\Gamma(z,n) \rightarrow \Gamma(z)$, this gives the required result.

9.5. Asymptotic expansions

A series
$$A_0+\frac{A_1}{z}+\frac{A_2}{z^2}+...+\frac{A_n}{z^n}+...,$$

which may either converge for large values of $|z|$ or diverge for all values of z, is called an *asymptotic expansion* of the function $F(z)$, valid in a given range of values of $\arg z$, if, for every fixed value of n, the expression

$$z^n\left\{F(z)-A_0-\frac{A_1}{z}-\frac{A_2}{z^2}-...-\frac{A_n}{z^n}\right\}$$

tends to zero as $|z| \rightarrow \infty$, whilst $\arg z$ remains in the given range. When this is the case, we denote the relationship between the function and the series by writing

$$F(z) \sim A_0+\frac{A_1}{z}+\frac{A_2}{z^2}+....$$

This definition, which is due to Poincaré,[†] implies that the difference between $F(z)$ and the sum of n terms of its asymptotic expansion is of the same order as the $(n+1)$th term when $|z|$ is large, a fact which often renders an asymptotic expansion more suited for numerical computation than a convergent series.

If a function $F(z)$ possesses an asymptotic expansion

$$F(z) \sim A_0+\frac{A_1}{z}+\frac{A_2}{z^2}+...,$$

† *Acta Math.* 8 (1886), 295–344.

the coefficients are determined successively by the equations

$$\lim_{|z|\to\infty} F(z) = A_0,$$

$$\lim_{|z|\to\infty} z\{F(z)-A_0\} = A_1,$$

$$\lim_{|z|\to\infty} z^2\left\{F(z)-A_0-\frac{A_1}{z}\right\} = A_2,$$

and so on. On the other hand, a knowledge of the asymptotic expansion does not determine the function, since two functions may possess the same asymptotic expansion. For example, $e^{1/z}$ and $e^{1/z}+e^{-z}$ have the same asymptotic expansion

$$1+\frac{1}{z.1!}+\frac{1}{z^2.2!}+\cdots$$

valid in the angle $|\arg z| < \tfrac{1}{2}\pi$.

9.51. A more general definition of an asymptotic expansion

It may happen that, even though the function $F(z)$ does not possess an asymptotic expansion, there exists a function $G(z)$ such that

$$\frac{F(z)}{G(z)} \sim A_0+\frac{A_1}{z}+\frac{A_2}{z^2}+\cdots$$

in a certain range of values of $\arg z$. In this case, we shall write

$$F(z) \sim G(z)\left\{A_0+\frac{A_1}{z}+\frac{A_2}{z^2}+\cdots\right\}.$$

The term $A_0 G(z)$ is called the dominant term of this asymptotic representation of $F(z)$.

Example 1. Show that, if $f(z) \sim \sum_0^\infty A_m z^{-m}$ and $g(z) \sim \sum_0^\infty B_m z^{-m}$ in the same range of values of $\arg z$, then

$$f(z)g(z) \sim \sum_0^\infty C_m z^{-m},$$

where $\qquad C_m = A_0 B_m+A_1 B_{m-1}+A_2 B_{m-2}+\cdots+A_m B_0.$

Example 2. Prove that, if $f(x) \sim \sum_2^\infty A_m x^{-m}$ when x is large and positive, then

$$\int_x^\infty f(x)\,dx \sim \sum_1^\infty \frac{A_{m+1}}{mx^m}.$$

9.52. Watson's lemma

The following lemma, due to G. N. Watson,† enables us to determine very simply the asymptotic expansion of a function defined by a definite integral. Although the type of integral considered is apparently very special, the lemma does, in fact, cover many of the cases which occur in analysis.

Let us suppose that $f(t)$ is an analytic function, regular, save possibly for a branch-point at the origin, when $|t| \leqslant a+\delta$, where a and δ are positive, and let

$$f(t) = \sum_{m=1}^{\infty} a_m t^{(m/r)-1}$$

when $|t| \leqslant a$, r being positive. Let us suppose, further, that, when t is positive and $t \geqslant a$,

$$|f(t)| < Ke^{bt}$$

where K and b are positive numbers independent of t. Then

$$F(z) \equiv \int\limits_{0}^{\infty} e^{-zt} f(t)\, dt \sim \sum_{m=1}^{\infty} a_m \, \Gamma(m/r)\, z^{-m/r}$$

when $|z|$ is large and $|\arg z| \leqslant \frac{1}{2}\pi - \Delta$, where Δ is an arbitrary positive number. The lemma states that the asymptotic expansion is obtained by substituting in the integral the series for $f(t)$ and then integrating formally term by term.

To prove this lemma, we observe that, having fixed a positive integer M, we can find a constant C such that the inequality

$$\left| f(t) - \sum_{m=1}^{M-1} a_m t^{(m/r)-1} \right| \leqslant Ct^{(M/r)-1} e^{bt}$$

is true when $t \geqslant 0$, no matter whether $t \leqslant a$ or not. Hence, if

$$F(z) = \sum_{m=1}^{M-1} \int\limits_{0}^{\infty} e^{-zt} a_m t^{(m/r)-1}\, dt + R_M,$$

$$= \sum_{m=1}^{M-1} a_m \, \Gamma(m/r) z^{-m/r} + R_M,$$

we have to show that $z^{M/r} R_M$ is bounded as $|z| \to \infty$.

† *Proc. London Math. Soc.* (2), **17** (1918), 133. See also Watson, *Bessel Functions* (1922), 236.

Writing $z = x+iy$, we find that

$$|R_M| = \left| \int_0^\infty e^{-zt} \left\{ f(t) - \sum_{m=1}^{M-1} a_m t^{(m/r)-1} \right\} dt \right|$$

$$\leqslant \int_0^\infty e^{-xt} C t^{(M/r)-1} e^{bt} dt$$

$$= \frac{C\,\Gamma(M/r)}{(x-b)^{M/r}},$$

provided that $x-b$ is positive. But from the condition $|\arg z| \leqslant \tfrac{1}{2}\pi - \Delta$, we have $x \geqslant |z| \sin \Delta$, so that $x-b$ is positive if $|z| > b \operatorname{cosec} \Delta$. Hence, when $|\arg z| \leqslant \tfrac{1}{2}\pi - \Delta < \tfrac{1}{2}\pi$ and $|z| > b \operatorname{cosec} \Delta$, we have

$$|z^{M/r} R_M| < \frac{C\Gamma(M/r)|z|^{M/r}}{(|z|\sin\Delta - b)^{M/r}} = O(1);$$

this completes the proof of the lemma.

9.53. The asymptotic expansion of $\Gamma(z)$

We shall now discuss the behaviour of $\Gamma(z)$ for large values of $|z|$ by finding the leading terms in its asymptotic expansion, valid when $|\arg z| < \pi$. One way of doing this involves proving first Stirling's[†] asymptotic series

$$\log \Gamma(z) \sim (z-\tfrac{1}{2})\log z - z + \tfrac{1}{2}\log(2\pi) + \sum_{r=1}^\infty \frac{(-1)^{r-1}B_r}{2r(2r-1)z^{2r-1}}.$$

In this formula, the coefficients B_r are Bernoulli's numbers defined by the expansion

$$\tfrac{1}{2}z \coth \tfrac{1}{2}z = 1 + \sum_{r=1}^\infty (-1)^{r-1} B_r \frac{z^{2r}}{(2r)!}.$$

The required asymptotic expansion of $\Gamma(z)$ can be deduced from that of its logarithm, though it is difficult to give any simple formula for the coefficient of the general term.

As this method[‡] involves a number of difficult preliminary transformations, we obtain here the asymptotic expansion of

---

† First published in his *Methodus differentialis* (London, 1730), 135.
‡ See Whittaker and Watson, *Modern Analysis* (1920), 246–53.

$\Gamma(z)$ directly from the definition as an integral, by a method based on Watson's[†] discussion of a closely related problem of Ramanujan.

When z is real and positive, the transformation $t = zu$ gives

$$\Gamma(z) = \frac{1}{z}\Gamma(1+z) = \frac{1}{z}\int_0^\infty e^{-t}t^z\, dt = z^z e^{-z}\int_0^\infty (ue^{1-u})^z\, du$$

and so

$$z^{-z}e^z\Gamma(z) = \int_0^\infty (ue^{1-u})^z\, du.$$

Although we have proved this formula by supposing that z is real and positive, it will also hold, by the theory of analytical continuation, in any closed domain in which $z^{-z}e^z\Gamma(z)$ is regular and the integral is uniformly convergent. The formula is, therefore, true when $\mathrm{Rl}\, z > 0$.

Let us suppose, then, that $\mathrm{Rl}\, z > 0$ and that $|z|$ is large. We observe that ue^{1-u} increases steadily from 0 to 1 as u increases from 0 to 1, and then decreases steadily from 1 to 0 as u increases from 1 to ∞. We now write

$$z^{-z}e^z\Gamma(z) = \int_0^1 (ue^{1-u})^z\, du + \int_1^\infty (Ue^{1-U})^z\, dU,$$

it being convenient to use different symbols for the variables in the different parts of the range of integration.

If, in the second integral, we make the substitution $e^{-t} = Ue^{1-U}$, t increases steadily from 0 to ∞ as U increases from 1 to ∞; on the other hand, if we put $e^{-t} = ue^{1-u}$ in the first integral, t decreases steadily from ∞ to 0 as u increases from 0 to 1. In this way we obtain the equation

$$z^{-z}e^z\Gamma(z) = \int_0^\infty e^{-zt}\!\left(\frac{dU}{dt} - \frac{du}{dt}\right) dt,$$

to which we may apply Watson's lemma.

Now U and u are the two real solutions of the equation

$$t = u - 1 - \log u.$$

† *Proc. London Math. Soc.* (2), **29** (1929), 293–308. See also Ex. 18 at the end of the present chapter.

In order to determine the nature of these solutions we consider the equation
$$\tfrac{1}{2}\zeta^2 = w - \log(1+w),$$

defining w as a function of the complex variable ζ.

Now ζ, regarded as a function of w, is two-valued in the neighbourhood of the origin, its two branches being

$$\zeta = \pm w(1 - \tfrac{2}{3}w + \tfrac{2}{4}w^2 - \dots)^{1/2}.$$

Since each branch is an analytic function of w, regular when $|w| < 1$, with a simple zero at $w = 0$, it follows, by §§ 6.22, 6.23, that the equation

$$\zeta = w(1 - \tfrac{2}{3}w + \tfrac{2}{4}w^2 - \dots)^{1/2}$$

possesses a unique solution

$$w = \zeta + a_2\zeta^2 + a_3\zeta^3 + \dots,$$

regular in a neighbourhood $|\zeta| < \rho$ of the origin. As we saw in § 6.23, the coefficients a_n are given by the fact that na_n is the residue of ζ^{-n} at $w = 0$; in particular,

$$a_2 = \tfrac{1}{3}, \qquad a_3 = \tfrac{1}{36}, \qquad a_4 = -\tfrac{1}{270}, \qquad a_5 = \tfrac{1}{4320}.$$

We shall denote this solution by $w_1(\zeta)$. Similarly, the solution of

$$\zeta = -w(1 - \tfrac{2}{3}w + \tfrac{2}{4}w^2 - \dots)^{1/2},$$

regular in $|\zeta| < \rho$, is $w = w_2(\zeta)$, where $w_2(\zeta) = w_1(-\zeta)$.

We have thus shown that the function $w(\zeta)$ defined by the equation

$$\tfrac{1}{2}\zeta^2 = w - \log(1+w)$$

has two branches $w = w_1(\zeta)$, $w = w_2(\zeta)$, each regular in a neighbourhood of the origin. The only branch-points or other singularities of $w(\zeta)$ are the points at which $dw/d\zeta$ is zero or infinite. Since

$$\frac{dw}{d\zeta} = \frac{\zeta(1+w)}{w},$$

these are $\zeta = 0$ and the points corresponding to $w = 0$ and $w = -1$. Of these, $\zeta = 0$ is not a branch-point of $w_1(\zeta)$, and the value of ζ corresponding to $w = -1$ is infinite; thus the only singularities of $w_1(\zeta)$ of finite affix are given by $\zeta^2 = 4n\pi i$, where n is a positive or negative integer. Similarly for $w_2(\zeta)$.

If we now put $\zeta^2 = 2t$, we see that the functions U, u are regular when $|\operatorname{Im} t| < 2\pi$, save for a branch-point at the origin, and that, when $|t| < 2\pi$,

$$U = 1 + (2t)^{1/2} + a_2(2t) + a_3(2t)^{3/2} + a_4(2t)^2 + \ldots,$$
$$u = 1 - (2t)^{1/2} + a_2(2t) - a_3(2t)^{3/2} + a_4(2t)^2 - \ldots,$$

the square roots being positive when t is real and positive.

Lastly, since

$$\frac{dU}{dt} - \frac{du}{dt} = \frac{U}{U-1} + \frac{u}{1-u} = \frac{1}{U-1} + \frac{1}{1-u},$$

$d(U-u)/dt$ is bounded when $t \geqslant \epsilon > 0$. The conditions of Watson's lemma are, therefore, all satisfied, and the asymptotic expansion of

$$\int\limits_0^\infty e^{-zt} \left(\frac{dU}{dt} - \frac{du}{dt} \right) dt$$

is obtained by substituting for U and u their expansions in powers of $\sqrt{(2t)}$ and integrating formally term by term. From this it follows that, when $|\arg z| \leqslant \frac{1}{2}\pi - \Delta < \frac{1}{2}\pi$ and $|z|$ is large,

$$z^{-z}e^z\Gamma(z) \sim \sqrt{(2/z)}[\Gamma(\tfrac{1}{2}) + 3\Gamma(\tfrac{3}{2})a_3(2/z) + 5\Gamma(\tfrac{5}{2})a_5(2/z)^2 + \ldots],$$
$$\sim \sqrt{(2\pi/z)}[1 + 3a_3/z + 15a_5/z^2 + \ldots].$$

Hence the required asymptotic expansion is

$$\Gamma(z) \sim e^{-z}z^z \sqrt{\left(\frac{2\pi}{z}\right)}\left[1 + \frac{1}{12z} + \frac{1}{288z^2} + \ldots\right].$$

9.54. The range of validity of the asymptotic expansion of $\Gamma(z)$

We next prove that this asymptotic expansion of $\Gamma(z)$ is valid for all large values of $|z|$, except when z lies in an arbitrarily small angle enclosing the negative part of the real axis.

The validity of the expansion when $\operatorname{Rl} z > 0$ followed from applying Watson's lemma to the formula

$$z^{-z}e^z\Gamma(z) = \int\limits_0^\infty e^{-zt}F(t)\,dt,$$

where $F(t) = d(U-u)/dt$. Now by applying Cauchy's theorem to the integral of $e^{-zt}F(t)$ round the complete boundary of the sector of $|t| \leqslant R$ bounded by $\arg t = 0$ and $\arg t = \alpha$, we easily show that, if $-\tfrac{1}{2}\pi < \alpha < \tfrac{1}{2}\pi$, then

$$\int_0^\infty e^{-zt}F(t)\,dt = \int_0^\infty \exp(-zte^{\alpha i})F(te^{\alpha i})e^{\alpha i}\,dt$$

when the real parts of z and $ze^{\alpha i}$ are positive. But the latter integral converges uniformly in any closed domain for which $\mathrm{Rl}(ze^{\alpha i}) > 0$ and represents an analytic function. The expression on the left-hand side of this equation is equal to $z^{-z}e^z\Gamma(z)$ when $\mathrm{Rl}\,z > 0$. Since the half-planes $\mathrm{Rl}\,z > 0$ and $\mathrm{Rl}(ze^{\alpha i}) > 0$ have an area in common, it follows, by analytical continuation, that

$$z^{-z}e^z\Gamma(z) = \int_0^\infty \exp(-zte^{\alpha i})F(te^{\alpha i})e^{\alpha i}\,dt$$

when $\mathrm{Rl}(ze^{\alpha i}) > 0$, provided that $-\tfrac{1}{2}\pi < \alpha < \tfrac{1}{2}\pi$.

Writing temporarily ζ for $ze^{\alpha i}$, we obtain, by Watson's lemma,

$$\int_0^\infty \exp(-zte^{\alpha i})F(te^{\alpha i})e^{\alpha i}\,dt = \int_0^\infty e^{-\zeta t}F(te^{\alpha i})e^{\alpha i}\,dt$$

$$\sim \left(\frac{2\pi e^{\alpha i}}{\zeta}\right)^{1/2}\left(1 + \frac{e^{\alpha i}}{12\zeta} + \frac{e^{2\alpha i}}{288\zeta^2} + \cdots\right)$$

$$= \left(\frac{2\pi}{z}\right)^{1/2}\left(1 + \frac{1}{12z} + \frac{1}{288z^2} + \cdots\right).$$

From this it follows that

$$\Gamma(z) \sim e^{-z}z^z\sqrt{\left(\frac{2\pi}{z}\right)}\left(1 + \frac{1}{12z} + \frac{1}{288z^2} + \cdots\right)$$

when $|\arg(ze^{\alpha i})| \leqslant \tfrac{1}{2}\pi - \Delta$, where Δ is an arbitrary positive number. But since α is any number between $\pm\tfrac{1}{2}\pi$, this implies that the asymptotic expansion is valid under the single restriction $|\arg z| \leqslant \pi - \delta$, where δ is any positive number.

9.55. The asymptotic behaviour of $|\Gamma(x+iy)|$ when y is large

Since $\Gamma(z)$ takes conjugate complex values at points which are symmetrical with respect to the real axis,† we have

$$|\Gamma(z)|^2 = \Gamma(z)\Gamma(\bar{z}),$$

---

† This is obvious from the canonical product for $1/\Gamma(z)$. Alternatively it is a consequence of Schwarz's principle of symmetry (§ 8.4), since $\Gamma(z)$ is real when z is real.

and so, when $|\arg z| < \pi$,

$$|\Gamma(z)|^2 \sim 2\pi e^{-z-\bar{z}} z^z \bar{z}^{\bar{z}} / |z|$$

Writing $z = x+iy$, this gives

$$|\Gamma(x+iy)|^2 \sim 2\pi e^{-2x}(x+iy)^{x+iy}(x-iy)^{x-iy}/|z|$$
$$= 2\pi e^{-2x}(x^2+y^2)^{x-1/2} e^{-2y \arg z}.$$

Now suppose that y increases indefinitely, whilst x remains finite. Then

$$|\Gamma(x+iy)|^2 \sim 2\pi e^{-2x} y^{2x-1}\left(1+\frac{x^2}{y^2}\right)^{x-1/2} e^{-\pi y + 2y \arctan(x/y)}$$

$$\sim 2\pi e^{-2x} y^{2x-1} e^{-\pi y + 2x} = 2\pi y^{2x-1} e^{-\pi y}.$$

When y is large and negative, the corresponding asymptotic formula

$$|\Gamma(x+iy)|^2 \sim 2\pi(-y)^{2x-1} e^{\pi y}$$

follows immediately if we remember that

$$|\Gamma(x+iy)| = |\Gamma(x-iy)|.$$

Combining these two results, we have, finally,

$$|\Gamma(x+iy)| \sim \surd(2\pi)\, |y|^{x-1/2} e^{-\pi|y|/2}$$

when x is finite and $|y|$ large.

9.56. Another proof of Legendre's duplication formula

We now give an alternative proof of Legendre's duplication formula, depending on the use of Liouville's theorem.

Let us consider the function

$$\phi(z) = 2^{2z}\Gamma(z)\Gamma(z+\tfrac{1}{2})/\Gamma(2z).$$

Its only possible singularities are the poles of the numerator and the zeros of the denominator. Now the numerator has simple poles at the points $2z = 0, -1, -2, -3,...$; but since these points are also simple poles of the denominator, they are not singularities of $\phi(z)$. The denominator $\Gamma(2z)$ never vanishes. Hence $\phi(z)$ has no singularity of finite affix and so is an integral function.

Again $\phi(z)$ is a periodic function of period 1, since

$$\frac{\phi(z+1)}{\phi(z)} = \frac{2^2 z(z+\tfrac{1}{2})}{(2z+1)2z} = 1,$$

by the recurrence formula for the Gamma function. Hence, if we can show that $\phi(z)$ is bounded when $\mathrm{R}l\, z \geqslant 1$, say, it will follow, by periodicity, that it is bounded all over the z-plane. But, by the asymptotic expansion of $\Gamma(z)$, we have

$$\phi(z) = 2\left(\frac{\pi}{e}\right)^{1/2}\left(1+\frac{1}{2z}\right)^z\left\{1+O\left(\frac{1}{|z|}\right)\right\} = 2\sqrt{\pi}\{1+O(1/|z|)\}$$

when $|z|$ is large and $|\arg z| < \pi$. Hence $\phi(z)$ is certainly bounded when $\mathrm{Rl}\,z \geqslant 1$.

We have thus shown that $\phi(z)$ is an integral function which remains bounded as $|z| \to \infty$ in any manner. By Liouville's theorem, this implies that $\phi(z)$ is a constant, its value $2\sqrt{\pi}$ being found by making $|z| \to \infty$. This completes the proof of Legendre's duplication formula

$$\pi^{\frac{1}{2}}\Gamma(2z) = 2^{2z-1}\Gamma(z)\Gamma(z+\tfrac{1}{2}).$$

Example. Prove Gauss's multiplication theorem that, if n is a positive integer,

$$\Gamma(z)\Gamma\left(z+\frac{1}{n}\right)\Gamma\left(z+\frac{2}{n}\right)\dots\Gamma\left(z+\frac{n-1}{n}\right) = (2\pi)^{\frac{1}{2}(n-1)}n^{\frac{1}{2}-nz}\Gamma(nz).$$

9.6. Hankel's contour integral for $1/\Gamma(z)$

The Eulerian integral of the second kind defined $\Gamma(z)$ only when the real part of z was positive. We now introduce a contour integral, due to Hankel,[†] which represents the Gamma function under much less restrictive conditions.

Let us consider the contour integral

$$\int_D e^t t^{-z}\, dt.$$

The integrand has, in general, a branch-point at the origin, but each branch is a one-valued function of t, regular in any domain of the complex plane supposed cut along the real axis from $-\infty$ to 0. We choose the branch for which

$$e^t t^{-z} = e^{t-z\log t},$$

where $\log t$ has its principal value.

Let D be a contour in the cut plane which starts at $-\rho$ on the lower edge of the cut, goes round the origin in the positive sense, and returns to $-\rho$ on the upper edge of the cut. This contour can be continuously deformed without crossing the cut,

---

† *Zeitschrift für Math. u. Phys.* **9** (1864), 7.

until it consists of the lower edge of the cut from $-\rho$ to $-\delta$, where $0 < \delta < \rho$, the circle $|t| = \delta$, and then the upper edge of the cut from $-\delta$ to $-\rho$. This deformation does not alter the value of the integral.

Now on the upper edge of the cut, we have $t = ue^{\pi i}$, where u is real and positive, and so the integrand takes there the value

$$e^{-u-z\log u - z\pi i} = e^{-u}u^{-z}e^{-z\pi i}.$$

Similarly on the lower edge of the cut $t = ue^{-\pi i}$, and the integrand is now

$$e^{-u}u^{-z}e^{z\pi i}.$$

Hence we have

$$\int_D e^t t^{-z}\, dt = (e^{z\pi i} - e^{-z\pi i})\int_\delta^\rho e^{-u}u^{-z}\, du + I,$$

where

$$I = \int_{-\pi}^{\pi} \exp(\delta e^{\theta i}) i \delta^{1-z} e^{(1-z)\theta i}\, d\theta.$$

But if $z = x + iy$,

$$|I| \leqslant \int_{-\pi}^{\pi} \delta^{1-x} e^{\delta \cos\theta + y\theta}\, d\theta \leqslant 2\pi \delta^{1-x} e^{\delta + \pi|y|},$$

and so I tends to zero with δ, provided that $x < 1$. We have thus shown that

$$\int_D e^t t^{-z}\, dt = 2i \sin\pi z \int_0^\rho e^{-u}u^{-z}\, dz,$$

provided that $\mathrm{Rl}(1-z) > 0$.

Now let C denote the contour obtained from D by making ρ tend to infinity. We then have

$$\int_C e^t t^{-z}\, dt = 2i \sin\pi z \int_0^\infty e^{-u}u^{-z}\, du = 2i \sin\pi z\, \Gamma(1-z).$$

Since $\Gamma(z)\Gamma(1-z) = \pi \operatorname{cosec}\pi z$, it follows that

$$\frac{1}{\Gamma(z)} = \frac{1}{2\pi i}\int_C e^t t^{-z}\, dt.$$

Although we have only proved this formula when $\mathrm{Rl}(1-z) > 0$, it does, in fact, hold for all values of z, by the theory of analytical continuation, since the expressions on each side of the equation are integral functions.

This completes the proof of Hankel's formula, that

$$\frac{1}{\Gamma(z)} = \frac{1}{2\pi i} \int_C e^t t^{-z}\, dt$$

for all values of z, where the contour C starts at the point $-\infty$ on the real axis, encircles the origin once in the positive sense, and returns to its starting-point.†

It should be observed that we have shown incidentally that

$$\Gamma(z) = \frac{1}{2i \sin \pi z} \int_C e^t t^{z-1}\, dt$$

for all values of z, save $0, \pm 1, \pm 2, \ldots$.

REFERENCES

N. Nielsen, *Handbuch der Theorie der Gamma-funktion* (Leipzig, 1906).

E. Lindelöf, *Le calcul des résidus* (Paris, 1905), Chap. IV.

MISCELLANEOUS EXAMPLES

1. By integrating $t^{z-1} e^{-t}$ round the complete boundary of a quadrant of a circle, indented at the origin, prove that

$$\int_0^\infty t^{z-1} e^{-it}\, dt = e^{-\pi z i/2} \Gamma(z)$$

provided that $0 < \mathrm{Rl}\, z < 1$. Deduce the values of

$$\int_0^\infty t^{z-1} \cos t\, dt, \qquad \int_0^\infty t^{z-1} \sin t\, dt.$$

2. By integrating $t^{z-1} e^{-t}$ round a suitable closed contour, show that

$$\int_0^\infty e^{-st} t^{z-1}\, dt = s^{-z} \Gamma(z)$$

provided that the real parts of s and z are positive. Deduce the values of

$$\int_0^\infty t^{x-1} e^{-\lambda t \cos \alpha} \genfrac{}{}{0pt}{}{\cos}{\sin} (\lambda t \sin \alpha)\, dt$$

when $\lambda > 0$, $x > 0$, and $-\tfrac{1}{2}\pi < \alpha < \tfrac{1}{2}\pi$.

3. Show that, when x is positive, $\Gamma(x)$ has a single minimum value which occurs between 1 and 2.

† We shall frequently write $\displaystyle\int_{-\infty}^{(0+)}$ for $\displaystyle\int_C$.

4. Show that
$$B(p,q) = \int_0^\infty \frac{t^{p-1}\, dt}{(1+t)^{p+q}},$$

provided that the real parts of p and q are positive. Deduce that $\Gamma(z)\Gamma(1-z) = \pi \operatorname{cosec} \pi z$.

5. Prove that
$$\int_0^{\pi/2} \sin^{2p-1}\theta \cos^{2q-1}\theta\, d\theta = \frac{\Gamma(p)\Gamma(q)}{2\Gamma(p+q)},$$

provided that the real parts of p and q are positive.

6. Show that, when the real parts of p and q are positive,
$$\int_0^1 \frac{t^{p-1}(1-t)^{q-1}}{(a+bt)^{p+q}}\, dt = \frac{B(p,q)}{(a+b)^p a^q},$$

provided that a/b is not a real number between 0 and -1.

7. Prove, by using the transformation $u = x+y+z$, $uv = y+z$, $uvw = z$, or otherwise, that, if $f(t)$ is continuous and α, β, γ are positive,

$$\iiint f(x+y+z)\, x^{\alpha-1}y^{\beta-1}z^{\gamma-1}\, dx\,dy\,dz = \frac{\Gamma(\alpha)\Gamma(\beta)\Gamma(\gamma)}{\Gamma(\alpha+\beta+\gamma)} \int_0^1 f(t)\, t^{\alpha+\beta+\gamma-1}\, dt,$$

where the triple integral is over the volume bounded by the coordinate planes and the plane $x+y+z = 1$.   (DIRICHLET.)

8. Prove, by using the transformation $xy = t$, $y = t+u$, or otherwise, that, if $f(t)$ is continuous and α and β are positive,

$$\int_0^1 dx \int_0^1 dy\, f(xy)(1-x)^{\alpha-1}y^\alpha(1-y)^{\beta-1} = \frac{\Gamma(\alpha)\Gamma(\beta)}{\Gamma(\alpha+\beta)} \int_0^1 f(t)(1-t)^{\alpha+\beta-1}\, dt.$$

9. Show that Euler's constant γ is given by

$$\gamma = \lim_{n\to\infty} \left[\int_0^1 \left\{1-\left(1-\frac{t}{n}\right)^n\right\} \frac{dt}{t} - \int_1^n \left(1-\frac{t}{n}\right)^n \frac{dt}{t} \right]$$

$$= \int_0^1 (1-e^{-t})\frac{dt}{t} - \int_1^\infty e^{-t}\frac{dt}{t}.$$

10. If $\psi(z)$ denotes the derivative of $\log \Gamma(z)$, prove that

$$\psi(z) = -\gamma - \frac{1}{z} + \sum_{n=1}^\infty \left(\frac{1}{n} - \frac{1}{n+z}\right).$$

Deduce that

$$\psi(1) = -\gamma, \qquad \psi(n+1) = -\gamma + \sum_{r=1}^{n} \frac{1}{r}.$$

Show also that

$$\psi'(z) = \sum_{n=0}^{\infty} \frac{1}{(n+z)^2}.$$

11. Show that

$$\psi(\tfrac{1}{2}) = -\gamma - 2\log 2, \qquad \psi'(\tfrac{1}{2}) = \tfrac{1}{2}\pi^2.$$

12. Prove that, when $\mathrm{Rl}\, z > 0$,

$$\psi(z) = \int_0^\infty \left(\frac{e^{-t}}{t} - \frac{e^{-zt}}{1-e^{-t}} \right) dt.$$

Deduce that

$$\psi(z+1) = \frac{1}{2z} + \log z - \int_0^\infty \left(\tfrac{1}{2}\coth \tfrac{1}{2}t - \frac{1}{t} \right) e^{-zt}\, dt.$$

13. Prove that, if $\mathrm{Rl}\, z > 0$,

$$\int_0^1 \frac{t^{2z-1}}{1+t}\, dt = \tfrac{1}{2}\psi(z+\tfrac{1}{2}) - \tfrac{1}{2}\psi(z).$$

Deduce that

$$\int_0^1 \frac{t^{2x-1} - t^{2y-1}}{(1+t)\log t}\, dt = \log \frac{\Gamma(x+\tfrac{1}{2})\Gamma(y)}{\Gamma(y+\tfrac{1}{2})\Gamma(x)},$$

provided that the real parts of x and y are positive.

14. Show that, if the real parts of a and b are positive,

$$\int_0^1 \frac{x^{a-1} - x^{b-1}}{1-x}\, dx = \psi(b) - \psi(a).$$

Deduce that

$$\int_0^1 \frac{(x^{a-1} - x^{b-1})(1-x^c)}{(1-x)\log x}\, dx = \log \frac{\Gamma(a+c)\Gamma(b)}{\Gamma(b+c)\Gamma(a)},$$

provided that the real parts of a, b, $c+a$, $b+c$ are all positive.

15. The logarithmic-integral function is defined by

$$\mathrm{li}(z) = \int_0^z \frac{dt}{\log t}.$$

Prove that

$$\mathrm{li}(e^{-z}) = -\int_z^\infty \frac{e^{-u}}{u}\, du,$$

and deduce that, when $|\arg z| \leqslant \tfrac{1}{2}\pi - \Delta < \tfrac{1}{2}\pi$,

$$-\mathrm{li}(e^{-z}) \sim e^{-z}\left\{\frac{1}{z} - \frac{1!}{z^2} + \frac{2!}{z^3} - \frac{3!}{z^4} + \ldots\right\}.$$

16. Show that, when $|\arg z| \leqslant \tfrac{1}{2}\pi - \Delta < \tfrac{1}{2}\pi$,

$$\int_z^\infty e^{-u}u^{\alpha-1}\,du \sim z^\alpha e^{-z}\left\{\frac{1}{z} + \frac{\alpha-1}{z^2} + \frac{(\alpha-1)(\alpha-2)}{z^3} + \ldots\right\}.$$

(LEGENDRE.)

17. The error function is defined by

$$\mathrm{Erfc}\,z = \int_z^\infty e^{-t^2}\,dt.$$

Prove that, when $|\arg z| \leqslant \tfrac{1}{4}\pi - \Delta < \tfrac{1}{4}\pi$,

$$\mathrm{Erfc}\,z \sim e^{-z^2}\left\{\frac{1}{2z} - \frac{1}{2^2 z^3} + \frac{1.3}{2^3 z^5} - \frac{1.3.5}{2^4 z^7} + \ldots\right\}.$$

18. Show that, if

$$1 + \frac{n}{1!} + \frac{n^2}{2!} + \ldots + \frac{n^{n-1}}{(n-1)!} + \frac{n^n}{n!}\theta_n = \tfrac{1}{2}e^n,$$

then

$$\theta_n = 1 + \tfrac{1}{2}n\left\{\int_0^1 (ue^{1-u})^n\,du - \int_1^\infty (Ue^{1-U})^n\,dU\right\}$$

Deduce that, as $n \to \infty$,

$$\theta_n \sim \frac{1}{3} + \frac{4}{135n} - \frac{8}{2835n^2} + \ldots.$$

(RAMANUJAN, WATSON.)

19. Prove that, if

$$1 - \frac{n}{1!} + \frac{n^2}{2!} - \ldots + (-1)^n\frac{n^n}{n!}\phi_n = e^{-n},$$

then

$$\phi_n = 1 - \int_0^n e^{-u}\left(1 - \frac{u}{n}\right)^n\,du.$$

Hence show that, as n increases from 0 to ∞, ϕ_n decreases steadily from 1 to $\tfrac{1}{2}$, and that

$$\phi_n \sim \frac{1}{2} + \frac{1}{8n} + \frac{1}{32n^2} + \ldots.$$

20. Deduce from Ex. 12 that, if $|z|$ is large and $|\arg z| < \tfrac{1}{2}\pi$, then

$$\psi(z+1) \sim \log z + \frac{1}{2z} - \frac{B_1}{2z^2} + \frac{B_2}{4z^4} - \frac{B_3}{6z^6} + \ldots.$$

Hence show that†

$$\log\Gamma(z+1) \sim (z+\tfrac{1}{2})\log z - z + \tfrac{1}{2}\log 2\pi + \sum_{r=1}^\infty \frac{(-1)^{r-1}B_r}{2r(2r-1)z^{2r-1}}.$$

† Use § 9.51, Ex. 2. The constant $\tfrac{1}{2}\log 2\pi$ is determined by using the dominant term of the asymptotic expansion of $\Gamma(z+1)$.

21. Find an asymptotic expansion, valid when $|z|$ is large and $\mathrm{Rl}\,z > 0$, of the function

$$\int_0^\infty e^{-zt}\,\frac{dt}{\sqrt{(1+t)}}.$$

Extend the range of validity of this expansion and deduce that

$$\int_z^\infty \frac{\cos t}{\sqrt{t}}\,dt = \frac{1}{\sqrt{z}}(X\cos z - Y\sin z),$$

$$\int_z^\infty \frac{\sin t}{\sqrt{t}}\,dt = \frac{1}{\sqrt{z}}(X\sin z + Y\cos z),$$

where, when $|z|$ is large and $\mathrm{Rl}\,z > 0$,

$$X \sim \frac{1}{2z} - \frac{1.3.5}{(2z)^3} + \frac{1.3.5.7.9}{(2z)^5} - \cdots,$$

$$Y \sim 1 - \frac{1.3}{(2z)^2} + \frac{1.3.5.7}{(2z)^4} - \cdots.$$

22. Show that, when $|z|$ is large and $|\arg z| \leqslant \frac{1}{2}\pi - \Delta < \frac{1}{2}\pi$,

$$\int_z^\infty \frac{\cos(t-z)}{t}\,dt \sim \frac{1}{z^2} - \frac{3!}{z^4} + \frac{5!}{z^6} - \cdots,$$

$$\int_z^\infty \frac{\sin(t-z)}{t}\,dt \sim \frac{1}{z} - \frac{2!}{z^3} + \frac{4!}{z^5} - \cdots.$$

23. By integrating $\pi z^{-s}\operatorname{cosec}\pi s/\Gamma(1-s)$, where z is positive, round the rectangle with vertices $\sigma \pm iR$, $-R \pm iR$, where σ is positive, show that

$$\frac{1}{2\pi i}\int_{\sigma-\infty i}^{\sigma+\infty i} z^{-s}\Gamma(s)\,ds = e^{-z}.$$

Prove that this formula also holds when $|\arg z| \leqslant \frac{1}{2}\pi - \delta$, where $\delta > 0$.

24. Deduce from Hankel's contour integral that

$$\frac{1}{\Gamma(z)} = \frac{1}{2\pi i}\int_{\sigma-\infty i}^{\sigma+\infty i} e^t t^{-z}\,dt,$$

where $\sigma > 0$, provided that $\mathrm{Rl}\,z > 0$.   (LAPLACE.)

25. $f(z)$ is an analytic function of z, regular in the half-plane $\mathrm{Rl}\,z < c$, where c is positive; a_r denotes the value of the rth derivative of $f(z)$ at

the origin. Show that the equation

$$\int_{-\infty}^{(0+)} f(z)z^{a-1}\, dz$$

$$= 2i \sin a\pi \int_0^\infty t^{a-1}\left\{f(-t)-a_0+a_1 t - \frac{a_2 t^2}{2!} + \ldots + (-1)^{k+1}\frac{a_k}{k!}t^k\right\}dt$$

is true, provided that the integer k lies between $\mathrm{Rl}(-a)$ and $\mathrm{Rl}(-a-1)$.

(CAUCHY.)

26. Prove that, when $\mathrm{Rl}\,z < 0$,

$$\Gamma(z) = \int_0^\infty t^{z-1}\left\{e^{-t}-1+t-\frac{t^2}{2!}+\ldots+(-1)^{k+1}\frac{t^k}{k!}\right\}dt,$$

where k is the integer which lies between $\mathrm{Rl}(-z)$ and $\mathrm{Rl}(-z-1)$.

(SAALSCHÜTZ.)

27. Show that the equation $\dfrac{1}{\Gamma(z+1)} = c$, where $c \neq 0$, has three infinite sets of roots, which behave asymptotically like

$$-n\{1+o(1)\},$$

$$\frac{\pi^2 n}{(\log n)^2}\{1+o(1)\} + \frac{2\pi n i}{\log n}\{1+o(1)\},$$

$$\frac{\pi^2 n}{(\log n)^2}\{1+o(1)\} - \frac{2\pi n i}{\log n}\{1+o(1)\},$$

as $n \to \infty$, one root of each set being associated with each large positive integer n. (HARDY.)

28. Show that the inverse factorial series

$$\sum_1^\infty \frac{a_n n!}{z(z+1)\ldots(z+n)}$$

converges whenever $\sum a_n n^{-z}$ is convergent, provided that z is not a negative integer or zero; and conversely.

Prove also that the convergence of either series is uniform in a bounded closed domain D, if it is uniform for the other, provided that D contains none of the points $0, -1, -2,\ldots$. (LANDAU.)

CHAPTER X

THE HYPERGEOMETRIC FUNCTIONS

10.1. Homogeneous linear differential equations

BEFORE we discuss in detail the properties of several important analytic functions defined by differential equations, it is desirable to consider whether there exists an analytic function $w(z)$ which satisfies the homogeneous linear differential equation

$$\frac{d^n w}{dz^n} + p_1(z)\frac{d^{n-1}w}{dz^{n-1}} + \dots + p_{n-1}(z)\frac{dw}{dz} + p_n(z)w = 0,$$

where the coefficients $p_1(z)$, $p_2(z)$,..., $p_n(z)$ are analytic functions whose only singularities of finite affix are poles, and, further, if such a solution does exist, to ask what effect the singularities of the coefficients have on the nature of the solution.

The simplest equation of this type

$$\frac{dw}{dz} + p(z)w = 0$$

presents little difficulty. Its variables are separable, and the solution is

$$w = \exp\left\{ -\int p(z)\, dz \right\}.$$

On the other hand, the equation of order two

$$\frac{d^2 w}{dz^2} + p(z)\frac{dw}{dz} + q(z)w = 0$$

has no such simple solution. We restrict our attention to this equation for two reasons; firstly, the analysis in this case is easily extended to the more general case, and, secondly, the particular functions with which we deal in the sequel do, in fact, satisfy second-order equations.

A point z_0 is said to be an *ordinary point* of this differential equation if the functions $p(z)$ and $q(z)$ are regular in a neighbourhood of z_0; all other points are called *singular points* of the differential equation.

10.11. The solution near an ordinary point

We now show that *if z_0 is an ordinary point of the equation*

$$\frac{d^2 w}{dz^2} + p(z)\frac{dw}{dz} + q(z)w = 0$$

and if a_0 and a_1 are two arbitrary constants, there exists a unique function $w(z)$ which is regular and satisfies the differential equation in a certain neighbourhood of z_0, and which also satisfies the initial conditions $w(z_0) = a_0$, $w'(z_0) = a_1$. This theorem, which is due to Fuchs,† shows that the only possible singularities of the function defined by the differential equation are the poles of the coefficients $p(z)$ and $q(z)$.

For simplicity we suppose that z_0 is zero.‡ Then since $p(z)$ and $q(z)$ are regular in a neighbourhood $|z| < R$ of the origin, they are expansible as Taylor series of the form

$$p(z) = \sum_0^\infty p_n z^n, \qquad q(z) = \sum_0^\infty q_n z^n,$$

the radius of convergence of each series being not less than R. We now try to find a formal solution by substituting

$$w = a_0 + a_1 z + a_2 z^2 + \dots$$

in the equation

$$\frac{d^2w}{dz^2} + \sum_0^\infty p_n z^n \frac{dw}{dz} + \sum_0^\infty q_n z^n w = 0$$

and equating coefficients. This gives

$$-2a_2 = a_1 p_0 + a_0 q_0,$$
$$-2.3a_3 = 2a_2 p_0 + a_1 p_1 + a_1 q_0 + a_0 q_1,$$

and, generally,

$$-(n-1)n\, a_n = (n-1)a_{n-1}p_0 + (n-2)a_{n-2}p_1 + \dots + a_1 p_{n-2} +$$
$$+ a_{n-2}q_0 + a_{n-3}q_1 + \dots + a_1 q_{n-3} + a_0 q_{n-2}.$$

These equations determine the coefficients a_n successively as linear combinations of a_0 and a_1.

We next show that this power series which satisfies the differential equation formally and also satisfies the given initial conditions, has a radius of convergence which is not less than R. The proof of this is rather difficult, since we know very little about the coefficients p_r and q_r.

Let us denote by M and N the maximum values, necessarily

† *Journal für Math.* **66** (1866), 121. See also Forsyth, *Theory of Differential Equations*, **4** (1902), Chap. I, and Bromwich, *Infinite Series* (1926), 162.

‡ This involves no loss of generality. For, if z_0 is not zero, we make the transformation $z' = z - z_0$.

finite, of $|p(z)|$ and $|q(z)|$ on the circle $|z| = r$, where $r < R$. Then, by Cauchy's inequality, we have

$$|p_n| \leqslant M/r^n, \qquad |q_n| \leqslant N/r^n,$$

and so

$$|p_n| \leqslant K/r^n, \qquad |q_n| \leqslant K/r^{n+1},$$

where K is the greater of M and Nr.

Writing b_0 and b_1 for $|a_0|$ and $|a_1|$ respectively, we have

$$2|a_2| \leqslant b_1|p_0| + b_0|q_0| \leqslant b_1 K + b_0 K/r \leqslant 2b_1 K + b_0 K/r,$$

and so

$$|a_2| \leqslant b_2$$

where

$$2b_2 = 2b_1 K + b_0 K/r.$$

Similarly,

$$2 . 3 |a_3| \leqslant 2|a_2||p_0| + b_1|p_1| + b_1|q_0| + b_0|q_1|$$
$$\leqslant 2b_2 K + 2b_1 Kr^{-1} + b_0 Kr^{-2}$$
$$\leqslant 3b_2 K + 2b_1 Kr^{-1} + b_0 Kr^{-2},$$

and so

$$|a_3| \leqslant b_3$$

where

$$2 . 3b_3 = 3b_2 K + 2b_1 Kr^{-1} + b_0 Kr^{-2}.$$

Proceeding in this way we find that $|a_n| \leqslant b_n$, where

$$(n-1)nb_n = nb_{n-1}K + (n-1)b_{n-2}Kr^{-1} + \ldots + b_0 Kr^{-n+1}.$$

From this equation we see that the coefficients b_n are connected by the recurrence formula

$$(n-1)nb_n - (n-2)(n-1)b_{n-1}r^{-1} = nb_{n-1}K.$$

But this gives

$$\frac{b_n}{b_{n-1}} = \frac{n-2}{nr} + \frac{K}{n-1} \to \frac{1}{r}$$

as $n \to \infty$, so that the radius of convergence of the power series $\sum b_n z^n$ is r. Since, however, $|a_n| \leqslant b_n$, it follows by the comparison test that the radius of convergence of $\sum a_n z^n$ cannot be less than r; moreover, as r was any number less than R, this shows that $\sum a_n z^n$ converges when $|z| < R$.

The function

$$w(z) = \sum_0^\infty a_n z^n$$

is, therefore, regular when $|z| < R$ and satisfies the prescribed conditions at the origin. The formal processes of term-by-term differentiation, multiplication, and rearrangement of power series by which this function was made to satisfy the differential equation are now seen to be completely justified, since all the series involved converge uniformly and absolutely in every closed domain within $|z| = R$. This completes the proof of the theorem.

Since a_n is a linear function of a_0 and a_1, we can express the solution we have just found in the form $w(z) = a_0 w_0(z) + a_1 w_1(z)$. The function $w_0(z)$ is a solution of the differential equation which satisfies the initial conditions $w_0(0) = 1$, $w_0'(0) = 0$, whereas $w_1(z)$ is a solution satisfying the conditions $w_1(0) = 0$, $w_1'(0) = 1$. Every solution of the differential equation regular in the neighbourhood of the origin is, therefore, a linear combination of the solutions $w_0(z)$ and $w_1(z)$, which we call a fundamental pair of solutions. Obviously $w_0(z)$ and $w_1(z)$ are linearly independent; by this we mean that there is no linear combination of them which is identically zero.

So far, the functions $w_0(z)$ and $w_1(z)$ are defined only in a neighbourhood of the origin. When we continue these functions analytically, they remain linearly independent solutions of the differential equation. The continuation can be carried out along any path which does not pass through a singular point of the differential equation, and so the solution will ultimately be defined all over the z-plane. In the next section we show that the continuation is not one-valued, by proving that a singularity of a differential equation is, in general, a branch-point of its complete solution.

Example 1. Prove that the necessary and sufficient condition that the two functions $f(z)$ and $g(z)$ should be linearly independent is that the determinant

$$\Delta(f, g) = \begin{vmatrix} f(z) & g(z) \\ f'(z) & g'(z) \end{vmatrix}$$

should not vanish. (This determinant is called the Wronskian of the two functions.)

Example 2. Show that, if $w_0(z)$ and $w_1(z)$ are two solutions of $w'' + p(z)w' + q(z)w = 0$, then

$$\frac{d}{dz}\Delta(w_0, w_1) + p(z)\,\Delta(w_0, w_1) = 0,$$

so that $\qquad \Delta(w_0, w_1) = C \exp\left\{ -\int p(z)\,dz \right\}.$

Deduce that, if $w_0(z)$ and $w_1(z)$ become $W_0(z)$ and $W_1(z)$ after analytical continuation round a closed curve Γ,

$$\Delta(W_0, W_1) = \Delta(w_0, w_1)e^{-2\pi i R},$$

where R is the sum of the residues of $p(z)$ at its poles within Γ.

10.12. The nature of the solution near a regular singularity

The point z_0 is a singularity of the differential equation $w'' + p(z)v' + q(z)w = 0$ if it is a pole of one or both of the functions $p(z)$ and $q(z)$. We call it a *regular singularity* if it is not a singularity of either of the functions $(z-z_0)p(z)$ and $(z-z_0)^2q(z)$; otherwise it is called an *irregular singularity*.

The reason for this distinction is simply explained. In a neighbourhood of a regular singularity, the differential equation possesses, as we shall shortly prove, two linearly independent solutions which are regular save possibly for a branch-point at the singularity. But near an irregular singularity, the method of solution by series breaks down and the singularity of the complete solution is of a much more complicated character. A general investigation of the behaviour of the complete solution near an irregular singularity is beyond the scope of the present book.†

If the origin is a regular singularity of the differential equation under consideration, the functions $zp(z)$ and $z^2q(z)$ are regular in a neighbourhood $|z| < R$ of the origin and so possess convergent Taylor expansions of the form

$$zp(z) = \sum_0^\infty p_r z^r, \qquad z^2q(z) = \sum_0^\infty q_r z^r,$$

where the coefficients p_0, q_0, and q_1 are not all zero. We now show that, in general, the equation possesses two linearly independent solutions of the form

$$w(z) = z^\alpha \sum_0^\infty a_r z^r,$$

where α is a root of a certain quadratic equation. When we substitute these power series in the differential equation and equate coefficients, we find that this expression is a formal solution of the equation if α and the coefficients a_r satisfy the conditions

$$a_0 F(\alpha) = 0,$$

† See Forsyth, *Theory of Differential Equations*, **4** (1902), or Ince, *Ordinary Differential Equations* (1927), 417–37.

and $\quad a_n F(\alpha+n) = -\sum_{s=0}^{n-1} a_s\{(\alpha+s)p_{n-s}+q_{n-s}\} \quad (n \geqslant 1),$

where $F(\alpha)$ denotes the quadratic $\alpha(\alpha-1)+p_0\alpha+q_0$.

The first equation is satisfied by choosing a_0 arbitrarily and making α a root of the quadratic equation $F(\alpha) = 0$. This equation is called the *indicial equation* and its roots the *exponents* of the regular singularity under consideration. The remaining equations determine successively the coefficients a_s as constant multiples of a_0, provided that $F(\alpha+n)$ does not vanish for any positive integral value of n. Hence, if the indicial equation has distinct roots which do not differ by an integer, this process gives two formal solutions, one corresponding to each root of the indicial equation.

If, however, the roots of the indicial equation are equal or differ by an integer, we may obtain only one formal solution. We leave this case for the moment as it presents certain difficulties which do not occur in the general case.

10.13. The convergence of the series solution near a regular singularity

We have just seen that the differential equation

$$w''+p(z)w'+q(z)w = 0$$

always has one formal solution $w = z^\alpha \sum_0^\infty a_n z^n$ valid near the regular singularity at the origin, and that it has two such solutions when the difference of the exponents is not an integer or zero. To prove that this formal series does represent a solution of the equation, we have to show either that the series $\sum a_n z^n$ terminates or else that it has a non-zero radius of convergence.

Let us suppose that the series does not terminate. We show that if $zp(z)$ and $z^2q(z)$ are regular when $|z| < R$, the radius of convergence of $\sum a_n z^n$ is not less than R. The proof is very similar to that of § 10.11.

If α' is the other root of the indicial equation, the coefficients a_n are given by

$$n(n+\alpha-\alpha')a_n = -\sum_{s=0}^{n-1} a_s\{(\alpha+s)p_{n-s}+q_{n-s}\}.$$

Let us write $b_n = |a_n|$ when $0 \leqslant n < \delta$, where $\delta = |\alpha-\alpha'|$ and

$\tau = |\alpha|$. Then if m is the least integer greater than δ, we have

$$m(m-\delta)|a_m| \leqslant |m(m+\alpha-\alpha')a_m|$$

$$= \left| \sum_{s=0}^{m-1} a_s\{(\alpha+s)p_{m-s}+q_{m-s}\} \right|$$

$$\leqslant \sum_{s=0}^{m-1} b_s\{(s+\tau)|p_{m-s}|+|q_{m-s}|\}.$$

But if M and N denote the maximum values, necessarily finite, of $|zp(z)|$ and $|z^2q(z)|$ respectively on the circle $|z| = r$, where $r < R$, Cauchy's inequality gives

$$|p_n| \leqslant M/r^n, \qquad |q_n| \leqslant N/r^n$$

and so

$$|p_n| \leqslant K/r^n, \qquad |q_n| \leqslant K/r^n,$$

where K is the greater of M and N. Substituting these bounds for $|p_n|$ and $|q_n|$, we find that $|a_m| \leqslant b_m$, where

$$m(m-\delta)b_m = K \sum_{s=0}^{m-1} (s+\tau+1)b_s/r^{m-s}.$$

Similarly we can show that $|a_n| \leqslant b_n$ when $n \geqslant m$, where

$$n(n-\delta)b_n = K \sum_{s=0}^{n-1} (s+\tau+1)b_s/r^{n-s}.$$

From this equation, we see that the coefficients b_n satisfy the recurrence formula

$$n(n-\delta)b_n - (n-1)(n-1-\delta)b_{n-1}/r = K(n+\tau)b_{n-1}/r.$$

But this gives

$$\frac{b_n}{b_{n-1}} = \frac{(n-1)(n-1-\delta)}{n(n-\delta)r} + \frac{K(n+\tau)}{n(n-\delta)r},$$

and so

$$\lim_{n\to\infty} (b_n/b_{n-1}) = 1/r.$$

The radius of convergence of the series $\sum b_n z^n$ is, therefore, r. Since, however, $|a_n| \leqslant b_n$, it follows by the comparison test that the radius of convergence of $\sum a_n z^n$ cannot be less than r; moreover, as r was any number less than R, this implies that this series is convergent when $|z| < R$.

The formal processes which made $w = z^\alpha \sum a_n z^n$ a solution are now seen to be completely justified since all the series in-

volved converge uniformly and absolutely in every closed
domain within $|z| = R$.

When the exponent-difference is not an integer or zero, we
derive in a similar manner a second independent solution
$w = z^{\alpha'} \sum a_n' z^n$ corresponding to the other root of the indicial
equation. In this case at least one of the solutions has a branch-
point at the origin.

10.14. Solutions valid for large values of $|z|$

To discuss the nature of the solution in the neighbourhood
of the point at infinity, we make the transformation $z = 1/t$.
The differential equation

$$\frac{d^2w}{dz^2} + p(z)\frac{dw}{dz} + q(z)w = 0$$

then becomes

$$\frac{d^2w}{dt^2} + \left\{\frac{2}{t} - \frac{1}{t^2}p\left(\frac{1}{t}\right)\right\}\frac{dw}{dt} + \frac{1}{t^4}q\left(\frac{1}{t}\right)w = 0.$$

The behaviour of the solution for large values of $|z|$ is now
determined by solving the transformed equation in the neighbourhood of the origin.

Accordingly we say that the point at infinity is an ordinary
point if

$$\frac{2}{t} - \frac{1}{t^2}p\left(\frac{1}{t}\right), \qquad \frac{1}{t^4}q\left(\frac{1}{t}\right)$$

are regular at the origin, that is, if

$$2z - z^2 p(z), \qquad z^4 q(z)$$

are regular at infinity. The complete solution of the equation,
valid in a neighbourhood of the point at infinity, is in this case
of the form

$$a_0 + \frac{a_1}{z} + \frac{a_2}{z^2} + \dots,$$

where a_0, a_1 are arbitrary constants.

Again, the point $t = 0$ is a regular singularity of the trans-
formed equation if $\frac{1}{t}p\left(\frac{1}{t}\right)$, $\frac{1}{t^2}q\left(\frac{1}{t}\right)$ are regular there; we say,
therefore, that the point at infinity is a regular singularity if
$zp(z)$ and $z^2q(z)$ are regular there. In this case, $p(z)$ and $q(z)$ are

expansible, by Laurent's theorem, in series of the form

$$p(z) = \frac{p_0}{z} + \frac{p_1}{z^2} + \frac{p_2}{z^3} + \dots,$$

$$q(z) = \frac{q_0}{z^2} + \frac{q_1}{z^3} + \frac{q_2}{z^4} + \dots,$$

convergent in a neighbourhood $|z| > R$ of the point at infinity.

It may now be shown, just as in § 10.13, that there exist in this neighbourhood two linearly independent solutions

$$w = z^{-\alpha} \sum a_n z^{-n}, \qquad w = z^{-\alpha'} \sum a_n' z^{-n},$$

where α and α' are the roots of the indicial equation

$$\alpha^2 - (p_0 - 1)\alpha + q_0 = 0,$$

provided that these roots do not differ by an integer or zero.

10.15. The solution when the exponent-difference is an integer or zero

When $\alpha - \alpha' = s$, where s is a positive integer or zero, the solution of § 10.13 fails. For if $s = 0$, the two solutions become identical, whilst if $s > 0$, all the coefficients in one of the solutions from some point onwards are either infinite or indeterminate. It is, however, well known[†] that a knowledge of one solution of a linear differential equation of order n enables us to depress the order to $n - 1$. In our case, we obtain in this way a linear equation of the first order which can be integrated immediately.

To effect this depression of order, we make, according to the usual rule, the change of independent variable

$$w = w_0(z)v,$$

where $w_0(z)$ is the known solution of exponent α. The function v is found to satisfy the equation

$$\frac{d^2v}{dz^2} + \left(\frac{2w_0'}{w_0} + p\right)\frac{dv}{dz} = 0,$$

whose solution is

$$v(z) = A + B \int^z \frac{1}{\{w_0(z)\}^2} \exp\left\{-\int^z p(z)\, dz\right\} dz,$$

† See, for example, Forsyth, *Treatise on Differential Equations* (1914), 130–3.

where A and B are arbitrary constants. Hence the required second solution, valid near the origin, is

$$w(z) = w_0(z) \int^z \frac{1}{\{w_0(z)\}^2} \exp\left\{ - \int^z p(z)\, dz \right\} dz.$$

Now α and $\alpha - s$ are the roots of the indicial equation

$$\alpha^2 + (p_0 - 1)\alpha + q_0 = 0,$$

so that $p_0 = 1 + s - 2\alpha$. Hence we have

$$\frac{1}{\{w_0(z)\}^2} \exp\left\{ - \int^z p(z)\, dz \right\}$$

$$= \frac{1}{z^{2\alpha}(a_0 + a_1 z + ...)^2} \exp\left\{ \int^z \left\{ \frac{2\alpha - 1 - s}{z} - p_1 - p_2 z - ... \right\} dz \right\}$$

$$= \frac{z^{-1-s}}{(a_0 + a_1 z + ...)^2} \exp\left\{ - \int^z (p_1 + p_2 z + ...)\, dz \right\}$$

$$= z^{-1-s} g(z),$$

where $g(0) = 1/a_0^2$. Since $a_0 \neq 0$, the function $(a_0 + a_1 z + ...)^{-2}$ is regular in a neighbourhood of the origin. Hence $g(z)$ is also regular there and can be expanded as a convergent Taylor series $g(z) = \sum g_n z^n$. Substituting this series for $g(z)$, we find that the second solution is

$$w = w_0(z) \int^z z^{1-s} \sum_0^\infty g_n z^n\, dz$$

$$= w_0(z) \left\{ \sum_{n=0}^{s-1} \frac{g_n z^{n-s}}{n-s} + g_s \log z + \sum_{n=s+1}^\infty \frac{g_n z^{n-s}}{n-s} \right\}.$$

In particular, when the exponent-difference s is zero, this solution can be written in the form

$$w = g_0 w_0(z) \log z + z^{\alpha+1} \sum_{n=0}^\infty b_n z^n.$$

As g_0 is not zero, this solution possesses a logarithmic branch-point at the origin. When the exponent-difference s is a positive integer, the second solution takes the form

$$w = g_s w_0(z) \log z + z^{\alpha'} \sum_{n=0}^\infty c_n z^n.$$

If it happens, as may be the case, that g_s is zero, the second solution does not involve a logarithmic term.

An alternative method of determining the second solution when the exponent-difference is an integer or zero is due to Frobenius.†

Example 1. Determine two linearly independent solutions of the equation
$$z^2(z+1)w'' - z^2w' + (3z+1)w = 0$$
valid (i) near $z = 0$, (ii) near $z = -1$.   (FORSYTH.)

Example 2. Determine two linearly independent solutions of Bessel's equation
$$zw'' + w' + zw = 0$$
valid near the origin.

Example 3. Prove that the equation
$$z^2w'' + (z+1)w' + w = 0$$
has an irregular singularity at the origin, and show that the method of solution by series gives only one integral of the equation valid near the origin.

Example 4. Show that the equation
$$z^3w'' + z^2w' + w = 0$$
has an irregular singularity at the origin, and that it is impossible to find a series solution valid near the origin.

10.2. The second-order differential equation with three regular singularities

If the only singularities of the differential equation
$$w'' + p(z)w' + q(z)w = 0$$
are regular singularities at ξ, η, and ζ, the functions
$$P(z) = (z-\xi)(z-\eta)(z-\zeta)p(z),$$
$$Q(z) = (z-\xi)^2(z-\eta)^2(z-\zeta)^2q(z)$$
are integral functions. Moreover, since the point at infinity is not a singularity of the differential equation, the functions $2z - z^2p(z)$ and $z^4q(z)$ are regular at infinity. This is the case if and only if $P(z)$ and $Q(z)$ are quadratics in z and the coefficient of z^2 in $P(z)$ is 2.

Accordingly we can write
$$p(z) = \frac{A}{z-\xi} + \frac{B}{z-\eta} + \frac{C}{z-\zeta},$$

† *Journal für Math.* **76** (1873), 214–24. See also Forsyth, *Treatise on Differential Equations* (1914), 243–58; Ince, *Ordinary Differential Equations* (1927), 396–403.

where $A+B+C = 2$, and

$$(z-\xi)(z-\eta)(z-\zeta)q(z) = \frac{D}{z-\xi} + \frac{E}{z-\eta} + \frac{F}{z-\zeta};$$

here the capital letters denote constants depending on th exponents of the singularities.

The indicial equation relating to the singularity ξ now take the form

$$k(k-1) + Ak + D/\{(\xi-\eta)(\xi-\zeta)\} = 0.$$

If the exponents at ξ are α and α', this gives

$$A = 1-\alpha-\alpha', \qquad D = (\xi-\eta)(\xi-\zeta)\alpha\alpha'.$$

Similarly if the exponents at η are β, β' and those at ζ ar γ, γ', we have

$$B = 1-\beta-\beta', \qquad E = (\eta-\zeta)(\eta-\xi)\beta\beta',$$

and

$$C = 1-\gamma-\gamma', \qquad F = (\zeta-\xi)(\zeta-\eta)\gamma\gamma'.$$

Moreover, since $A+B+C = 2$, the six exponents are not arbi trary, but are connected by the relation

$$\alpha+\alpha'+\beta+\beta'+\gamma+\gamma' = 1.$$

The differential equation is therefore of the form

$$\frac{d^2w}{dz^2} + \left\{ \frac{1-\alpha-\alpha'}{z-\xi} + \frac{1-\beta-\beta'}{z-\eta} + \frac{1-\gamma-\gamma'}{z-\zeta} \right\} \frac{dw}{dz} -$$

$$-\left\{ \frac{\alpha\alpha'}{(z-\xi)(\eta-\zeta)} + \frac{\beta\beta'}{(z-\eta)(\zeta-\xi)} + \frac{\gamma\gamma'}{(z-\zeta)(\xi-\eta)} \right\} \times$$

$$\times \frac{(\xi-\eta)(\eta-\zeta)(\zeta-\xi)}{(z-\xi)(z-\eta)(z-\zeta)} w = 0.$$

In the notation introduced by Riemann, we express the fac that w is a solution of this differential equation by writing

$$w = P \begin{Bmatrix} \xi & \eta & \zeta & \\ \alpha & \beta & \gamma & z \\ \alpha' & \beta' & \gamma' & \end{Bmatrix}.$$

Example 1. A linear differential equation of the second order ha but one singularity, a regular singularity at the origin. Show that th equation is $zw'' + 2w' = 0$.

Example 2. A linear differential equation of the second order ha but two singularities. These are a regular singularity of exponents α an α' at the origin and a regular singularity of exponents β and β' at infinit Find the equation and show that $\alpha+\alpha'+\beta+\beta' = 0$, $\alpha\alpha' = \beta\beta'$.

Example 3. Show that the differential equation satisfied by the function

$$w = P \begin{Bmatrix} \xi & \infty & \zeta \\ \alpha & \beta & \gamma & z \\ \alpha' & \beta' & \gamma' \end{Bmatrix}$$

is

$$\frac{d^2w}{dz^2} + \left\{ \frac{1-\alpha-\alpha'}{z-\xi} + \frac{1-\gamma-\gamma'}{z-\zeta} \right\} \frac{dw}{dz} +$$

$$+ \left\{ \frac{\alpha\alpha'(\xi-\zeta)}{z-\xi} + \beta\beta' + \frac{\gamma\gamma'(\zeta-\xi)}{z-\zeta} \right\} \frac{w}{(z-\xi)(z-\zeta)} = 0.$$

Example 4. Prove, by transforming the differential equation, that

$$z^p(1-z)^q P \begin{Bmatrix} 0 & \infty & 1 \\ \alpha & \beta & \gamma & z \\ \alpha' & \beta' & \gamma' \end{Bmatrix} = P \begin{Bmatrix} 0 & \infty & 1 \\ \alpha+p & \beta-p-q & \gamma+q & z \\ \alpha'+p & \beta'-p-q & \gamma'+q \end{Bmatrix},$$

and also that

$$P \begin{Bmatrix} 0 & \infty & 1 \\ \alpha & \beta & \gamma & z \\ \alpha' & \beta' & \gamma' \end{Bmatrix} = P \begin{Bmatrix} 1 & 0 & \infty \\ \alpha & \beta & \gamma & 1/(1-z) \\ \alpha' & \beta' & \gamma' \end{Bmatrix}.$$

Example 5. Prove that

$$\left(\frac{z-\xi}{z-\eta}\right)^p \left(\frac{z-\zeta}{z-\eta}\right)^q P \begin{Bmatrix} \xi & \eta & \zeta \\ \alpha & \beta & \gamma & z \\ \alpha' & \beta' & \gamma' \end{Bmatrix} = P \begin{Bmatrix} \xi & \eta & \zeta \\ \alpha+p & \beta-p-q & \gamma+q & z \\ \alpha'+p & \beta'-p-q & \gamma'+q \end{Bmatrix},$$

and also that

$$P \begin{Bmatrix} \xi & \eta & \zeta \\ \alpha & \beta & \gamma & z \\ \alpha' & \beta' & \gamma' \end{Bmatrix} = P \begin{Bmatrix} \xi_1 & \eta_1 & \zeta_1 \\ \alpha & \beta & \gamma & z_1 \\ \alpha' & \beta' & \gamma' \end{Bmatrix},$$

where $z_1, \xi_1, \eta_1, \zeta_1$ are derived from z, ξ, η, ζ respectively by the same homographic transformation.

10.21. The hypergeometric equation

If we make the homographic transformation

$$t = \frac{(z-\xi)(\eta-\zeta)}{(z-\eta)(\xi-\zeta)}$$

and use the results of Exx. 4, 5 of the preceding section, we find that

$$P \begin{Bmatrix} \xi & \eta & \zeta \\ \alpha & \beta & \gamma & z \\ \alpha' & \beta' & \gamma' \end{Bmatrix} = P \begin{Bmatrix} 0 & \infty & 1 \\ \alpha & \beta & \gamma & t \\ \alpha' & \beta' & \gamma' \end{Bmatrix}$$

$$= t^\alpha(1-t)^\gamma P \begin{Bmatrix} 0 & \infty & 1 \\ 0 & \alpha+\beta+\gamma & 0 & t \\ \alpha'-\alpha & \alpha+\beta'+\gamma & \gamma'-\gamma \end{Bmatrix}$$

Hence, in order to determine the properties of the solution of the second-order equation with three regular singularities, it suffices to discuss the behaviour of the function

$$w = P \left\{ \begin{matrix} 0 & \infty & 1 \\ 0 & a & 0 & t \\ 1-c & b & c-a-b \end{matrix} \right\},$$

which satisfies the equation

$$t(1-t)w'' + \{c-(a+b+1)t\}w' - abw = 0.$$

This is called the differential equation of the hypergeometric function, or, more briefly, the hypergeometric equation.

To avoid difficulties regarding the possible occurrence of logarithmic terms in the complete solution of this equation, we shall suppose in the present chapter that none of the exponent-differences $c-1$, $a-b$, $a+b-c$ is an integer or zero.[†]

10.22. The generalized hypergeometric equation

If we introduce the operator $\vartheta = z\,d/dz$, we find that the hypergeometric equation

$$z(1-z)\frac{d^2w}{dz^2} + \{c-(a+b+1)z\}\frac{dw}{dz} - abw = 0$$

takes the simple form

$$\vartheta(\vartheta+c-1)w = z(\vartheta+a)(\vartheta+b)w,$$

a fact which is of importance in the formal solution of the equation by series.

A differential equation is said to be of *generalized hypergeometric type* if it can be written in the form

$$\vartheta(\vartheta+\rho_1-1)(\vartheta+\rho_2-1)...(\vartheta+\rho_q-1)w$$
$$= z(\vartheta+\alpha_1)(\vartheta+\alpha_2)...(\vartheta+\alpha_p)w;$$

the order of this equation is equal to the greater of p and $q+1$.

10.3. The hypergeometric function

To discuss the nature of the solution of the hypergeometric equation $$\vartheta(\vartheta+c-1)w = z(\vartheta+a)(\vartheta+b)w$$

---

† The case of zero or integer exponent-differences has been discussed by Lindelöf, *Acta Soc. Scient. Fennicae*, **19** (1893), No. 1, and W. L. Ferrar, *Proc. Edinburgh Math. Soc.* (1), **43** (1925), 39–47.

near the regular singularity at the origin, we substitute formally the series

$$w = z^\alpha \sum_0^\infty a_n z^n$$

and equate coefficients. We find that the exponent α satisfies the indicial equation

$$\alpha(\alpha+c-1) = 0$$

and that the coefficients a_n satisfy the recurrence formula

$$(\alpha+n)(\alpha+c-1+n)a_n = (\alpha+a+n-1)(\alpha+b+n-1)a_{n-1}.$$

From the recurrence formula, we deduce that

$$a_n = \frac{\Gamma(\alpha+a+n)\Gamma(\alpha+b+n)}{\Gamma(\alpha+1+n)\Gamma(\alpha+c+n)} A,$$

where A is an arbitrary constant, and so we obtain two formal solutions

$$\sum_0^\infty \frac{\Gamma(a+n)\Gamma(b+n)}{\Gamma(c+n)\,n!} z^n, \quad z^{1-c} \sum_0^\infty \frac{\Gamma(a-c+1+n)\Gamma(b-c+1+n)}{\Gamma(2-c+n)\,n!} z^n.$$

But since the two power series converge absolutely and uniformly with respect to z in every closed domain within the unit circle, the validity of these solutions when $|z| < 1$ follows immediately.

We now define the hypergeometric function $F(a, b; c; z)$ by the equation

$$\frac{\Gamma(a)\Gamma(b)}{\Gamma(c)} F(a, b; c; z) = \sum_{n=0}^\infty \frac{\Gamma(a+n)\Gamma(b+n)}{\Gamma(c+n)} \frac{z^n}{n!}$$

when $|z| < 1$, and by analytical continuation when $|z| \geqslant 1$; it is an analytic function of z, which is certainly regular† when $|z| < 1$.

In terms of this new function, the two solutions of the hypergeometric equation valid near the regular singularity at the origin are

$$F(a, b; c; z), \quad z^{1-c}F(1+a-c, 1+b-c; 2-c; z).$$

Example 1. Show that

$$(1-z)^{-\alpha} = F(\alpha, \beta; \beta; z),$$

$$\log\frac{1}{1-z} = zF(1, 1; 2; z),$$

$$e^z = \lim_{\alpha\to\infty} F\left(\alpha, \beta; \beta; \frac{z}{\alpha}\right).$$

† We shall see later that it has branch-points at 1 and ∞.

Example 2. Prove that

$$\frac{d}{dz} F(a,b;c;z) = \frac{ab}{c} F(a+1,b+1;c+1;z).$$

Example 3. Show that, when $c = 1$, two independent solutions of the hypergeometric equation, valid when $|z| < 1$, are $F(a,b;1;z)$ and

$$\Gamma(a)\Gamma(b)F(a,b;1;z)\log z + \sum_{1}^{\infty} s_r \frac{\Gamma(a+r)\Gamma(b+r)}{r!\,r!} z^r,$$

where

$$s_r = \sum_{1}^{r} \left(\frac{1}{a+n-1} + \frac{1}{b+n-1} - \frac{2}{n} \right).$$

10.31. An integral representation of $F(a,b;c;z)$

The series defining the hypergeometric function can be written in the form

$$\frac{\Gamma(a)\Gamma(b)}{\Gamma(c)} F(a,b;c;z) = \frac{1}{\Gamma(c-b)} \sum_{n=0}^{\infty} \Gamma(a+n)\mathrm{B}(b+n,c-b)\frac{z^n}{n!}.$$

Using the Eulerian integral of the first kind, we deduce that, when $\mathrm{Rl}\,c > \mathrm{Rl}\,b > 0$,

$$\frac{\Gamma(a)\Gamma(b)}{\Gamma(c)} F(a,b;c;z)$$

$$= \frac{1}{\Gamma(c-b)} \sum_{n=0}^{\infty} \int_0^1 t^{b+n-1}(1-t)^{c-b-1}\Gamma(a+n)\frac{z^n}{n!}\,dt,$$

it being understood that the many-valued functions under the sign of integration are made definite by taking

$$\arg t = \arg(1-t) = 0.$$

Now when $|z| < 1$, the series $\sum \Gamma(a+n)z^n t^n/n!$ converges uniformly with respect to t over the whole range of integration, and so we can invert the order of integration and summation to obtain

$$\frac{\Gamma(a)\Gamma(b)}{\Gamma(c)} F(a,b;c;z) = \int_0^1 t^{b-1}(1-t)^{c-b-1} \sum_{n=0}^{\infty} \frac{\Gamma(a+n)}{\Gamma(c-b)} \frac{(zt)^n}{n!}\,dt$$

$$= \frac{\Gamma(a)}{\Gamma(c-b)} \int_0^1 t^{b-1}(1-t)^{c-b-1}(1-zt)^{-a}\,dt,$$

where $(1-zt)^{-a}$ has its principal value. We have thus shown that, when $|z| < 1$ and $\mathrm{Rl}\,c > \mathrm{Rl}\,b > 0$,

$$\frac{\Gamma(b)\Gamma(c-b)}{\Gamma(c)} F(a,b;c;z) = \int_0^1 t^{b-1}(1-t)^{c-b-1}(1-zt)^{-a}\,dt.$$

The integral on the right-hand side of this equation is, however, uniformly convergent in any closed domain of the z-plane, supposed cut along the real axis from 1 to $+\infty$, and so represents an analytic function, regular in the cut plane. Hence this integral representation of $F(a,b;c;z)$ provides the analytical continuation of the hypergeometric function in the case when $\mathrm{Rl}\,c > \mathrm{Rl}\,b > 0$.

If we had used Pochhammer's double-circuit integral for the Beta function (see § 9.3) instead of the Eulerian integral, we should have obtained a double-circuit integral for $F(a,b;c;z)$, valid in the cut plane, without any restrictions on the parameters b and c. For the details of this, we refer the reader to Pochhammer's memoir already cited.

10.32. The value of $F(a,b;c;1)$ when $\mathrm{Rl}(c-a-b) > 0$.

Since $\Gamma(a+n)/\Gamma(n) \sim n^a$ when n is large and positive,[†] we have

$$\frac{\Gamma(a+n)\Gamma(b+n)}{\Gamma(c+n)\,n!} \sim \frac{1}{n^{c-a-b+1}}.$$

Hence the hypergeometric series $F(a,b;c;1)$ converges if and only if $\mathrm{Rl}(c-a-b) > 0$. When this condition is satisfied, it follows from Abel's theorem on the continuity of power series[‡] that

$$F(a,b;c;1) = \lim_{x\to 1-0} F(a,b;c;x).$$

If, in addition, the condition $\mathrm{Rl}\,c > \mathrm{Rl}\,b > 0$ is satisfied, we deduce from the integral formula of § 10.31 that

$$F(a,b;c;1) = \lim_{x\to 1-0} \frac{\Gamma(c)}{\Gamma(b)\Gamma(c-b)} \int_0^1 t^{b-1}(1-t)^{c-b-1}(1-xt)^{-a}\,dt$$

$$= \frac{\Gamma(c)}{\Gamma(b)\Gamma(c-b)} \int_0^1 t^{b-1}(1-t)^{c-a-b-1}\,dt$$

$$= \frac{\Gamma(c)\Gamma(c-a-b)}{\Gamma(c-a)\Gamma(c-b)}.$$

† See § 9.22, Ex. 4. ‡ § 5.22, Ex. 1.

The additional restrictions on the real parts of b and c are, however, quite unnecessary for the truth of this result, and only arise on account of the particular method of proof adopted. Although the restrictions can be removed by an appeal to the principle of analytical continuation, it is simpler to give a direct proof, as follows.

If we write

$$F(a,b;c;z) = \sum_0^\infty A_n z^n, \qquad F(a,b;c+1;z) = \sum_0^\infty B_n z^n,$$

it is easily verified that

$$c(c-a-b)A_n = (c-a)(c-b)B_n + cnA_n - c(n+1)A_{n+1},$$

from which it follows that

$$c(c-a-b)\sum_0^N A_n = (c-a)(c-b)\sum_0^N B_n - c(N+1)A_{N+1}.$$

But since $(N+1)A_{N+1} \sim 1/N^{c-a-b}$, this equation gives

$$F(a,b;c;1) = \frac{(c-a)(c-b)}{c(c-a-b)} F(a,b;c+1;1),$$

provided that $\mathrm{Rl}(c-a-b) > 0$. From this we easily deduce that

$$\frac{\Gamma(c-a)\Gamma(c-b)}{\Gamma(c)\Gamma(c-a-b)} F(a,b;c;1)$$

$$= \frac{\Gamma(c+m-a)\Gamma(c+m-b)}{\Gamma(c+m)\Gamma(c+m-a-b)} F(a,b;c+m;1)$$

for every positive integral value of m, and hence

$$\frac{\Gamma(c-a)\Gamma(c-b)}{\Gamma(c)\Gamma(c-a-b)} F(a,b;c;1) = \lim_{m\to\infty} F(a,b;c+m;1).$$

Let us now write

$$F(a,b;c+m;z) = 1 + \sum_1^\infty C_n z^n.$$

Then, since $C_n \sim 1/n^{c-a-b+m+1}$ when n is large, we can find an integer N, independent of m, such that, when $n > N$,

$$|C_n| < \frac{2}{n^{\kappa+m+1}} < \frac{2}{N^m}\frac{1}{n^{\kappa+1}},$$

where $\kappa = \mathrm{Rl}(c-a-b)$. Hence we have

$$\left| \sum_1^\infty C_n \right| \leqslant \sum_1^N |C_n| + \frac{2}{N^m} \sum_{N+1}^\infty \frac{1}{n^{\kappa+1}} < \sum_1^N |C_n| + \frac{K}{N^m},$$

where K is independent of m. Since, for every fixed value of n, C_n tends to zero as $m \to \infty$, this inequality implies that $\sum\limits_1^\infty C_n$ also tends to zero and hence that

$$\lim_{m \to \infty} F(a, b; c+m; 1) = 1.$$

This completes the proof that the equation

$$F(a, b; c; 1) = \frac{\Gamma(c)\Gamma(c-a-b)}{\Gamma(c-a)\Gamma(c-b)},$$

is true when the real part of $c-a-b$ is positive.

10.33. The analytical continuation of $F(a, b; c; z)$

If we put $z = 1-t$ in the hypergeometric equation satisfied by $F(a, b; c; z)$, we find that

$$t(1-t)\frac{d^2w}{dt^2} + \{(1+a+b-c)-(a+b+1)t\}\frac{dw}{dt} - abw = 0,$$

which is also of hypergeometric type. From this it follows that the hypergeometric equation has two linearly independent solutions

$$F(a, b; 1+a+b-c; 1-z),$$

$$(1-z)^{c-a-b}F(c-a, c-b; 1+c-a-b; 1-z)$$

valid when $|1-z| < 1$. We make the second solution definite by giving to $(1-z)^{c-a-b}$ its principal value.

The region in which these two solutions are defined has an area in common with the region $|z| < 1$ in which $F(a, b; c; z)$ was defined. In this common area, the three solutions must be connected by a linear relation

$$F(a, b; c; z) = A F(a, b; 1+a+b-c; 1-z) +$$
$$+ B(1-z)^{c-a-b}F(c-a, c-b; 1+c-a-b; 1-z).$$

To determine the constants A and B, we suppose that $\mathrm{Rl}(a+b) < \mathrm{Rl}\,c < 1$, so that the three series

$$F(a, b; c; 1), \qquad F(a, b; 1+a+b-c; 1),$$

$$F(c-a, c-b; 1+c-a-b; 1)$$

are convergent.

If we make z tend to 1 along the real axis, we find that

$$F(a, b; c; 1) = A.$$

Similarly, making z tend to zero, we have

$$1 = AF(a,b; 1+a+b-c; 1) + BF(c-a, c-b; 1+c-a-b; 1).$$

By § 10.32, the first equation gives

$$A = \frac{\Gamma(c)\Gamma(c-a-b)}{\Gamma(c-a)\Gamma(c-b)}.$$

The second equation now becomes

$$1 = \frac{\Gamma(c)\Gamma(1-c)\Gamma(c-a-b)\Gamma(1+a+b-c)}{\Gamma(c-a)\Gamma(1+a-c)\Gamma(c-b)\Gamma(1+b-c)} +$$

$$+ B\frac{\Gamma(1-c)\Gamma(1+c-a-b)}{\Gamma(1-b)\Gamma(1-a)}$$

from which it is not difficult to deduce† that

$$B = \frac{\Gamma(c)\Gamma(a+b-c)}{\Gamma(a)\Gamma(b)}.$$

We have thus proved that the relation

$$F(a,b;c;z) = \frac{\Gamma(c)\Gamma(c-a-b)}{\Gamma(c-a)\Gamma(c-b)} F(a,b; 1+a+b-c; 1-z) +$$

$$+ \frac{\Gamma(c)\Gamma(a+b-c)}{\Gamma(a)\Gamma(b)}(1-z)^{c-a-b}F(c-a, c-b; 1+c-a-b; 1-z)$$

holds when $|z| < 1$, $|1-z| < 1$, provided that

$$\mathrm{Rl}(a+b) < \mathrm{Rl}\,c < 1.$$

This restriction on the parameters a, b, c is not necessary for the truth of this result, and arises as a result of the method of proof adopted. An alternative proof, valid for all values of the parameters, will be found in Barnes's memoir cited below.

The importance of the result lies in the fact that it provides the analytical continuation of $F(a,b;c;z)$ into the region $|1-z| < 1$ and shows that this function has a branch-point at $z = 1$.

10.4. Barnes's contour integral for $F(a,b;c;z)$

Barnes,‡ following Pincherle§ and Mellin,|| has represented the hypergeometric function by means of a contour integral

---

† By using the formula $\Gamma(z)\Gamma(1-z) = \pi\,\mathrm{cosec}\,\pi z$.
‡ *Proc. London Math. Soc.* (2), **6** (1908), 141-77.
§ *Atti d. R. Accademia dei Lincei, Rendiconti* (4), **4** (1888), 694-700, 792-9.
|| *Acta Soc. Scient. Fennicae,* **20** (1895), No. 7.

whose integrand involves Gamma functions. A particular case of Barnes's formula is

$$-\frac{1}{2\pi i} \int_{\sigma-\infty i}^{\sigma+\infty i} \frac{\pi}{\sin \pi s}(-z)^s \, ds = 1+z+z^2+\dots,$$

valid when $|z| < 1$, $|\arg(-z)| < \pi$, the path of integration being the straight line $\mathrm{Rl}\, s = \sigma$, where $-1 < \sigma < 0$; this has already been given as an exercise for the reader.†

Now if ϑ denotes the operator $z \, d/dz$, we have formally

$$\frac{\Gamma(a)\Gamma(b)}{\Gamma(c)} F(a,b;c;z) = \frac{\Gamma(a+\vartheta)\Gamma(b+\vartheta)}{\Gamma(c+\vartheta)\Gamma(1+\vartheta)}(1+z+z^2+\dots)$$

$$= -\frac{1}{2\pi i} \frac{\Gamma(a+\vartheta)\Gamma(b+\vartheta)}{\Gamma(c+\vartheta)\Gamma(1+\vartheta)} \int_{\sigma-\infty i}^{\sigma+\infty i} \frac{\pi}{\sin \pi s}(-z)^s \, ds$$

$$= -\frac{1}{2\pi i} \int_{\sigma-\infty i}^{\sigma+\infty i} \frac{\Gamma(a+s)\Gamma(b+s)}{\Gamma(c+s)\Gamma(1+s)} \frac{\pi}{\sin \pi s}(-z)^s \, ds$$

$$= \frac{1}{2\pi i} \int_{\sigma-\infty i}^{\sigma+\infty i} \frac{\Gamma(a+s)\Gamma(b+s)\Gamma(-s)}{\Gamma(c+s)}(-z)^s \, ds.$$

This is Barnes's contour integral for $F(a,b;c;z)$.

Let us consider, then, the integral

$$\frac{1}{2\pi i} \int_{-\infty i}^{\infty i} \frac{\Gamma(a+s)\Gamma(b+s)\Gamma(-s)}{\Gamma(c+s)}(-z)^s \, ds$$

in the case when $|z| < 1$, $|\arg(-z)| \leqslant \pi-\epsilon$, where ϵ is an arbitrary positive number. The path of integration is the imaginary axis, modified, if necessary, by loops to make the poles of $\Gamma(-s)$ lie to the right of the path and those of $\Gamma(a+s)\Gamma(b+s)$ to its left; this is always possible, provided that neither a nor b is a negative integer.‡ We suppose, as before, that none of the exponent-differences $c-1$, $a-b$, $a+b-c$ is an integer or zero.§

This integral may be evaluated by Cauchy's theory of resi-

† Replace $e^{-\alpha}$ by $-z$, z by $-s$, in Ex. 18 on page 153.

‡ The case when a or b is a negative integer is unimportant, since $F(a,b;c;z)$ is then a polynomial.

§ Barnes's formula does, in fact, provide a solution of the hypergeometric equation when this condition is not satisfied.

dues. Let C denote the closed contour formed by three sides of the rectangle whose vertices are $\pm iN$, $N+\frac{1}{2}\pm iN$, together with the portion of the path of integration from iN to $-iN$. We take N to be an integer, greater than $|\operatorname{Im} a|$ and $|\operatorname{Im} b|$, so that no poles of the integrand lie on C. We then have

$$\frac{1}{2\pi i}\int_C \frac{\Gamma(a+s)\Gamma(b+s)\Gamma(-s)}{\Gamma(c+s)}(-z)^s\,ds$$

$$= \text{sum of residues of } \frac{\Gamma(a+s)\Gamma(b+s)\Gamma(-s)}{\Gamma(c+s)}(-z)^s \text{ at the poles within } C$$

$$= -\sum_{n=0}^{N} \frac{\Gamma(a+n)\Gamma(b+n)}{\Gamma(c+n)\Gamma(1+n)}z^n,$$

and so

$$\frac{1}{2\pi i}\int_{-iN}^{iN} \frac{\Gamma(a+s)\Gamma(b+s)\Gamma(-s)}{\Gamma(c+s)}(-z)^s\,ds$$

$$= \sum_{n=0}^{N} \frac{\Gamma(a+n)\Gamma(b+n)}{\Gamma(c+n)}\frac{z^n}{n!}+\frac{1}{2\pi i}J,$$

where J denotes the integral along the remainder of C. We shall now show that J tends to zero as $N \to \infty$.

We find it convenient to write

$$J = \int_{-iN}^{-iN+N+\frac{1}{2}} + \int_{N+\frac{1}{2}-iN}^{N+\frac{1}{2}+iN} - \int_{iN}^{iN+N+\frac{1}{2}}$$

$$= J_1+J_2-J_3, \text{ say,}$$

and to consider J_1, J_2, J_3 separately.

Now, when $|s|$ is large and $|\arg s| < \pi$,

$$\frac{\Gamma(a+s)\Gamma(b+s)}{\Gamma(c+s)\Gamma(1+s)} = s^{\alpha+i\beta}[1+o(1)],$$

where $\alpha+i\beta = a+b-c-1$, and so

$$\left|\frac{\Gamma(a+s)\Gamma(b+s)}{\Gamma(c+s)\Gamma(1+s)}\right| = |s|^{\alpha}e^{-\beta \arg s}[1+o(1)].$$

Hence, in J_1, J_2, J_3, we have

$$\left|\frac{\Gamma(a+s)\Gamma(b+s)}{\Gamma(c+s)\Gamma(1+s)}\right| < AN^{\alpha},$$

where A is a constant, independent of N.

But in J_1, $s = \sigma - iN$, so that, when N is large,

$$|\Gamma(-s)\Gamma(1+s)| = \frac{2\pi}{|e^{\pi(N+\sigma i)} - e^{-\pi(N+\sigma i)}|} < 4\pi e^{-\pi N},$$

$$|(-z)^s| = |z|^\sigma e^{N \arg(-z)} < |z|^\sigma e^{(\pi-\epsilon)N}.$$

These inequalities give immediately

$$|J_1| < 4\pi A N^\alpha e^{-\epsilon N} \int_0^{N+\frac{1}{2}} |z|^\sigma \, d\sigma < 2(2N+1)\pi A N^\alpha e^{-\epsilon N},$$

since $|z| < 1$; this implies that J_1 tends to zero as N tends to infinity. In a similar manner we prove that J_3 tends to zero.

In J_2, however, we have $s = N+\frac{1}{2}+it$, where $-N \leqslant t \leqslant N$, and so

$$|\Gamma(-s)\Gamma(1+s)| = \frac{\pi}{|\sin\pi(N+\frac{1}{2}+it)|} = \frac{\pi}{|\cosh\pi t|} < 2\pi e^{-\pi|t|},$$

and

$$|(-z)^s| = |z|^{N+\frac{1}{2}} e^{-t \arg(-z)}.$$

It follows that

$$|J_2| < 2\pi A N^\alpha |z|^{N+\frac{1}{2}} \int_{-N}^{N} e^{-\pi|t|-t\arg(-z)} \, dt$$

$$< 2\pi A N^\alpha |z|^{N+\frac{1}{2}} \int_{-N}^{N} e^{-\epsilon|t|} \, dt$$

$$< 4\pi A N^\alpha |z|^{N+\frac{1}{2}}/\epsilon.$$

But since $|z| < 1$, this implies that J_2 tends to zero as N tends to infinity.

We have thus shown that

$$\frac{1}{2\pi i} \int_{-Ni}^{Ni} \frac{\Gamma(a+s)\Gamma(b+s)\Gamma(-s)}{\Gamma(c+s)} (-z)^s \, ds -$$

$$- \sum_{n=0}^{N} \frac{\Gamma(a+n)\Gamma(b+n)}{\Gamma(c+n)} \frac{z^n}{n!} \to 0$$

as $N \to \infty$, so that,† when $|z| < 1$ and $|\arg(-z)| < \pi$,

$$\frac{\Gamma(a)\Gamma(b)}{\Gamma(c)} F(a,b;c;z) = \frac{1}{2\pi i} \int_{-\infty i}^{\infty i} \frac{\Gamma(a+s)\Gamma(b+s)\Gamma(-s)}{\Gamma(c+s)} (-z)^s \, ds.$$

† That the integral on the right-hand side actually converges and is not a Cauchy principal value, will be easily proved by the reader.

Finally, we show that *the integral*

$$\frac{1}{2\pi i} \int_{-\infty i}^{\infty i} \frac{\Gamma(a+s)\Gamma(b+s)\Gamma(-s)}{\Gamma(c+s)}(-z)^s\, ds$$

represents an analytic function, regular in the z-plane supposed cut along the real axis from 0 to ∞, and so provides the analytical continuation of

$$\frac{\Gamma(a)\Gamma(b)}{\Gamma(c)} F(a,b;c;z)$$

all over this cut plane.

For in any closed domain of the cut plane, there holds an inequality $|\arg(-z)| \leqslant \pi-\epsilon$, where ϵ is a positive constant. It easily follows that, if $s = it$ where t is real and $|t|$ large, then

$$\left| \frac{\Gamma(a+s)\Gamma(b+s)\Gamma(-s)}{\Gamma(c+s)}(-z)^s \right| < K|t|^\alpha e^{-\epsilon|t|},$$

where K is independent of z and t. This implies that Barnes's integral converges uniformly in the closed domain and so represents a regular analytic function. As the value of the integral has been shown to be $\Gamma(a)\Gamma(b)F(a,b;c;z)/\Gamma(c)$ when $|z| < 1$, the result stated follows immediately.

10.41. The behaviour of $F(a,b;c;z)$ near the point at infinity

By an argument similar to that of § 10.4, it can be shown without much difficulty that, if m is a positive integer,

$$\frac{1}{2\pi i} \int_{-\infty i}^{\infty i} \frac{\Gamma(a+s)\Gamma(b+s)\Gamma(-s)}{\Gamma(c+s)}(-z)^s\, ds$$

$$= \frac{1}{2\pi i} \int_{-m-\infty i}^{-m+\infty i} \frac{\Gamma(a+s)\Gamma(b+s)\Gamma(-s)}{\Gamma(c+s)}(-z)^s\, ds +$$

$$+ \sum_{n=0}^{p} (\text{residue at } s = -a-n) + \sum_{n=0}^{q} (\text{residue at } s = -b-n),$$

where p and q are integers, not exceeding m, which tend to infinity with m. The path of integration in the second integral is obtained by translating that of the first integral a distance m to the left. If a or b is a positive integer, the new contour is

dented so that the pole, which would otherwise lie on it, lies
its left.

Now the residue at $s = -a-n$ is

$$(-1)^n \frac{\Gamma(a+n)\Gamma(b-a-n)}{\Gamma(1+n)\Gamma(c-a-n)}(-z)^{-a-n}$$

$$= (-z)^{-a}\frac{\Gamma(a+n)\Gamma(1+a-c+n)}{\Gamma(1+n)\Gamma(1+a-b+n)}\frac{\sin \pi(a+n-c)}{\sin \pi(a+n-b)}z^{-n}$$

$$= \frac{\sin \pi(a-c)}{\sin \pi(a-b)}(-z)^{-a}\frac{\Gamma(a+n)\Gamma(1+a-c+n)}{\Gamma(1+n)\Gamma(1+a-b+n)}z^{-n},$$

here, as usual, $|\arg(-z)| < \pi$. A similar result holds at
$= -b-n$.

Hence we have

$$\frac{\Gamma(a)\Gamma(b)}{\Gamma(c)}F(a,b;c;z)-I$$

$$= \frac{\sin \pi(a-c)}{\sin \pi(a-b)}(-z)^{-a}\sum_{n=0}^{p}\frac{\Gamma(a+n)\Gamma(1+a-c+n)}{\Gamma(1+a-b+n)}\frac{z^{-n}}{n!}+$$

$$+\frac{\sin \pi(b-c)}{\sin \pi(b-a)}(-z)^{-b}\sum_{n=0}^{q}\frac{\Gamma(b+n)\Gamma(1+b-c+n)}{\Gamma(1+b-a+n)}\frac{z^{-n}}{n!},$$

where

$$I = \frac{1}{2\pi i}\int_{-m-\infty i}^{-m+\infty i}\frac{\Gamma(a+s)\Gamma(b+s)\Gamma(-s)}{\Gamma(c+s)}(-z)^s\,ds$$

$$= -\frac{1}{2\pi i}z^{-m}\int_{-\infty i}^{\infty i}\frac{\Gamma(a-m+s)\Gamma(b-m+s)}{\Gamma(c-m+s)\Gamma(1-m+s)}\frac{\pi}{\sin \pi s}(-z)^s\,ds$$

$$= -z^{-m}J, \text{ say.}$$

But when $|\arg(-z)| \leqslant \pi-\epsilon$ where $\epsilon > 0$, J is a bounded func-
ion of m and z; hence $I \to 0$ as $m \to \infty$ provided that $|z| > 1$.

We have thus shown that, when z lies in the part of the cut
plane for which $|z| > 1$,

$$\frac{\Gamma(a)\Gamma(b)}{\Gamma(c)}F(a,b;c;z)$$

$$= \frac{\Gamma(a)\Gamma(b-a)}{\Gamma(c-a)}(-z)^{-a}F(a,1+a-c;1+a-b;z^{-1})+$$

$$+\frac{\Gamma(b)\Gamma(a-b)}{\Gamma(c-b)}(-z)^{-b}F(b,1+b-c;1+b-a;z^{-1}).$$

This equation provides the analytical continuation of $F(a,b;c;z)$ outside its circle of convergence and shows that the function so defined possesses a branch-point at infinity.

We have now proved that the function $F(a,b;c;z)$ defined by the power series

$$\frac{\Gamma(c)}{\Gamma(a)\Gamma(b)} \sum_{n=0}^{\infty} \frac{\Gamma(a+n)\Gamma(b+n)}{\Gamma(c+n)} \frac{z^n}{n!}$$

when $|z| < 1$, and defined by analytical continuation when $|z| \geqslant 1$, is a one-valued analytic function, regular in the whole plane supposed cut along the real axis from 1 to $+\infty$.

10.5. The relations between contiguous hypergeometric functions

Let us denote by $P(z)$ a solution of a second-order linear differential equation with three regular singularities. If λ and μ are any two exponents of this differential equation, the function $P_{\lambda+1,\mu-1}(z)$, obtained by replacing λ and μ in $P(z)$ by $\lambda+1$ and $\mu-1$ respectively, is said to be contiguous to $P(z)$. Since $P(z)$ has two exponents at each of its singularities, there are thirty functions contiguous to $P(z)$. Riemann† proved that the function $P(z)$ and any two functions contiguous to it are connected by a linear relation whose coefficients are polynomials in z. The recurrence formulae satisfied by the Legendre functions are particular cases of this general theorem.

Now if we transform $P(z)$ and its contiguous functions to the hypergeometric form

$$P \left\{ \begin{array}{cccc} 0 & \infty & 1 & \\ 0 & a & 0 & z \\ 1-c & b & c-a-b & \end{array} \right\},$$

as in § 10.21, we find that Riemann's theorem is a consequence of an earlier one due to Gauss. According to Gauss, the function $F(a',b';c';z)$ is contiguous to $F(a,b;c;z)$ if it is obtained by increasing or decreasing one and only one of the parameters a, b, c by unity. There are, then, six hypergeometric functions contiguous to $F(a,b;c;z)$, and these may be conveniently denoted by $F_{a+}, F_{a-}, F_{b+}, F_{b-}, F_{c+}, F_{c-}$ in an obvious notation.

† *Abh. d. Ges. d. Wiss. zu Göttingen (Math. Klasse)*, **7** (1857), 1–24.

Gauss† showed that, *between $F(a, b; c; z)$ and any two hypergeometric functions contiguous to it, there exists a linear relation with polynomial coefficients.* There will then be fifteen such linear relations.

The simplest method of proof consists in determining the required linear relation when $|z| < 1$ from the series definition of the hypergeometric function, and deducing the result in general by analytical continuation.

For example,

$$(a-b)\frac{\Gamma(a)\Gamma(b)}{\Gamma(c)} F(a, b; c; z)$$

$$= (a-b) \sum_{n=0}^{\infty} \frac{\Gamma(a+n)\Gamma(b+n)}{\Gamma(c+n)} \frac{z^n}{n!}$$

$$= \sum_{n=0}^{\infty} \frac{\Gamma(a+n+1)\Gamma(b+n)}{\Gamma(c+n)} \frac{z^n}{n!} - \sum_{n=0}^{\infty} \frac{\Gamma(a+n)\Gamma(b+n+1)}{\Gamma(c+n)} \frac{z^n}{n!}$$

$$= \frac{\Gamma(a)\Gamma(b)}{\Gamma(c)} \{aF_{a+} - bF_{b+}\}.$$

Thus the equation

$$(a-b)F = aF_{a+} - bF_{b+}$$

holds when $|z| < 1$, and hence generally.

10.6. The generalized hypergeometric function

If we attempt to solve the generalized hypergeometric equation

$$\vartheta(\vartheta+\rho_1-1)(\vartheta+\rho_2-1)\ldots(\vartheta+\rho_q-1)w$$
$$= z(\vartheta+\alpha_1)(\vartheta+\alpha_2)\ldots(\vartheta+\alpha_p)w$$

by a series of the form $z^\gamma \sum_{n=0}^{\infty} c_n z^n$, we find that

$$w = z^\gamma \sum_{n=0}^{\infty} \frac{\Gamma(\gamma+\alpha_1+n)\Gamma(\gamma+\alpha_2+n)\ldots\Gamma(\gamma+\alpha_p+n)}{\Gamma(\gamma+\rho_1+n)\Gamma(\gamma+\rho_2+n)\ldots\Gamma(\gamma+\rho_q+n)} \frac{z^n}{n!}$$

provides a formal solution when γ is a root of the equation

$$\gamma(\gamma+\rho_1-1)(\gamma+\rho_2-1)\ldots(\gamma+\rho_q-1) = 0.$$

Apart from the case when the series terminates and so represents a polynomial multiplied by z^γ, this formal series solution will be valid only within its circle of convergence. Now the radius of convergence of the series is 0, 1, or ∞ according as $p-1 >$, $=$, or $< q$. If $p-1 > q$, the formal solution breaks down completely. When $p-1 \leqslant q$, we obtain $q+1$ solutions, provided that none of the coefficients becomes infinite or indeterminate. If $p-1 < q$, each solution is an integral function, multiplied, possibly, by a power of z, and so is valid all over the z-plane. But when $p-1 = q$, the series solutions are valid only within the circle $|z| = 1$ and must be defined outside this circle by analytical continuation.

The solution of exponent zero at the origin is usually denoted by $_pF_q(\alpha_1, \alpha_2, ..., \alpha_p; \rho_1, \rho_2, ..., \rho_q; z)$, where

$$\frac{\Gamma(\alpha_1)\Gamma(\alpha_2)...\Gamma(\alpha_p)}{\Gamma(\rho_1)\Gamma(\rho_2)...\Gamma(\rho_q)}\,_pF_q(\alpha_1, \alpha_2, ..., \alpha_p; \rho_1, \rho_2, ..., \rho_q; z)$$

$$= \sum_{n=0}^{\infty} \frac{\Gamma(\alpha_1+n)\Gamma(\alpha_2+n)...\Gamma(\alpha_p+n)}{\Gamma(\rho_1+n)\Gamma(\rho_2+n)...\Gamma(\rho_q+n)} \frac{z^n}{n!}.$$

In this notation, the ordinary hypergeometric function is $_2F_1(a, b; c; z)$.

In dealing with asymptotic expansions we shall find it convenient to use this notation when $p-1 > q$, even though the series diverges.

10.61. The function $_1F_1(\alpha; \rho; z)$

The function $_1F_1(\alpha; \rho; z)$ satisfies the differential equation

$$\vartheta(\vartheta+\rho-1)w = z(\vartheta+\alpha)w.$$

If we write this in the form

$$z\frac{d^2w}{dz^2} + (\rho-z)\frac{dw}{dz} - \alpha w = 0,$$

we see that it has an irregular singularity at infinity and a regular singularity of exponents 0 and $1-\rho$ at the origin. When ρ is not an integer, two linearly independent solutions of this equation are $_1F_1(\alpha; \rho; z)$ and $z^{1-\rho}\,_1F_1(\alpha-\rho+1; 2-\rho; z)$; these are valid all over the z-plane, since $_1F_1$ is an integral function.

It is easily shown that

$$_1F_1(\alpha; \rho; z) = \lim_{\beta \to \infty} F(\alpha, \beta; \rho; z/\beta),$$

so that the irregular singularity at infinity arises from the 'confluence' of the singularities at β and infinity of the equation satisfied by $F(\alpha,\beta;\rho;z/\beta)$. Many of the properties of $_1F_1(\alpha;\rho;z)$, which is usually called a confluent hypergeometric function, can be obtained by this limiting process, though a rigorous proof is often difficult. But since a direct proof by the methods of this chapter is generally quite straightforward, the most important formulae and certain deductions from them are given as exercises for the reader.

Example 1. Prove that, when $\mathrm{Rl}\,\alpha > 0$ and $\mathrm{Rl}(\rho-\alpha) > 0$,

$$\Gamma(\alpha)\Gamma(\rho-\alpha)_1F_1(\alpha;\rho;z) = \Gamma(\rho)\int_0^1 e^{zt}t^{\alpha-1}(1-t)^{\rho-\alpha-1}\,dt,$$

where $t^{\alpha-1}$ and $(1-t)^{\rho-\alpha-1}$ have their principal values.

Example 2. Prove, by a transformation of the differential equation or otherwise, that

$$_1F_1(\alpha;\rho;z) = e^z {}_1F_1(\rho-\alpha;\rho;-z),$$

provided that ρ is not a negative integer or zero.† (Kummer's‡ first transformation.)

Example 3. Show that the function $w = {}_0F_1(\rho;z)$ satisfies the equation

$$z\frac{d^2w}{dz^2} + \rho\frac{dw}{dz} - w = 0.$$

Hence show that

$$_1F_1(\alpha;2\alpha;2z) = e^z {}_0F_1(\alpha+\tfrac{1}{2};\tfrac{1}{4}z^2),$$

provided that 2α is not a negative integer or zero. (Kummer's second transformation.)

Example 4. Prove that, when $|\arg(-z)| < \tfrac{1}{2}\pi$ and α is not a negative integer or zero,

$$\Gamma(\alpha)_1F_1(\alpha;\rho;z) = \frac{\Gamma(\rho)}{2\pi i}\int_{-\infty i}^{\infty i} \frac{\Gamma(\alpha+s)}{\Gamma(\rho+s)}\Gamma(-s)(-z)^s\,ds,$$

where the path of integration is the imaginary axis, modified, if necessary, by loops to make the negative poles lie to its left and the positive ones to its right.§ (BARNES.)

Example 5. Show that, when $|\arg z| < \tfrac{1}{2}\pi$,

$$z^n e^{-z} = \frac{1}{2\pi i}\int_{-\infty i}^{\infty i} \Gamma(n-s)z^s\,ds.$$

Deduce Kummer's first transformation. (BARNES.)

---

† For a discussion of the case when ρ is a negative integer, see Watson, *Bessel Functions* (1922), § 4.42.   ‡ *Journal für Math.* **15** (1836), 138–41.

§ In proving this result, it is necessary to use the asymptotic formula of § 9.55.

Example 6. Prove that, when $|\arg z| < \tfrac{3}{2}\pi$ and ρ is not an integer,

$$\frac{1}{2\pi i} \int_{-\infty i}^{\infty i} \Gamma(-s)\Gamma(1-\rho-s)\Gamma(\alpha+s)z^s\, ds$$

$$= \Gamma(1-\rho)\Gamma(\alpha){}_1F_1(\alpha;\rho;z) + \Gamma(\rho-1)\Gamma(1+\alpha-\rho)z^{1-\rho}{}_1F_1(1+\alpha-\rho;2-\rho;z)$$

provided that the right-hand side exists. The contour is the imaginary axis, modified, if necessary, by loops to make the positive poles lie to its right and the negative poles to its left. (BARNES.)

10.62. An asymptotic expansion

It is possible to obtain an asymptotic expansion of ${}_1F_1(\alpha;\rho;z)$ when $|z|$ is large and $\mathrm{Rl}\, z < 0$ by applying the method of § 10.41 to the integral

$$\frac{\Gamma(\alpha)}{\Gamma(\rho)}{}_1F_1(\alpha;\rho;z) = \frac{1}{2\pi i}\int_{-\infty i}^{\infty i} \frac{\Gamma(\alpha+s)}{\Gamma(\rho+s)}\Gamma(-s)(-z)^s\, ds,$$

and then deducing the corresponding expansion when $\mathrm{Rl}\, z > 0$ by the aid of Kummer's first transformation. If, however, we use the result of Ex. 6 of the previous section, namely that, when $|\arg z| \leqslant \tfrac{3}{2}\pi - \epsilon < \tfrac{3}{2}\pi$,

$$\frac{1}{2\pi i} \int_{-\infty i}^{\infty i} \Gamma(-s)\Gamma(1-\rho-s)\Gamma(\alpha+s)z^s\, ds$$

$$= \Gamma(1-\rho)\Gamma(\alpha){}_1F_1(\alpha;\rho;z) +$$
$$+ \Gamma(\rho-1)\Gamma(1+\alpha-\rho)z^{1-\rho}{}_1F_1(1+\alpha-\rho;2-\rho;z),$$

we can determine the required asymptotic expansion over a much wider range of values of $\arg z$.

Let us consider,[†] then, the integral

$$I = \frac{1}{2\pi i}\int_C \Gamma(-s)\Gamma(1-\rho-s)\Gamma(\alpha+s)z^s\, ds,$$

where C is the rectangle with vertices at iM, $-K+iM$, $-K-iN$, $-iN$, modified in the following manner. In the first place, the right-hand side of the contour is provided with loops, if necessary, so that the positive poles of the integrand lie to its right and the negative ones to its left. Secondly, we take

---

† The analysis which follows is a slightly modified form of the work of Barnes, *Cambridge Phil. Trans.* **20** (1904–8), 259–61.

$K - \mathrm{Rl}\,\alpha = m$, a positive integer, and indent the left-hand side so that the pole $-\alpha - m$ lies within the contour.

By Cauchy's theory of residues, we have

$$I = \text{sum of residues of integrand at poles } -\alpha - n \text{ within } C$$

$$= z^{-\alpha} \sum_{n=0}^{m} \frac{\Gamma(\alpha+n)\Gamma(1+\alpha-\rho+n)}{n!} \left(-\frac{1}{z}\right)^{n}.$$

If we can show that the integrals along the sides parallel to the real axis tend to zero as M and N tend to infinity, it will follow that

$$\frac{1}{2\pi i} \int_{-\infty i}^{\infty i} \Gamma(-s)\Gamma(1-\rho-s)\Gamma(\alpha+s)z^{s}\, ds$$

$$= z^{-\alpha} \sum_{n=0}^{m} \frac{\Gamma(\alpha+n)\Gamma(1+\alpha-\rho+n)}{n!} \left(-\frac{1}{z}\right)^{n} +$$

$$+ \frac{1}{2\pi i} \int_{-K-\infty i}^{-K+\infty i} \Gamma(-s)\Gamma(1-\rho-s)\Gamma(\alpha+s)z^{s}\, ds.$$

Now on the upper side of the rectangle C, we have $s = \sigma + iM$ where $-K \leqslant \sigma \leqslant 0$. K being kept fixed, it follows from the formula of § 9.55 that, if M is large and s lies on this side of C, then

$$|\Gamma(-s)\Gamma(1-\rho-s)\Gamma(\alpha+s)z^{s}|$$

$$\sim (2\pi)^{3/2} e^{-\pi \operatorname{Im}(\rho+\alpha)/2} e^{-M(\arg z + 3\pi/2)} M^{\mathrm{Rl}(\alpha-\rho-1/2)} |z/M|^{\sigma}$$

$$\leqslant (2\pi)^{3/2} e^{-\pi \operatorname{Im}(\rho+\alpha)/2} e^{-\epsilon M} M^{\mathrm{Rl}(\alpha-\rho-1/2)} |z/M|^{\sigma},$$

since $|\arg z| \leqslant \frac{3}{2}\pi - \epsilon < \frac{3}{2}\pi$. Hence the absolute value of the integral along the upper side of C does not exceed

$$A M^{\mathrm{Rl}(\alpha-\rho-1/2)} e^{-\epsilon M} \int_{-K}^{0} |z/M|^{\sigma}\, d\sigma,$$

where A is independent of M and z. As this expression evidently tends to zero as $M \to \infty$, so also does the integral along the upper side of C. In a similar way it can be shown that the integral along the lower side of C tends to zero as $N \to \infty$.

We have thus proved that, when $|\arg z| < \frac{3}{2}\pi$,

$$\frac{1}{2\pi i} \int_{-\infty i}^{\infty i} \Gamma(-s)\Gamma(1-\rho-s)\Gamma(\alpha+s)z^s\, ds$$

$$= z^{-\alpha} \sum_{n=0}^{m} \frac{\Gamma(\alpha+n)\Gamma(1+\alpha-\rho+n)}{n!\,(-z)^n} + z^{-\alpha-m}J,$$

where

$$J = \frac{z^{\alpha+m}}{2\pi i} \int_{-\alpha-m-\infty i}^{-\alpha-m+\infty i} \Gamma(-s)\Gamma(1-\rho-s)\Gamma(\alpha+s)z^s\, ds$$

$$= \frac{1}{2\pi i} \int_{-\infty i}^{\infty i} \Gamma(\alpha+m-s)\Gamma(1+\alpha-\rho+m-s)\Gamma(s-m)z^s\, ds$$

$$= O(1)$$

when $|z|$ is large. Hence we see that

$$\Gamma(\alpha)\Gamma(1-\rho)\,_1F_1(\alpha;\rho;z)+$$

$$+\Gamma(1+\alpha-\rho)\Gamma(\rho-1)z^{1-\rho}\,_1F_1(1+\alpha-\rho;2-\rho;z)$$

$$\sim \Gamma(\alpha)\Gamma(1+\alpha-\rho)z^{-\alpha}\,_2F_0\left(\alpha,1+\alpha-\rho;-\frac{1}{z}\right),$$

the series on the right-hand side being an asymptotic expansion valid when $|z|$ is large and $|\arg z| < \frac{3}{2}\pi$; for the error caused by terminating the series at the mth term is

$$z^{-\alpha-m}\left[\frac{\Gamma(\alpha+m)\Gamma(1+\alpha-\rho+m)}{(-1)^m m!} + J\right] = O(z^{-\alpha-m}),$$

which is of the order of the first term omitted.

10.63. The asymptotic expansion of $_1F_1(\alpha;\rho;z)$

If we write

$$\Gamma(\alpha)\Gamma(1-\rho)\,_1F_1(\alpha;\rho;z) = P,$$

$$\Gamma(1+\alpha-\rho)\Gamma(\rho-1)\,_1F_1(1+\alpha-\rho;2-\rho;z) = Q,$$

$$\Gamma(\alpha)\Gamma(1+\alpha-\rho)\,_2F_0(\alpha,1+\alpha-\rho;-z^{-1}) = R,$$

the result of the previous section is that, when $|\arg z| < \frac{3}{2}\pi$,

$$P + z^{1-\rho}Q \sim z^{-\alpha}R$$

for large values of $|z|$. In particular, this holds when

$$\tfrac{1}{2}\pi < \arg z \leqslant \pi.$$

But when $\frac{1}{2}\pi < \arg z \leqslant \pi$, we have $-\frac{3}{2}\pi < \arg(ze^{-2\pi i}) \leqslant -\pi$, and so this asymptotic formula holds when z is replaced by $ze^{-2\pi i}$. This gives

$$P + z^{1-\rho}e^{-2\pi i(1-\rho)}Q \sim z^{-\alpha}e^{2\pi i\alpha}R,$$

since P, Q, R are unaltered. Eliminating Q, we find that

$$P \sin \pi\rho \sim e^{\pi\alpha i}z^{-\alpha}R \sin \pi(\rho-\alpha).$$

In a similar manner it can be shown that, when

$$-\pi \leqslant \arg z < -\tfrac{1}{2}\pi,$$

$$P \sin \pi\rho \sim e^{-\pi\alpha i}z^{-\alpha}R \sin \pi(\rho-\alpha)$$

for large values of $|z|$. These two results can be combined into the single formula

$$P \sin \pi\rho \sim (-z)^{-\alpha}R \sin \pi(\rho-\alpha)$$

valid when $\mathrm{Rl}\, z < 0$, provided that $(-z)^{-\alpha}$ has its principal value.

We have thus proved that, when $\mathrm{Rl}\, z < 0$,

$$_1F_1(\alpha;\rho;z) \sim \frac{\Gamma(\rho)}{\Gamma(\rho-\alpha)}(-z)^{-\alpha}\,_2F_0(\alpha, 1+\alpha-\rho; -z^{-1}).$$

From this we deduce, by Kummer's first transformation (§ 10.61, Ex. 2), that when $\mathrm{Rl}\, z > 0$,

$$_1F_1(\alpha;\rho;z) \sim \frac{\Gamma(\rho)e^z}{\Gamma(\alpha)z^{\rho-\alpha}}\,_2F_0(\rho-\alpha, 1-\alpha; z^{-1}),$$

provided that $z^{\rho-\alpha}$ has its principal value.

REFERENCES

H. BATEMAN, *Partial Differential Equations of Mathematical Physics* (Cambridge, 1932).

A. R. FORSYTH, *Theory of Differential Equations*, **4** (Cambridge, 1902).

E. L. INCE, *Ordinary Differential Equations* (London, 1927).

F. KLEIN, *Vorlesungen über die hypergeometrische Funktion* (Berlin, 1933).

G. SZEGÖ, *Orthogonal Polynomials* (New York, 1939).

E. T. WHITTAKER and G. N. WATSON, *Modern Analysis* (Cambridge, 1920).

MISCELLANEOUS EXAMPLES

1. Show that the hypergeometric series $F(a, b; c; -1)$ is convergent when $\mathrm{Rl}(1+c-a-b) > 0$.

Prove that, when $\mathrm{Rl}\, b < 1$,

$$F(a, b; a-b+1; -1) = \frac{\Gamma(a-b+1)\Gamma(\tfrac{1}{2})}{2^a \Gamma(\tfrac{1}{2}a-b+1)\Gamma(\tfrac{1}{2}a+\tfrac{1}{2})}. \quad \text{(Kummer.)}$$

2. Prove that, when z is not a negative integer or zero,

$$\frac{\Gamma(z)\Gamma(\tfrac{1}{2})}{\Gamma(z+\tfrac{1}{2})} = \sum_{n=0}^{\infty} \frac{(2n)!}{2^{2n} n!\, n!} \frac{1}{z+n}.$$

3. Denoting by $[z]^\alpha$ the ratio $\Gamma(1+z)/\Gamma(1+z-\alpha)$, show that, if $\mathrm{Rl}(z+h+1) > 0$,

$$[z+h]^\alpha = C_0[z]^\alpha + C_1[z]^{\alpha-1}[h]^1 + C_2[z]^{\alpha-2}[h]^2 + \cdots,$$

where C_0, C_1, $C_2, \ldots$ are the coefficients in the expansion of $(1+h)^\alpha$ in powers of h.

4. Show that, when $\mathrm{Rl}\, z > 0$,

$$\frac{\Gamma(z)\sqrt{z}}{\Gamma(z+\tfrac{1}{2})}$$
$$= \sqrt{\left\{ 1 + \frac{1^2}{4(z+1)} + \frac{1^2 \cdot 3^2}{4 \cdot 8 \cdot (z+1)(z+2)} + \frac{1^2 \cdot 3^2 \cdot 5^2}{4 \cdot 8 \cdot 12 \cdot (z+1)(z+2)(z+3)} + \cdots \right\}}.$$

5. If the two sums

$$|a_1 + a_2 + \ldots + a_n|, \qquad |a_1| + |a_2| + \ldots + |a_n|$$

both tend to infinity with n in such a way that

$$|a_1| + |a_2| + \ldots + |a_n| < K|a_1 + a_2 + \ldots + a_n|,$$

where K is independent of n, prove that

$$\lim_{n \to \infty} \frac{b_1 + b_2 + \ldots + b_n}{a_1 + a_2 + \ldots + a_n} = \lim_{n \to \infty} \frac{b_n}{a_n},$$

provided that the right-hand limit exists. (Jensen.)

6. Prove that $a_n = \Gamma(\alpha+n)/n!$ satisfies the conditions of Ex. 5 only when $\mathrm{Rl}\, \alpha > 0$ or when $\alpha = 0$.

Deduce that, if s_n denotes the sum of the first n terms of the series $F(a, b; c; 1)$, then

$$s_n \sim \frac{\Gamma(c) n^{a+b-c}}{\Gamma(a)\Gamma(b)(a+b-c)}$$

when $\mathrm{Rl}(c-a-b) < 0$, and

$$s_n \sim \frac{\Gamma(a+b)}{\Gamma(a)\Gamma(b)} \log n$$

when $c = a+b$. (M. J. M. Hill.†)

† *Proc. London Math. Soc.* (2), **5** (1907), 335; **6** (1908), 339. The proof indicated in this exercise is a modification of one due to Bromwich, ibid. **7** (1909), 101.

7. If the series $\sum a_n z^n$, $\sum b_n z^n$ converge when $|z| < 1$, and if, moreover, the coefficients a_n satisfy the conditions that (i) $\sum |a_n|$ is divergent, (ii) $\sum |a_n| x^n < K \left| \sum a_n x^n \right|$ when $0 < x < 1$, the constant K being independent of x, prove that

$$\lim_{x \to 1-0} \frac{\sum b_n x^n}{\sum a_n x^n} = \lim_{n \to \infty} \frac{b_n}{a_n},$$

provided that the right-hand limit exists.†

8. Show that, if $\mathrm{Rl}(c-a-b) < 0$,

$$\lim_{x \to 1-0} \frac{F(a,b;c;x)}{(1-x)^{c-a-b}} = \frac{\Gamma(c)\Gamma(a+b-c)}{\Gamma(a)\Gamma(b)}.$$

Prove also that $\qquad \lim\limits_{x \to 1-0} \dfrac{F(a,b;a+b;x)}{\log[1/(1-x)]} = \dfrac{\Gamma(a+b)}{\Gamma(a)\Gamma(b)}.$ (GAUSS.)

9. Show that, when $\mathrm{Rl}(c-a-b) < 0$,

$$\lim_{x \to 1-0} \Bigg[F(a,b;c;x) -$$

$$- \sum_{n=0}^{k} (-1)^n \frac{\Gamma(a+b-c-n)\Gamma(c-a+n)\Gamma(c-b+n)\Gamma(c)}{n!\,\Gamma(c-a)\Gamma(c-b)\Gamma(a)\Gamma(b)} (1-x)^{n+c-a-b} \Bigg]$$

$$= \frac{\Gamma(c-a-b)\Gamma(c)}{\Gamma(c-a)\Gamma(c-b)},$$

k being the integer such that $k \leqslant \mathrm{Rl}(a+b-c) < k+1$. (HARDY.)

10. Determine the fifteen relations with polynomial coefficients which connect $F(a,b;c;z)$ with a pair of contiguous hypergeometric functions. (GAUSS.)

11. Show that the complete solution, valid when $|z-\tfrac{1}{2}| < \tfrac{1}{2}$, of the equation

$$z(1-z)\frac{d^2w}{dz^2} + \tfrac{1}{2}(\alpha+\beta+1)(1-2z)\frac{dw}{dz} - \alpha\beta w = 0$$

is

$$w = A\,F\{\tfrac{1}{2}\alpha, \tfrac{1}{2}\beta; \tfrac{1}{2}; (1-2z)^2\} + B(1-2z)F\{\tfrac{1}{2}(\alpha+1), \tfrac{1}{2}(\beta+1); \tfrac{3}{2}; (1-2z)^2\},$$

where A and B are arbitrary constants.

12. Show that, if $\mathrm{Rl}(a-b) > 0$,

$$\frac{\Gamma(c+\lambda-b)}{\Gamma(c+\lambda)} F(a,b;c+\lambda;z) \sim \sum_{0}^{\infty} \frac{k_s\,\Gamma(b+s)}{\Gamma(b)\lambda^{s+b}}$$

when $|\lambda|$ is large and $|\arg\lambda| \leqslant \tfrac{1}{2}\pi$, the coefficients k_s being defined by

$$\sum_{s=0}^{\infty} k_s \tau^{s+b-1} = (1-e^{-\tau})^{b-1} e^{-\tau(c-b)} (1-z+ze^{-\tau})^{-a}.$$

† For an account of this and other generalizations of a well-known theorem of Cesàro, see Pringsheim, *Acta Math.* **28** (1904), 1.

Show also that the asymptotic expansion is valid when $|\arg\lambda| \leqslant \pi-\delta$, where $\delta > 0$, provided that $|1-z^{-1}| \leqslant 1$. (WATSON.†)

13. Deduce from Ex. 12, the asymptotic expansion of
$$F(a+\lambda, b+\lambda; c+\lambda; z).$$

14.‡ Show that, when $|z| < 1$,
$$\Gamma(a)\Gamma(b)F(a,b;\tfrac{1}{2};z) = \int\limits_0^\infty \int\limits_0^\infty e^{-u-v}\cosh 2\sqrt{(uvz)}\, u^{a-1}v^{b-1}\, du\, dv,$$

provided that the real parts of a and b are positive. (WHITTAKER.)

15. Prove that, when $|\arg h| \leqslant \pi-\delta$, where $\delta > 0$,
$$\frac{\Gamma(a)\Gamma(b)}{\Gamma(c)} F(a,b;c;z-h)$$
$$= \frac{1}{2\pi i} \int\limits_{-\infty i}^{\infty i} \frac{\Gamma(-s)\Gamma(a+s)\Gamma(b+s)}{\Gamma(c+s)} F(a+s,b+s;c+s;z)h^s\, ds,$$

provided that $|\arg(1-z)| < \delta$. (WHITTAKER.)

16. Show that, when $0 < \mathrm{Rl}\, s < \mathrm{Rl}\, a \leqslant \mathrm{Rl}\, b$,
$$\frac{\Gamma(s)\Gamma(a-s)\Gamma(b-s)}{\Gamma(c-s)} F(a-s,b-s;c-s;z)$$
$$= \frac{\Gamma(a)\Gamma(b)}{\Gamma(c)} \int\limits_0^\infty F(a,b;c;z-t)t^{s-1}\, dt. \qquad \text{(WHITTAKER.)}$$

17. Show that, if
$$(1-z)^{a+b-c}F(2a,2b;2c;z) = \sum_0^\infty a_n z^n,$$
then
$$F(a,b;c+\tfrac{1}{2};z)F(c-a,c-b;c+\tfrac{1}{2};z) = \frac{\Gamma(c+\tfrac{1}{2})}{\Gamma(c)} \sum_0^\infty a_n \frac{\Gamma(c+n)}{\Gamma(c+n+\tfrac{1}{2})} z^n.$$

18. The Incomplete Gamma Function is defined, when the real part of ν is positive, by the equation
$$\gamma(\nu,z) = \int\limits_0^z e^{-t}t^{\nu-1}\, dt.$$
Show that
$$\nu\gamma(\nu,z) = z^\nu\, {}_1F_1(\nu;\nu+1;-z).$$

---

† *Cambridge Phil. Trans.* **22** (1912–23), 277–308. In this paper, Watson determines the asymptotic expansion of $F(a+\epsilon_1\lambda,\, b+\epsilon_2\lambda;\, c+\epsilon_3\lambda; z)$, where $\epsilon_1, \epsilon_2, \epsilon_3$ take the values 0, 1, or −1 for large values of $|\lambda|$.

‡ The results contained in Exx. 14, 15, 16 were obtained by E. T. Whittaker by applying contact transformations to the solution of differential equations by definite integrals: *Proc. Edinburgh Math. Soc.* (2), **2** (1931), 189–204.

19. Prove that the Error Function

$$\text{Erf}\,z = \int\limits_0^z \exp(-t^2)\,dt$$

is equal to $z\,{}_1F_1(\tfrac{1}{2};\tfrac{3}{2};-z^2)$.

20. The generalized Laguerre polynomial[†] $L_n^{(\alpha)}(z)$ is defined by the equation

$$L_n^{(\alpha)}(z) = \frac{\Gamma(\alpha+1+n)}{n!\,\Gamma(\alpha+1)}\,{}_1F_1(-n;\alpha+1;z),$$

n being a positive integer or zero. Prove that

(i) $L_n^{(\alpha)}(z) = \dfrac{e^z z^{-\alpha}}{n!}\,\dfrac{d^n}{dz^n}\,(e^{-z}z^{n+\alpha})$,

(ii) $L_n^{(\alpha)}(z) = \dfrac{\Gamma(\alpha+1+n)}{n!\,2\pi i}\displaystyle\int\limits_{-\infty}^{(0+)}\left(1-\frac{z}{t}\right)^n e^t\,\dfrac{dt}{t^{\alpha+1}}$.

21. Show that, when $|t| < 1$,

$$\sum_0^\infty t^n L_n^{(\alpha)}(z) = (1-t)^{-\alpha-1}e^{-zt/(1-t)}.$$

22. Prove that the integral

$$\int\limits_0^\infty e^{-x}x^\alpha L_m^{(\alpha)}(x)L_n^{(\alpha)}(x)\,dx$$

converges when $\mathrm{Rl}\,\alpha > -1$ and that it has the value $\Gamma(\alpha+n+1)/n!$ or zero according as the integers m and n are equal or unequal.

Deduce that, if $f(z)$ can be expanded as a series of the form[‡] $\sum_0^\infty c_n L_n^{(\alpha)}(z)$ and term-by-term integration is valid, then

$$c_n = \frac{n!}{\Gamma(n+\alpha+1)}\int\limits_0^\infty e^{-x}x^\alpha f(x)L_n^{(\alpha)}(x)\,dx.$$

23. Show that, if $m+n$ is a positive integer or zero,

$$L_n^{(m)}(z) = \frac{(-1)^m e^z}{n!}\,\frac{d^{m+n}}{dz^{m+n}}\,(e^{-z}z^n).$$

Deduce that $\dfrac{(t-1)^n e^{tz}}{n!} = \displaystyle\sum_{r=-n}^\infty z^r L_n^{(r)}(z)\,\dfrac{t^{n+r}}{(n+r)!}$.   (DERUYTS.)

[†] The polynomial discussed by Laguerre (*Bull. Soc. math. de France*, **7** (1879), 72–81) is obtained by putting $\alpha = 0$. The generalized Laguerre polynomial was introduced by Sonine, *Math. Annalen*, **16** (1880), 1–80 (41–2).

[‡] The question of the convergence of such a series may often be settled by the use of Fejér's asymptotic formula (*Comptes Rendus*, **147** (1908), 1040),

$$L_n^{(\alpha)}(z) = \sqrt{\left(\frac{e^z n^{\alpha-1/2}}{\pi z^{\alpha+1/2}}\right)}\cos\{2\sqrt{(nz)}-(2\alpha+1)\pi/4\}+O(n^{\alpha/2-3/4}),$$

valid when n is large and z finite.

24. Prove that

$$\int_0^\infty e^{-zt} t^\alpha L_n^{(\alpha)}(t)\, dt = \frac{\Gamma(\alpha+n+1)(z-1)^n}{n!\, z^{\alpha+n+1}},$$

provided that the real parts of z and $\alpha+1$ are positive. (SONINE.)

25. Prove that

$$\int_0^1 t^\alpha (1-t)^{\rho-1} L_n^{(\alpha)}(zt)\, dt = \frac{\Gamma(\rho)\Gamma(\alpha+n+1)}{\Gamma(\rho+\alpha+n+1)} L_n^{(\alpha+\rho)}(z),$$

provided that the real parts of ρ and $\alpha+1$ are positive. (KOSHLIAKOV.)

26. Show that

$$L_n^{(\alpha)}(2z) = \Gamma(\alpha+1+n) \sum_{r=0}^n \frac{2^{n-r}(-1)^r}{\Gamma(\alpha+1+n-r)r!} L_{n-r}^{(\alpha)}(z). \quad \text{(B. M. WILSON.)}$$

27. Show that

$$e^{-z} z^{\frac{1}{2}\alpha} L_n^{(\alpha)}(z) = \frac{1}{n!} \int_0^\infty e^{-t} t^{n+\frac{1}{2}\alpha} J_\alpha\{2\sqrt{(zt)}\}\, dt,$$

provided that the real part of $n+\alpha+1$ is positive. Here $J_\alpha(u)$ denotes the Bessel function

$$(\tfrac{1}{2}u)^\alpha \sum_0^\infty \frac{(-\tfrac{1}{4}u^2)^n}{n!\, \Gamma(\alpha+n+1)}.$$

28. Prove that

(i) $L_n^{(\alpha)}(z) - L_{n-1}^{(\alpha)}(z) = L_n^{(\alpha-1)}(z),$

(ii) $\dfrac{d}{dz} L_n^{(\alpha)}(z) = -L_{n-1}^{(\alpha+1)}(z),$

(iii) $n L_n^{(\alpha)}(z) = (2n+\alpha-1-z) L_{n-1}^{(\alpha)}(z) - (n+\alpha-1) L_{n-2}^{(\alpha)}(z).$

Deduce that, if α is not a negative integer,

$$\sum_{r=0}^n \frac{r!}{\Gamma(\alpha+r+1)} L_r^{(\alpha)}(x) L_r^{(\alpha)}(y)$$

$$= \frac{(n+1)!}{\Gamma(n+\alpha+1)(x-y)} \{ L_n^{(\alpha)}(x) L_{n+1}^{(\alpha)}(y) - L_{n+1}^{(\alpha)}(x) L_n^{(\alpha)}(y) \}.$$

29. Show that

$$\sum_{n=0}^\infty t^n L_n^{(\alpha)}(z)/\Gamma(\alpha+n+1) = e^t (zt)^{-\frac{1}{2}\alpha} J_\alpha\{2\sqrt{(zt)}\}.$$

30. Prove that† when $|t| < 1$,

$$\sum_{n=0}^\infty L_n^{(\alpha)}(x) L_n^{(\alpha)}(y) t^n n!/\Gamma(\alpha+n+1) = \frac{(xyt)^{-\frac{1}{2}\alpha}}{1-t} e^{-(x+y)t/(1-t)} I_\alpha\left\{\frac{2\sqrt{(xyt)}}{1-t}\right\},$$

where

$$I_\alpha(u) = (\tfrac{1}{2}u)^\alpha \sum_{n=0}^\infty \frac{(\tfrac{1}{4}u^2)^n}{n!\, \Gamma(\alpha+n+1)}.$$

† See Hardy, *Journal London Math. Soc.* **7** (1932), 138; Watson, ibid. **8** (1933), 189.

31. The Hermite polynomials are defined by the expansion

$$\exp(2tz - t^2) = \sum_{n=0}^{\infty} H_n(z) t^n / n!$$

Prove that

(i) $H_n(z) = (-1)^n \exp z^2 \dfrac{d^n}{dz^n} \exp(-z^2),$

(ii) $H_{2n}(z) = (-1)^n 2^{2n} n! \, L_n^{(-\frac{1}{2})}(z^2),$

(iii) $H_{2n+1}(z) = (-1)^n 2^{2n+1} n! \, z L_n^{(\frac{1}{2})}(z^2).$

32. Show that

(i) $\dfrac{d}{dz} H_n(z) = 2n H_{n-1}(z),$

(ii) $H_{n+1}(z) - 2z H_n(z) + 2n H_{n-1}(z) = 0.$

Deduce that $w = H_n(z)$ is a solution of

$$\frac{d^2 w}{dz^2} - 2z \frac{dw}{dz} + 2nw = 0.$$

33. Show that the value of the integral

$$\int_{-\infty}^{\infty} e^{-x^2} H_m(x) H_n(x) \, dx$$

is $2^n n! \sqrt{\pi}$ or zero according as the integers m and n are equal or unequal.

34. Prove that,† when $|t| < 1$,

$$\sum_{0}^{\infty} H_n(x) H_n(y) \frac{t^n}{2^n n!} = (1 - t^2)^{-1/2} \exp\left\{ \frac{2xyt - (x^2 + y^2) t^2}{1 - t^2} \right\}.$$

† See Watson, loc. cit.

CHAPTER XI

LEGENDRE FUNCTIONS

11.1. Legendre's differential equation

IN the last chapter we discussed the solution of the hyper-geometric equation under the assumption that none of the exponent-differences was an integer or zero. We shall now con-sider in detail an equation of hypergeometric type in which this condition is not satisfied, namely *Legendre's differential equation*

$$(1-z^2)\frac{d^2w}{dz^2} - 2z\frac{dw}{dz} + n(n+1)w = 0,$$

where n is an integer or zero.

This equation, which is of importance in mathematical physics, arises when one tries to find a solution of Laplace's equation
$$\frac{\partial^2 V}{\partial X^2} + \frac{\partial^2 V}{\partial Y^2} + \frac{\partial^2 V}{\partial Z^2} = 0$$

which is a polynomial of degree n in X, Y, and Z. Such a solu-tion is called a solid harmonic of degree n. If we transform this partial differential equation to spherical polar coordinates (r, θ, ϕ) defined by the equations

$$X = r\sin\theta\cos\phi, \qquad Y = r\sin\theta\sin\phi, \qquad Z = r\cos\theta,$$

it becomes

$$\frac{\partial^2 V}{\partial r^2} + \frac{2}{r}\frac{\partial V}{\partial r} + \frac{1}{r^2}\frac{\partial^2 V}{\partial \theta^2} + \frac{\cot\theta}{r^2}\frac{\partial V}{\partial \theta} + \frac{1}{r^2\sin^2\theta}\frac{\partial^2 V}{\partial \phi^2} = 0.$$

It follows that every solid harmonic of degree n is of the form $r^n S_n(\theta, \phi)$, where $S_n(\theta, \phi)$ is a polynomial in $\sin\theta$, $\cos\theta$, $\sin\phi$, $\cos\phi$ and satisfies the partial differential equation

$$\operatorname{cosec}\theta\frac{\partial}{\partial\theta}\left(\sin\theta\frac{\partial S_n}{\partial\theta}\right) + \operatorname{cosec}^2\theta\frac{\partial^2 S_n}{\partial\phi^2} + n(n+1)S_n = 0.$$

$S_n(\theta, \phi)$ is called a spherical surface harmonic of degree n.

In particular, if

$$S_n(\theta, \phi) = f(\theta)\cos m(\phi+\epsilon),$$

where m and ϵ are constants, we find that $w = f(\theta)$ is a solu-tion of

$$\operatorname{cosec}\theta\frac{d}{d\theta}\left(\sin\theta\frac{dw}{d\theta}\right)+\{n(n+1)-m^2\operatorname{cosec}^2\theta\}w=0,$$

or, putting $z=\cos\theta$,

$$(1-z^2)\frac{d^2w}{dz^2}-2z\frac{dw}{dz}+\left\{n(n+1)-\frac{m^2}{1-z^2}\right\}w=0.$$

This differential equation, which reduces to Legendre's equation when $m=0$, is called the *associated Legendre equation*. Its solution is seen, without much difficulty, to be of the form

$$w=P\left\{\begin{matrix}-1 & \infty & 1 & \\ \tfrac{1}{2}m & n+1 & \tfrac{1}{2}m & z \\ -\tfrac{1}{2}m & -n & -\tfrac{1}{2}m & \end{matrix}\right\},$$

in Riemann's notation (§ 10.2).

In the problem of determining solid harmonics of degree n, the parameter m can take only the values 0, 1, 2,..., n, and this is the case of greatest interest since the exponent-differences are then all integers. We shall show that the associated Legendre equation has, in this case, only one solution which is a polynomial in z and $\sqrt{(1-z^2)}$; it is denoted by $P_n^m(z)$ when m is not zero and by $P_n(z)$ when m is zero. It follows from this that there are only $2n+1$ linearly independent spherical harmonics of degree n, namely

$$P_n(\cos\theta),\quad P_n^m(\cos\theta)\cos m\phi,\quad P_n^m(\cos\theta)\sin m\phi,\quad (m=1,2,...,n).$$

Any other spherical harmonic of degree n is a linear combination of harmonics of this set.

In the present chapter, we consider the form of the complete solutions of Legendre's equation and of the associated equation only in the case when m and n are positive integers or zero and m does not exceed n.

11.11. The Legendre polynomials

When n is a positive integer or zero, the point at infinity is a regular singularity of Legendre's differential equation, the exponents there being $n+1$ and $-n$. If we attempt to satisfy the equation by a series of the form

$$w=z^{-c}\{a_0+a_1z^{-1}+a_2z^{-2}+...\},$$

T

we find that the solution of exponent $-n$ is

$$w = Az^n\left\{1 - \frac{n(n-1)}{2(2n-1)}z^{-2} + \frac{n(n-1)(n-2)(n-3)}{2.4(2n-1)(2n-3)}z^{-4} - \ldots\right\} +$$

$$+ Bz^{-n-1}\left\{1 + \frac{(n+1)(n+2)}{2(2n+3)}z^{-2} + \right.$$

$$\left. + \frac{(n+1)(n+2)(n+3)(n+4)}{2.4(2n+3)(2n+5)}z^{-4} + \ldots\right\}$$

$$= Aw_1 + Bw_2$$

say, where A and B are two arbitrary constants. The second constant B arises from the fact that the equation which should determine a_{2n+1} turns out to be an identity. The solution of exponent $n+1$ is found to be

$$w = Cw_2,$$

where C is an arbitrary constant. We have thus found formally two linearly independent solutions of Legendre's equation, viz.

$$w = Aw_1, \qquad w = Cw_2.$$

The first solution Aw_1 is a polynomial in z of degree n and so certainly satisfies Legendre's equation for all values of z. The second solution is a non-terminating series of descending powers of z which converges when $|z| > 1$; the formal processes which made it a solution are thus completely justified. A discussion of the analytical continuation of the second solution within the unit circle is deferred for the moment.

Taking $A = (2n)!/\{2^n(n!)^2\}$, we can write the polynomial solution in the form $w = P_n(z)$, where

$$P_n(z) = \sum_{r=0}^{p} \frac{(-1)^r(2n-2r)!}{2^n r!\,(n-r)!\,(n-2r)!}z^{n-2r},$$

where the integer p is $\frac{1}{2}n$ or $\frac{1}{2}(n-1)$ according as n is even or odd. We call $P_n(z)$ Legendre's polynomial of degree n. In particular,

$$P_0(z) = 1, \quad P_1(z) = z, \quad P_2(z) = \tfrac{1}{2}(3z^2-1), \quad P_3(z) = \tfrac{1}{2}(5z^3-3z).$$

From this definition we deduce that

$$P_n(z) = \sum_{r=0}^{p} \frac{(-1)^r}{2^n r!\,(n-r)!}\frac{d^n}{dz^n}(z^{2n-2r})$$

$$= \frac{1}{2^n n!} \frac{d^n}{dz^n} \sum_{r=0}^{p} \frac{(-1)^r n!}{r!\,(n-r)!} z^{2n-2r}$$

$$= \frac{1}{2^n n!} \frac{d^n}{dz^n} \sum_{r=0}^{n} \frac{(-1)^r n!}{r!\,(n-r)!} z^{2n-2r}$$

and so $$P_n(z) = \frac{1}{2^n n!} \frac{d^n}{dz^n} (z^2-1)^n.$$

This is Rodrigues's formula for Legendre's polynomial.

Using Cauchy's formula for the nth derivative of an analytic function, we obtain from Rodrigues's formula the following contour integral formula, due to Schläfli:

$$P_n(z) = \frac{1}{2\pi i} \int_C \frac{(t^2-1)^n}{2^n(t-z)^{n+1}}\, dt,$$

where C is a closed contour surrounding the point $t = z$.

Example 1. Deduce from Rodrigues's formula that the n zeros of $P_n(z)$ are all real and lie between ± 1.

Example 2. Prove that

$$P_n(z) = \frac{(2n)!}{2^n(n!)^2} z^n F(-\tfrac{1}{2}n, \tfrac{1}{2}-\tfrac{1}{2}n; \tfrac{1}{2}-n; z^{-2}).$$

Example 3. Show that

$$P_n(z) = F(n+1, -n; 1; \tfrac{1}{2}(1-z)).$$

Example 4. Prove that $P_n(z)$ is equal to

$$(-1)^{n/2} \frac{n!}{2^n\{(\tfrac{1}{2}n)!\}^2} F(-\tfrac{1}{2}n, \tfrac{1}{2}(n+1); \tfrac{1}{2}; z^2)$$

or

$$(-1)^{(n-1)/2} \frac{n!}{2^{n-1}\{(\tfrac{1}{2}n-\tfrac{1}{2})!\}^2} z F(-\tfrac{1}{2}n+\tfrac{1}{2}, \tfrac{1}{2}n+1; \tfrac{3}{2}; z^2)$$

according as n is even or odd.

Example 5. Show, by using Rodrigues's formula and integrating by parts, that

$$\int_{-1}^{1} z^k P_n(z)\, dz = 0$$

when $k = 0, 1, 2,..., n-1$. Deduce that

$$\int_{-1}^{1} P_m(z) P_n(z)\, dz = 0$$

when the integers m and n are unequal.

Example 6. Prove that

$$\int_{-1}^{1} z^n P_n(z)\, dz = \frac{2^{n+1}(n!)^2}{(2n+1)!}.$$

Deduce that

$$\int_{-1}^{1} \{P_n(z)\}^2\, dz = \frac{2}{2n+1}.$$

Example 7. Show that a polynomial $f(z)$ of degree n can be expressed in the form

$$f(z) = \sum_{r=0}^{n} a_r P_r(z),$$

where

$$a_r = \frac{2r+1}{2} \int_{-1}^{1} f(z) P_r(z)\, dz.$$

More generally, prove that if $f(z)$ is an analytic function which can be expanded as a series

$$f(z) = \sum_{r=0}^{\infty} a_r P_r(z)$$

which converges uniformly when $-1 \leqslant z \leqslant 1$, the coefficients a_r are given by the above formula.

11.12. Laplace's integral for the Legendre polynomials

We shall now deduce from Schläfli's integral a definite-integral formula for $P_n(z)$, due to Laplace. Let us take as the contour C the circle $|t-z| = \sqrt{|z^2-1|}$. Then on C we have

$$t = z + (z^2-1)^{\frac{1}{2}} e^{i\phi},$$

where ϕ varies from $-\pi$ to π. Evidently it is immaterial which branch of $\sqrt{(z^2-1)}$ is taken.

Making this change of variable, we find that

$$t^2-1 = 2(z^2-1)^{\frac{1}{2}} e^{i\phi}\{z+(z^2-1)^{\frac{1}{2}}\cos\phi\} = 2(t-z)\{z+(z^2-1)^{\frac{1}{2}}\cos\phi\}$$

and hence that

$$P_n(z) = \frac{1}{2\pi} \int_{-\pi}^{\pi} \{z+(z^2-1)^{\frac{1}{2}}\cos\phi\}^n\, d\phi.$$

Since the integrand is an even function of ϕ, it follows that

$$P_n(z) = \frac{1}{\pi} \int_{0}^{\pi} \{z+(z^2-1)^{\frac{1}{2}}\cos\phi\}^n\, d\phi.$$

This formula is known as *Laplace's first integral* for the Legendre polynomial $P_n(z)$.

Example. By making the transformation

$$\{z+(z^2-1)^{1/2}\cos\phi\}\{z-(z^2-1)^{1/2}\cos\psi\} = 1$$

when z is real and greater than unity, show that

$$P_n(z) = \frac{1}{\pi}\int_0^\pi \{z+(z^2-1)^{1/2}\cos\omega\}^{-n-1}\,d\omega$$

when $z > 1$. By appealing to the principle of analytical continuation, prove *Laplace's second integral formula*, that

$$P_n(z) = \pm\frac{1}{\pi}\int_0^\pi \{z+(z^2-1)^{1/2}\cos\omega\}^{-n-1}\,d\omega,$$

where the upper or lower sign is taken according as the real part of z is positive or negative. Show also that Laplace's second integral diverges when z is purely imaginary.

11.2. A generating function for the Legendre polynomials

The Legendre polynomials can also be defined as the coefficients in the expansion of $(1-2hz+h^2)^{-1/2}$ as a series of ascending powers of h, a result which enables us to determine very simply many of the properties of $P_n(z)$. To prove this, we sum the series $\sum h^n P_n(z)$.

Using Laplace's first integral, we find that

$$\sum_0^\infty h^n P_n(z) = \frac{1}{\pi}\sum_0^\infty \int_0^\pi h^n\{z+(z^2-1)^{\frac12}\cos\phi\}^n\,d\phi$$

$$= \frac{1}{\pi}\int_0^\pi \sum_0^\infty h^n\{z+(z^2-1)^{\frac12}\cos\phi\}^n\,d\phi,$$

provided that we can justify this inversion of the order of integration and summation.

Let us suppose that

$$|h| \leqslant (1-\epsilon)/(|z|+\sqrt{|z^2-1|}),$$

where $0 < \epsilon < 1$. We then have

$$|h\{z+(z^2-1)^{\frac12}\cos\phi\}| \leqslant |h|\{|z|+|z^2-1|^{\frac12}\} \leqslant 1-\epsilon,$$

and so the series $\sum_0^\infty h^n\{z+(z^2-1)^{\frac12}\cos\phi\}^n$

converges absolutely and uniformly with respect to the real

variable ϕ. The inversion of order is thus valid. It follows that

$$\sum_{n=0}^{\infty} h^n P_n(z) = \frac{1}{\pi} \int_0^{\pi} \{1 - hz - h(z^2 - 1)^{\frac{1}{2}} \cos \phi\}^{-1} d\phi$$

$$= (1 - 2hz + h^2)^{-1/2},$$

the branch of this function being determined by the fact that it is equal to 1 when $h = 0$.

Now $(1 - 2hz + h^2)^{-1/2}$, regarded as a function of h, has but two singularities, and these are branch-points at $h = z \pm (z^2 - 1)^{\frac{1}{2}}$. Hence, by Taylor's theorem, this function is expansible as a series of powers of h whose radius of convergence is the smaller of $|z \pm (z^2 - 1)^{\frac{1}{2}}|$. But we have seen that, for sufficiently small values of h, the function is expansible in the form $\sum h^n P_n(z)$. As the Taylor expansion of an analytic function is unique, we have thus shown that

$$(1 - 2hz + h^2)^{-1/2} = \sum_{n=0}^{\infty} h^n P_n(z)$$

provided that $|h| < |z \pm (z^2 - 1)^{\frac{1}{2}}|$. In particular, the radius of convergence of this series is unity when $-1 \leqslant z \leqslant 1$.

Example 1. Prove that

$$P_n(1) = 1, \quad P_n(-1) = (-1)^n, \quad P_{2n}(0) = \frac{(-1)^n (2n)!}{2^{2n} (n!)^2}, \quad P_{2n+1}(0) = 0.$$

Example 2. Use the identity $(1 - 2h \cos \theta + h^2) = (1 - he^{\theta i})(1 - he^{-\theta i})$ to prove that $P_n(\cos \theta)$ is equal to

$$\frac{(2n)!}{2^{2n}(n!)^2}\Big\{ 2 \cos n\theta + \frac{1(2n)}{2(2n-1)} 2 \cos(n-2)\theta +$$

$$+ \frac{1 \cdot 3(2n)(2n-2)}{2 \cdot 4(2n-1)(2n-3)} 2 \cos(n-4)\theta + ... \Big\}.$$

Deduce that $|P_n(\cos \theta)| \leqslant 1$ when θ is real.

Example 3. Show that, if $h + 1/h = 2/k$, then

$$\frac{(1 + h^2)}{(1 - 2hz + h^2)} = \frac{1}{(1 - zk)}.$$

Deduce that z^n is equal to

$$\frac{2^n (n!)^2}{(2n+1)!}\Big\{ (2n+1) P_n(z) + (2n-3) \frac{2n+1}{2} P_{n-2}(z) +$$

$$+ (2n-7) \frac{(2n+1)(2n-1)}{2 \cdot 4} P_{n-4}(z) + ... \Big\}.$$

11.21. The recurrence formulae

We shall now find the recurrence formulae connecting Legendre polynomials of different orders by using their generating function

$$V(z,h) = (1-2hz+h^2)^{-1/2}.$$

This generating function is easily seen to satisfy the partial differential equation

$$(1-2hz+h^2)\frac{\partial V}{\partial h} = (z-h)V.$$

Hence we have

$$(1-2hz+h^2)\sum_0^\infty nh^{n-1}P_n(z) = (z-h)\sum_0^\infty h^n P_n(z),$$

where the infinite series converge absolutely provided that

$$|h| < |z\pm(z^2-1)^{\frac{1}{2}}|.$$

Equating coefficients of h^{n-1}, we find that

$$nP_n(z)-(2n-1)zP_{n-1}(z)+(n-1)P_{n-2}(z) = 0, \qquad \text{(i)}$$

which is the first of the recurrence formulae.

Similarly, from the relation

$$h\frac{\partial V}{\partial h} = (z-h)\frac{\partial V}{\partial z},$$

we deduce that

$$z\frac{dP_n(z)}{dz} - \frac{dP_{n-1}(z)}{dz} = nP_n(z). \qquad \text{(ii)}$$

If we now differentiate (i) with respect to z, we obtain

$$n\left\{\frac{dP_n(z)}{dz} - z\frac{dP_{n-1}(z)}{dz}\right\} - (n-1)\left\{z\frac{dP_{n-1}(z)}{dz} - \frac{dP_{n-2}(z)}{dz}\right\}$$

$$= (2n-1)P_{n-1}(z),$$

from which it follows by formula (ii) (with $n-1$ for n), that

$$\frac{dP_n(z)}{dz} - z\frac{dP_{n-1}(z)}{dz} = nP_{n-1}(z). \qquad \text{(iii)}$$

From these three formulae, it is easy to deduce that

$$\frac{dP_{n+1}(z)}{dz} - \frac{dP_{n-1}(z)}{dz} = (2n+1)P_n(z), \qquad \text{(iv)}$$

$$(z^2-1)\frac{dP_n(z)}{dz} = nzP_n(z) - nP_{n-1}(z), \qquad \text{(v)}$$

$$(z^2-1)\frac{dP_n(z)}{dz} = -(n+1)zP_n(z)+(n+1)P_{n+1}(z). \qquad \text{(vi)}$$

It should be observed that the six recurrence formulae of this paragraph are really particular cases of the formulae of Gauss connecting contiguous hypergeometric functions (§ 10.5).

11.22. The integral of a product of Legendre polynomials

The polynomials $P_m(z)$, $P_n(z)$ satisfy the differential equations

$$\frac{d}{dz}\{(1-z^2)P'_m\}+m(m+1)P_m = 0,$$

$$\frac{d}{dz}\{(1-z^2)P'_n\}+n(n+1)P_n = 0,$$

where dashes denote differentiation with respect to z. If we multiply these equations by P_n and P_m respectively and subtract, we obtain

$$(m-n)(m+n+1)P_m P_n = P_m \frac{d}{dz}\{(1-z^2)P'_n\}-P_n\frac{d}{dz}\{(1-z^2)P'_m\}$$

$$= \frac{d}{dz}\{(1-z^2)(P_m P'_n - P'_m P_n)\}.$$

Hence, by integration, we have

$$(m-n)(m+n+1)\int_{z_1}^{z_2} P_m P_n \, dz = [(1-z^2)(P_m P'_n - P'_m P_n)]_{z_1}^{z_2}.$$

But, by the recurrence formula (v),

$$(1-z^2)(P_m P'_n - P'_m P_n) = nP_m P_{n-1} - mP_{m-1}P_n + (m-n)zP_m P_n,$$

so that, when $m \neq n$,

$$\int_{z_1}^{z_2} P_m P_n \, dz = \left[\frac{nP_m P_{n-1} - mP_{m-1}P_n + (m-n)zP_m P_n}{(m-n)(m+n+1)}\right]_{z_1}^{z_2},$$

a formula which enables us to integrate the product of two different Legendre polynomials between any limits.

To determine the corresponding formula for the integral of the square of a Legendre polynomial,† we observe that, by the

† See Hargreaves, *Proc. London Math. Soc.* (1), **29** (1898), 115–23.

recurrence formulae (ii) and (iii),

$$(2n+1)P_n^2-(2n-1)P_{n-1}^2$$
$$= 2P_n(zP_n'-P_{n-1}')-2P_{n-1}(P_n'-zP_{n-1}')+P_n^2+P_{n-1}^2$$
$$= \frac{d}{dz}[zP_n^2+zP_{n-1}^2-2P_{n-1}P_n],$$

and so

$$(2n+1)\int_{z_1}^{z_2} P_n^2\,dz -(2n-1)\int_{z_1}^{z_2} P_{n-1}^2\,dz = [zP_n^2+zP_{n-1}^2-2P_{n-1}P_n]_{z_1}^{z_2}.$$

If we now put $n = 1, 2,..., m$ and add, we obtain

$$(2m+1)\int_{z_1}^{z_2} P_m^2\,dz - \int_{z_1}^{z_2} P_0^2\,dz = [zP_0^2+2z(P_1^2+P_2^2+...+P_{m-1}^2)+$$
$$+zP_m^2-2(P_0P_1+P_1P_2+...+P_{m-1}P_m)]_{z_1}^{z_2},$$

or, since $P_0(z) = 1$, $P_1(z) = z$,

$$(2m+1)\int_{z_1}^{z_2} P_m^2\,dz = [2z(P_1^2+P_2^2+...+P_{m-1}^2)+$$
$$+zP_m^2-2(P_1P_2+P_2P_3+...+P_{m-1}P_m)]_{z_1}^{z_2}.$$

In particular, since $P_n(1) = 1$, $P_n(-1) = (-1)^n$, we see that

$$\int_{-1}^{1} P_m(z)P_n(z)\,dz = \frac{2}{2n+1} \quad\text{or } 0$$

according as the integers m and n are equal or unequal. This result can also be proved by using Rodrigues's formula and integrating by parts, as suggested in § 11.11, Exx. 7 and 8.

Example 1. Show that, if $m \geqslant n$ and $m-n$ is even,

$$\int_0^1 P_m(z)P_n(z)\,dz$$

is equal to 0 or $1/(2n+1)$ according as $m >$ or $= n$.

Example 2. Prove that

$$\int_0^1 P_{2r}(z)P_{2s+1}(z)\,dz = \frac{(-1)^{r+s+1}(2r)!(2s+1)!}{4^{r+s}(2r-2s-1)(2r+2s+2)(r!)^2(s!)^2}.$$

(RAYLEIGH.)

Example 3. Show that

$$\int_{z_1}^{z_2} (1-z^2)P'_m(z)P'_n(z)\,dz = [(1-z^2)P_m(z)P'_n(z)]_{z_1}^{z_2} + n(n+1)\int_{z_1}^{z_2} P_m(z)P_n(z)\,dz.$$

Deduce the value of

$$\int_{-1}^{1} (1-z^2)P'_m(z)P'_n(z)\,dz. \qquad\qquad \text{(Hargreaves.)}$$

Example 4. Show that

$$P'_n(z) = (2n-1)P_{n-1} + (2n-5)P_{n-3} + (2n-9)P_{n-5} + \cdots,$$

the last term being $3P_1$ or P_0 according as n is even or odd. Hence or otherwise show that, if $m \geqslant n$,

$$\int_{-1}^{1} P'_m(z)P'_n(z)\,dz = n(n+1) \quad \text{or } 0$$

according as $m-n$ is even or odd.

11.3. Legendre polynomials of large degree

In many of the applications of Legendre polynomials it is necessary to discuss the convergence of series of the form $\sum a_n P_n(z)$, and therefore to know how $P_n(z)$ behaves when its degree is large. We shall now give an account of Darboux's† method of deducing the asymptotic expansion of the Legendre polynomials of large degree from their generating function.

Let us consider, in the first place, the case when the point z does not lie on the real axis between ± 1, so that $z = \cosh \zeta$, where $\mathrm{Rl}\,\zeta > 0$. We then have

$$\sum_{0}^{\infty} h^n P_n(\cosh \zeta) = \frac{1}{\sqrt{\{(e^{\zeta}-h)(e^{-\zeta}-h)\}}},$$

provided that $|h| < |e^{-\zeta}|$. The generating function of the polynomials $P_n(\cosh \zeta)$ is, therefore, of the form $(e^{-\zeta}-h)^{-\frac{1}{2}}F(h)$, where $F(h)$ is regular when $|h| < |e^{\zeta}|$.

We can, however, write

$$F(h) = (2\sinh \zeta + e^{-\zeta} - h)^{-1/2}$$

$$= \sum_{r=0}^{\infty} (-\tfrac{1}{2}, r)(e^{-\zeta} - h)^r / (2\sinh \zeta)^{r+\frac{1}{2}},$$

† *Journal de Math.* (3), **4** (1878), 5 and 377. It will be seen that the method is applicable to many of the functions defined by a generating function.

where (α, r) denotes the binomial coefficient

$$\Gamma(\alpha+1)/\{r!\,\Gamma(\alpha+1-r)\}.$$

This power series converges when $|e^{-\zeta}-h| < 2|\sinh \zeta|$. From this it follows that, for any positive integral value of p,

$$F(h) = \sum_{r=0}^{p} (-\tfrac{1}{2}, r)(e^{-\zeta}-h)^r/(2 \sinh \zeta)^{r+\frac{1}{2}} + (e^{-\zeta}-h)^{p+1} G(h),$$

where $G(h)$ is regular when $|h| < |e^{\zeta}|$.

We have thus shown that

$$(e^{-\zeta}-h)^{p+\frac{1}{2}} G(h)$$

$$= \sum_{n=0}^{\infty} h^n P_n(\cosh \zeta) - \sum_{r=0}^{p} (-\tfrac{1}{2}, r)(e^{-\zeta}-h)^{r-\frac{1}{2}}/(2 \sinh \zeta)^{r+\frac{1}{2}}$$

$$= \sum_{n=0}^{\infty} h^n \left\{ P_n(\cosh \zeta) - \sum_{r=0}^{p} (-\tfrac{1}{2}, r)(r-\tfrac{1}{2}, n)\frac{(-1)^n e^{(n+\frac{1}{2}-r)\zeta}}{(2 \sinh \zeta)^{r+\frac{1}{2}}} \right\}$$

$$= \sum_{n=0}^{\infty} a_n h^n$$

say. By Taylor's theorem, this expansion is valid when

$$|h| < |e^{-\zeta}|.$$

The coefficients a_n are given by

$$a_n = \frac{1}{2\pi i} \int_C (e^{-\zeta}-h)^{p+\frac{1}{2}} G(h) \frac{dh}{h^{n+1}},$$

where C denotes a circle concentric with and interior to the circle of convergence. We can, however, deform the contour, without altering the value of the integral, until it consists of the circle of convergence $|h| = |e^{-\zeta}|$ indented at the singularity $e^{-\zeta}$. Moreover, the integral round the indentation tends to zero with the radius of the indentation.

Accordingly, if we write $h = e^{-\zeta+\theta i}$ on the modified contour, where θ varies from 0 to 2π, we obtain

$$a_n = \frac{1}{2\pi} e^{(n-p-\frac{1}{2})\zeta} \int_0^{2\pi} e^{-n\theta i}(1-e^{\theta i})^{p+\frac{1}{2}} G(e^{-\zeta+\theta i})\, d\theta$$

$$= \frac{1}{2\pi} e^{(n-p-\frac{1}{2})\zeta} \int_0^{2\pi} e^{-n\theta i} f(\theta)\, d\theta$$

say. The first p derivatives of $f(\theta)$ are continuous, whilst its derivative of order $p+1$, being of the form $(1-e^{\theta i})^{-\frac{1}{2}} g(\theta)$, where

$g(\theta)$ is continuous, is discontinuous at 0 and 2π. We can therefore integrate $p+1$ times by parts to obtain

$$a_n = \frac{1}{2\pi} \frac{e^{(n-p-\frac{1}{2})\zeta}}{(ni)^{p+1}} \int_0^{2\pi} e^{-n\theta i}(1-e^{\theta i})^{-\frac{1}{2}}g(\theta)\,d\theta.$$

But this integral remains finite as $n \to \infty$, and so $n^{p+1}e^{-n\zeta}a_n$ is uniformly bounded† as $n \to \infty$, provided that ζ lies in a closed domain where the inequality $\mathrm{Rl}\,\zeta > 0$ is satisfied.

We therefore see that, when $\mathrm{Rl}\,\zeta > 0$,

$$P_n(\cosh \zeta)$$
$$= \sum_{r=0}^{p} (-\tfrac{1}{2},r)(r-\tfrac{1}{2},n)\frac{(-1)^n e^{(n+\frac{1}{2}-r)\zeta}}{(2\sinh\zeta)^{r+\frac{1}{2}}} + a_n$$
$$= \frac{1}{\sqrt{\pi}} \sum_{r=0}^{p} \frac{\Gamma(\frac{1}{2}+r)\Gamma(\frac{1}{2}+r)}{n!\,r!\,\Gamma(\frac{1}{2}-n+r)}(-1)^{n+r}\frac{e^{(n+\frac{1}{2}-r)\zeta}}{(2\sinh\zeta)^{r+\frac{1}{2}}} + O\!\left(\frac{e^{n\zeta}}{n^{p+1}}\right).$$

But since the term corresponding to $r=p$ is $O(e^{n\zeta}/n^{p+\frac{1}{2}})$ when n is large, this equation can be written

$$P_n(\cosh\zeta)$$
$$= \frac{(-1)^n e^{(n+\frac{1}{2})\zeta}}{n!\,\sqrt{(2\pi\sinh\zeta)}}\sum_{r=0}^{p-1}\frac{\Gamma(\frac{1}{2}+r)\Gamma(\frac{1}{2}+r)}{r!\,\Gamma(\frac{1}{2}-n+r)}\left(-\frac{e^{-\zeta}}{2\sinh\zeta}\right)^r + O\!\left(\frac{e^{n\zeta}}{n^{p+\frac{1}{2}}}\right).$$

In other words,

$$P_n(\cosh\zeta) \sim \frac{(-1)^n e^{(n+\frac{1}{2})\zeta}}{n!\,\sqrt{(2\pi\sinh\zeta)}}\sum_{r=0}^{\infty}\frac{\Gamma(\frac{1}{2}+r)\Gamma(\frac{1}{2}+r)}{r!\,\Gamma(\frac{1}{2}-n+r)}\left(-\frac{e^{-\zeta}}{2\sinh\zeta}\right)^r,$$

the series on the right-hand side being an asymptotic expansion in Poincaré's sense when $\mathrm{Rl}\,\zeta > 0$, since the error caused by terminating the series at any term has the same order of magnitude as the first term omitted. It should be observed that this asymptotic expansion may be written in the form

$$P_n(\cosh\zeta) \sim \frac{\Gamma(n+\frac{1}{2})e^{(n+\frac{1}{2})\zeta}}{n!\,\sqrt{(2\pi\sinh\zeta)}}\,F\!\left(\tfrac{1}{2},\tfrac{1}{2};\,-n+\tfrac{1}{2};\,-\frac{e^{-\zeta}}{2\sinh\zeta}\right)$$

and, in particular, that

$$P_n(\cosh\zeta) = \frac{e^{(n+\frac{1}{2})\zeta}}{\sqrt{(2n\pi\sinh\zeta)}}\left\{1+O\!\left(\frac{1}{n}\right)\right\}.$$

This analysis has to be modified slightly when z is a real

† It can, in fact, be shown that $n^{p+1}e^{-n\zeta}a_n$ tends to zero uniformly, so that O in the next equation can be replaced by o. This is, however, of no importance here.

number lying between ± 1, since the branch-points of the generating function then both lie on the circle $|h| = 1$. In this case we write $z = \cos\theta$, where $0 < \theta < \pi$, and make use of the fact that

$$(1 - 2h\cos\theta + h^2)^{-1/2} - \sum_{r=0}^{p} (-\tfrac{1}{2}, r)\frac{(e^{-\theta i} - h)^{r-\frac{1}{2}}}{(2i\sin\theta)^{r+\frac{1}{2}}} -$$

$$- \sum_{r=0}^{p} (-\tfrac{1}{2}, r)\frac{(e^{\theta i} - h)^{r-\frac{1}{2}}}{(-2i\sin\theta)^{r+\frac{1}{2}}}$$

is regular save at the branch-points $e^{\pm\theta i}$; moreover, at $e^{\theta i}$ this function behaves like $(e^{\theta i} - h)^{p+\frac{1}{2}}G(h)$, where $G(h)$ is regular when $|e^{\theta i} - h| < 2\sin\theta$, and similarly at $e^{-\theta i}$. If we now expand in powers of h and apply the same argument as before, we find that, if $\epsilon \leqslant \theta \leqslant \pi - \epsilon$ where $\epsilon > 0$, then

$$P_n(\cos\theta)$$

$$\sim \left(\frac{2}{\pi\sin\theta}\right)^{1/2}\frac{(-1)^n}{n!} \sum_{r=0}^{\infty} \frac{\{\Gamma(r+\tfrac{1}{2})\}^2}{r!\,\Gamma(r+\tfrac{1}{2}-n)} \frac{\cos\{(n-r+\tfrac{1}{2})\theta + \tfrac{1}{4}(2r-1)\pi\}}{2^r\sin^r\theta},$$

and, in particular, that

$$P_n(\cos\theta) = \left(\frac{2}{n\pi\sin\theta}\right)^{1/2}\cos\{(n+\tfrac{1}{2})\theta - \tfrac{1}{4}\pi\} + O(n^{-3/2}).$$

This approximation is valid only when $\epsilon \leqslant \theta \leqslant \pi - \epsilon$, where ϵ is any positive number. It can, however, be shown that

$$|P_n(\cos\theta)| < \frac{\sqrt{2}}{\sqrt{(n\pi\sin\theta)}}$$

under the less restrictive condition $0 < \theta < \pi$. A proof of this will be found in Szegö's *Orthogonal Polynomials*.

11.4. The complete solution of Legendre's equation when n is an integer

Since the exponent-differences of Legendre's differential equation at the points ± 1 are both zero, the complete solution has a logarithmic singularity at these points. To discuss the nature of the complete solution near these singular points we apply the usual rule for solving a linear differential equation when one solution is known, that is, we make the substitution

$$w = P_n(z)u.$$

We find that u satisfies the equation

$$(1-z^2)P_n(z)\frac{d^2u}{dz^2}+2\{(1-z^2)P_n'(z)-zP_n(z)\}\frac{du}{dz}=0,$$

from which it follows that

$$u=A+B\int^z\frac{dz}{(z^2-1)\{P_n(z)\}^2},$$

where A and B are arbitrary constants. Hence the complete solution of Legendre's differential equation is

$$w=AP_n(z)+BP_n(z)\int^z\frac{dz}{(z^2-1)\{P_n(z)\}^2}.$$

Now $P_n(z)$ is a polynomial of degree n, with n distinct zeros $z_1, z_2,..., z_n$, say, no zero being equal to ±1. Accordingly we have, by the theory of partial fractions,

$$\frac{1}{(z^2-1)\{P_n(z)\}^2}=\frac{1}{2(z-1)}-\frac{1}{2(z+1)}+\sum_{r=1}^{n}\left\{\frac{a_r}{z-z_r}+\frac{b_r}{(z-z_r)^2}\right\}.$$

Here a_r is the residue of $1/[(z^2-1)\{P_n(z)\}^2]$ at $z=z_r$. If we write $P_n(z)=(z-z_r)F(z)$, we easily find that

$$a_r=\frac{2\{z_r F(z_r)-(1-z_r^2)F'(z_r)\}}{(1-z_r^2)\{F(z_r)\}^3}.$$

But if we substitute $(z-z_r)F(z)$ for $P_n(z)$ in Legendre's differential equation, we obtain

$$\tfrac{1}{2}(z-z_r)\{(1-z^2)F''(z)-2zF'(z)+n(n+1)F(z)\}+$$
$$+\{(1-z^2)F'(z)-zF(z)\}=0;$$

putting $z=z_r$, we find that $a_r=0$. Substituting the value of $1/[(z^2-1)\{P_n(z)\}^2]$ so obtained, we have as the complete solution of Legendre's differential equation

$$w=AP_n(z)-B\left\{\tfrac{1}{2}P_n(z)\log\frac{z+1}{z-1}+P_n(z)\sum_{r=1}^{n}\frac{b_r}{z-z_r}\right\}$$

$$=AP_n(z)-B\left\{\tfrac{1}{2}P_n(z)\log\frac{z+1}{z-1}-W_{n-1}(z)\right\},$$

where A and B are arbitrary constants and $W_{n-1}(z)$ is a polynomial of degree $n-1$.

The second solution of Legendre's differential equation

$$Q_n(z) = \tfrac{1}{2}P_n(z)\log\frac{z+1}{z-1} - W_{n-1}(z),$$

which we have just determined, has logarithmic branch-points at $z = \pm 1$, but any branch of the function is one-valued and regular in the z-plane supposed cut along the real axis from -1 to 1. We now define $Q_n(z)$ in this cut plane by assigning to the logarithms their principal values; we call this solution the *Legendre function of the second kind*. This is equivalent to taking

$$Q_n(z) = P_n(z)\int\limits_{\infty}^{z}\frac{dz}{(z^2-1)\{P_n(z)\}^2},$$

where the path of integration does not cross the cut.

The cut is a line of discontinuity of $Q_n(z)$. For, if $-1 < \mu < 1$, we have

$$\lim_{\epsilon\to+0} Q_n(\mu\pm\epsilon i) = \tfrac{1}{2}P_n(\mu)\left\{\log\frac{1+\mu}{1-\mu}\mp\pi i\right\} - W_{n-1}(\mu)$$

and so

$$Q_n(\mu+0i) - Q_n(\mu-0i) = -\pi i\, P_n(\mu).$$

When μ is a point on the cut, it is convenient to define $Q_n(\mu)$ as the arithmetic mean of $Q_n(\mu\pm 0i)$. With this convention we have

$$Q_n(\mu) = \tfrac{1}{2}P_n(\mu)\log\frac{1+\mu}{1-\mu} - W_{n-1}(\mu),$$

when $-1 < \mu < 1$.

11.41. The behaviour of $Q_n(z)$ at infinity

When $|z| > 1$, we can expand the function

$$Q_n(z) = \tfrac{1}{2}P_n(z)\log\frac{z+1}{z-1} - W_{n-1}(z)$$

as a series of the form

$$Q_n(z) = P_n(z)\left\{\frac{1}{z}+\frac{1}{3z^3}+\frac{1}{5z^5}+...\right\} - W_{n-1}(z)$$

$$= z^{n-1}\{a_0+a_1 z^{-1}+a_2 z^{-2}+...\}$$

say, the coefficients a_r being constants. If a_m is the first non-vanishing coefficient, this solution has the exponent $m-n+1$ at infinity.

We saw, however, in § 11.11 that the exponents of Legendre's equation at the regular singular point at infinity are $-n$ and $n+1$. Evidently $Q_n(z)$ cannot be the solution of exponent $-n$. Accordingly, we identify $Q_n(z)$ with the solution of exponent $n+1$, viz.

$$Q_n(z) = Cz^{-n-1}\left\{1 + \frac{(n+1)(n+2)}{2(2n+3)}z^{-2} + \right.$$
$$\left. + \frac{(n+1)(n+2)(n+3)(n+4)}{2.4(2n+3)(2n+5)}z^{-4} + \ldots\right\},$$

where C is a constant.

It should be observed that a_{2n} is the first non-zero coefficient, a fact which enables us to determine the polynomial $W_{n-1}(z)$. To determine C, we equate coefficients of z^{-n-1} in the two expansions. This gives

$$C = a_{2n}$$
$$= \frac{(2n)!}{2^n(n!)^2}\left\{\frac{1}{2n+1} - \frac{n(n-1)}{2(2n-1)^2} + \frac{n(n-1)(n-2)(n-3)}{2.4(2n-1)(2n-3)^2} - \ldots\right\}$$
$$= \int_0^1 \mu^n P_n(\mu)\,d\mu = \frac{1}{2^n n!}\int_0^1 \mu^n \frac{d^n}{d\mu^n}(\mu^2-1)^n\,d\mu$$
$$= \frac{1}{2^n}\int_0^1 (1-\mu^2)^n\,d\mu = \frac{n!\,\sqrt{\pi}}{2^{n+1}\Gamma(n+\frac{3}{2})}.$$

We have thus proved that, when $|z| > 1$,

$$Q_n(z) = \frac{n!\,\sqrt{\pi}}{2^{n+1}\Gamma(n+\frac{3}{2})}z^{-n-1}\left\{1 + \frac{(n+1)(n+2)}{2(2n+3)}z^{-2} + \right.$$
$$\left. + \frac{(n+1)(n+2)(n+3)(n+4)}{2.4(2n+3)(2n+5)}z^{-4} + \ldots\right\},$$

a result which can be expressed most simply in the form

$$Q_n(z) = \frac{n!\,\sqrt{\pi}}{2^{n+1}\Gamma(n+\frac{3}{2})}z^{-n-1}F(\tfrac{1}{2}n+\tfrac{1}{2}, \tfrac{1}{2}n+1; n+\tfrac{3}{2}; z^{-2}).$$

Example 1. Show that

$$Q_0(z) = \tfrac{1}{2}\log\frac{z+1}{z-1}, \qquad Q_1(z) = \tfrac{1}{2}z\log\frac{z+1}{z-1} - 1,$$

$$Q_2(z) = \tfrac{1}{2}P_2(z)\log\frac{z+1}{z-1} - \tfrac{3}{2}z,$$

$$Q_3(z) = \tfrac{1}{2}P_3(z)\log\frac{z+1}{z-1} - \tfrac{5}{2}z^2 + \tfrac{2}{3}.$$

Example 2. Show that

$$P_n(z) = \frac{(2n)!}{2^n(n!)^2}(z-1)^n F\left(-n, -n; -2n; \frac{2}{1-z}\right),$$

$$Q_n(z) = \frac{2^n(n!)^2}{(2n+1)!}(z-1)^{-n-1} F\left(n+1, n+1; 2n+2; \frac{2}{1-z}\right),$$

the latter formula being valid when $|z-1| > 2$. What is the corresponding formula, valid when $|z+1| > 2$?

Example 3. Prove that, if we replace the factorials in the functions of Ex. 2 by Gamma functions, the functions so obtained are linearly independent solutions of Legendre's differential equation for general values of the parameter n. [The functions $P_n(z)$ and $Q_n(z)$ so defined are called the Legendre functions of the first and second kinds respectively.]

11.42. An integral formula for $Q_n(z)$

Using the duplication formula for the Gamma function, we find that we can write the hypergeometric series for $Q_n(z)$ (§ 11.41) in the form

$$Q_n(z) = \frac{1}{(2z)^{n+1}} \sum_{s=0}^{\infty} \frac{(n+2s)!}{(2s)!} \frac{\Gamma(s+\frac{1}{2})}{\Gamma(n+s+\frac{3}{2})} z^{-2s}$$

when $|z| > 1$. But, by the Eulerian integral of the first kind, we have

$$\frac{n!\,\Gamma(s+\frac{1}{2})}{\Gamma(n+s+\frac{3}{2})} = \int_0^1 (1-u)^n u^{s-\frac{1}{2}}\,du = \int_{-1}^1 (1-t^2)^n t^{2s}\,dt$$

and so

$$Q_n(z) = \frac{1}{(2z)^{n+1}} \sum_{s=0}^{\infty} \frac{(n+2s)!}{n!\,(2s)!} \int_{-1}^1 (1-t^2)^n \left(\frac{t}{z}\right)^{2s}\,dt.$$

If we insert vanishing terms of the form

$$\frac{(n+2s+1)!}{n!\,(2s+1)!} \int_{-1}^1 (1-t^2)^n \left(\frac{t}{z}\right)^{2s+1}\,dt$$

in this infinite series, we find that

$$Q_n(z) = \frac{1}{(2z)^{n+1}} \sum_{r=0}^{\infty} \frac{(n+r)!}{n!\,r!} \int_{-1}^1 (1-t^2)^n \left(\frac{t}{z}\right)^{r}\,dt.$$

We can invert the order of integration and summation in this last equation; for, since $|z| > 1$, the series

$$\sum_{r=0}^{\infty} \frac{(n+r)!}{n!\,r!} \left(\frac{t}{z}\right)^{r}$$

converges uniformly when $-1 \leqslant t \leqslant 1$. It follows that

$$Q_n(z) = \frac{1}{(2z)^{n+1}} \int_{-1}^{1} (1-t^2)^n \sum_{r=0}^{\infty} \frac{(n+r)!}{n!\, r!} \left(\frac{t}{z}\right)^r dt$$

$$= \frac{1}{(2z)^{n+1}} \int_{-1}^{1} (1-t^2)^n \left(1-\frac{t}{z}\right)^{-n-1} dt,$$

or, finally, $\quad Q_n(z) = \dfrac{1}{2^{n+1}} \displaystyle\int_{-1}^{1} \dfrac{(1-t^2)^n}{(z-t)^{n+1}} \, dt.$

This formula, which is the analogue of Schläfli's integral for $P_n(z)$, has been proved under the assumption that $|z| > 1$. The integral is, however, uniformly convergent when z lies in any closed domain of the z-plane supposed cut along the real axis from -1 to $+1$. Hence, by the principle of analytical continuation, this formula for $Q_n(z)$ holds everywhere in the cut plane.

Example. Prove that $Q_n(z)$ satisfies recurrence formulae of the same type as those satisfied by $P_n(z)$.

11.43. Heine's integrals for $Q_n(z)$

We shall now deduce from the formula

$$Q_n(z) = \frac{1}{2^{n+1}} \int_{-1}^{1} \frac{(1-t^2)^n}{(z-t)^{n+1}} \, dt$$

two integral representations of $Q_n(z)$ which are analogous to Laplace's integrals for $P_n(z)$.

Let us suppose, in the first place, that z is real and greater than unity, so that the transformation

$$t = z - (z^2-1)^{\frac{1}{2}} e^{\theta}$$

is a real one. If we take the positive square root, we find that, as t varies from -1 to 1, θ varies from α to $-\alpha$, where

$$\alpha = \tfrac{1}{2} \log \frac{z+1}{z-1} = \operatorname{arccoth} z,$$

the real value of the logarithm being taken. From this it follows by direct substitution that, when $z > 1$,

$$Q_n(z) = \tfrac{1}{2} \int_{-\alpha}^{\alpha} \{z - (z^2-1)^{\frac{1}{2}} \cosh \theta\}^n \, d\theta,$$

and so, since the integrand is an even function of θ,

$$Q_n(z) = \int_0^\alpha \{z - (z^2 - 1)^{\frac{1}{2}} \cosh \theta\}^n \, d\theta.$$

This formula is important since it enables us to calculate simply the functions $Q_n(z)$. For example,

$$Q_0(z) = \alpha = \tfrac{1}{2} \log \frac{z+1}{z-1},$$

$$Q_1(z) = z\alpha - (z^2-1)^{\frac{1}{2}} \sinh \alpha = \tfrac{1}{2} z \log \frac{z+1}{z-1} - 1,$$

and so on. For the more difficult discussion of this formula when z is complex, we refer the reader elsewhere.[†]

If we now make the substitution

$$\{z + (z^2-1)^{\frac{1}{2}} \cosh \phi\}\{z - (z^2-1)^{\frac{1}{2}} \cosh \theta\} = 1,$$

we find that, as θ varies from 0 to α, ϕ varies from 0 to $+\infty$, and hence, after a little easy manipulation, that, when $z > 1$,

$$Q_n(z) = \int_0^\infty \{z + (z^2-1)^{\frac{1}{2}} \cosh \phi\}^{-n-1} \, d\phi.$$

This formula, which is due to Heine,[‡] is the analogue of Laplace's second integral for $P_n(z)$.

If we wish to extend this formula to the case when z is complex, we must first ensure that the integral is one-valued and convergent. This is the case if we take the branch of $(z^2-1)^{\frac{1}{2}}$ which is positive when $z > 1$, and make a cut[§] in the z-plane along the real axis from $-\infty$ to 1. If z lies in a bounded closed domain within the cut plane, the integral

$$\int_0^\infty \{z + (z^2-1)^{\frac{1}{2}} \cosh \phi\}^{-n-1} \, d\phi$$

converges uniformly with respect to z, and so represents a regular analytic function which is equal to $Q_n(z)$ when $z > 1$. From

---

[†] See, for example, Hobson's memoir published in *Phil. Trans.* (A) **187** (1896), 443–531, or his *Spherical and Ellipsoidal Harmonics* (Cambridge, 1931), Chap. V.

[‡] *Journal für Math.* **42** (1851), 73–5.

[§] The cut from -1 to 1 is required to make $(z^2-1)^{\frac{1}{2}}$ one-valued, whilst that from $-\infty$ to -1 ensures that $z + (z^2-1)^{\frac{1}{2}} \cosh \phi$ never vanishes when $\phi \geqslant 0$.

this it follows, by analytical continuation, that *the formula*

$$Q_n(z) = \int_0^\infty \{z + (z^2-1)^{\frac{1}{2}}\cosh\phi\}^{-n-1}\, d\phi$$

holds everywhere in the z-plane, supposed cut along the real axis from $-\infty$ *to* $+1$, *it being understood that* $(z^2-1)^{\frac{1}{2}}$ *has its principal value.* The value of $Q_n(z)$ on the cut is determined by the equation

$$Q_n(-z) = (-1)^{n+1}Q_n(z)$$

when $z < -1$, and by the convention of § 11.4 when $-1 < z < 1$.

11.5. Neumann's integral for $Q_n(z)$

F. Neumann† showed that *if z is any point of the z-plane, supposed cut along the real axis from* -1 *to* $+1$, $Q_n(z)$ *can be expressed in terms of Legendre's polynomial by the relation*

$$Q_n(z) = \tfrac{1}{2}\int_{-1}^{1} P_n(u)\,\frac{du}{z-u}.$$

We deduce this result from Cauchy's integral formula (§ 4.31, Ex.).

Let z be any fixed point of the w-plane which does not lie on the real axis between -1 and $+1$. We choose a closed contour C_1 which surrounds the points ± 1 but not the point z, and which does not cross the cut; we also take the circle C_2 whose equation is $|w| = R$, where $R > |z|$. Since $Q_n(w)$ is regular in the annulus bounded by C_1 and C_2, Cauchy's formula gives

$$Q_n(z) = \frac{1}{2\pi i}\int_{C_2} Q_n(w)\frac{dw}{w-z} - \frac{1}{2\pi i}\int_{C_1} Q_n(w)\frac{dw}{w-z}.$$

We now modify the expression on the right-hand side of this equation by making R tend to infinity.

It follows from § 11.41 that, for all sufficiently large values of $|w|$, $\qquad |Q_n(w)| \leqslant A/|w|^{n+1}$,

where $\qquad\qquad A = \dfrac{n!\,\sqrt{\pi}}{2^n\,\Gamma(n+\tfrac{3}{2})}.$

† *Journal für Math.* **37** (1848), 24.

Hence we have

$$\left| \int_{C_2} Q_n(w) \frac{dw}{w-z} \right| \leqslant \frac{2\pi A}{R^n(R-|z|)},$$

and this implies that the integral round C_2 tends to zero as R tends to infinity.

We have thus shown that

$$Q_n(z) = \frac{1}{2\pi i} \int_{C_1} Q_n(w) \frac{dw}{z-w}.$$

But since $Q_n(w)$ is regular in the cut plane, we can deform the contour C_1, without altering the value of the integral, until it consists of the two sides of the cut from $-1+\epsilon$ to $1-\eta$ joined by the circles $|w+1| = \epsilon$, $|w-1| = \eta$. Moreover, since

$$Q_n(w) = \tfrac{1}{2} P_n(w) \log \frac{w+1}{w-1} - W_{n-1}(w),$$

the integrals round these small circles tend to zero as ϵ and η tend to zero. It follows that

$$Q_n(z) = \frac{1}{2\pi i} \int_{-1}^{1} \{Q_n(u-0i) - Q_n(u+0i)\} \frac{du}{z-u}.$$

Finally, since

$$Q_n(u-0i) - Q_n(u+0i) = \pi i\, P_n(u)$$

when $-1 < u < 1$, this formula can be written in the form

$$Q_n(z) = \frac{1}{2} \int_{-1}^{1} P_n(u) \frac{du}{z-u},$$

which is Neumann's result.

11.51. Heine's expansion of $(z-u)^{-1}$ as a series of Legendre polynomials

Let us suppose that it is possible to expand $1/(z-u)$ as a series of Legendre polynomials of the form

$$\frac{1}{z-u} = \sum_{m=0}^{\infty} a_m P_m(u).$$

Then, by § 11.11, Ex. 7, the coefficients a_m are given by

$$a_m = \frac{2m+1}{2} \int_{-1}^{1} P_n(u)\frac{du}{z-u} = (2m+1)Q_m(z).$$

This suggests that the formula

$$\frac{1}{z-u} = \sum_{m=0}^{\infty} (2m+1)Q_m(z)P_n(u)$$

is probably true, provided that certain restrictions are made concerning z and u. This result, which is due to Heine,[†] is of great importance; for on it depends the theory of the expansion of a class of analytic functions as series of Legendre polynomials. The proof given below is due to Christoffel.[‡]

When $m \geqslant 1$, it follows from the recurrence formulae

$$(2m+1)zQ_m(z) = (m+1)Q_{m+1}(z)+mQ_{m-1}(z),$$
$$(2m+1)uP_m(u) = (m+1)P_{m+1}(u)+mP_{m-1}(u),$$

that

$$(2m+1)(z-u)Q_m(z)P_m(u)$$
$$= (m+1)\{Q_{m+1}(z)P_m(u)-Q_m(z)P_{m+1}(u)\}-$$
$$-m\{Q_m(z)P_{m-1}(u)-Q_{m-1}(z)P_m(u)\}.$$

The corresponding formula when $m = 0$ is

$$(z-u)Q_0(z)P_0(u) = \{Q_1(z)P_0(u)-Q_0(z)P_1(u)\}+1.$$

From these two formulae we have, by addition,

$$\sum_{m=0}^{n} (2m+1)Q_m(z)P_m(u)$$
$$= \frac{1}{z-u}+\frac{n+1}{z-u}\{Q_{n+1}(z)P_n(u)-Q_n(z)P_{n+1}(u)\}.$$

To prove Heine's formula, we have therefore to show that

$$(n+1)\{Q_{n+1}(z)P_n(u)-Q_n(z)P_{n+1}(u)\}$$

tends to zero as n tends to infinity.

Now, if $z = \cosh(\alpha+i\beta)$ where $\alpha > 0$, and if ϕ is real, we have

$$|z+(z^2-1)^{\frac{1}{2}}\cosh\phi| = |\cosh(\alpha+i\beta)+\sinh(\alpha+i\beta)\cosh\phi|$$
$$= \sqrt{\{\tfrac{1}{2}(\cosh 2\alpha+\cos 2\beta)+\sinh 2\alpha\cosh\phi+}$$
$$+\tfrac{1}{2}(\cosh 2\alpha-\cos 2\beta)\cosh^2\phi\}$$
$$\geqslant \sqrt{\{\cosh 2\alpha+\sinh 2\alpha\cosh\phi\}} \geqslant e^{\alpha}.$$

† *Journal für Math.* **42** (1851), 72.   ‡ Ibid. **55** (1858), 61–82.

It follows from Heine's integral (§ 11.43) that

$$|Q_n(z)| = \left| \int_0^\infty \{z+(z^2-1)^{\frac{1}{2}}\cosh\phi\}^{-n-1}\, d\phi \right|$$

$$\leqslant \int_0^\infty \{\cosh 2\alpha + \sinh 2\alpha \cos\phi\}^{-(n+1)/2}\, d\phi$$

$$\leqslant e^{-(n-1)\alpha} \int_0^\infty \{\cosh 2\alpha + \sinh 2\alpha \cos\phi\}^{-1}\, d\phi$$

$$= e^{-(n-1)\alpha} Q_0(\cosh 2\alpha).$$

Similarly, if $u = \cosh(\gamma+i\delta)$ where $\gamma \geqslant 0$, and if θ is real, we have

$$|u+(u^2-1)^{\frac{1}{2}}\cos\theta|$$

$$= |\cosh(\gamma+i\delta)+\sinh(\gamma+i\delta)\cos\theta|$$

$$= \sqrt{\{\tfrac{1}{2}(\cosh 2\gamma+\cos 2\delta)+\sinh 2\gamma\cos\theta+\tfrac{1}{2}(\cosh 2\gamma-\cos 2\delta)\cos^2\theta\}}$$

$$\leqslant \sqrt{\{\cosh 2\gamma+\sinh 2\gamma\}} = e^\gamma,$$

and so, by Laplace's first integral (§ 11.12),

$$|P_n(u)| = \frac{1}{\pi}\left| \int_0^\pi \{u+(u^2-1)^{\frac{1}{2}}\cos\theta\}^n\, d\theta \right| \leqslant e^{n\gamma}.$$

Now suppose that α is fixed and that ϵ is an arbit: ary positive number less than α. Then, when $0 \leqslant \gamma \leqslant \alpha-\epsilon$, we find that

$$(n+1)|Q_{n+1}(z)P_n(u)-Q_n(z)P_{n+1}(u)|$$

$$\leqslant (n+1)\{e^{-n\alpha}Q_0(\cosh 2\alpha)e^{n\gamma}+e^{-(n-1)\alpha}Q_0(\cosh 2\alpha)e^{(n+1)\gamma}\}$$

$$= (n+1)Q_0(\cosh 2\alpha)e^{n(\gamma-\alpha)}\{1+e^{\alpha+\gamma}\}$$

$$< (n+1)Q_0(\cosh 2\alpha)e^{-n\epsilon}\{1+e^{2\alpha}\}.$$

This last expression does not depend on β, γ, or δ, and tends to zero as n tends to infinity. It follows that the series

$$\sum_0^\infty (2n+1)Q_n(z)P_n(u)$$

converges uniformly with respect to β, γ, and δ and has sum $1/(z-u)$.

The simplest way of stating this result is to use geometrical language. If we keep α fixed and vary β, the point $z = \cosh(\alpha+i\beta)$ traces out an ellipse with foci at the points of affix ± 1 and major axis of length $2\cosh\alpha$. The condition

$0 \leqslant \gamma \leqslant \alpha - \epsilon$ means that $u = \cosh(\gamma + i\delta)$ lies within or on the smaller confocal ellipse of major axis $2\cosh(\alpha - \epsilon)$. The result we have just proved can therefore be stated in the following form. *The series*

$$\sum_0^\infty (2n+1)Q_n(z)P_n(u)$$

converges uniformly with respect to z and u when z lies on a fixed ellipse C with foci at the points of affix ± 1 and u lies in any closed domain definitely within C. The sum of the series is $1/(z-u)$.

11.52. Neumann's expansion theorem

If $f(z)$ is an analytic function, regular within and on an ellipse C with foci at the points of affix ± 1, it can be expanded as a series of Legendre polynomials

$$f(z) = \sum_0^\infty a_n P_n(z)$$

which converges uniformly when z lies within or on a smaller ellipse C_1, confocal with C.

For if u is any point within or on C_1, we have

$$f(u) = \frac{1}{2\pi i} \int_C f(z) \frac{dz}{z-u}$$

$$= \frac{1}{2\pi i} \int_C f(z) \sum_0^\infty (2n+1)Q_n(z)P_n(u) \, dz$$

$$= \frac{1}{2\pi i} \sum_0^\infty \int_C f(z)(2n+1)Q_n(z)P_n(u) \, dz,$$

the inversion of the order of integration and summation being valid since the infinite series under the sign of integration is uniformly convergent with respect to z and u when z lies on C. From this it follows that $f(u)$ can be expressed as a uniformly convergent series

$$f(u) = \sum_0^\infty a_n P_n(u),$$

where

$$a_n = \frac{2n+1}{2\pi i} \int_C f(z)Q_n(z) \, dz.$$

This completes the proof of K. Neumann's expansion theorem.

The actual determination of the constants a_n is best carried out by deforming the contour C, as in § 11.5, until it consists of the two sides of the cut from $-1+\epsilon$ to $1-\eta$, joined together by the circles $|z+1| = \epsilon$, $|z-1| = \eta$. This does not alter the value of the integral for a_n. It easily follows that

$$a_n = \frac{2n+1}{2\pi i} \int_{-1}^{1} f(x)\{Q_n(x-0i) - Q_n(x+0i)\} \, dx$$

and hence that

$$a_n = \frac{2n+1}{2} \int_{-1}^{1} f(x) P_n(x) \, dx.$$

Alternatively we can integrate term by term in the equation

$$\int_{-1}^{1} f(x) P_n(x) \, dx = \int_{-1}^{1} \sum_{r=0}^{\infty} a_r P_r(x) P_n(x) \, dx$$

which leads to the same result; this process is valid on account of the uniform convergence of Neumann's series.

For theorems of a similar nature relating to functions of a real variable, we refer the reader to Chapter VII of Hobson's *Spherical and Ellipsoidal Harmonics*.

Example. The function $f(z)$ is an analytic function regular in an annulus bounded externally by an ellipse C_2 with foci at the points of affix ± 1, and internally by a smaller confocal ellipse C_1. Show that $f(z)$ can be expanded as a series of the form

$$f(z) = \sum_{0}^{\infty} a_n P_n(z) + \sum_{0}^{\infty} b_n Q_n(z),$$

where

$$a_n = \frac{2n+1}{2\pi i} \int_{C_2} f(z) Q_n(z) \, dz,$$

$$b_n = \frac{2n+1}{2\pi i} \int_{C_1} f(z) P_n(z) \, dz.$$

Prove also that the series converges uniformly in any closed domain definitely within the annulus. (K. NEUMANN.)

11.6. The associated Legendre functions

We saw in § 11.1 that the problem of finding all the spherical harmonics of degree n depends on solving the associated Legendre differential equation

$$(1-z^2)\frac{d^2w}{dz^2} - 2z\frac{dw}{dz} + \left\{n(n+1) - \frac{m^2}{1-z^2}\right\}w = 0,$$

where n and m $(\leqslant n)$ are positive integers or zero. This differential equation has three regular singularities, its complete solution being of the form

$$w = P \left\{ \begin{matrix} -1 & \infty & 1 \\ \tfrac{1}{2}m & -n & \tfrac{1}{2}m \\ -\tfrac{1}{2}m & n+1 & -\tfrac{1}{2}m \end{matrix} \quad z \right\}.$$

If we make the substitution $w = (z^2-1)^{\frac{1}{2}m}u$, the exponents at ± 1 are changed to 0 and $-m$, and the exponents at infinity to $m-n$ and $m+n+1$. But this function u satisfies the differential equation

$$(1-z^2)\frac{d^2u}{dz^2} - 2(m+1)z\frac{du}{dz} + (n-m)(n+m+1)u = 0,$$

and this, by Leibniz's theorem, can be written in the form

$$\frac{d^m}{dz^m}\left\{ (1-z^2)\frac{d^2v}{dz^2} - 2z\frac{dv}{dz} + n(n+1)v \right\} = 0,$$

where $u = d^m v/dz^m$. Hence, if v is any solution of Legendre's differential equation, the function

$$w = (z^2-1)^{\frac{1}{2}m}\frac{d^m v}{dz^m}$$

satisfies the associated Legendre equation.

Accordingly we take as the two linearly independent solutions of this equation the functions

$$P_n^m(z) = (z^2-1)^{\frac{1}{2}m}\frac{d^m P_n(z)}{dz^m}, \qquad Q_n^m(z) = (z^2-1)^{\frac{1}{2}m}\frac{d^m Q_n(z)}{dz^m},$$

it being supposed that the z-plane is cut along the real axis from -1 to 1 and that $(z^2-1)^{\frac{1}{2}}$ has its principal value. These functions are called the *associated Legendre functions*.

When m is odd, $P_n^m(z)$ is undefined on the cut from -1 to 1. We complete the definition when $-1 < x < 1$ by writing

$$P_n^m(x) = (-1)^m(1-x^2)^{\frac{1}{2}m}\frac{d^m P_n(x)}{dx^m},$$

where the positive value of the square root is taken; it must, however, be remembered that, although $P_n^m(z)$ is now defined everywhere, it is discontinuous across the cut, since

$$P_n^m(x) = \lim_{\epsilon \to +0} e^{\frac{1}{2}m\pi i}P_n^m(x+i\epsilon) = \lim_{\epsilon \to +0} e^{-\frac{1}{2}m\pi i}P_n^m(x-i\epsilon).$$

When m is even, $P_n^m(z)$ is a polynomial of degree n, and so is regular everywhere; but as it is undesirable to have differences in definition according as m is even or odd, we suppose that, when $-1 < x < 1$, the equation

$$P_n^m(x) = (-1)^m (1-x^2)^{\frac{1}{2}m} \frac{d^m P_n(x)}{dx^m}$$

holds for all values of m.†

Similarly it is convenient to define $Q_n^m(x)$, when $-1 < x < 1$, by the equation

$$(-1)^m Q_n^m(x) = \tfrac{1}{2} \lim_{\epsilon \to +0} \{ e^{-\frac{1}{2}m\pi i} Q_n^m(x+\epsilon i) + e^{\frac{1}{2}m\pi i} Q_n^m(x-\epsilon i) \},$$

which agrees with the definition of $Q_n(x)$ when $m = 0$. The functions $P_n^m(x)$, $Q_n^m(x)$ so defined evidently satisfy the differential equation for real values of x.

Example 1. Prove that $P_n^m(z)$ is even or odd according as n is even or odd.

Example 2. Prove that

$$P_n^m(z) = \frac{(z^2-1)^{m/2}}{2^n \cdot n!} \frac{d^{n+m}}{dz^{n+m}} (z^2-1)^n.$$

Deduce that

$$P_n^m(z) = \frac{(2n)!}{2^n \cdot n!(n-m)!} (z^2-1)^{m/2} \Big\{ z^{n-m} - \frac{(n-m)(n-m-1)}{2 \cdot (2n-1)} z^{n-m-2} + $$
$$+ \frac{(n-m)(n-m-1)(n-m-2)(n-m-3)}{2 \cdot 4 \cdot (2n-1)(2n-3)} z^{n-m-4} - \ldots \Big\}.$$

Example 3. Show that

$$P_n^m(z) = \frac{1}{2^n \cdot (n-m)!} \left(\frac{z-1}{z+1} \right)^{m/2} \frac{d^n}{dz^n} \{ (z-1)^{n-m}(z+1)^{n+m} \}$$
$$= \frac{1}{2^n \cdot (n-m)!} \left(\frac{z+1}{z-1} \right)^{m/2} \frac{d^n}{dz^n} \{ (z+1)^{n-m}(z-1)^{n+m} \}.$$

Example 4. Show that

$$\int_{-1}^{1} P_n^m(z) P_r^m(z) \, dz = \frac{2}{2n+1} \frac{(n+m)!}{(n-m)!} \quad \text{or } 0$$

according as n is or is not equal to r.

Example 5. Prove that

$$\int_{-1}^{1} P_n^m(x) P_n^k(x) \frac{dx}{1-x^2} = \frac{1}{m} \frac{(n+m)!}{(n-m)!} \quad \text{or } 0$$

according as m is or is not equal to k.

---

† This is Hobson's definition. The factor $(-1)^m$ is sometimes omitted; to distinguish the two cases, it is usual to write $T_n^m(x) = (1-x^2)^{m/2} d^m P_n(x)/dx^m$, a notation due to Ferrers (*Spherical Harmonics* (1877), 76).

Example 6. Show that, if $r \leqslant n$,

$$\int_{-1}^{1} x P_n^m(x) P_r^m(x)\, dx$$

vanishes, save when $r = n-1$, when its value is

$$\frac{2}{4n^2-1}\, \frac{(n+m)!}{(n-m-1)!}.$$

Example 7. Show that, if $-1 < x < 1$,

$$(-1)^m Q_n^m(x \pm 0i) = e^{\pm m\pi i/2}\{Q_n^m(x) \mp \tfrac{1}{2}\pi i\, P_n^m(x)\}.$$

11.61. A lemma of Jacobi

Before we discuss the representation of $P_n^m(z)$ by definite integrals, it is convenient to prove that, if $\mu = \cos\phi$,

$$\frac{d^{m-1}\sin^{2m-1}\phi}{d\mu^{m-1}} = \frac{(-1)^{m-1}}{m}\, \frac{(2m)!}{2^m m!}\sin m\phi,$$

an interesting result due to Jacobi.†

The result is true when $m = 2$; for, in this case, it is easily shown that

$$\frac{d\sin^3\phi}{d\mu} = -\tfrac{3}{2}\sin 2\phi.$$

We shall show that the lemma is true generally by the method of induction.

Let us suppose that the lemma is true for some particular value of m. Then, writing

$$K = \frac{(-1)^{m-1}}{m}\, \frac{(2m)!}{2^m m!},$$

we deduce that

$$\frac{d^m \sin^{2m-1}\phi}{d\mu^m} = K\frac{d\sin m\phi}{d\mu} = -K\frac{m\cos m\phi}{\sin\phi}$$

and

$$\frac{d^{m+1}\sin^{2m-1}\phi}{d\mu^{m+1}} = -K\frac{m^2\sin m\phi \sin\phi + m\cos m\phi \cos\phi}{\sin^3\phi}.$$

Hence, by Leibniz's theorem, we have

$$\frac{d^{m+1}\sin^{2m+1}\phi}{d\mu^{m+1}} = \frac{d^{m+1}\{(1-\mu^2)\sin^{2m-1}\phi\}}{d\mu^{m+1}}$$

$$= K\{-m^2\sin m\phi - m\cos m\phi \cot\phi +$$
$$+ 2m(m+1)\cos m\phi \cot\phi - m(m+1)\sin m\phi\}$$

† *Journal für Math.* **15** (1836), 3–4. The proof given here is that of Ferrar, *Proc. London Math. Soc.* (2), **23** (1925), (*Records*) xxx.

$$= Km(2m+1)\cos(m+1)\phi/\sin\phi$$

$$= -\frac{d}{d\mu}\left\{K\frac{(2m+1)m}{m+1}\sin(m+1)\phi\right\}.$$

If we now integrate with respect to μ, we find that

$$\frac{d^m\sin^{2m+1}\phi}{d\mu^m} = \frac{(-1)^m}{m+1}\frac{(2m+2)!}{2^{m+1}(m+1)!}\sin(m+1)\phi,$$

the constant of integration vanishing since the expression on each side of the equation is an odd function of ϕ.

We have thus shown that, if the lemma is true for any particular value of m, it is true for the next greater. But since it is true for $m = 2$, it is true generally.

11.62. Integral representations of $P_n^m(z)$

The simplest integral formula for $P_n^m(z)$ is the analogue of Schläfli's integral for the Legendre polynomial, namely

$$P_n^m(z) = \frac{(n+m)!}{2^n n!}(z^2-1)^{\frac{1}{2}m}\frac{1}{2\pi i}\int_C\frac{(t^2-1)^n}{(t-z)^{n+m+1}}\,dt,$$

where C is a simple closed contour within which the point z lies. This follows immediately from the generalized Rodrigues's formula

$$P_n^m(z) = \frac{(z^2-1)^{\frac{1}{2}m}}{2^n n!}\frac{d^{n+m}}{dz^{n+m}}(z^2-1)^n,$$

by using Cauchy's integral for the $(n+m)$th derivative.

When z does not lie on the real axis between ± 1, we can take as C the circle $|t-z| = \sqrt{|z^2-1|}$. Then on C we have

$$t = z+(z^2-1)^{\frac{1}{2}}e^{\phi i},$$

where $(z^2-1)^{\frac{1}{2}}$ has its principal value and ϕ varies from 0 to 2π. It now follows, exactly as in § 11.12, that

$$P_n^m(z) = \frac{(n+m)!}{n!}\frac{1}{\pi}\int_0^\pi\{z+(z^2-1)^{\frac{1}{2}}\cos\phi\}^n\cos m\phi\,d\phi.$$

Now by the lemma of § 11.61 we have

$$\cos m\phi = (-1)^{m-1}\frac{2^m m!}{(2m)!}\frac{d^m\sin^{2m-1}\phi}{d\mu^m}\frac{d\mu}{d\phi},$$

where μ denotes $\cos\phi$. We can, therefore, write this definite integral for $P_n^m(z)$ in the form

$$P_n^m(z) = \frac{2^m m!\,(n+m)!}{(2m)!\,n!}\frac{(-1)^m}{\pi}\int_{-1}^{1}\{z+(z^2-1)^{\frac12}\mu\}^n\frac{d^m\sin^{2m-1}\phi}{d\mu^m}\,d\mu.$$

Integrating by parts m times, we deduce that

$$P_n^m(z) = \frac{2^m m!\,(n+m)!}{(2m)!\,(n-m)!}\frac{(z^2-1)^{\frac12 m}}{\pi}\int_{-1}^{1}\{z+(z^2-1)^{\frac12}\mu\}^{n-m}\sin^{2m-1}\phi\,d\mu.$$

Finally, putting $\mu = \cos\phi$, we obtain a second definite-integral formula for $P_n^m(z)$, namely

$$P_n^m(z) = \frac{2^m m!\,(n+m)!}{(2m)!\,(n-m)!}\frac{(z^2-1)^{\frac12 m}}{\pi}\int_{0}^{\pi}\{z+(z^2-1)^{\frac12}\cos\phi\}^{n-m}\sin^{2m}\phi\,d\phi,$$

valid when the z-plane is cut along the real axis from -1 to 1 and $(z^2-1)^{\frac12}$ has its principal value.

It should be observed that the two integrals of this paragraph reduce to Laplace's first integral for the Legendre polynomial when m is zero.

Example 1. Show that, when the z-plane is cut from -1 to 1 and $(z^2-1)^{1/2}$ has its principal value,

$$\{z+(z^2-1)^{1/2}\cos\phi\}^n = P_n(z)+2\sum_{m=1}^{n}\frac{n!}{(n+m)!}P_n^m(z)\cos m\phi.$$

Example 2. By applying the transformation

$$\{z+(z^2-1)^{1/2}\cos\phi\}\{z-(z^2-1)^{1/2}\cos\psi\} = 1$$

when $z > 1$ to the second definite integral of § 11.62, show that

$$P_n^m(z) = \frac{2^m m!}{(2m)!}\frac{(n+m)!}{(n-m)!}(z^2-1)^{m/2}\frac{1}{\pi}\int_{0}^{\pi}\{z+(z^2-1)^{1/2}\cos\omega\}^{-n-m-1}\sin^{2m}\omega\,d\omega.$$

Deduce that, when the z-plane is cut from -1 to 1,

$$P_n^m(z) = \pm\frac{2^m m!}{(2m)!}\frac{(n+m)!}{(n-m)!}(z^2-1)^{m/2}\frac{1}{\pi}\int_{0}^{\pi}\{z+(z^2-1)^{1/2}\cos\omega\}^{-n-m-1}\sin^{2m}\omega\,d\omega,$$

where the upper or lower sign is taken according as $\mathrm{Rl}\,z >$ or < 0. Show also that the integral diverges when $\mathrm{Rl}\,z = 0$.

Example 3. By using Jacobi's lemma, show that

$$P_n^m(z) = \pm(-1)^m \frac{n!}{(n-m)!} \frac{1}{\pi} \int_0^\pi \{z+(z^2-1)^{1/2}\cos\omega\}^{-n-1}\cos m\omega \, d\omega,$$

where the upper or lower sign is taken according as $\mathrm{Rl}\,z > $ or < 0.

Example 4. Show that, if $0 < \theta < \pi$,

$$(\cos\theta \pm i\sin\theta\cos\phi)^n$$

$$= P_n(\cos\theta) + 2\sum_{m=1}^n (\pm 1)^m e^{-m\pi i/2} \frac{n!}{(n+m)!} P_n^m(\cos\theta)\cos m\phi.$$

11.63. Integral representations of $Q_n^m(z)$

We have seen in § 11.42 that, when z does not lie on the real axis between -1 and 1,

$$Q_n(z) = \frac{1}{2^{n+1}} \int_{-1}^1 \frac{(1-t^2)^n}{(z-t)^{n+1}} \, dt.$$

From this it easily follows by differentiation under the sign of integration that the equation

$$Q_n^m(z) = (-1)^m \frac{(n+m)!}{2^{n+1}n!}(z^2-1)^{\frac{1}{2}m} \int_{-1}^1 \frac{(1-t^2)^n}{(z-t)^{n+m+1}} \, dt$$

holds everywhere in the cut z-plane. This is the fundamental definite-integral representation of $Q_n^m(z)$, and from it the generalizations of Heine's integrals (§ 11.43) can be deduced. As the analysis runs on exactly similar lines to that of § 11.43 and § 11.62, we state the results as exercises for the reader.

Example 1. Prove that, when z is real and greater than unity,

$$Q_n^m(z) = \frac{(-1)^m(n+m)!}{n!} \int_0^\alpha \{z-(z^2-1)^{1/2}\cosh\theta\}^n\cosh m\theta \, d\theta,$$

where $\alpha = \operatorname{arccoth} z$.

Example 2. Show that, if $\mu = \cosh\theta$,

$$\cosh m\theta = \frac{2^m m!}{(2m)!}\sinh\theta \frac{d^m\sinh^{2m-1}\theta}{d\mu^m}.$$

Hence prove that, when $z > 1$,

$$Q_n^m(z) = \frac{(-1)^m(n+m)!\,m!\,2^m}{(2m)!\,(n-m)!}(z^2-1)^{m/2}\int_0^\alpha \{z-(z^2-1)^{1/2}\cosh\theta\}^{n-m}\sinh^{2m}\theta \, d\theta.$$

Example 3. Deduce from Ex. 3 that the equations

$$Q_n^m(z) = \frac{(-1)^m(n+m)!\,m!\,2^m}{(2m)!\,(n-m)!}(z^2-1)^{m/2} \times$$

$$\times \int_0^\infty \{z+(z^2-1)^{1/2}\cosh\phi\}^{-n-m-1}\sinh^{2m}\phi\,d\phi,$$

$$Q_n^m(z) = \frac{(-1)^m n!}{(n-m)!}\int_0^\infty \{z+(z^2-1)^{1/2}\cosh\phi\}^{-n-1}\cosh m\phi\,d\phi$$

hold everywhere in the cut z-plane.

11.7. The addition-theorem for the Legendre polynomials

If Θ denotes the angle between a fixed line OA and the radius vector to the point of spherical polar coordinates (r,θ,ϕ), the function $P_n(\cos\Theta)$ is a spherical harmonic of degree n. Accordingly we can express this harmonic as a series of the form

$$P_n(\cos\Theta) = a_0 P_n(\cos\theta) + \sum_{m=1}^n (a_m \cos m\phi + b_m \sin m\phi)P_n^m(\cos\theta),$$

where the coefficients a_m and b_m are independent of θ and ϕ. In particular, if A has polar coordinates $(r_1,\theta_1,0)$, this expansion becomes

$$P_n(\cos\theta\cos\theta_1 + \sin\theta\sin\theta_1\cos\phi)$$

$$= a_0 P_n(\cos\theta) + \sum_{m=1}^n (a_m \cos m\phi + b_m \sin m\phi)P_n^m(\cos\theta),$$

a result which is called the addition-theorem for the Legendre polynomials.

If we write z and z_1 for $\cos\theta$ and $\cos\theta_1$ respectively, this addition-theorem takes the form

$$P_n(\zeta) = a_0 P_n(z) + \sum_{m=1}^n (a_m \cos m\phi + b_m \sin m\phi)P_n^m(z),$$

where
$$\zeta = zz_1 - (z^2-1)^{\frac{1}{2}}(z_1^2-1)^{\frac{1}{2}}\cos\phi.$$

In the present section we propose to determine the coefficients a_m and b_m for general complex values of z and z_1.

Let us suppose, in the first instance, that z and z_1 are real and greater than unity and that $0 \leqslant \phi \leqslant \pi$, so that ζ is certainly positive. The expansion

$$\sum_{n=0}^\infty h^n P_n(\zeta) = (1-2h\zeta+h^2)^{-1/2}$$

then holds for all sufficiently small values of h. We now express the function on the right-hand side of this equation as a definite integral and deduce the addition-theorem by equating coefficients of powers of h.

When h is real, it is easily shown that

$$(1-2h\zeta+h^2)^{-1/2}$$

$$= [(z-hz_1)^2-\{(z^2-1)-2h(z^2-1)^{\frac{1}{2}}(z_1^2-1)^{\frac{1}{2}}\cos\phi+h^2(z_1^2-1)\}]^{-\frac{1}{2}}$$

$$= \frac{1}{2\pi}\int_{-\pi}^{\pi}[(z-hz_1)+\{(z^2-1)-2h(z^2-1)^{\frac{1}{2}}(z_1^2-1)^{\frac{1}{2}}\cos\phi+$$

$$+h^2(z_1^2-1)\}^{\frac{1}{2}}\cos(\omega-\alpha)]^{-1}\,d\omega$$

for every real value of α. In particular, if we take

$$\tan\alpha = \frac{h(z_1^2-1)^{\frac{1}{2}}\sin\phi}{(z^2-1)^{\frac{1}{2}}-h(z_1^2-1)^{\frac{1}{2}}\cos\phi},$$

we obtain

$$(1-2h\zeta+h^2)^{-1/2}$$

$$= \frac{1}{2\pi}\int_{-\pi}^{\pi}[(z-hz_1)+\{(z^2-1)^{\frac{1}{2}}-h(z_1^2-1)^{\frac{1}{2}}\cos\phi\}\cos\omega+$$

$$+h(z_1^2-1)^{\frac{1}{2}}\sin\phi\sin\omega]^{-1}\,d\omega$$

$$= \frac{1}{2\pi}\int_{-\pi}^{\pi}[z+(z^2-1)^{\frac{1}{2}}\cos\omega-h\{z_1+(z_1^2-1)^{\frac{1}{2}}\cos(\omega+\phi)\}]^{-1}\,d\omega.$$

This formula also holds, by the theory of analytical continuation, for all sufficiently small complex values of h.

For any fixed value of h which satisfies the inequality

$$|h| < \frac{z-\sqrt{(z^2-1)}}{z_1+\sqrt{(z_1^2-1)}},$$

we can expand the integrand of the last integral as a power-series in h which converges uniformly with respect to ω when $-\pi \leqslant \omega \leqslant \pi$. Accordingly we can integrate term by term to obtain

$$\sum_{n=0}^{\infty} h^n P_n(\zeta) = (1-2h\zeta+h^2)^{-1/2}$$

$$= \sum_{n=0}^{\infty} h^n \frac{1}{2\pi}\int_{-\pi}^{\pi}\frac{\{z_1+(z_1^2-1)^{\frac{1}{2}}\cos(\omega+\phi)\}^n}{\{z+(z^2-1)^{\frac{1}{2}}\cos\omega\}^{n+1}}\,d\omega.$$

Equating coefficients, we deduce that

$$P_n(\zeta) = \frac{1}{2\pi} \int_{-\pi}^{\pi} \frac{\{z_1 + (z_1^2 - 1)^{\frac{1}{2}} \cos(\omega + \phi)\}^n}{\{z + (z^2 - 1)^{\frac{1}{2}} \cos \omega\}^{n+1}} \, d\omega.$$

If we substitute in this equation the value of

$$\{z_1 + (z_1^2 - 1)^{\frac{1}{2}} \cos(\omega + \phi)\}^n$$

given in § 11.62, Ex. 1, we find that $P_n(\zeta)$ is equal to

$$\frac{P_n(z_1)}{2\pi} \int_{-\pi}^{\pi} \frac{d\omega}{\{z + (z^2 - 1)^{\frac{1}{2}} \cos \omega\}^{n+1}} +$$

$$+ \sum_{m=1}^{n} \frac{n!}{(n+m)!} \frac{P_n^m(z_1)}{\pi} \int_{-\pi}^{\pi} \frac{\cos m(\omega + \phi) \, d\omega}{\{z + (z^2 - 1)^{\frac{1}{2}} \cos \omega\}^{n+1}}.$$

But

$$\int_{-\pi}^{\pi} \frac{\cos m(\omega + \phi) \, d\omega}{\{z + (z^2 - 1)^{\frac{1}{2}} \cos \omega\}^{n+1}} = \cos m\phi \int_{-\pi}^{\pi} \frac{\cos m\omega \, d\omega}{\{z + (z^2 - 1)^{\frac{1}{2}} \cos \omega\}^{n+1}}$$

$$\pm \sin m\phi \int_{-\pi}^{\pi} \frac{\sin m\omega \, d\omega}{\{z + (z^2 - 1)^{\frac{1}{2}} \cos \omega\}^{n+1}}$$

$$= 2\pi(-1)^m \frac{(n-m)!}{n!} P_n^m(z) \cos m\phi,$$

by § 11.62, Ex. 3, the integral involving $\sin m\omega$ vanishing since its integrand is an odd function of ω.

We have thus shown that, when z and z_1 are real and greater than unity,

$$P_n\{zz_1 - (z^2 - 1)^{\frac{1}{2}}(z_1^2 - 1)^{\frac{1}{2}} \cos \phi\}$$

$$= P_n(z)P_n(z_1) + 2 \sum_{m=1}^{n} \frac{(n-m)!}{(n+m)!} (-1)^m P_n^m(z) P_n^m(z_1) \cos m\phi.$$

To complete the proof of the addition-theorem, we have only to extend this result to general complex values of z, z_1, and ϕ.

Let us suppose that the Argand plane is cut along the real axis from -1 to 1 and that $(z^2 - 1)^{\frac{1}{2}}$ and $(z_1^2 - 1)^{\frac{1}{2}}$ have their principal values. When z is any point of this cut plane, $z_1 \, (> 1)$ and ϕ being real, the expressions on each side of the last equation are regular analytic functions of z which are equal when

z is real and greater than unity. By the principle of analytical continuation, the equation still holds for such complex values of z, z_1 and ϕ remaining real. The restriction on z_1 is next removed in the same way. Finally it is not necessary to suppose that ϕ is real, since the addition-theorem expresses the equality of two polynomials in $e^{\phi i}$ and $e^{-\phi i}$.

We have thus shown that *if z and z_1 are any two points of the Argand plane supposed cut along the real axis from -1 to 1, and if ϕ is any complex number, the equation*

$$P_n(\zeta) = P_n(z)P_n(z_1) + 2\sum_{m=1}^{n} \frac{(n-m)!}{(n+m)!}(-1)^m P_n^m(z)P_n^m(z_1)\cos m\phi,$$

where $\zeta = zz_1 - (z^2-1)^{\frac{1}{2}}(z_1^2-1)^{\frac{1}{2}}\cos\phi$, holds provided that $(z^2-1)^{\frac{1}{2}}$ and $(z_1^2-1)^{\frac{1}{2}}$ have their principal values.

Example. Prove that, when θ, θ_1 and ϕ are real,

$$P_n(\cos\theta\cos\theta_1 + \sin\theta\sin\theta_1\cos\phi)$$

$$= P_n(\cos\theta)P_n(\cos\theta_1) + 2\sum_{m=1}^{n}\frac{(n-m)!}{(n+m)!}P_n^m(\cos\theta)P_n^m(\cos\theta_1)\cos m\phi.$$

1.8. Legendre functions of non-integral order

In the present chapter we have only discussed the solution of the associated Legendre equation in the case when $m \leqslant n$ and m and n are positive integers or zero, the case which is of most frequent occurrence in physical problems. For a discussion of the solution in the general case when m and n have any real or complex values, we refer the reader to the original memoirs, in particular those of Barnes[†] and Hobson[‡].

REFERENCES

H. BATEMAN, *Partial Differential Equations of Mathematical Physics* (Cambridge, 1932), Chap. VI.

E. W. HOBSON, *The Theory of Spherical and Ellipsoidal Harmonics* (Cambridge, 1931).

G. SZEGÖ, *Orthogonal Polynomials* (New York, 1939).

E. T. WHITTAKER and G. N. WATSON, *Modern Analysis* (Cambridge, 1920), Chap. XV.

[†] *Quarterly Journal of Math.* **39** (1908), 97–204.
[‡] *Phil. Trans.* (A), **187** (1896), 443–531. See also Hobson's book cited above.

MISCELLANEOUS EXAMPLES

1. Show that the value of the integral

$$\int_{-1}^{1} z(1-z^2)P'_m(z)P'_n(z)\,dz$$

is zero unless $m = n \pm 1$. Find the value of the integral in these exceptional cases.

2. Prove that, if $m \geqslant n$,

$$\int_{-1}^{1} P''_m(z)P''_n(z)\,dz = \frac{(n+2)!}{4!(n-2)!}\{3m(m+1)-n(n+1)+6\} \quad \text{or} \quad 0$$

according as $m-n$ is even or odd.

3. Prove that

$$P_n(z) = \frac{1}{2\pi i} \int_C \frac{dh}{h^{n+1}(1-2hz+h^2)^{1/2}},$$

where C is a simple closed contour enclosing the origin but neither of the points $z\pm(z^2-1)^{1/2}$; the branch of $(1-2hz+h^2)^{1/2}$ is that which reduces to 1 when $h = 0$.

4. Deduce from Ex. 3 that

$$P_n(z) = \frac{1}{2\pi i} \int_{\Gamma} \frac{h^n\,dh}{(1-2hz+h^2)^{1/2}},$$

where Γ is a simple closed contour enclosing both the points $z\pm(z^2-1)^{1/2}$; the branch of $(1-2hz+h^2)^{1/2}$ is specified by the condition

$$(1-2hz+h^2)^{1/2}/h \to 1$$

as $h \to \infty$.

Hence prove that, when $0 < \theta < \pi$,

$$P_n(\cos\theta) = \frac{\sqrt{2}}{\pi} \int_0^{\theta} \frac{\cos(n+\tfrac{1}{2})\phi}{(\cos\phi - \cos\theta)^{1/2}}\,d\phi,$$

the positive square root being taken.†

5. Show that if $R^2 = X^2 + Y^2 + Z^2$, the numbers involved being real,

$$P_n(Z/R) = \frac{(-1)^n R^{n+1}}{n!}\frac{\partial^n}{\partial Z^n}\left(\frac{1}{R}\right),$$

$$Q_n(Z/R) = \frac{(-1)^n R^{n+1}}{n!}\frac{\partial^n}{\partial Z^n}\left(\frac{1}{2R}\log\frac{R+Z}{R-Z}\right),$$

where R is regarded as a function of the independent variables X, Y and Z.

† This is the Dirichlet-Mehler integral for the Legendre polynomials. To prove it, deform the contour Γ until it consists of two small circles about $e^{\pm\theta i}$, joined by an arc of $|h| = 1$, covered twice.

6. Prove that the polynomial $W_{n-1}(z)$ satisfies the differential equation

$$(1-z^2)\frac{d^2w}{dz^2} - 2z\frac{dw}{dz} + n(n+1)w = 2P_n'(z).$$

Deduce that

$$W_{n-1}(z) = \frac{2n-1}{n}P_{n-1}(z) + \frac{2n-5}{3(n-1)}P_{n-3}(z) + \frac{2n-9}{5(n-2)}P_{n-5}(z) + \dots .$$

(CHRISTOFFEL.)

7. Show that

$$W_{n-1}(z) = \frac{1}{n}P_0(z)P_{n-1}(z) + \frac{1}{n-1}P_1(z)P_{n-2}(z) + \dots + P_{n-1}(z)P_0(z).$$

8. Prove the following generalization of Rodrigues's formula:

$$Q_n(z) = (-1)^{n+1}2^n n! \, D^{-n-1}(z^2-1)^{-n-1},$$

where D^{-1} denotes integration from the point at infinity to z.

9. Show that

$$P_n(z)Q_{n-1}(z) - P_{n-1}(z)Q_n(z) = \frac{1}{n}.$$

Deduce that

$$Q_n(z) = \tfrac{1}{2}P_n(z)\log\frac{z+1}{z-1} - P_n(z)\sum_{r=1}^{n}\frac{1}{rP_{r-1}(z)P_r(z)}.$$

10. Prove that

$$\int_1^\infty (2n+1)\{Q_n(z)\}^2\,dz - \int_1^\infty (2n-1)\{Q_{n-1}(z)\}^2\,dz = -\frac{1}{n^2},$$

$$\int_0^1 (2n+1)\{Q_n(z)\}^2\,dz - \int_0^1 (2n-1)\{Q_{n-1}(z)\}^2\,dz = \frac{1}{n^2}.$$

Hence show that

$$\int_1^\infty (2n+1)\{Q_n(z)\}^2\,dz = \sum_{n+1}^\infty \frac{1}{r^2},$$

$$\int_0^1 (2n+1)\{Q_n(z)\}^2\,dz = \frac{\pi^2}{4} - \sum_{n+1}^\infty \frac{1}{r^2}.$$

(HARGREAVES.)

11. Prove that

$$P_n(z)Q_n'(z) - P_n'(z)Q_n(z) = 1/(1-z^2).$$

12. Show that

$$(1-z^2)(P_n'Q_n' - P_{n+1}'Q_{n+1}') = (n+1)^2(P_{n+1}Q_{n+1} - P_nQ_n).$$

Deduce that, when z does not lie between ± 1,

$$\int_1^z (2n+3)P_{n+1}Q_{n+1}\,dz - \int_1^z (2n+1)P_nQ_n\,dz$$

$$= z(P_{n+1}Q_{n+1} + P_nQ_n) - (P_nQ_{n+1} + P_{n+1}Q_n).$$

Show also that

$$(2n+1) \int_0^1 P_n(x)Q_n(x)\, dx - (2n+3) \int_0^1 P_{n+1}(x)Q_{n+1}(x)\, dx = \frac{(-1)^n}{n+1}.$$

Hence evaluate $\displaystyle \int_0^1 P_n(x)Q_n(x)\, dx.$ (HARGREAVES.)

13. Prove that
$$P_{n+1}(z)Q_{n-1}(z) - P_{n-1}(z)Q_{n+1}(z) = \frac{(2n+1)z}{n(n+1)}.$$

14. Show that
$$\int_{-1}^1 (1+x)^{m+n}P_m(x)P_n(x)\, dx = \frac{2^{m+n+1}\{(m+n)!\}^4}{\{m!\,n!\}^2(2m+2n+1)!}.$$
$$\text{(TITCHMARSH.)}$$

15. Show that
$$(m-n)(m+n+1)\int_{-1}^1 P_m(x)Q_n(x)\, dx = 1-(-1)^{m+n}.$$

Deduce that, if $m+n$ is odd,
$$(m-n)(m+n+1)\int_0^1 P_m(x)Q_n(x)\, dx = 1. \quad \text{(NICHOLSON.)}$$

16. Prove that
$$(2n-2m)(2m+2n+1)\int_0^1 P_{2n}(x)Q_{2m}(x)\, dx$$
$$= 1-(-1)^{m+n}\frac{(2n)!}{(2m)!}\left\{\frac{2^m m!}{2^n n!}\right\}^2. \quad \text{(NICHOLSON.)}$$

17. Show, by the aid of the addition theorem or otherwise, that
$$\int_{-1}^1 \frac{P_n(x)}{\sqrt{(1-x^2)}}\, dx = \pi\{P_n(0)\}^2.$$

Hence show that
$$\frac{1}{\sqrt{(1-x^2)}} = \tfrac12\pi \sum_{n=0}^\infty (4n+1)\left(\frac{1.3\ldots(2n-1)}{2.4\ldots(2n)}\right)^2 P_{2n}(x).$$

Deduce Catalan's expansion
$$\sin^{-1}x = \tfrac12\pi P_1(x) + \tfrac12\pi \sum_{n=1}^\infty \left(\frac{1.3\ldots(2n-1)}{2.4\ldots(2n)}\right)^2 \{P_{2n+1}(x) - P_{2n-1}(x)\}.$$
$$\text{(NICHOLSON.)}$$

18. Prove that, if $n \geqslant m$,
$$\int_0^\pi P_n(\cos\theta)\cos m\theta\, d\theta = \frac{\Gamma(\tfrac12 n + \tfrac12 m + \tfrac12)\Gamma(\tfrac12 n - \tfrac12 m + \tfrac12)}{\Gamma(\tfrac12 n + \tfrac12 m + 1)\Gamma(\tfrac12 n - \tfrac12 m + 1)} \quad \text{or} \quad 0$$

according as $n-m$ is even or odd. Deduce that

$$\sin(2m\cos^{-1}z) = -m \sum_{n=m}^{\infty} \frac{\Gamma(n+m+\frac{1}{2})\Gamma(n-m+\frac{1}{2})}{\Gamma(n+m+1)\Gamma(n-m+1)}\{P_{2n+1}(z) - P_{2n-1}(z)\}$$

and

$$\sin\{(2m+1)\cos^{-1}z\}$$

$$= -(m+\tfrac{1}{2}) \sum_{n=m}^{\infty} \frac{\Gamma(n+m+\frac{3}{2})\Gamma(n-m+\frac{1}{2})}{\Gamma(n+m+2)\Gamma(n-m+1)}\{P_{2n+2}(z) - P_{2n}(z)\}.$$

(Nicholson.)

19. Show that

$$\int_0^\pi P_n(\cos\theta)\sin m\theta \, d\theta = \frac{\Gamma(\frac{1}{2}m+\frac{1}{2}n+\frac{1}{2})\Gamma(\frac{1}{2}m-\frac{1}{2}n)}{\Gamma(\frac{1}{2}m-\frac{1}{2}n+\frac{1}{2})\Gamma(\frac{1}{2}m+\frac{1}{2}n+1)}$$

when $m > n$ and $m-n$ is odd, and that the value of the integral is zero in all other cases. (Heine.)

20. The equation of a nearly spherical surface of revolution is $r = a\{1+\epsilon P_n(\cos\theta)\}$, where ϵ is small. Show that, if ϵ^3 be neglected, its volume and surface are respectively

$$\frac{4\pi a^3}{3}\left\{1+\frac{3\epsilon^2}{2n+1}\right\}, \qquad 4\pi a^2\left\{1+\tfrac{1}{2}\epsilon^2\frac{n^2+n+2}{2n+1}\right\}.$$

21. Show that if $m \geqslant n$ and $s \geqslant 0$,

$$\int_{-1}^{1} P_m(x)P_n(x)P_{m+n-2s}(x)\,dx = \frac{2A_{m-s}A_{n-s}A_s}{(2m+2n-2s+1)A_{m+n-s}},$$

where $\qquad\qquad m!A_m = 1.3.5\dots(2m-1).$ (Ferrers.)

22. Prove that $\quad \sum_0^\infty h^n P_n(z)P_n(zh) = \dfrac{2K}{\pi(1-z^2h^2)^{1/2}},$

where K denotes the complete elliptic integral† of modulus

$$h\bigg/\sqrt{\left(\frac{1-z^2}{1-h^2z^2}\right)}.$$

(Geronimus.)

23. Show that, if $|h|$ is sufficiently small,

$$\sum_{n=0}^\infty h^n Q_n(z) = (1-2hz+h^2)^{-1/2}\operatorname{arccosh}\frac{h-z}{(z^2-1)^{1/2}}.$$

24. Prove that

$$\{z+(z^2-1)^{1/2}\}^{-n-1}$$

$$= -(n+1)\sum_{m=0}^\infty \frac{(2m+n+\frac{1}{2})\Gamma(m-\frac{1}{2})\Gamma(m+n+\frac{1}{2})}{2\pi.m!(m+n+1)!}Q_{2m+n}(z).$$

† The complete elliptic integral of modulus k is $\int_0^1 dt/\sqrt{\{(1-t^2)(1-k^2t^2)\}}$. See § 14.42.

25. If $x > 1$ and $y = \sqrt{(x^2-1)}$, show that

$$\int_0^\pi P_n(1+2y^2\sin^2\phi)\, d\phi = \pi\{P_n(x)\}^2. \qquad \text{(Nicholson.)}$$

26. Prove that, if $-1 < x_1 < 1$ and $-1 < x_2 < 1$,

$$\int_0^{2\pi} d\phi \int_{-1}^1 dx\, P_n(\xi_1)P_n(\xi_2) = \frac{4\pi}{2n+1} P_n(\xi),$$

where

$$\xi_1 = xx_1+(1-x^2)^{1/2}(1-x_1^2)^{1/2}\cos(\phi-\phi_1),$$
$$\xi_2 = xx_2+(1-x^2)^{1/2}(1-x_2^2)^{1/2}\cos(\phi-\phi_2),$$
$$\xi\ = x_1x_2+(1-x_1^2)^{1/2}(1-x_2^2)^{1/2}\cos(\phi_1-\phi_2).$$

CHAPTER XII

BESSEL FUNCTIONS

12.1. Bessel's differential equation

In the present chapter we determine the complete solution of Bessel's differential equation

$$\frac{d^2w}{dz^2} + \frac{1}{z}\frac{dw}{dz} + \left(1 - \frac{\nu^2}{z^2}\right)w = 0,$$

where ν is a constant. It is an equation of the confluent hypergeometric type considered in § 10.61, and has a regular singularity of exponents $\pm\nu$ at the origin and an irregular singularity at infinity.

This differential equation is of frequent occurrence in physical problems. For example, it arises in the determination of the solutions of Laplace's equation associated with the circular cylinder, and so its solutions are sometimes called cylinder functions. For suppose we transform Laplace's equation

$$\frac{\partial^2 V}{\partial X^2} + \frac{\partial^2 V}{\partial Y^2} + \frac{\partial^2 V}{\partial Z^2} = 0$$

to cylindrical coordinates (ρ, ϕ, Z) defined by the equations

$$X = \rho\cos\phi, \qquad Y = \rho\sin\phi;$$

this gives

$$\frac{\partial^2 V}{\partial\rho^2} + \frac{1}{\rho}\frac{\partial V}{\partial\rho} + \frac{1}{\rho^2}\frac{\partial^2 V}{\partial\phi^2} + \frac{\partial^2 V}{\partial Z^2} = 0.$$

It follows that the expression

$$V = e^{kZ}w(\rho)\cos(\nu\phi+\epsilon),$$

where k, ν, and ϵ are constants, is a solution of Laplace's equation provided that w satisfies Bessel's equation

$$\frac{d^2w}{d\rho^2} + \frac{1}{\rho}\frac{dw}{d\rho} + \left(k^2 - \frac{\nu^2}{\rho^2}\right)w = 0$$

with independent variable $k\rho$.

In most physical problems V must be a one-valued function of position in space, and so ν must be an integer. In this case the exponent-difference at the origin is an integer and it turns out that it is impossible to express the complete solution in powers of z. It will, therefore, be necessary to distinguish between formulae which hold for general values of ν and those which are valid only when ν is an integer. We do this by adopting the convention, usual in this subject, that *the parameter occurring in Bessel's equation will be denoted by a Roman letter instead of a Greek one in any formula which holds only for integral values of that parameter.*

12.11. The Bessel functions

If we write $z^2 = 4x$ and denote by ϑ the operator $x\,d/dx$, Bessel's equation becomes

$$(\vartheta^2 - \tfrac{1}{4}\nu^2)w + xw = 0.$$

This equation is satisfied formally by the series

$$w = x^\alpha \sum_{r=0}^{\infty} c_r x^r,$$

provided that α is a root of the indicial equation $\alpha^2 - \tfrac{1}{4}\nu^2 = 0$, the coefficients c_r being connected by the recurrence formula

$$\{(\alpha+r)^2 - \tfrac{1}{4}\nu^2\}c_r + c_{r-1} = 0.$$

Now if we take $\alpha = \tfrac{1}{2}\nu$, the recurrence formula becomes

$$(\nu+r)rc_r + c_{r-1} = 0,$$

which is satisfied by taking

$$c_r = \frac{A(-1)^r}{r!\,\Gamma(\nu+r+1)},$$

where A is independent of r. Hence

$$w = Ax^{\frac{1}{2}\nu} \sum_{r=0}^{\infty} \frac{(-x)^r}{r!\,\Gamma(\nu+r+1)}$$

is a series solution of the equation in question. But since this infinite series converges uniformly and absolutely in every circle $|x| \leqslant R$, the formal processes by which this solution was obtained are valid all over the x-plane. We have thus shown that

$$w = Ax^{\frac{1}{2}\nu} \sum_{r=0}^{\infty} \frac{(-x)^r}{r!\,\Gamma(\nu+r+1)}$$

and, similarly,

$$w = Bx^{-\frac{1}{2}\nu} \sum_{r=0}^{\infty} \frac{(-x)^r}{r!\,\Gamma(-\nu+r+1)},$$

where $z^2 = 4x$, are two solutions, not necessarily independent, of Bessel's differential equation of order ν.

We now define the Bessel function of the first kind of order ν to be the function

$$J_\nu(z) = (\tfrac{1}{2}z)^\nu \sum_{r=0}^{\infty} \frac{(-1)^r(\tfrac{1}{2}z)^{2r}}{r!\,\Gamma(\nu+r+1)},$$

where $(\tfrac{1}{2}z)^\nu = \exp(\nu \log \tfrac{1}{2}z)$, the logarithm having its principal value. The function $(\tfrac{1}{2}z)^{-\nu}J_\nu(z)$ is thus an integral function.

In this notation, the expression

$$w = AJ_\nu(z) + BJ_{-\nu}(z)$$

is a solution of Bessel's differential equation depending on two arbitrary constants; it remains to determine whether it is the complete solution or not. In the first place, it is obviously not the complete solution when $\nu = 0$, since it then reduces to a constant multiple of $J_0(z)$. Again, if n is a positive integer, we have

$$J_{-n}(z) = (\tfrac{1}{2}z)^{-n} \sum_{r=0}^{\infty} \frac{(-1)^r(\tfrac{1}{2}z)^{2r}}{r!\,\Gamma(-n+r+1)}$$

$$= (\tfrac{1}{2}z)^{-n} \sum_{r=n}^{\infty} \frac{(-1)^r(\tfrac{1}{2}z)^{2r}}{r!\,\Gamma(-n+r+1)}$$

$$= (\tfrac{1}{2}z)^{n} \sum_{s=0}^{\infty} \frac{(-1)^{n+s}(\tfrac{1}{2}z)^{2s}}{\Gamma(n+s+1)s!} = (-1)^n J_n(z),$$

since $1/\Gamma(t)$ vanishes when t is a negative integer or zero. The solution we have just obtained is therefore not the complete solution when ν is an integer, since it then reduces to a constant multiple of $J_\nu(z)$. The nature of the complete solution in this case accordingly requires further investigation.

When ν is not an integer each coefficient in the expansions of $J_\nu(z)$ and $J_{-\nu}(z)$ is finite and non-zero. The functions $J_\nu(z)$ and $J_{-\nu}(z)$ are, in this case, evidently linearly independent solutions of Bessel's differential equation.

Example. Prove that the Wronskian of $J_\nu(z)$ and $J_{-\nu}(z)$ is

$$\Delta(J_\nu, J_{-\nu}) = -\frac{2\sin\nu\pi}{\pi z}.$$

By § 10.11, Ex. 2, we have $\Delta(J_\nu, J_{-\nu}) = C/z$, where C is a constant. Now when $|z|$ is small,

$$J_\nu(z) = \frac{(\tfrac{1}{2}z)^\nu}{\Gamma(\nu+1)}\{1+O(z^2)\}, \qquad J_\nu'(z) = \frac{(\tfrac{1}{2}z)^{\nu-1}}{2\Gamma(\nu)}\{1+O(z^2)\}.$$

Hence

$$\Delta(J_\nu, J_{-\nu}) = J_\nu(z)J'_{-\nu}(z) - J'_\nu(z)J_{-\nu}(z)$$

$$= \left[\frac{1}{\Gamma(1+\nu)\Gamma(-\nu)} - \frac{1}{\Gamma(1-\nu)\Gamma(\nu)}\right]\left[\frac{1}{z} + O(z)\right]$$

$$= -\frac{2\sin\nu\pi}{\pi z} + O(z).$$

Comparing the two expressions for the Wronskian, we find that

$$\Delta(J_\nu, J_{-\nu}) = -\frac{2\sin\nu\pi}{\pi z}.$$

This result shows that $J_\nu(z)$ and $J_{-\nu}(z)$ are linearly independent if ν is not an integer or zero.

12.12. The recurrence formulae for $J_\nu(z)$

As $J_\nu(z)$ is the limiting form of a certain hypergeometric function, we should naturally expect that Gauss's formulae connecting contiguous hypergeometric functions would provide, in the limit, recurrence formulae connecting Bessel functions. This is indeed the case, but it is much simpler to prove these recurrence formulae directly from the definition of $J_\nu(z)$.

The first recurrence formula states that

$$J_{\nu-1}(z) + J_{\nu+1}(z) = \frac{2\nu}{z}J_\nu(z). \tag{i}$$

For

$$J_{\nu-1}(z) + J_{\nu+1}(z)$$

$$= (\tfrac{1}{2}z)^{\nu-1}\sum_{r=0}^{\infty}\frac{(-\tfrac{1}{4}z^2)^r}{r!\,\Gamma(\nu+r)} + (\tfrac{1}{2}z)^{\nu+1}\sum_{r=0}^{\infty}\frac{(-\tfrac{1}{4}z^2)^r}{r!\,\Gamma(\nu+r+2)}$$

$$= (\tfrac{1}{2}z)^{\nu-1}\left[\sum_{r=0}^{\infty}\frac{(-\tfrac{1}{4}z^2)^r}{r!\,\Gamma(\nu+r)} - \sum_{r=0}^{\infty}\frac{(-\tfrac{1}{4}z^2)^{r+1}}{r!\,\Gamma(\nu+r+2)}\right]$$

$$= (\tfrac{1}{2}z)^{\nu-1}\left[\frac{1}{\Gamma(\nu)} + \sum_{r=1}^{\infty}\left\{\frac{1}{r!\,\Gamma(\nu+r)} - \frac{1}{(r-1)!\,\Gamma(\nu+r+1)}\right\}(-\tfrac{1}{4}z^2)^r\right]$$

$$= \nu(\tfrac{1}{2}z)^{\nu-1}\sum_{r=0}^{\infty}\frac{(-\tfrac{1}{4}z^2)^r}{r!\,\Gamma(\nu+r+1)}$$

$$= \frac{2\nu}{z}J_\nu(z),$$

the reordering of the terms of the two infinite series being justifiable on account of their absolute convergence.

Similarly we see that

$$J_{\nu-1}(z)-J_{\nu+1}(z)$$

$$= (\tfrac{1}{2}z)^{\nu-1}\left[\frac{1}{\Gamma(\nu)}+\sum_{r=1}^{\infty}\left\{\frac{1}{r!\,\Gamma(\nu+r)}+\frac{1}{(r-1)!\,\Gamma(\nu+r+1)}\right\}\left(-\frac{z^2}{4}\right)^r\right]$$

$$= (\tfrac{1}{2}z)^{\nu-1}\sum_{r=0}^{\infty}\frac{\nu+2r}{r!\,\Gamma(\nu+r+1)}\left(-\frac{z^2}{4}\right)^r,$$

and so
$$J_{\nu-1}(z)-J_{\nu+1}(z) = 2J_{\nu}'(z), \tag{ii}$$

where the accent denotes differentiation with respect to z. From (i) and (ii), the remaining recurrence formulae

$$\frac{\nu}{z}J_{\nu}(z)+J_{\nu}'(z) = J_{\nu-1}(z), \tag{iii}$$

and
$$\frac{\nu}{z}J_{\nu}(z)-J_{\nu}'(z) = J_{\nu+1}(z), \tag{iv}$$

may be easily obtained.

Example 1. Prove by induction that, when m is an integer,

$$(\tfrac{1}{2}z)^m = \sum_{n=0}^{\infty}\frac{(m+2n)(m+n-1)!}{n!}J_{m+2n}(z).$$

Example 2. Show that, if m is any positive integer,

$$\left(\frac{d}{z\,dz}\right)^m\{z^{\nu}J_{\nu}(z)\} = z^{\nu-m}J_{\nu-m}(z),$$

$$\left(\frac{d}{z\,dz}\right)^m\{z^{-\nu}J_{\nu}(z)\} = (-1)^m z^{-\nu-m}J_{\nu+m}(z).$$

Example 3. Prove that, if ν is real, there lies precisely one zero of $z^{-\nu}J_{\nu+1}(z)$ between any two consecutive real zeros of $z^{-\nu}J_{\nu}(z)$.

Example 4. Show that

$$J_{\nu}(z)J_{1-\nu}(z)+J_{-\nu}(z)J_{\nu-1}(z) = \frac{2\sin\nu\pi}{\pi z}.$$

Example 5. Prove that

$$J_{\frac{1}{2}}(z) = \left(\frac{2}{\pi z}\right)^{\frac{1}{2}}\sin z, \qquad J_{-\frac{1}{2}}(z) = \left(\frac{2}{\pi z}\right)^{\frac{1}{2}}\cos z.$$

Deduce the values of $J_{\pm\frac{3}{2}}(z)$.

Example 6. Show that, if $\alpha \neq \beta$ and $\nu > -1$,

$$(\alpha^2-\beta^2)\int_0^x t\,J_{\nu}(\alpha t)J_{\nu}(\beta t)\,dt = x\left\{J_{\nu}(\alpha x)\frac{dJ_{\nu}(\beta x)}{dx}-J_{\nu}(\beta x)\frac{dJ_{\nu}(\alpha x)}{dx}\right\},$$

$$2\alpha^2\int_0^x t\{J_{\nu}(\alpha t)\}^2\,dt = (\alpha^2 x^2-\nu^2)\{J_{\nu}(\alpha x)\}^2+\left\{x\frac{dJ_{\nu}(\alpha x)}{dx}\right\}^2.$$

(LOMMEL.)

Example 7. Prove that, if $\nu > -1$ and α and β are distinct zeros of $J_\nu(x)$, then

$$\int_0^1 t J_\nu(\alpha t) J_\nu(\beta t)\, dt = 0,$$

$$\int_0^1 t\{J_\nu(\alpha t)\}^2\, dt = \tfrac{1}{2}\{J_{\nu+1}(\alpha)\}^2.$$

Hence show that, when $\nu > -1$, the zeros of $J_\nu(x)$, apart from $x = 0$, are all real and distinct. (LOMMEL.)

12.13. Schläfli's contour integral for $J_\nu(z)$

If we use Hankel's formula

$$\frac{1}{\Gamma(\nu+r+1)} = \frac{1}{2\pi i} \int_{-\infty}^{(0+)} e^t t^{-\nu-r-1}\, dt,$$

where $|\arg t| \leqslant \pi$ on the path of integration, we obtain

$$(\tfrac{1}{2}z)^{-\nu} J_\nu(z) = \sum_{r=0}^{\infty} (-\tfrac{1}{4}z^2)^r \frac{1}{2\pi i\, r!} \int_{-\infty}^{(0+)} e^t t^{-\nu-r-1}\, dt.$$

We consider, therefore, the function

$$F(z) = \frac{1}{2\pi i} \int_{-\infty}^{(0+)} \exp\!\left(t - \frac{z^2}{4t}\right) t^{-\nu-1}\, dt$$

obtained by inverting the order of integration and summation in this last expression.

By applying the theorem of § 5.51, we find that $F(z)$ is an integral function whose derivatives of all orders can be obtained by differentiating under the sign of integration. It follows that the Taylor expansion of $F(z)$ is

$$F(z) = \sum_{r=0}^{\infty} (-\tfrac{1}{4}z^2)^r \frac{1}{2\pi i\, r!} \int_{-\infty}^{(0+)} e^t t^{-\nu-r-1}\, dt.$$

Thus $F(z)$ and $(\tfrac{1}{2}z)^{-\nu} J_\nu(z)$ are integral functions with the same Taylor expansion and so are identical. Hence we have

$$J_\nu(z) = \frac{(\tfrac{1}{2}z)^\nu}{2\pi i} \int_{-\infty}^{(0+)} \exp\!\left(t - \frac{z^2}{4t}\right) t^{-\nu-1}\, dt,$$

where $|\arg t| \leqslant \pi$ on the path of integration. This result is due to Schläfli.†

12.2. The Bessel functions of integral order

When n is a positive or negative integer or zero, Schläfli's integral

$$J_n(z) = \frac{(\tfrac{1}{2}z)^n}{2\pi i} \int_{-\infty}^{(0+)} \exp\!\left(t - \frac{z^2}{4t}\right) t^{-n-1}\, dt$$

has as integrand a one-valued analytic function of t whose only singularity of finite affix is an essential singularity at the origin. Hence we can deform the path of integration, without altering the value of the integral, until it consists of the circle $|t| = \tfrac{1}{2}|z|R$, provided that z is not zero. Making the substitution $t = \tfrac{1}{2}zu$, we find that this gives

$$J_n(z) = \frac{1}{2\pi i} \int_C \exp\{\tfrac{1}{2}z(u - u^{-1})\}\, u^{-n-1}\, du,$$

where C denotes the circle $|u| = R$. This formula evidently holds also when C is any simple closed contour encircling the origin.

In particular, if we take for C the circle $|u| = 1$, on which $u = e^{\theta i}$ where $-\pi \leqslant \theta \leqslant \pi$, we obtain the formula

$$J_n(z) = \frac{1}{2\pi} \int_{-\pi}^{\pi} e^{-in\theta + iz\sin\theta}\, d\theta$$

$$= \frac{1}{2\pi} \int_0^{\pi} \{e^{-in\theta + iz\sin\theta} + e^{in\theta - iz\sin\theta}\}\, d\theta,$$

and hence

$$J_n(z) = \frac{1}{\pi} \int_0^{\pi} \cos(n\theta - z\sin\theta)\, d\theta.$$

This is Bessel's‡ integral for $J_n(z)$.

Example 1. Show that

$$J_n(z) = \frac{1}{\pi} \int_0^{\pi} \cos(z\cos\theta - \tfrac{1}{2}n\pi)\cos n\theta\, d\theta.$$

---

† *Ann. di Mat.* (2), **5** (1873), 204.   ‡ *Berliner Abh.* (1824), 1–24.

Deduce, by the use of Jacobi's lemma, Poisson's integral formula

$$J_n(z) = \frac{(\tfrac{1}{2}z)^n}{\Gamma(n+\tfrac{1}{2})\Gamma(\tfrac{1}{2})} \int\limits_0^\pi \cos(z\cos\theta)\sin^{2n}\theta \, d\theta,$$

where $n \geqslant 0$.

Example 2. Show from the series definition that

$$J_\nu(z) = \frac{(\tfrac{1}{2}z)^\nu}{\Gamma(\nu+\tfrac{1}{2})\Gamma(\tfrac{1}{2})} \int\limits_0^\pi \cos(z\cos\theta)\sin^{2\nu}\theta \, d\theta,$$

provided that $\mathrm{Rl}(\nu+\tfrac{1}{2}) > 0$.

Example 3. Prove that, if $z = x+iy$ and if ν is real and not less than $-\tfrac{1}{2}$,

$$|J_\nu(z)| \leqslant \frac{|\tfrac{1}{2}z|^\nu e^{|y|}}{\Gamma(\nu+1)}.$$

Example 4. Show that

$$\int\limits_0^\pi \cos(\nu\theta - z\sin\theta) \, d\theta$$

satisfies Bessel's equation of order ν only when ν is an integer.

Example 5. Show that

$$J_n(z) = \frac{1}{2\pi i} \int\limits_{-\pi i}^{\pi i} e^{z\sinh t - nt} \, dt,$$

where the path of integration is any curve joining the points $\pm\pi i$.

12.21. The generating function for $J_n(z)$

We have just proved that

$$J_n(z) = \frac{1}{2\pi i} \int\limits_C e^{\tfrac{1}{2}z(u-1/u)} \frac{du}{u^{n+1}},$$

where C denotes any circle with centre at the origin. Since the only singularity of the integrand is at the origin, it follows immediately from Laurent's theorem (§ 4.52) that

$$e^{\tfrac{1}{2}z(u-1/u)} = \sum_{-\infty}^\infty u^n J_n(z),$$

the series converging uniformly with respect to u and z when u lies in any annulus $0 < R_1 \leqslant |u| \leqslant R_2$ and z lies in any bounded closed domain.

The functions $J_n(z)$ are therefore the coefficients in the expansion of the generating function $e^{\frac{1}{2}z(u-1/u)}$ as a Laurent series in u, and, for this reason, are sometimes called the *Bessel coefficients*. This expansion was, in fact, Schlömilch's† definition of the Bessel coefficients, and from it he derived many of their principal properties.

Example 1. Show by means of Schlömilch's generating function that the Bessel coefficients satisfy the recurrence formulae of § 12.12, and hence that they are solutions of Bessel's differential equation.

Show also that $\quad J_{-n}(z) = J_n(-z) = (-1)^n J_n(z)$.

Example 2. Prove that

$$e^{iz\sin\theta} = J_0(z) + 2\sum_1^\infty J_{2n}(z)\cos 2n\theta + 2i\sum_0^\infty J_{2n+1}(z)\sin(2n+1)\theta,$$

and deduce the Fourier series for $\cos(z\sin\theta)$ and $\sin(z\sin\theta)$. (JACOBI.)

Example 3. Prove that

$$1 = J_0(z) + 2\sum_1^\infty J_{2n}(z),$$

$$z = 2\sum_1^\infty (2n+1)J_{2n+1}(z),$$

$$\tfrac{1}{2}z\cos z = J_1(z) - 9J_3(z) + 25J_5(z) - ...,$$

$$\tfrac{1}{2}z\sin z = 4J_2(z) - 16J_4(z) + 36J_6(z) - ....\qquad \text{(LOMMEL.)}$$

Example 4. Show that

$$J_n(z+z') = \sum_{-\infty}^\infty J_m(z)J_{n-m}(z'). \qquad \text{(K. NEUMANN.)}$$

12.3. The solution of Bessel's equation by complex integrals

We have already seen (§ 12.2, Ex. 5) that Bessel's differential equation

$$z^2\frac{d^2w}{dz^2} + z\frac{dw}{dz} + (z^2 - \nu^2)w = 0$$

is satisfied by $\quad w = \displaystyle\int_{-\pi i}^{\pi i} e^{z\sinh t - \nu t}\, dt$

when ν is an integer. We now propose to determine whether there exist solutions of the form

$$w = \int_a^b e^{z\sinh t - \nu t}\, dt$$

for general values of ν.

† *Zeitschrift für Math. und Phys.* **2** (1857), 137–65.

It should be observed that the integrand is an integral function of t, so that the integral is independent of the particular path of integration which joins the points a and b. It is, moreover, useless to consider integrals of this type round closed contours since they all vanish identically.

When the limits a and b are finite, we can differentiate w under the sign of integration to obtain

$$z^2\frac{d^2w}{dz^2}+z\frac{dw}{dz}+(z^2-\nu^2)w$$

$$= \int_a^b e^{z\sinh t-\nu t}(z^2\cosh^2 t+z\sinh t-\nu^2)\,dt$$

$$= \left[e^{z\sinh t-\nu t}(z\cosh t+\nu)\right]_a^b.$$

This result also holds when one or both of the limits are infinite provided that the integral for w converges uniformly. If we can choose a and b so that this last expression vanishes, w is a solution of Bessel's equation.

When the limits are $\pm\pi i$, we have

$$\left[e^{z\sinh t-\nu t}(z\cosh t+\nu)\right]_{-\pi i}^{\pi i} = 2i(z-\nu)\sin\nu\pi.$$

Hence
$$w = \int_{-\pi i}^{\pi i} e^{z\sinh t-\nu t}\,dt$$

is a solution of Bessel's equation if and only if ν is an integer or zero.

When ν is not an integer or zero, the appropriate values of a and b are given by the considerations which follow.

Let us consider now a path of integration consisting of the negative part of the straight line $\mathrm{Im}\,t = \alpha$, the imaginary axis from αi to βi, and the positive part of the straight line $\mathrm{Im}\,t = \beta$. The limits of integration are then $-\infty+\alpha i$ and $+\infty+\beta i$ in the usual notation. We suppose, moreover, that $z = re^{\theta i}$ lies in a bounded closed domain D for which $-\frac{1}{2}\pi+\alpha+\delta \leqslant \theta \leqslant \frac{1}{2}\pi+\alpha-\delta$, where δ is an arbitrary positive number.

When R is positive, we have

$$\mathrm{Rl}\{z\sinh(-R+\alpha i)\}$$

$$= \tfrac{1}{2}re^{-R}\cos(\theta+\alpha)-\tfrac{1}{2}re^{R}\cos(\theta-\alpha) \leqslant \tfrac{1}{2}re^{-R}-\tfrac{1}{2}re^{R}\sin\delta.$$

If $\nu = \lambda + i\mu$, it follows that

$$\left|e^{z\sinh t - \nu t}(z\cosh t + \nu)\right|_{t=-R+\alpha i}$$
$$\leqslant (r\cosh R + |\nu|)\exp(\tfrac{1}{2}re^{-R} - \tfrac{1}{2}re^{R}\sin\delta + \lambda R + \mu\alpha).$$

Since by hypothesis r is bounded in D, we deduce that

$$\left[e^{z\sinh t - \nu t}(z\cosh t + \nu)\right]_{t=-R+\alpha i} \to 0$$

as $R \to \infty$, the convergence being uniform with respect to z when z lies in D. In a similar manner we can show that

$$\left[e^{z\sinh t - \nu t}(z\cosh t + \nu)\right]_{t=R+\beta i} \to 0$$

as $R \to \infty$, provided that $\beta = \pm\pi - \alpha$, the convergence being uniform with respect to z when z lies in D.

Lastly, it can be shown without much difficulty that, under these conditions, the integral

$$w = \int_{-\infty+\alpha i}^{\infty+\beta i} e^{z\sinh t - \nu t}\, dt$$

converges uniformly with respect to z when z lies in D. Hence w is an analytic function, regular in D, whose derivatives can be found by differentiation under the sign of integration, and so w satisfies all the conditions necessary to make it a solution of Bessel's equation of order ν.

We have thus shown that the functions

$$\int_{-\infty+\alpha i}^{\infty+(\pi-\alpha)i} e^{z\sinh t - \nu t}\, dt, \qquad \int_{-\infty+\alpha i}^{\infty-(\pi+\alpha)i} e^{z\sinh t - \nu t}\, dt$$

are solutions of Bessel's equation of order ν, valid when z lies in the angle $-\tfrac{1}{2}\pi + \alpha + \delta \leqslant \arg z \leqslant \tfrac{1}{2}\pi + \alpha - \delta$, where δ is an arbitrary positive number. It is evident, moreover, that the paths of integration can be any contours which are asymptotic to the particular contours defined above.

12.31. The Hankel functions

In particular, we find, by taking $\alpha = 0$, that

$$H_\nu^{(1)}(z) = \frac{1}{\pi i} \int_{-\infty}^{\infty+\pi i} e^{z\sinh t - \nu t}\, dt,$$

$$H_\nu^{(2)}(z) = -\frac{1}{\pi i} \int_{-\infty}^{\infty - \pi i} e^{z \sinh t - \nu t}\, dt,$$

are solutions of Bessel's equation of order ν, valid when $|\arg z| < \tfrac{1}{2}\pi$. These functions are called *the Bessel functions of the third kind*, or, more briefly, *the Hankel functions*† of order ν.

The analytical continuation of these functions for other ranges of values of $\arg z$ is provided by the formulae

$$H_\nu^{(1)}(z) = \frac{1}{\pi i} \int_{-\infty + \alpha i}^{\infty + (\pi - \alpha)i} e^{z \sinh t - \nu t}\, dt,$$

$$H_\nu^{(2)}(z) = -\frac{1}{\pi i} \int_{-\infty + \alpha i}^{\infty - (\pi + \alpha)i} e^{z \sinh t - \nu t}\, dt,$$

where $-\tfrac{1}{2}\pi + \alpha + \delta \leqslant \arg z \leqslant \tfrac{1}{2}\pi + \alpha - \delta$ and $\delta > 0$. The argument by which this is proved may be illustrated by considering the case when $\alpha = \tfrac{1}{2}\pi$.

$H_\nu^{(1)}(z)$ is defined when $|\arg z| < \tfrac{1}{2}\pi$, whilst

$$\frac{1}{\pi i} \int_{-\infty + \frac{1}{2}\pi i}^{\infty + \frac{1}{2}\pi i} e^{z \sinh t - \nu t}\, dt$$

is a solution of Bessel's equation when $0 < \arg z < \pi$. We have to show that these two functions are identical in the first quadrant, their common region of definition.

Let us suppose that $0 < \delta \leqslant \arg z \leqslant \tfrac{1}{2}\pi - \delta$. If we apply Cauchy's theorem to the rectangle with vertices $\tfrac{1}{2}\pi i$, $R + \tfrac{1}{2}\pi i$, $R + \pi i$, πi, we find that

$$\int_{\frac{1}{2}\pi i}^{R + \pi i} e^{z \sinh t - \nu t}\, dt = \int_{\frac{1}{2}\pi i}^{R + \frac{1}{2}\pi i} e^{z \sinh t - \nu t}\, dt + \int_{R + \frac{1}{2}\pi i}^{R + \pi i} e^{z \sinh t - \nu t}\, dt.$$

But, on account of our restrictions on $\arg z$, the second integral on the right-hand side tends to zero as $R \to \infty$, and so

$$\int_{\frac{1}{2}\pi i}^{\infty + \pi i} e^{z \sinh t - \nu t}\, dt = \int_{\frac{1}{2}\pi i}^{\infty + \frac{1}{2}\pi i} e^{z \sinh t - \nu t}\, dt.$$

---

† So called because it was Hankel who first realized their importance. The definition adopted here is not the usual one, but is essentially equivalent to that of Hopf and Sommerfeld, *Archiv der Math. und Phys.* (3), **18** (1911), 1–16.

Similarly we can show that

$$\int_{-\infty}^{\frac{1}{2}\pi i} e^{z \sinh t - \nu t}\, dt = \int_{-\infty+\frac{1}{2}\pi i}^{\frac{1}{2}\pi i} e^{z \sinh t - \nu t}\, dt.$$

Hence, when z lies in the first quadrant,

$$\int_{-\infty}^{\infty+\pi i} e^{z \sinh t - \nu t}\, dt = \int_{-\infty-\frac{1}{2}\pi i}^{\infty+\frac{1}{2}\pi i} e^{z \sinh t - \nu t}\, dt,$$

which is the required result.

In this way the Hankel functions are continued analytically all over the z-plane. It will, however, be observed that the functions so defined are not one-valued, but possess a branch-point at the origin, even in the case when ν is an integer.†

Example 1. Show that $H^{(1)}_{-\nu}(z)$, $H^{(2)}_{-\nu}(z)$ are also solutions of Bessel's equation of order ν by proving that

$$H^{(1)}_{-\nu}(z) = e^{\nu\pi i}H^{(1)}_{\nu}(z), \qquad H^{(2)}_{-\nu}(z) = e^{-\nu\pi i}H^{(2)}_{\nu}(z).$$

Example 2. Prove that the Hankel functions $H^{(1)}_{\nu}(z)$, $H^{(2)}_{\nu}(z)$ satisfy the same recurrence formulae as $J_{\nu}(z)$.

Example 3. Show that‡

$$H^{(1)}_{\nu}(ze^{\pi i}) = -e^{-\nu\pi i}H^{(2)}_{\nu}(z),$$
$$H^{(2)}_{\nu}(ze^{\pi i}) = 2\cos\nu\pi\, H^{(2)}_{\nu}(z) + e^{\nu\pi i}H^{(1)}_{\nu}(z).$$

Hence prove that

$$H^{(1)}_{\nu}(ze^{2\pi i}) = -H^{(1)}_{\nu}(z) - 2\cos\nu\pi\, e^{-\nu\pi i}H^{(2)}_{\nu}(z),$$
$$H^{(2)}_{\nu}(ze^{2\pi i}) = (4\cos^2\nu\pi - 1)H^{(2)}_{\nu}(z) + 2\cos\nu\pi\, e^{\nu\pi i}H^{(1)}_{\nu}(z).$$

(WEBER; GRAF.)

12.32. The connexion between the Bessel and Hankel functions

We shall now show that *the Hankel and Bessel functions are connected by the relations*

$$2J_{\nu}(z) = H^{(1)}_{\nu}(z) + H^{(2)}_{\nu}(z),$$
$$2J_{-\nu}(z) = e^{\nu\pi i}H^{(1)}_{\nu}(z) + e^{-\nu\pi i}H^{(2)}_{\nu}(z),$$

provided that§ $|\arg z| < \pi$.

† See Ex. 3.
‡ It is simplest to prove these formulae in the first instance when $|\arg z| < \frac{1}{2}\pi$; in this case $\frac{1}{2}\pi < \arg(ze^{\pi i}) < \frac{3}{2}\pi$. The formulae for general values of z follow by analytical continuation.
§ This restriction is needed since the Bessel functions are not defined outside this range of values of $\arg z$. The formulae we are about to prove may be used to extend their range of definition.

If $z = re^{\theta i}$, where $-\pi < \theta < \pi$, the formulae of the previous section give

$$H_\nu^{(1)}(z) = \frac{1}{\pi i} \int_{-\infty+\theta i}^{\infty+(\pi-\theta)i} \exp(re^{\theta i}\sinh t - \nu t)\, dt,$$

$$H_\nu^{(2)}(z) = -\frac{1}{\pi i} \int_{-\infty+\theta i}^{\infty-(\pi+\theta)i} \exp(re^{\theta i}\sinh t - \nu t)\, dt.$$

Hence we have

$$\tfrac{1}{2}\{H_\nu^{(1)}(z)+H_\nu^{(2)}(z)\} = \frac{1}{2\pi i} \int_{\infty-\theta i-\pi i}^{\infty-\theta i+\pi i} \exp(re^{\theta i}\sinh t - \nu t)\, dt,$$

the path of integration being the positive part of the line $\operatorname{Im} t = -\pi - \theta$, the imaginary axis from $-(\pi+\theta)i$ to $(\pi-\theta)i$, and the positive part of the line $\operatorname{Im} t = \pi - \theta$. If we make, in turn, the two substitutions $t = u - \theta i$, $e^u = 2v/r$, we obtain

$$\tfrac{1}{2}\{H_\nu^{(1)}(z)+H_\nu^{(2)}(z)\} = \frac{1}{2\pi i} \int_{\infty-\pi i}^{\infty+\pi i} \exp\{re^{\theta i}\sinh(u-\theta i) - \nu u + \nu\theta i\}\, du$$

$$= \frac{1}{2\pi i} \int_{\infty-\pi i}^{\infty+\pi i} \exp\{\tfrac{1}{2}re^u - \tfrac{1}{2}re^{2\theta i}e^{-u}\}\frac{e^{\nu\theta i}}{e^{\nu u}}\, du$$

$$= \frac{1}{2\pi i} \int_{-\infty}^{(0+)} \exp\left\{v - \frac{r^2 e^{2\theta i}}{4v}\right\}\frac{r^\nu e^{\nu\theta i}}{2^\nu v^\nu}\frac{dv}{v}$$

$$= \frac{1}{2\pi i}(\tfrac{1}{2}z)^\nu \int_{-\infty}^{(0+)} \exp\left\{v - \frac{z^2}{4v}\right\}\frac{dv}{v^{\nu+1}}.$$

But this last expression is Schläfli's integral for $J_\nu(z)$, and therefore

$$J_\nu(z) = \tfrac{1}{2}\{H_\nu^{(1)}(z)+H_\nu^{(2)}(z)\}.$$

From this we deduce that

$$J_{-\nu}(z) = \tfrac{1}{2}\{H_{-\nu}^{(1)}(z)+H_{-\nu}^{(2)}(z)\} = \tfrac{1}{2}\{e^{\nu\pi i}H_\nu^{(1)}(z)+e^{-\nu\pi i}H_\nu^{(2)}(z)\},$$

a result which reduces to $J_{-n}(z) = (-1)^n J_n(z)$ when n is an integer.

12.33. The complete solution of Bessel's equation

Although the Hankel functions are merely linear combinations of the functions $J_\nu(z)$ and $J_{-\nu}(z)$ when ν is not an integer, they possess, as we shall prove, the remarkable property of being linearly independent solutions of Bessel's equation for all values of the parameter ν, so that the complete solution is

$$w = A H_\nu^{(1)}(z) + B H_\nu^{(2)}(z),$$

where A and B are arbitrary constants.

For when ν is not an integer, the Wronskian† of $J_\nu(z)$ and $J_{-\nu}(z)$ is given by

$$\Delta(J_\nu, J_{-\nu}) = J_\nu(z) J'_{-\nu}(z) - J'_\nu(z) J_{-\nu}(z)$$

$$= \tfrac{1}{4}\bigg[\{H_\nu^{(1)}(z) + H_\nu^{(2)}(z)\} \frac{d}{dz}\{e^{\nu\pi i} H_\nu^{(1)}(z) + e^{-\nu\pi i} H_\nu^{(2)}(z)\} -$$

$$- \{e^{\nu\pi i} H_\nu^{(1)}(z) + e^{-\nu\pi i} H_\nu^{(2)}(z)\} \frac{d}{dz}\{H_\nu^{(1)}(z) + H_\nu^{(2)}(z)\} \bigg]$$

$$= -\tfrac{1}{2} i \sin \nu\pi \, \Delta(H_\nu^{(1)}, H_\nu^{(2)}),$$

and so, by the example of § 12.11,

$$\Delta(H_\nu^{(1)}, H_\nu^{(2)}) = \frac{4}{\pi i z}.$$

But, for any fixed value of z, the Hankel functions are integral functions of ν, and so, by continuity, the Wronskian of $H_\nu^{(1)}(z)$ and $H_\nu^{(2)}(z)$ is $4/(\pi i z)$ for all values of ν. Since the Wronskian never vanishes, $H_\nu^{(1)}(z)$ and $H_\nu^{(2)}(z)$ are linearly independent solutions of Bessel's equation.

12.4. The Bessel function of the second kind

In view of the fact that the behaviour of $J_\nu(z)$ near the origin is much simpler than that of the Hankel functions, it is very desirable to retain it as one of the standard solutions of Bessel's equation. As a second solution we take Weber's‡ function $Y_\nu(z)$, defined by the equation

$$Y_\nu(z) = \frac{1}{2i}\{H_\nu^{(1)}(z) - H_\nu^{(2)}(z)\},$$

for all values of the parameter ν. Remembering that

$$J_\nu(z) = \tfrac{1}{2}\{H_\nu^{(1)}(z) + H_\nu^{(2)}(z)\},$$

we see that the linear independence of $J_\nu(z)$ and $Y_\nu(z)$ follows

† See § 10.11, Exx. 1, 2.

‡ *Journal für Math.* **76** (1873), 9; *Math. Ann.* **6** (1873), 148. There are several other definitions of a second solution of Bessel's equation, the present one being the most satisfactory. See Watson, *Bessel Functions*, § 3.5 et seq.

from that of the Hankel functions. $Y_\nu(z)$ is usually called the *Bessel function of the second kind*. Evidently $Y_\nu(z)$ satisfies the same recurrence formulae as $J_\nu(z)$.

When ν is not an integer, it follows from the formulae of § 12.32 that

$$Y_\nu(z) = \frac{\cos \nu\pi J_\nu(z) - J_{-\nu}(z)}{\sin \nu\pi}.$$

When ν is an integer, this formula fails because the numerator and denominator are then both zero. But since the Hankel functions are continuous functions of ν, so also is $Y_\nu(z)$. Hence the value of Weber's function of integral order is given by the equation

$$Y_n(z) = \lim_{\nu \to n} \frac{\cos \nu\pi \, J_\nu(z) - J_{-\nu}(z)}{\sin \nu\pi}.$$

12.41. The series for $Y_n(z)$

If we substitute in the formula

$$Y_\nu(z) = \frac{\cos \nu\pi \, J_\nu(z) - J_{-\nu}(z)}{\sin \nu\pi}$$

the power series for the Bessel functions, we obtain the expansion

$$Y_\nu(z) = \cot \nu\pi \, (\tfrac{1}{2}z)^\nu \sum_{r=0}^{\infty} \frac{(-\tfrac{1}{4}z^2)^r}{r! \, \Gamma(\nu+r+1)} -$$

$$- \operatorname{cosec} \nu\pi \, (\tfrac{1}{2}z)^{-\nu} \sum_{r=0}^{\infty} \frac{(-\tfrac{1}{4}z^2)^r}{r! \, \Gamma(-\nu+r+1)}$$

valid when ν is not an integer. This formula fails when ν is an integer.

Now by the ordinary rule for finding the limit of a quotient, we have

$$Y_n(z) = \lim_{\nu \to n} \frac{\cos \nu\pi J_\nu(z) - J_{-\nu}(z)}{\sin \nu\pi}$$

$$= \lim_{\nu \to n} \left\{ \cos \nu\pi \, \frac{\partial J_\nu}{\partial \nu} - \pi \sin \nu\pi J_\nu - \frac{\partial J_{-\nu}}{\partial \nu} \right\} \Big/ \{\pi \cos \nu\pi\}$$

$$= \frac{1}{\pi} \lim_{\nu \to n} \left\{ \frac{\partial J_\nu}{\partial \nu} - (-1)^n \frac{\partial J_{-\nu}}{\partial \nu} \right\}.$$

Moreover, since $Y_{-n}(z) = (-1)^n Y_n(z)$, it suffices to consider only the case when n is positive or zero.

Denoting the derivative of $\log \Gamma(t)$ by $\psi(t)$, we find that

$$\frac{\partial J_\nu}{\partial \nu} = (\tfrac{1}{2}z)^\nu \sum_{r=0}^\infty \frac{(-\tfrac{1}{4}z^2)^r}{r!\,\Gamma(\nu+r+1)} \{\log(\tfrac{1}{2}z) - \psi(\nu+r+1)\}$$

$$\to (\tfrac{1}{2}z)^n \sum_{r=0}^\infty \frac{(-\tfrac{1}{4}z^2)^r}{r!\,(n+r)!} \{\log(\tfrac{1}{2}z) - \psi(n+r+1)\}$$

as $\nu \to n$.

When n is positive, we have to consider separately the first n terms of the series for $\partial J_{-\nu}/\partial \nu$ since $\Gamma(-\nu+r+1)$ and $\psi(-\nu+r+1)$ have poles at $\nu = n$ when r takes the values $0, 1, 2,..., n-1$. This difficulty does not arise when n is zero.

When $r = 0, 1, 2,..., n-1$, we have

$$\frac{\partial}{\partial \nu}\left[(-1)^r(\tfrac{1}{2}z)^{-\nu+2r} \frac{1}{r!\,\Gamma(-\nu+r+1)}\right] = \frac{\partial}{\partial \nu}\left[(\tfrac{1}{2}z)^{-\nu+2r} \frac{\sin \nu\pi\, \Gamma(\nu-r)}{\pi r!}\right]$$

$$= (\tfrac{1}{2}z)^{-\nu+2r} \frac{\Gamma(\nu-r)}{\pi r!}\left[-\sin \nu\pi \log \tfrac{1}{2}z + \pi \cos \nu\pi + \sin \nu\pi\, \psi(\nu-r)\right]$$

$$\to (-1)^n(\tfrac{1}{2}z)^{-n+2r} \frac{(n-r-1)!}{r!}$$

as $\nu \to n$. Treating the terms for which $r \geqslant n$ in the straightforward way, we see that

$$(-1)^n \frac{\partial J_{-\nu}}{\partial \nu} \to \sum_{r=0}^{n-1} \frac{(n-r-1)!}{r!}(\tfrac{1}{2}z)^{2r-n} +$$

$$+ \sum_{s=0}^\infty (-1)^s \frac{(\tfrac{1}{2}z)^{n+2s}}{s!\,(n+s)!}\{\psi(s+1) - \log(\tfrac{1}{2}z)\}$$

as $\nu \to n$. Hence, when n is a positive integer, Weber's function can be expanded as a series of the form

$$Y_n(z) = \frac{(\tfrac{1}{2}z)^n}{\pi} \sum_{r=0}^\infty \frac{(-\tfrac{1}{4}z^2)^r}{r!\,(n+r)!}\{2\log(\tfrac{1}{2}z) - \psi(r+1) - \psi(n+r+1)\} -$$

$$- \frac{1}{\pi} \sum_{r=0}^{n-1} \frac{(n-r-1)!}{r!}(\tfrac{1}{2}z)^{2r-n}.$$

This formula also holds when $n = 0$, the terms in the second line being omitted. It is sometimes useful to modify this formula by writing

$$\psi(1) = -\gamma, \qquad \psi(m+1) = 1 + \frac{1}{2} + \frac{1}{3} + ... + \frac{1}{m} - \gamma,$$

where γ denotes Euler's constant.

12.5. The asymptotic expansions of the Bessel functions

Although we have now represented the complete solution of
Bessel's equation by series of ascending powers of z (multiplied
in some cases by $\log z$), which are convergent for all values of z,
the convergence is, unfortunately, so slow when $|z|$ is large that
an examination of the initial terms of such a series gives
practically no information regarding the value of its sum. To
overcome this difficulty, we now propose to determine, by means
of the method of steepest descents,[†] expansions of the Bessel
functions in inverse powers of z which are asymptotic in Poincaré's sense, even though they are divergent for all values of z.

The method of steepest descents,[‡] which was devised by
Debye[§] to obtain asymptotic expansions of Bessel functions of
large order, consists essentially in representing the function
under consideration by an integral along a path with a particular
geometrical property.

Let us suppose that we wish to find the asymptotic behaviour,
when $|z|$ is large, of a function defined by a contour integral of
the form

$$\int e^{zf(w)} F(w)\, dw$$

which converges when Rl z is positive, the functions $f(w)$ and
$F(w)$ being analytic functions of w, regular in a region of the
w-plane which contains the path of integration. The path of
integration is to be deformed, if possible, until the following
conditions are satisfied:

(i) the path of integration goes through a zero w_0 of $f'(w)$;

(ii) the imaginary part of $f(w)$ is constant on the path.

To obtain a geometrical picture of this, we consider the surface defined by the equations

$$w = u + iv, \qquad t = \mathrm{Rl}\, f(w)$$

in a space in which (u, v, t) are rectangular Cartesian coordinates.

---

† For an account of other methods of determining these asymptotic expansions, see Watson, *Bessel Functions*, Chap. VII. The only application of the
method of steepest descents to the present problem seems to be that of Meijer
(*Proc. Kon. Akad. Wet. Amsterdam*, **35** (1932), 657–67, 852–66), although
Sommerfeld and Hopf (loc. cit., p. 324) used it to find the dominant term.

‡ Sometimes called the saddle-point method.

§ *Math. Ann.* **67** (1909), 535–58; *Münchener Sitzungsberichte* (5), **40** (1910).

The height of a point on this surface above the plane $t = 0$ can never be a true maximum or minimum, since t satisfies the partial differential equation

$$\frac{\partial^2 t}{\partial u^2} + \frac{\partial^2 t}{\partial v^2} = 0.$$

The surface may, however, possess points at which the tangent plane is parallel to $t = 0$, and these are necessarily saddle-points. At such a saddle-point, $\partial t/\partial u$ and $\partial t/\partial v$ both vanish, and hence, by the Cauchy-Riemann conditions, $f'(w)$ also vanishes there.

If we construct a map of this surface on the (u, v)-plane by means of contour lines, the curves of this map on which the imaginary part of $f(w)$ is constant are everywhere orthogonal to the contour lines and so are the projections of the paths of steepest ascent or descent on the surface.

Let us suppose that it is possible to modify the path of integration in this way without altering the value of the integral and so to express the function as a sum of integrals along paths of steepest descent starting at a saddle-point w_0. Integrals along paths of steepest ascent cannot occur as they evidently diverge. On a path of steepest descent, $f(w) = f(w_0) - \tau$, where τ is real and positive and increases indefinitely as we move away from the saddle-point. We have, therefore, to consider the behaviour of a sum of integrals of the form

$$e^{zf(w_0)} \int_0^\infty e^{-z\tau} F(w) \frac{dw}{d\tau} d\tau$$

when $|z|$ is large. To each of these we can, in general, apply the result of Watson's lemma (§ 9.52), and so deduce the required asymptotic expansion.

This brief explanation of the method of steepest descents will be made clearer by a consideration of the following section.

12.51. The asymptotic expansions of the Hankel functions

In the present section we find an asymptotic expansion of the Hankel function $H_\nu^{(1)}(z)$ by applying the method of steepest descents to the integral

$$H_\nu^{(1)}(z) = \frac{1}{\pi i} \int_{-\infty+\alpha i}^{\infty+(\pi-\alpha)i} e^{z \sinh t - \nu t}\, dt$$

where $|\arg(ze^{-\alpha i})| < \frac{1}{2}\pi$. From this the asymptotic formulae for the other solutions of Bessel's equations are easily deduced.

The saddle-points are given by the equation $\cosh t = 0$ and so are $t = (n+\frac{1}{2})\pi i$, where n is an integer. Of these, $t = \frac{1}{2}\pi i$ lies on the path of integration for all values of α. If we make the substitution $t = \frac{1}{2}\pi i + w$, we find that

$$\pi i e^{\frac{1}{2}\nu\pi i} H_\nu^{(1)}(z) = \int_{\infty-\frac{1}{2}(\pi-\alpha)i}^{\infty+\frac{1}{2}(\pi-\alpha)i} \exp\{ze^{\frac{1}{2}\pi i}\cosh w - \nu w\}\, dw$$

$$= 2 \int_0^{\infty+\frac{1}{2}(\pi-\alpha)i} \exp\{ze^{\frac{1}{2}\pi i}\cosh w\} \cosh \nu w\, dw.$$

To bring this formula into agreement with the theory of the previous section, we write $z = \zeta e^{\alpha i}$, so that $|\arg \zeta| < \frac{1}{2}\pi$. This gives

$$\pi i e^{\frac{1}{2}\nu\pi i} H_\nu^{(1)}(\zeta e^{\alpha i}) = 2 \int_0^{\infty+(\pi-\beta)i} \exp\{\zeta e^{\beta i}\cosh w\} \cosh \nu w\, dw,$$

where $\beta = \alpha + \frac{1}{2}\pi$. We have now to see whether there exists a path of steepest descent which starts at the origin and goes to infinity in the required direction.

Let us suppose that $0 < \beta < 2\pi$. The steepest paths through the origin are given by the equation

$$e^{\beta i}\cosh w = e^{\beta i} - \tau,$$

where τ is real. If we solve for w, we find that

$$e^{\pm w} = 1 - \tau e^{-\beta i} - (\tau^2 e^{-2\beta i} - 2\tau e^{-\beta i})^{1/2},$$

so that $\arg w \to \pm\frac{1}{2}(\pi-\beta)$ as $\tau \to +0$ and $\arg w \to \pm\frac{1}{2}\beta$ as $\tau \to -0$. There are therefore four steepest paths through $w = 0$, the paths of steepest descent being given by $\tau \geqslant 0$. Moreover, as $\tau \to +\infty$,

$$e^{\pm w} \sim 1 + 2\tau e^{(\pi-\beta)i}$$

and so $w \to \infty + (\pi-\beta)i$ or $-\infty - (\pi-\beta)i$. Hence there is a path of steepest descent which leaves the origin in the direction $\arg w = \frac{1}{2}(\pi-\beta)$ and tends to infinity in the direction

$\infty + (\pi - \beta)i$; we can take this as path of integration without altering the value of the integral. Hence we have

$$\pi i e^{\frac{1}{2}\nu\pi i} H_\nu^{(1)}(\zeta e^{\alpha i}) = 2\exp(\zeta e^{\beta i}) \int_0^\infty e^{-\zeta\tau}\cosh\nu w \,\frac{dw}{d\tau}\, d\tau$$

$$= \frac{2}{\nu}\exp(\zeta e^{\beta i}) \int_0^\infty e^{-\zeta\tau}\frac{d\sinh\nu w}{d\tau}\, d\tau.$$

In order to apply Watson's lemma to this integral, we must first show that
$$F(\tau) = \frac{d\sinh\nu w}{d\tau},$$

regarded as a function of the *complex* variable τ, satisfies all the conditions of the lemma; these are as follows:

(i) $F(\tau)$ is regular, save possibly for a branch-point at the origin, when $|\tau| \leqslant a + \delta$, where a and δ are positive;

(ii) $|F(\tau)| < Ke^{b\tau}$ holds when $\tau \geqslant a$, K and b being positive numbers independent of τ;

(iii) $F(\tau)$ can be expanded as a series of the form
$$F(\tau) = \sum_{m=1}^\infty a_m \tau^{(m-r)/r}$$

valid when $|\tau| \leqslant a$, r being positive.

Now, from the equation
$$e^{\beta i}\cosh w = e^{\beta i} - \tau$$

we find that
$$\sinh \tfrac{1}{2}w = e^{\frac{1}{2}(\pi-\beta)i}\sqrt{(\tfrac{1}{2}\tau)}.$$

Since $\arg w \to \tfrac{1}{2}(\pi-\beta)$ as $\tau \to +0$, $\sqrt{(\tfrac{1}{2}\tau)}$ is positive on the path of integration. Moreover, $\sinh\tfrac{1}{2}w$ is an analytic function of τ, regular save for the branch-point at the origin.

On the other hand, $\sinh\nu w$ is an analytic function of $\sinh\tfrac{1}{2}w$, regular when $|\sinh\tfrac{1}{2}w| < 1$. Its Taylor expansion is

$$2\nu\sinh\tfrac{1}{2}w\left[1 + \sum_{r=1}^\infty \frac{(4\nu^2-1^2)(4\nu^2-3^2)\ldots(4\nu^2-(2r-1)^2)}{(2r+1)!\,2^r}\sinh^{2r}\tfrac{1}{2}w\right].$$

From this it follows that $\sinh\nu w$ is an analytic function of τ, regular, apart from a branch-point at 0, when $|\tau| < 2$. Also, for such values of τ the expansion

$$\sinh \nu w = 2\nu e^{\frac{1}{2}(\pi-\beta)i}\sqrt{(\tfrac{1}{2}\tau)} \times$$

$$\times \left[1 + \sum_{r=1}^{\infty} \frac{(4\nu^2-1^2)(4\nu^2-3^2)\ldots\left(4\nu^2-(2r-1)^2\right)}{(2r+1)!\, 2^r} \{e^{(\pi-\beta)i}\tau\}^r \right]$$

is valid. This implies that, apart from a branch-point at the origin, $F(\tau)$ is regular when $|\tau| < 2$ and can then be represented by the series

$$F(\tau)$$

$$= \frac{\nu e^{\frac{1}{2}(\pi-\beta)i}}{\sqrt{(2\tau)}} \left[1 + \sum_{r=1}^{\infty} \frac{(4\nu^2-1^2)(4\nu^2-3^2)\ldots\left(4\nu^2-(2r-1)^2\right)}{2^r(2r)!} e^{r(\pi-\beta)i}\tau^r \right].$$

Hence conditions (i) and (iii) of Watson's lemma are satisfied.

Finally, when τ is large and positive,

$$e^w \sim 1 + 2\tau e^{(\pi-\beta)i}$$

and

$$\frac{dw}{d\tau} \sim \frac{1}{\tau}.$$

It follows that there exists a positive number τ_1 with the property that

$$|e^w| < 3\tau, \qquad |e^{-w}| < 1/\tau, \qquad |dw/d\tau| < 2/\tau$$

when $\tau > \tau_1$. But since

$$F(\tau) = \nu \cosh \nu w \frac{dw}{d\tau}$$

this implies that there exists a constant A such that

$$|F(\tau)| < A\tau^{\mathrm{Rl}\,\nu-1} < Ae^\tau$$

when $\tau \geqslant \tau_1$. Since $|F(\tau)|$ is bounded when $1 \leqslant \tau \leqslant \tau_1$, condition (ii) of the lemma is also satisfied.

By the formal term-by-term integration whose validity is a consequence of Watson's lemma, we now deduce that, when $|\zeta|$ is large and $|\arg \zeta| < \tfrac{1}{2}\pi$,

$$\pi i e^{\frac{1}{2}\nu\pi i} H_\nu^{(1)}(\zeta e^{\alpha i}) = \frac{2}{\nu} \exp(\zeta e^{\beta i}) \int_0^\infty e^{-\zeta\tau} F(\tau)\, d\tau.$$

$$\sim \left(\frac{2}{\zeta}\right)^{1/2} \exp\{\zeta e^{\beta i} + \tfrac{1}{2}(\pi-\beta)i\}\left[\Gamma(\tfrac{1}{2}) + \right.$$

$$\left. + \sum_{r=1}^{\infty} \Gamma(r+\tfrac{1}{2}) \frac{(4\nu^2-1^2)(4\nu^2-3^2)...(4\nu^2-(2r-1)^2)}{2^r(2r)!} \left(\frac{e^{(\pi-\beta)i}}{\zeta}\right)^r\right]$$

$$= \left(\frac{2\pi}{\zeta e^{\alpha i}}\right)^{1/2} \exp\{i\zeta e^{\alpha i} + \tfrac{1}{4}\pi i\} \times$$

$$\times \left[1 + \sum_{r=1}^{\infty} (-1)^r \frac{(4\nu^2-1^2)(4\nu^2-3^2)...(4\nu^2-(2r-1)^2)}{2^{2r}r!\,(2i\zeta e^{\alpha i})^r}\right].$$

In obtaining the expression in the last line we have used the duplication formula for the Gamma function.

If we restore the original variable z, we find that

$$H_\nu^{(1)}(z) \sim \left(\frac{2}{\pi z}\right)^{1/2} \exp\{i(z-\tfrac{1}{2}\nu\pi-\tfrac{1}{4}\pi)\} \times$$

$$\times \left[1 + \sum_{r=1}^{\infty} \frac{(-1)^r(4\nu^2-1^2)(4\nu^2-3^2)...(4\nu^2-(2r-1)^2)}{2^{2r}r!\,(2iz)^r}\right]$$

is the asymptotic expansion of $H_\nu^{(1)}(z)$, valid when $|z|$ is large and $|\arg(ze^{-\alpha i})| < \tfrac{1}{2}\pi$.

In proving this formula we assumed that $|\arg(ze^{-\alpha i})| < \tfrac{1}{2}\pi$, where the only restriction upon α is that $\beta = \alpha + \tfrac{1}{2}\pi$ must lie between 0 and 2π. If we allow β to vary over this range, we find that the asymptotic expansion is valid when $|z|$ is large, provided only that $-\pi < \arg z < 2\pi$.

We have now shown that, *when $-\pi < \arg z < 2\pi$ and $|z|$ is large, the Hankel function $H_\nu^{(1)}(z)$ is represented asymptotically by the series*

$$H_\nu^{(1)}(z) \sim \left(\frac{2}{\pi z}\right)^{1/2} \exp\{i(z-\tfrac{1}{2}\nu\pi-\tfrac{1}{4}\pi)\}\left[1 + \sum_{r=1}^{\infty} \frac{(-1)^r(\nu,r)}{(2iz)^r}\right],$$

where $$(\nu,r) = \frac{(4\nu^2-1^2)(4\nu^2-3^2)...(4\nu^2-(2r-1)^2)}{2^{2r}r!}.$$

This result, for general complex values of ν and z, was first obtained by Hankel.†

Since the Hankel functions are connected by the relation

$$H_\nu^{(2)}(z) = -e^{\nu\pi i}H_\nu^{(1)}(ze^{\pi i}),$$

it follows immediately from the asymptotic expansion of $H_\nu^{(1)}(z)$

† *Math. Ann.* **1** (1869), 491–5.

that, *when* $-2\pi < \arg z < \pi$ *and* $|z|$ *is large,* $H_\nu^{(2)}(z)$ *has the asymptotic expansion*

$$H_\nu^{(2)}(z) \sim \left(\frac{2}{\pi z}\right)^{1/2} \exp\{-i(z-\tfrac{1}{2}\nu\pi-\tfrac{1}{4}\pi)\}\left[1+\sum_{r=1}^{\infty}\frac{(\nu,r)}{(2iz)^r}\right].$$

The asymptotic expansions of the Hankel functions for other ranges of values of $\arg z$ may be deduced from the formulae of § 12.31, Ex. 3.

Although these asymptotic expansions are in the form of divergent series, they may be used for computing the value of the Hankel functions, since the error incurred by terminating the series at any point is of the same order of magnitude as the first term omitted. More precise information on the magnitude of the error will be found in § 7.3 of Watson's treatise and also in the series of papers by Meijer already cited.

Example 1. Prove that the formulae

$$J_\nu(z) \sim \left(\frac{2}{\pi z}\right)^{1/2}\left[\cos(z-\tfrac{1}{2}\nu\pi-\tfrac{1}{4}\pi)\sum_{r=0}^{\infty}\frac{(-1)^r(\nu,2r)}{(2z)^{2r}}-\right.$$

$$\left.-\sin(z-\tfrac{1}{2}\nu\pi-\tfrac{1}{4}\pi)\sum_{r=0}^{\infty}\frac{(-1)^r(\nu,2r+1)}{(2z)^{2r+1}}\right],$$

$$Y_\nu(z) \sim \left(\frac{2}{\pi z}\right)^{1/2}\left[\sin(z-\tfrac{1}{2}\nu\pi-\tfrac{1}{4}\pi)\sum_{r=0}^{\infty}\frac{(-1)^r(\nu,2r)}{(2z)^{2r}}+\right.$$

$$\left.+\cos(z-\tfrac{1}{2}\nu\pi-\tfrac{1}{4}\pi)\sum_{r=0}^{\infty}\frac{(-1)^r(\nu,2r+1)}{(2z)^{2r+1}}\right],$$

hold for large values of $|z|$ provided that $|\arg z| < \pi$.

Example 2. Show that the asymptotic expansions for the Hankel functions terminate when ν is half of an odd integer. Deduce that, if $\nu = n+\tfrac{1}{2}$ where n is a positive integer or zero,

$$J_\nu(z) = \left(\frac{2}{\pi z}\right)^{1/2}\left[\sin(z-\tfrac{1}{2}n\pi)\sum_{r=0}^{\leqslant n/2}\frac{(-1)^r(n+2r)!}{(2r)!\,(n-2r)!\,(2z)^{2r}}+\right.$$

$$\left.+\cos(z-\tfrac{1}{2}n\pi)\sum_{r=0}^{\leqslant(n-1)/2}\frac{(-1)^r(n+2r+1)!}{(2r+1)!\,(n-2r-1)!\,(2z)^{2r+1}}\right],$$

$$J_{-\nu}(z) = \left(\frac{2}{\pi z}\right)^{1/2}\left[\cos(z+\tfrac{1}{2}n\pi)\sum_{r=0}^{\leqslant n/2}\frac{(-1)^r(n+2r)!}{(2r)!\,(n-2r)!\,(2z)^{2r}}-\right.$$

$$\left.-\sin(z+\tfrac{1}{2}n\pi)\sum_{r=0}^{\leqslant(n-1)/2}\frac{(-1)^r(n+2r+1)!}{(2r+1)!\,(n-2r-1)!\,(2z)^{2r+1}}\right].$$

12.6. The Neumann polynomials

We now propose to investigate the properties of certain polynomials associated with the Bessel coefficients which are of importance in the theory of the expansion of an arbitrary analytic function $f(z)$ as a series of the form

$$f(z) = \sum_0^\infty a_n J_n(z).$$

These are the Neumann† polynomials $O_n(t)$, defined by the expansion

$$\frac{1}{t-z} = J_0(z)O_0(t) + 2\sum_{n=1}^\infty J_n(z)O_n(t).$$

We start from the formula

$$(t-z)^{-1} = \int_0^\infty e^{-(t-z)\sinh w}\cosh w \, dw$$

which is valid when $\mathrm{Rl}(t-z) > 0$, and use Schlömilch's generating function in the form

$$e^{z\sinh w} = J_0(z) + \sum_{n=1}^\infty \{e^{nw} + (-1)^n e^{-nw}\}J_n(z).$$

This gives

$$(t-z)^{-1} = \int_0^\infty e^{-t\sinh w}\cosh w \Big[J_0(z) + \sum_{n=1}^\infty \{e^{nw} + (-1)^n e^{-nw}\}J_n(z)\Big] \, dw$$

$$= J_0(z)\int_0^\infty e^{-t\sinh w}\cosh w \, dw +$$

$$+ \sum_{n=1}^\infty J_n(z)\int_0^\infty e^{-t\sinh w}\cosh w \{e^{nw} + (-1)^n e^{-nw}\} \, dw,$$

provided that it is permissible to invert the order of integration and summation.

A sufficient condition for the validity of this process is the convergence of the series

$$\sum_{n=1}^\infty \int_0^\infty |e^{-t\sinh w}\cosh w \{e^{nw} + (-1)^n e^{-nw}\}J_n(z)| \, dw.$$

† K. Neumann, *Journal für Math.* 67 (1867), 310. The Neumann polynomial was formerly called the Bessel function of the second kind, by analogy with the corresponding formula in the theory of the Legendre polynomials. But the terminology is misleading as $O_n(t)$ is not a solution of Bessel's equation.

But if $\mathrm{Rl}\,t = \tau > 0$ and $\mathrm{Im}\,z = y$, we have

$$\int_0^\infty |e^{-t\sinh w}\cosh w\,\{e^{nw}+(-1)^n e^{-nw}\}\,J_n(z)|\,dw$$

$$\leqslant 4|J_n(z)|e^{\frac{1}{2}\tau}\int_0^\infty e^{-\frac{1}{2}\tau e^w}e^{(n+1)w}\,dw$$

$$< 4|J_n(z)|e^{\frac{1}{2}\tau}\int_{-\infty}^\infty e^{-\frac{1}{2}\tau e^w}e^{(n+1)w}\,dw$$

$$= 4|J_n(z)|e^{\frac{1}{2}\tau}(2/\tau)^{n+1}n!$$

$$< 8|z|^n e^{\frac{1}{2}\tau+|y|}/\tau^{n+1},$$

by § 12.2, Ex. 3. The interchange is thus certainly valid when $|z| < \tau$.

We have thus shown that, when $\mathrm{Rl}\,t > |z|$,

$$(t-z)^{-1} = J_0(z)O_0(t)+2\sum_{n=1}^\infty J_n(z)O_n(t)$$

where

$$O_n(t) = \int_0^\infty e^{-t\sinh w}\cosh w\,{\cosh \atop \sinh}\,nw\,dw,$$

the upper or lower function being taken according as n is even or odd.

The functions $O_n(t)$ have, so far, been defined only when $\mathrm{Rl}\,t > 0$. We now extend their region of definition and show that the expansion of $(t-z)^{-1}$ is valid under the less restrictive condition $|z| < |t|$.

Now, when $n > 0$, we know that†

$${\cosh \atop \sinh}\,nw = 2^{n-1}\Big\{\sinh^n w+\frac{n(n-1)}{2(2n-2)}\sinh^{n-2}w+$$

$$+\frac{n(n-1)(n-2)(n-3)}{2\,.\,4(2n-2)(2n-4)}\sinh^{n-4}w+\ldots\Big\}$$

the upper or lower function being taken according as n is even or odd. If we make the substitution $u = \sinh w$, we find that,

† See Hobson, *Plane Trigonometry* (1911), 105.

when $n > 0$ and $\mathrm{Rl}\,t > 0$,

$$O_n(t) = \int\limits_0^\infty e^{-tu} 2^{n-1} \left\{ u^n + \frac{n(n-1)}{2(2n-2)} u^{n-2} + \right.$$

$$\left. + \frac{n(n-1)(n-2)(n-3)}{2\,.\,4\,.\,(2n-2)(2n-4)} u^{n-4} + \ldots \right\} du,$$

and so

$$O_n(t) = \frac{2^{n-1}n!}{t^{n+1}} \left\{ 1 + \frac{t^2}{2(2n-2)} + \frac{t^4}{2\,.\,4\,.\,(2n-2)(2n-4)} + \ldots \right\},$$

the series inside the brackets ending with a term involving t^{n-1} or t^n according as n is odd or even. On the other hand,

$$O_0(t) = \int\limits_0^\infty e^{-t\sinh w} \cosh w \, dw = \frac{1}{t}.$$

We now define $O_n(t)$ to mean these polynomials in $1/t$, for all values of $\arg t$.

From this definition we see that, when $n > 0$,

$$|O_n(t)| \leqslant \frac{2^{n-1}n!}{|t|^{n+1}} \exp(\tfrac{1}{4}|t|^2),$$

so that, by § 12.2, Ex. 3,

$$|J_n(z)O_n(t)| \leqslant \frac{|z|^n}{2\,|t|^{n+1}} \exp(\tfrac{1}{4}|t|^2 + |\mathrm{Im}\,z|).$$

Hence, when $|z| \leqslant R$ and t lies in a bounded closed domain for which $|t| \geqslant R + \epsilon$, where ϵ is positive, the series

$$J_0(z)O_0(t) + 2 \sum_{n=1}^\infty J_n(z)O_n(t)$$

converges absolutely and uniformly with respect to z and t. Since its sum is $(t-z)^{-1}$ when $\mathrm{Rl}\,t > |z|$, it follows by analytical continuation that this will still be the sum when $|t| > |z|$.

We have thus shown that

$$(t-z)^{-1} = J_0(z)O_0(t) + 2 \sum_{n=1}^\infty J_n(z)O_n(t),$$

provided only that $|z| < |t|$.

Example 1. Prove that the Neumann polynomials are connected by the recurrence formulae

$$(n-1)O_{n+1}(t) + (n+1)O_{n-1}(t) - \frac{2}{t}(n^2-1)O_n(t) = \frac{2}{t}n\sin^2\tfrac{1}{2}n\pi \qquad (n \geqslant 1),$$

$$O_{n-1}(t) - O_{n+1}(t) = 2O_n'(t) \qquad (n \geqslant 1),$$

$$-O_1(t) = O_0'(t),$$

where accents denote differentiation with respect to t.

Example 2. Show that $O_n(t)$ satisfies the differential equation

$$\frac{d^2w}{dt^2} + \frac{3}{t}\frac{dw}{dt} + \left(1 - \frac{n^2 - 1}{t^2}\right)w = g_n(t),$$

where $g_n(t)$ denotes $1/t$ or n/t^2 according as n is even or odd.

Example 3. Show that, if C denotes any simple closed contour about the origin,

$$\int_C O_m(z)O_n(z)\,dz = 0,$$

$$\int_C J_m(z)O_n(z)\,dz = 0 \qquad (m \neq n),$$

$$\int_C J_m(z)O_m(z)\,dz = \pi i \qquad (m \geqslant 1).$$

12.61. Neumann's expansion theorem

K. Neumann showed that *if $f(z)$ is an analytic function, regular when $|z| \leqslant R$, it can be expanded as a series of the form*

$$f(z) = a_0 J_0(z) + 2\sum_1^\infty a_n J_n(z),$$

which converges uniformly in every closed domain within $|z| = R$. The coefficients a_n are given by the relation

$$a_n = \frac{1}{2\pi i}\int_{|t|=R} f(t)O_n(t)\,dt.$$

For if z lies in a closed domain within the circle $|z| = R$, we have

$$f(z) = \frac{1}{2\pi i}\int_{|t|=R} f(t)\frac{dt}{t-z}$$

$$= \frac{1}{2\pi i}\int_{|t|=R} f(t)\left[J_0(z)O_0(t) + 2\sum_1^\infty J_n(z)O_n(t)\right]dt.$$

Since the series occurring under the sign of integration converges uniformly with respect to z and t, we can integrate it term by term to obtain Neumann's result.

REFERENCES

H. BATEMAN, *Partial Differential Equations of Mathematical Physics* (Cambridge, 1932), Chap. VII.

A. GRAY, G. B. MATHEWS, and T. M. MACROBERT, *A Treatise on Bessel Functions* (London, 1922).

G. N. Watson, *A Treatise on the Theory of Bessel Functions* (Cambridge, 1922).

E. T. Whittaker and G. N. Watson, *Modern Analysis* (Cambridge, 1920), Chap. XVII.

MISCELLANEOUS EXAMPLES

1. Prove that
$$\lim_{n \to \infty} \left(-\frac{1}{n}\right)^m P_n^m\left(\cos\frac{x}{n}\right) = J_m(x)$$

provided that x is positive.

2. Show that, when n is an integer,
$$\int_{-1}^{1} e^{izt} P_n(t)\, dt = \sqrt{\left(\frac{2\pi}{z}\right)} i^n J_{n+\frac{1}{2}}(z),$$

and deduce that
$$e^{izt} = \sqrt{\left(\frac{\pi}{2z}\right)} \sum_{n=0}^{\infty} (2n+1) i^n J_{n+\frac{1}{2}}(z) P_n(t). \qquad \text{(Bauer.)}$$

3. Prove that
$$\int_{-\infty}^{\infty} J_{m+\frac{1}{2}}(x) J_{n+\frac{1}{2}}(x) \frac{dx}{x}$$

is equal to $2/(2n+1)$ or 0 according as the integers m and n are equal or unequal.

4. Show that, when $\cos\theta$ is positive,
$$P_n^m(\cos\theta) = \frac{(-1)^m}{(n-m)!} \int_0^{\infty} e^{-z\cos\theta} J_m(x\sin\theta) x^n\, dx. \qquad \text{(Hobson.)}$$

5. Prove that the product $J_\mu(z) J_\nu(z)$ is equal to
$$\left(\tfrac{1}{2}z\right)^{\mu+\nu} \sum_{n=0}^{\infty} \frac{\Gamma(\mu+\nu+2n+1)(-z^2/4)^n}{n!\,\Gamma(\mu+\nu+n+1)\Gamma(\mu+n+1)\Gamma(\nu+n+1)}.$$

6. Show that   (Schläfli.)
$$J_\nu(z) = \frac{1}{\pi} \int_0^{\pi} \cos(z\sin\theta - \nu\theta)\, d\theta - \frac{\sin\nu\pi}{\pi} \int_0^{\infty} e^{-z\sinh\phi - \nu\phi}\, d\phi,$$

$$Y_\nu(z) = \frac{1}{\pi} \int_0^{\pi} \sin(z\sin\theta - \nu\theta)\, d\theta - \frac{1}{\pi} \int_0^{\infty} e^{-z\sinh\phi}(e^{\nu\phi} + e^{-\nu\phi}\cos\nu\pi)\, d\phi$$

provided that the real part of z is positive. (Schläfli.)

7. Prove, by term-by-term integration, that the equation
$$\int_0^{\infty} e^{-at} J_\nu(bt) t^{\mu-1}\, dt = \frac{b^\nu \Gamma(\mu+\nu)}{2^\nu a^{\mu+\nu} \Gamma(\nu+1)}\, F\left(\frac{\mu+\nu}{2}, \frac{\mu+\nu+1}{2}; \nu+1; -\frac{b^2}{a^2}\right)$$

holds when $\mathrm{Rl}(\mu+\nu) > 0$, $\mathrm{Rl}\,a > 0$ and $|b| < |a|$. Apply the principle of analytical continuation to show that the equation is true under the less restrictive conditions $\mathrm{Rl}(\mu+\nu) > 0$ and $\mathrm{Rl}(a \pm ib) > 0$. (HANKEL.)

8. Show that

$$\int\limits_0^\infty J_\nu(at)\exp(-p^2t^2)t^{\mu-1}\,dt = \frac{\Gamma(\tfrac12\mu+\tfrac12\nu)a^\nu}{\Gamma(\nu+1)2^{\nu+1}p^{\mu+\nu}}\,{}_1F_1\!\left(\frac{\mu+\nu}{2};\nu+1;-\frac{a^2}{4p^2}\right)$$

provided that $|\arg p| < \tfrac14\pi$ and $\mathrm{Rl}(\mu+\nu) > 0$. (HANKEL.)

9. Prove that, when $\mathrm{Rl}\,\nu > -1$,

$$J_\nu(z) = \frac{(\tfrac12 z)^\nu}{2\pi i}\int\limits_{c-\infty i}^{c+\infty i} t^{-\nu-1}\exp\!\left(t-\frac{z^2}{4t}\right)dt,$$

the path of integration being the straight line $\mathrm{Rl}\,t = c > 0$. (SONINE.)

10. By using the formula for $J_{\nu+1}(tu)$ given in Ex. 9, prove that, when $\mathrm{Rl}\,\nu > -1$, $u > 0$, $c > 0$,

$$\int\limits_0^\infty J_\nu(t)J_{\nu+1}(ut)\,dt = \frac{1}{2\pi i u^{\nu+1}}\int\limits_{c-\infty i}^{c+\infty i} e^{x(u^2-1)}\frac{dx}{x}.$$

Deduce that $\qquad\displaystyle\int\limits_0^\infty J_\nu(t)J_{\nu+1}(ut)\,dt = \frac{\epsilon}{u^{\nu+1}},$

where ϵ is equal to 0, $\tfrac12$, or 1 according as u is less than, equal to, or greater than unity.

11. Prove that the relation

$$F(x) = \int\limits_0^\infty \left(\frac{x}{t}\right)^{\nu+1} J_{\nu+1}(xt)\Phi'(t)\,dt$$

implies that $\qquad\displaystyle\Phi(t)-\Phi(0) = \int\limits_0^\infty \left(\frac{t}{u}\right)^{\nu+1} J_{\nu+1}(tu)F'(u)\,du \quad (t > 0)$

provided that we can differentiate the first integral under the sign of integration and invert the order of a certain repeated integral. [This is the *Hankel Transform Theorem*. Sufficient conditions for its validity are given by Burkill, *Proc. London Math. Soc.* (2), **25** (1926), 513–24. See also Titchmarsh, *Proc. Camb. Phil. Soc.* **21** (1922–3), 463–73.

The more usual form of the theorem is obtained by writing

$$F'(x) = x^{\nu+1}f(x), \qquad \Phi'(t) = t^{\nu+1}\phi(t);$$

it then states that $\qquad\displaystyle f(x) = \int\limits_0^\infty t\phi(t)J_\nu(xt)\,dt$

implies that
$$\phi(t) = \int_0^\infty uf(u)J_\nu(tu)\,du.]$$

12. Prove that, when the real parts of $\mu+1$ and ν are positive,

$$z^{(\mu+\nu)/2}J_{\mu+\nu}(2\sqrt{z}) = \frac{1}{\Gamma(\nu)}\int_0^z v^{\mu/2}J_\mu(2\sqrt{v})(z-v)^{\nu-1}\,dv.$$

Hence show that, when n is an integer,

$$z^{(\mu+n)/2}J_{\mu+n}(2\sqrt{z}) = \int_0^z\int_0^z \cdots \int_0^z z^{\mu/2}J_\mu(2\sqrt{z})\,dz,$$

integration being performed n times. (SONINE.)

13. Show that

$$(z+h)^{-\nu/2}J_\nu\{2\sqrt{(z+h)}\} = \sum_{m=0}^\infty \frac{(-h)^m}{m!}z^{-(\nu+m)/2}J_{\nu+m}(2\sqrt{z}),$$

$$(z+h)^{\nu/2}J_\nu\{2\sqrt{(z+h)}\} = \sum_{m=0}^\infty \frac{h^m}{m!}z^{(\nu-m)/2}J_{\nu-m}(2\sqrt{z}),$$

the latter expansion being valid only when $|h| < |z|$.

14. Show that, when $\mathrm{Rl}(\tfrac{1}{2}\nu-\tfrac{1}{4}) > \mathrm{Rl}\,\mu > -1$,

$$\int_0^\infty (t+z)^{-\nu/2}J_\nu\{2\sqrt{(t+z)}\}t^\mu\,dt = \frac{\Gamma(\mu+1)}{z^{(\nu-\mu-1)/2}}J_{\nu-\mu-1}(2\sqrt{z}). \quad \text{(SONINE.)}$$

15. Show that, when $\mathrm{Rl}(\nu+\tfrac{1}{2}) > 0$,

$$\int_C e^{izt}(t^2-1)^{\nu-1/2}\,dt = 4i\cos\nu\pi\int_0^1 \cos zu(1-u^2)^{\nu-1/2}\,du,$$

where the contour C, on which $|\arg(t^2-1)| \leqslant \pi$, is a figure of eight which goes round $t = 1$ once positively and $t = -1$ once negatively.

Deduce that $\quad J_\nu(z) = \dfrac{\Gamma(\tfrac{1}{2}-\nu)(\tfrac{1}{2}z)^\nu}{2\pi i\,\Gamma(\tfrac{1}{2})}\displaystyle\int_C e^{izt}(t^2-1)^{\nu-1/2}\,dt,$

provided only that $\nu+\tfrac{1}{2}$ is not a positive integer. (HANKEL.)

16. By using the result of Ex. 5, prove that

$$\int_0^\pi J_0(2z\sin\psi)\cos 2n\psi\,d\psi = \pi\{J_n(z)\}^2,$$

and also that
$$\int_0^\pi J_{2n}(2z\sin\psi)\,d\psi = \pi\{J_n(z)\}^2.$$

17. Show that, if $Z^2 = z^2 + z_1^2 - 2zz_1 \cos\theta$,

$$J_0(Z) = \sum_{-\infty}^{\infty} J_m(z)J_m(z_1)e^{m\theta i}.$$

18. By integrating round a semicircle in the upper half-plane, show that, if $x > a$,

$$\int_{-\infty}^{\infty} \frac{H_\nu^{(1)}(xu)}{H_\nu^{(1)}(au)} \frac{du}{u} = \pi i \cdot \frac{a^\nu}{x^\nu},$$

this being a Cauchy principal value.

Deduce that $\int_0^\infty \dfrac{J_\nu(au)Y_\nu(xu) - J_\nu(xu)Y_\nu(au)}{\{J_\nu(au)\}^2 + \{Y_\nu(au)\}^2} \dfrac{du}{u} = \dfrac{\pi a^\nu}{2x^\nu}.$ (TITCHMARSH.)

19. Show that, for all values of the parameter ν, the complete primitive of the differential equation

$$\frac{d^2w}{dz^2} + \frac{1}{z}\frac{dw}{dz} - \left(1 + \frac{\nu^2}{z^2}\right)w = 0$$

is $w = AI_\nu(z) + BK_\nu(z),$

where

$$I_\nu(z) = \sum_{m=0}^{\infty} \frac{(\tfrac{1}{2}z)^{\nu+2m}}{m!\,\Gamma(\nu+m+1)},$$

$$K_\nu(z) = \tfrac{1}{2}\pi i e^{\nu\pi i/2} H_\nu^{(1)}(e^{\pi i/2}z).$$

20. Prove that, when $|\arg z| < \tfrac{1}{2}\pi$ and $|z|$ is large,

$$I_\nu(z) \sim \frac{e^z}{\sqrt{(2\pi z)}}, \qquad K_\nu(z) \sim \sqrt{\left(\frac{\pi}{2z}\right)}e^{-z}.$$

21. Show that, when $|\arg z| < \tfrac{1}{2}\pi$,

$$I_\nu(z) = \frac{1}{2\pi i} \int_{\infty - \pi i}^{\infty + \pi i} e^{z\cosh w - \nu w}\,dw,$$

$$K_\nu(z) = \int_0^\infty e^{-z\cosh w}\cosh\nu w\,dw,$$

the path of integration in the former integral being along straight lines from $\infty - \pi i$ to $-\pi i$, from $-\pi i$ to πi, and from πi to $\infty + \pi i$.

22. If $x > 0$, $-1 < \mathrm{Rl}\,\nu < 1$,

$$H_\nu^{(1)}(x) = \frac{e^{-\frac{1}{2}\nu\pi i}}{\pi i} \int_{-\infty}^{\infty} e^{ix\cosh t - \nu t}\,dt,$$

$$H_\nu^{(2)}(x) = -\frac{e^{\frac{1}{2}\nu\pi i}}{\pi i} \int_{-\infty}^{\infty} e^{-ix\cosh t - \nu t}\,dt.$$

CHAPTER XIII

THE ELLIPTIC FUNCTIONS OF WEIERSTRASS

13.1. Periodic functions

A FUNCTION $f(z)$ is said to be periodic if there exists a non-zero constant 2ω such that the equation

$$f(z+2\omega) = f(z)$$

holds for all values of z. The number 2ω is called a period of $f(z)$; evidently, if n is a positive or negative integer, $2n\omega$ is also a period. We call 2ω a fundamental period if no submultiple of it is a period.

A periodic function which has only one fundamental period is said to be simply-periodic. For example, e^z is simply-periodic, its fundamental period being $2\pi i$. A function which possesses more than one fundamental period is said to be multiply-periodic. In the present chapter we show that multiply-periodic functions exist by constructing Weierstrass's doubly-periodic function $\wp(z)$, which has two fundamental periods whose ratio is not real; every other period is a sum of multiples of these two fundamental periods.

The existence of such a function naturally suggests the following questions:

(i) Does there exist an analytic function, regular save for poles, which has two fundamental periods whose ratio is real?

(ii) Does there exist an analytic function, regular save for poles, which possesses more than two independent fundamental periods?

These questions were first asked by Jacobi,† who showed in each case that such a function is necessarily constant.

Example. The function $f(z)$ has two periods $2\omega_1$ and $2\omega_2$. Show that, if m and n denote positive or negative integers or zero, the number $2m\omega_1 + 2n\omega_2$ is also a period.

---

† See the earlier part of Jacobi's paper, *Journal für Math.* **13** (1835), 55–78, which is reprinted in his *Ges. Werke*, **2** (1882), 25–50.

13.11. The lower bound of the periods of an analytic function

As a preliminary step in proving† the results established by Jacobi, we show that *a periodic analytic function which is not a constant cannot possess arbitrarily small periods.*

Let $f(z)$ be an analytic function which has a set of periods 2ω, where the lower bound of $|\omega|$ is zero. If z_0 is a point at which $f(z)$ is regular, the function $f(z)-f(z_0)$ has a zero at each of the points $z_0+2\omega$. But since the lower bound of $|\omega|$ is zero, there exists a point of the set $z_0+2\omega$ in every neighbourhood of z_0. This is impossible‡ unless $f(z)-f(z_0)$ is identically zero. Hence the result.

13.12. Jacobi's first question

We now answer Jacobi's first question by showing that *if an analytic function $f(z)$, other than a constant, has a set of periods 2ω, $2\lambda\omega$, where λ is real, each of these periods is a multiple of a single fundamental period.*

If the only values which λ takes are positive or negative integers, there is nothing to be proved; 2ω is then the fundamental period.

If, however, there are periods $2\lambda\omega$ with non-integral values of λ, each such period is expressible in the form $2m\omega+2\alpha\omega$, where m is a positive or negative integer or zero and $0 < \alpha < 1$. Evidently $2\alpha\omega$ is itself a period, since it is the difference between the periods $2\lambda\omega$ and $2m\omega$. Thus corresponding to every period $2\lambda\omega$ which is not a multiple of 2ω, there exists a period $2\alpha\omega$, where $0 < \alpha < 1$.

There can, however, be only a finite number of periods of the form $2\alpha\omega$. For if there were an infinite number, they would possess a limiting-point in virtue of the Bolzano-Weierstrass theorem; as the difference of any two of the periods $2\alpha\omega$ is also a period, this would imply that there exist periods of arbitrarily small modulus, which is impossible by § 13.11.

Let us write $2\omega_1 = 2\alpha_1\omega$, where α_1 is the least of the numbers

---

† In framing the general argument of §§ 13.11–13.13 I am materially indebted to Mr. W. L. Ferrar and Mr. J. Hodgkinson, and I wish to take this opportunity of thanking them.

‡ See § 4.51.

κ. Then 2ω and each of the periods $2\lambda\omega$ are multiples of $2\omega_1$. For if not, by a repetition of the previous argument we could find a period $2\alpha_2\,\omega_1$, where $0 < \alpha_2 < 1$, and this is impossible by the definition of $2\omega_1$. This completes the proof of the theorem.

It should be observed that we have shown incidentally that *if an analytic function, other than a constant, has distinct periods 2ω and $2\lambda\omega$, where λ is real, then λ is necessarily rational.* For 2ω and $2\lambda\omega$ are multiples of a fundamental period $2\omega_1$.

Finally, it is evident that *if all the periods of an analytic function are of the form $2\lambda\omega$, where λ is real, the function is simply-periodic.*

13.13. Jacobi's second question

Let $f(z)$ be an analytic function, other than a constant, which possesses two fundamental periods $2\omega_1$ and $2\omega_2$ whose ratio is not real. Such a function cannot be simply-periodic. We now answer Jacobi's second question by showing that it must be doubly-periodic, in the sense that every period is a sum of multiples of a certain pair of fundamental periods, not necessarily $2\omega_1$ and $2\omega_2$.

Since ω_2/ω_1 is not real, we can express any period 2ω uniquely in the form $2\lambda\omega_1+2\mu\omega_2$, where λ and μ are real, by solving the simultaneous equations†

$$\mathrm{Rl}\,\omega = \lambda\,\mathrm{Rl}\,\omega_1+\mu\,\mathrm{Rl}\,\omega_2,$$

$$\mathrm{Im}\,\omega = \lambda\,\mathrm{Im}\,\omega_1+\mu\,\mathrm{Im}\,\omega_2.$$

If it turns out that the only values of λ and μ which occur are positive or negative integers or zero, there is nothing more to be proved, since every period is a sum of multiples of $2\omega_1$ and $2\omega_2$.

If, however, there are periods which are not of the form $2l\omega_1+2m\omega_2$, where l and m are integers or zero, each such period is expressible in the form

$$2l\omega_1+2m\omega_2+2\alpha\omega_1+2\beta\omega_2;$$

† These equations do determine λ and μ, since their determinant is

$$\mathrm{Rl}\,\omega_1\,\mathrm{Im}\,\omega_2 - \mathrm{Im}\,\omega_1\,\mathrm{Rl}\,\omega_2 = |\omega_1\,\omega_2|\sin\arg(\omega_2/\omega_1),$$

and this, by hypothesis, is not zero.

here l and m denote integers or zero, and

$$0 \leqslant \alpha < 1, \qquad 0 \leqslant \beta < 1,$$

α and β not being simultaneously zero. Evidently the number

$$2\alpha\omega_1 + 2\beta\omega_2$$

is itself a period. We now see that neither α nor β can be zero; for if β were zero, α would not be zero, by hypothesis, and $f(z)$ would have periods $2\omega_1$ and $2\alpha\omega_1$. This is impossible, by § 13.12, since $2\omega_1$ is given to be a fundamental period.

We have thus proved that, corresponding to each period 2ω which is not of the form $2l\omega_1 + 2m\omega_2$, where l and m are integers, there exists a point $2\alpha\omega_1 + 2\beta\omega_2$ which represents a period and lies within the parallelogram with vertices $0, 2\omega_1, 2\omega_1 + 2\omega_2, 2\omega_2$. There can be only a finite number of such points; for, if there were an infinite number of them, it is easily seen† that $f(z)$ would have periods of arbitrarily small modulus, which is impossible. Moreover, no two periods of the set have the same value of β; for if $2\alpha\omega_1 + 2\beta\omega_2$ and $2\alpha'\omega_1 + 2\beta\omega_2$ were two such periods, $2|\alpha - \alpha'|\omega_1$ would also be a period, and this is impossible.

We see, then, that there exists a unique point of the set $2\alpha\omega_1 + 2\beta\omega_2$ for which the value of β is least. Let us call it $2\omega_2'$. Every period of $f(z)$ can be expressed as a sum of multiples of $2\omega_1$ and $2\omega_2'$. For if not, a repetition of the preceding argument shows that we can find a period of the form $2\alpha'\omega_1 + 2\beta'\omega_2'$, where $0 < \alpha' < 1, 0 < \beta' < 1$. But since

$$2\alpha'\omega_1 + 2\beta'\omega_2' = 2(\alpha' + \alpha\beta')\omega_1 + 2\beta\beta'\omega_2,$$

this contradicts the definition of $2\omega_2'$. We have thus proved that *if $f(z)$ is an analytic function, other than a constant, which possesses periods whose ratio is not real, it is necessarily doubly-periodic*.

If 2ω and $2\omega'$ are two periods of a doubly-periodic function with the property that every other period is a sum of multiples of 2ω and $2\omega'$, we say that 2ω and $2\omega'$ form *a pair of primitive periods*. The periods $2\omega_1$ and $2\omega_2'$ evidently form such a pair. When a pair of primitive periods is known, an unlimited number

† Cf. § 13.12.

of other pairs can be found. For if we write

$$\Omega_1 = a\omega_1 + b\omega_2', \qquad \Omega_2 = c\omega_1 + d\omega_2',$$

where a, b, c, and d are integers connected by the relation†
$ad - bc = 1$, then $2\Omega_1$ and $2\Omega_2$ are also periods. Moreover

$$\omega_1 = d\Omega_1 - b\Omega_2, \qquad \omega_2' = -c\Omega_1 + a\Omega_2.$$

As any period is expressible as a sum of multiples of $2\omega_1$ and $2\omega_2'$, it is therefore also expressible as a sum of multiples of $2\Omega_1$ and $2\Omega_2$; thus $2\Omega_1$ and $2\Omega_2$ form a pair of primitive periods.

Example. Show that any three periods $2\omega_1$, $2\omega_2$, $2\omega_3$ of a multiply-periodic analytic function are connected by a relation

$$2l\omega_1 + 2m\omega_2 + 2n\omega_3 = 0,$$

where l, m, and n are integers.

13.2. The definition of an elliptic function

An elliptic function is defined to be a doubly-periodic analytic function whose only possible singular points in the finite part of the plane are poles. Before we actually construct special elliptic functions, it is convenient to consider some of the properties of elliptic functions in general.

Let $f(z)$ be an elliptic function with a pair of primitive periods $2\omega_1$ and $2\omega_2$. The imaginary part of ω_2/ω_1 is not zero; we suppose, as we may without loss of generality, that it is positive.‡ With this convention, the points 0, $2\omega_1$, $2\omega_1 + 2\omega_2$, $2\omega_2$, taken in order, are the vertices of a parallelogram described in the positive sense. We call it a *primitive period-parallelogram* of $f(z)$; there are evidently an unlimited number of primitive period-parallelograms. Since, as we have proved, the only periods of $f(z)$ are of the form $2m\omega_1 + 2n\omega_2$, where m and n are integers, the vertices are the only points within or on a primitive period-parallelogram whose affixes are periods.

Now mark in the Argand plane the points of affix

$$\Omega_{m,n} = 2m\omega_1 + 2n\omega_2,$$

† Evidently the integers a and b must be prime to each other. When a and b are fixed, c and d can be found by the process of repeated division used in determining the G.C.M. of two numbers. See Chrystal, *Algebra*, **1** (1910), 45; **2** (1919), 436.

‡ For if $\mathrm{Im}(\omega_2/\omega_1)$ is negative, we consider instead the pair of primitive periods $2\omega_1$ and $-2\omega_2$.

where m and n take the values $0, \pm1, \pm2, \ldots$. Then the fou points $\Omega_{p,q}, \Omega_{p+1,q}, \Omega_{p+1,q+1}, \Omega_{p,q+1}$ are the vertices of a parallelo gram, which is obtained from the primitive period-parallelogram by a translation without rotation; it is called a *period parallelogram*, or, more briefly, a *mesh*. The Argand plane i completely covered by this system of non-overlapping meshes.

The points $z+\Omega_{p,q}$ and $z+\Omega_{r,s}$ obviously lie in differen meshes; if we translate one mesh until it coincides with th second, these two points become coincident. Accordingly we say that the point $z+\Omega_{p,q}$ is congruent to the point $z+\Omega_{r,s}$. The since $\Omega_{r,s}-\Omega_{p,q}$ is a period of $f(z)$, it follows that $f(z)$ takes th same value at every one of a set of congruent points. Th behaviour of an elliptic function is therefore completely deter mined by a knowledge of its values in a primitive period parallelogram.

From this it follows that *an elliptic function must possess poles* For if $f(z)$ is an elliptic function which is regular in a primitiv period-parallelogram, it satisfies there an inequality $|f(z)| < K$ where K is a finite constant. But since $f(z)$ repeats in every mesh the values it takes in a primitive period-parallelogram $f(z)$ is an integral function which satisfies everywhere the in equality $|f(z)| < K$; hence, by Liouville's theorem, it is a con stant.

An elliptic function has only a finite number of poles in any mesh. For if it had an infinite number, the set of poles would possess at least one limiting-point, and this is impossible since a limiting-point of poles is an essential singularity. Similarly we see that *an elliptic function has only a finite number of zeros in any mesh.*

When we wish to calculate the number of poles (or zeros) of an elliptic function in a given mesh, it is inconvenient to have poles (or zeros) on the boundary of the mesh. But as there are only a finite number of poles and zeros in each mesh, we can always translate the mesh without rotation until no pole or zero lies on its boundary. The parallelogram obtained in this way is called a *cell*. The set of poles (or zeros) in a given cell is called an irreducible set.

Example 1. Show that, if $f(z)$ is an elliptic function, so also is $f'(z)$.

Example 2. Show that all primitive period-parallelograms associated with a given elliptic function are of the same area.

13.21. The irreducible poles and zeros of an elliptic function

We prove, first of all, that *the sum of the residues of an elliptic function at its poles in any cell is zero.* For if C is a cell, the sum of the residues of the elliptic function $f(z)$ at its poles within C is

$$\frac{1}{2\pi i} \int_C f(z)\, dz,$$

and this is zero, since the integrals along opposite sides of C cancel on account of the periodicity of $f(z)$.

The number of poles of an elliptic function in any cell, each pole being counted according to its multiplicity, is called the *order*[†] of the function. The order of an elliptic function is at least two, since an elliptic function of order one would have one irreducible pole of residue zero, which is impossible.

We next show that *an elliptic function of order m has m zeros in each cell*, multiple zeros being counted according to their multiplicity. For if the elliptic function $f(z)$ of order m has n zeros in a cell, $n-m$ is equal to the sum of the residues of $f'(z)/f(z)$ at its poles in the cell.[‡] But $f'(z)$ is obviously an elliptic function with the same periods as $f(z)$, and therefore so also is $f'(z)/f(z)$; hence $n-m = 0$, which proves the theorem.[§]

Finally we prove that *the sum of the affixes of the zeros of an elliptic function in any cell*[||] *exceeds the sum of the affixes of its poles in that cell by a period.* For if $f(z)$ is an elliptic function with primitive periods $2\omega_1$ and $2\omega_2$, the sum of the affixes of its zeros in the cell C exceeds the sum of the affixes of its poles there by[††]

$$\frac{1}{2\pi i} \int_C \frac{zf'(z)}{f(z)}\, dz.$$

[†] It should be observed that the word *order* has different meanings in the theory of elliptic functions and the theory of integral functions.

[‡] See § 6.2.

[§] More generally, a being any constant, the elliptic function $f(z)$ of order m takes the value a m times in each cell.

[||] Multiple zeros (or poles) are repeated in these sums according to their multiplicity.

[††] See § 6.2, Ex. 1.

If the vertices of C are t, $t+2\omega_1$, $t+2\omega_1+2\omega_2$, $t+2\omega_2$, this difference is

$$\frac{1}{2\pi i}\int_t^{t+2\omega_1}\left\{\frac{zf'(z)}{f(z)}-\frac{(z+2\omega_2)f'(z+2\omega_2)}{f(z+2\omega_2)}\right\}dz -$$

$$-\frac{1}{2\pi i}\int_t^{t+2\omega_2}\left\{\frac{zf'(z)}{f(z)}-\frac{(z+2\omega_1)f'(z+2\omega_1)}{f(z+2\omega_1)}\right\}dz$$

$$=\frac{1}{2\pi i}\left\{2\omega_1\int_t^{t+2\omega_2}\frac{f'(z)}{f(z)}dz-2\omega_2\int_t^{t+2\omega_1}\frac{f'(z)}{f(z)}dz\right\}$$

$$=\frac{1}{2\pi i}\left\{2\omega_1[\log f(z)]_t^{t+2\omega_2}-2\omega_2[\log f(z)]_t^{t+2\omega_1}\right\}$$

since $f(z)$ and $f'(z)$ have the periods $2\omega_1$ and $2\omega_2$.

Now $f(z)$ takes the same value at each vertex of C. Hence the sum of the affixes of the zeros of $f(z)$ in the cell C exceeds the sum of the affixes of its poles there by

$$\frac{1}{\pi i}\{2m\pi i\omega_1-2n\pi i\omega_2\} = 2m\omega_1-2n\omega_2,$$

where m and n are integers. As $2m\omega_1-2n\omega_2$ is a period, the required result is now established.

13.3. Weierstrass's Sigma function

Let $f(z)$ be a simply-periodic analytic function of period π, which has simple zeros $z_1, z_2,..., z_m$ and simple poles $p_1, p_2,..., p_n$ in the strip $0 < \mathrm{Rl}\, z \leqslant \pi$. It is easily seen that

$$f(z) = g(z)e^{ikz}\frac{\displaystyle\prod_1^m\sin(z-z_r)}{\displaystyle\prod_1^n\sin(z-p_r)},$$

where $g(z)$ is an integral function of period π and $k = 0$ or 1 according as $m-n$ is even or odd.

If we wish to exhibit in a similar manner the way in which an elliptic function with primitive periods $2\omega_1$ and $2\omega_2$ depends on its zeros and poles, we must first construct an integral function with simple zeros at the points $\Omega_{m,n}$, which is to play a part similar to that of $\sin z$ in the theory of simply-periodic functions. The simplest function with the required property is Weierstrass's canonical product.

In order to construct this canonical product, we must determine the exponent of convergence of its zeros. If $\theta = \arg(\omega_2/\omega_1)$, we have

$$|m\omega_1 + n\omega_2|^2 = m^2|\omega_1|^2 + n^2|\omega_2|^2 + 2mn\cos\theta|\omega_1\omega_2|.$$

But since $0 < \theta < \pi$, $\cos\theta = \pm\mu$, where $0 \leqslant \mu < 1$. Hence

$$
\begin{aligned}
|m\omega_1 + n\omega_2|^2 &= m^2|\omega_1|^2 + n^2|\omega_2|^2 \pm 2mn\mu|\omega_1\omega_2| \\
&= (1-\mu)(m^2|\omega_1|^2 + n^2|\omega_2|^2) + \mu(m|\omega_1| \pm n|\omega_2|)^2 \\
&\geqslant (1-\mu)(m^2|\omega_1|^2 + n^2|\omega_2|^2) \\
&\geqslant (1-\mu)a^2(m^2 + n^2),
\end{aligned}
$$

where a is the smaller of $|\omega_1|$ and $|\omega_2|$. Similarly we see that

$$|m\omega_1 + n\omega_2|^2 \leqslant (1+\mu)b^2(m^2 + n^2),$$

where b is the greater of $|\omega_1|$ and $|\omega_2|$.

From these two inequalities it follows that the double series

$$\sum{}' |\Omega_{m,n}|^{-\alpha},$$

where summation is extended over all positive and negative integral and zero values of m and n, save $m = n = 0$, converges or diverges with the series

$$\sum{}' (m^2 + n^2)^{-\alpha/2}.$$

But it is easily shown by the integral test† that the latter series is convergent when $\alpha > 2$ and divergent when $\alpha \leqslant 2$. Hence the exponent of convergence of the zeros $\Omega_{m,n}$ is 2.

It now follows from the general theory of canonical products‡ that the doubly-infinite product

$$\sigma(z|\omega_1,\omega_2) = z \prod_{m,n}{}' \left\{ \left(1 - \frac{z}{\Omega_{m,n}}\right) \exp\left(\frac{z}{\Omega_{m,n}} + \frac{z^2}{2\Omega_{m,n}^2}\right) \right\},$$

where multiplication is extended over all positive and negative integral and zero values of m and n, save $m = n = 0$, converges uniformly and absolutely in any bounded closed domain of the z-plane which contains none of the points $\Omega_{m,n}$, and represents an integral function $\sigma(z|\omega_1,\omega_2)$, of order 2, with simple zeros at the points $\Omega_{m,n}$. This function is *Weierstrass's Sigma function*.

† See, for example, Bromwich, *Infinite Series* (1926), 86.
‡ § 7.2.

A a

When there is no need to emphasize the parameters ω_1 and ω_2 on which the Sigma function depends, we shall denote it more briefly by $\sigma(z)$.

It should be observed that $\sigma(z)$ is not an elliptic function; for if it were, it would be identically zero in virtue of the theorem of § 13.2, and this is certainly not the case.

In the canonical product for $\sigma(z)$ we can arrange the factors in pairs, such as

$$\left(1-\frac{z}{\Omega_{m,n}}\right)\exp\left(\frac{z}{\Omega_{m,n}}+\frac{z^2}{2\Omega_{m,n}^2}\right), \quad \left(1+\frac{z}{\Omega_{m,n}}\right)\exp\left(-\frac{z}{\Omega_{m,n}}+\frac{z^2}{2\Omega_{m,n}^2}\right),$$

the second factor being derived from the first by replacing m and n by $-m$ and $-n$. But since these two factors interchange when we replace z by $-z$, it follows that $\sigma(z)$ is an odd function of z.

13.31. Weierstrass's elliptic function $\wp(z)$

Before we show how elliptic functions can be constructed as quotients of products of Sigma functions, it is convenient to discuss the properties of Weierstrass's elliptic function $\wp(z)$, which is very closely connected with $\sigma(z)$.

The function $\log \sigma(z)$ can be written as a double series

$$\log \sigma(z) = \log z + \sum{}' \left\{\log\left(1-\frac{z}{\Omega_{m,n}}\right)+\frac{z}{\Omega_{m,n}}+\frac{z^2}{2\Omega_{m,n}^2}\right\},$$

which converges absolutely and uniformly in any bounded closed domain D which contains none of the points $\Omega_{m,n}$. *Weierstrass's Zeta function*† is defined by the equation

$$\zeta(z) = \frac{d}{dz}\log \sigma(z);$$

term-by-term differentiation gives at once

$$\zeta(z) = \frac{1}{z} + \sum{}' \left\{\frac{1}{z-\Omega_{m,n}}+\frac{1}{\Omega_{m,n}}+\frac{z}{\Omega_{m,n}^2}\right\},$$

the double series being uniformly and absolutely convergent in the domain D, since its general term is $O(|\Omega_{m,n}|^{-3})$. $\zeta(z)$ is

---

† This function is not to be confused with Riemann's Zeta function

$$\zeta(s) = \sum_1^\infty n^{-s},$$

which is of importance in the analytic theory of numbers.

therefore an analytic function with a simple pole of residue 1 at each of the points $\Omega_{m,n}$.

If we replace m and n by $-m$ and $-n$, the series for $\zeta(z)$ becomes

$$\zeta(z) = \frac{1}{z} + \sum' \left\{ \frac{1}{z+\Omega_{m,n}} - \frac{1}{\Omega_{m,n}} + \frac{z}{\Omega_{m,n}^2} \right\}.$$

Hence

$$\zeta(-z) = -\frac{1}{z} + \sum' \left\{ \frac{1}{-z+\Omega_{m,n}} - \frac{1}{\Omega_{m,n}} - \frac{z}{\Omega_{m,n}^2} \right\} = -\zeta(z),$$

so that $\zeta(z)$ is an odd function. $\zeta(z)$ is not an elliptic function, since the residue at each of its poles is 1, whereas the sum of the residues of an elliptic function at a set of irreducible poles is zero.

Weierstrass's[†] *elliptic function* $\wp(z)$ is now defined by the equation

$$\wp(z) = -\frac{d\zeta(z)}{dz}.$$

It follows that $\wp(z)$ is represented by a double series

$$\wp(z) = \frac{1}{z^2} + \sum' \left\{ \frac{1}{(z-\Omega_{m,n})^2} - \frac{1}{\Omega_{m,n}^2} \right\},$$

which converges uniformly and absolutely in every bounded closed domain containing none of the points $\Omega_{m,n}$. Hence $\wp(z)$ is an even analytic function whose only singularities are double poles of residue zero at each of the points $\Omega_{m,n}$.

To show that $\wp(z)$ is an elliptic function, we consider the behaviour of its derivative when z is increased by $2\omega_1$ or $2\omega_2$. This derivative $\wp'(z)$ is given by the equation

$$\wp'(z) = - \sum \frac{2}{(z-\Omega_{m,n})^3},$$

where summation is now extended over all positive and negative integral and zero values of m and n without exception. From this, we see that

$$\wp'(z+2\omega_1) = - \sum \frac{2}{(z+2\omega_1-\Omega_{m,n})^3} = - \sum \frac{2}{(z-\Omega_{m-1,n})^3};$$

but since the set of points $\Omega_{m-1,n}$ is the same as the set $\Omega_{m,n}$, this equation becomes

$$\wp'(z+2\omega_1) = \wp'(z).$$

† Weierstrass, *Ges. Werke*, **2** (1895), 245-55.

Thus $\wp'(z)$ has the period $2\omega_1$; similarly we can show that it has the period $2\omega_2$. The function $\wp'(z)$ is, therefore, an elliptic function, for it is doubly-periodic with a triple pole of residue zero at each of the points $\Omega_{m,n}$.

Moreover, $2\omega_1$ and $2\omega_2$ form a pair of primitive periods of $\wp'(z)$. For if not, there would exist a network of period-parallelograms, each having a smaller area than the parallelogram with vertices 0, $2\omega_1$, $2\omega_1 + 2\omega_2$, $2\omega_2$; some of these would evidently contain no singularity of $\wp'(z)$, and this is impossible.

By integrating the equation

$$\wp'(z+2\omega_1) = \wp'(z),$$

we obtain

$$\wp(z+2\omega_1) = \wp(z)+C.$$

The value of the constant C can be found by putting $z = -\omega_1$. Since $\wp(z)$ is an even function and $\wp(\pm\omega_1)$ is finite, this gives

$$C = \wp(\omega_1)-\wp(-\omega_1) = 0,$$

so that $2\omega_1$ is a period. Similarly $2\omega_2$ is also a period. Hence $\wp(z)$ is a doubly-periodic function whose only singularities are poles, and so is an elliptic function. Evidently $2\omega_1$ and $2\omega_2$ form a pair of primitive periods of $\wp(z)$.

When it is desirable to put in evidence the primitive periods $2\omega_1$ and $2\omega_2$ with which $\wp(z)$ is constructed, we denote it by $\wp(z|\omega_1, \omega_2)$.

13.32. The pseudo-periodicity of $\zeta(z)$ and $\sigma(z)$

If we integrate the equation $\wp(z+2\omega_1) = \wp(z)$, we obtain the relation

$$\zeta(z+2\omega_1) = \zeta(z)+2\eta_1,$$

where $2\eta_1$ is a constant of integration; putting $z = -\omega_1$, we have

$$2\eta_1 = \zeta(\omega_1)-\zeta(-\omega_1) = 2\zeta(\omega_1),$$

since $\zeta(z)$ is odd. Hence $\eta_1 = \zeta(\omega_1)$. Similarly

$$\zeta(z+2\omega_2) = \zeta(z)+2\eta_2,$$

where $\eta_2 = \zeta(\omega_2)$. The numbers η_1 and η_2 are not both zero; for if they were, $\zeta(z)$ would be an elliptic function, which we know is not the case. The function $\zeta(z)$ has, therefore, a pseudo-periodicity, in that the function is reproduced, apart from an additive constant, when z is increased by a period of $\wp(z)$.

The constants η_1 and η_2 are connected by the relation

$$\eta_1\omega_2 - \eta_2\omega_1 = \tfrac{1}{2}\pi i.$$

For the only singularity of $\zeta(z)$ within or on the cell C of vertices $\omega_1 - \omega_2$, $\omega_1 + \omega_2$, $-\omega_1 + \omega_2$, $-\omega_1 - \omega_2$ is a simple pole at the origin of residue 1; hence

$$2\pi i = \int_C \zeta(z)\,dz$$

$$= \int_{\omega_1 - \omega_2}^{\omega_1 + \omega_2} \{\zeta(z) - \zeta(z - 2\omega_1)\}\,dz + \int_{-\omega_1 - \omega_2}^{\omega_1 - \omega_2} \{\zeta(z) - \zeta(z + 2\omega_2)\}\,dz$$

$$= 2\eta_1 \int_{\omega_1 - \omega_2}^{\omega_1 + \omega_2} dz - 2\eta_2 \int_{-\omega_1 - \omega_2}^{\omega_1 - \omega_2} dz$$

$$= 4\eta_1\omega_2 - 4\eta_2\omega_1,$$

which gives the required result.

It is frequently convenient to make use of the period $2\omega_3$, where $\omega_1 + \omega_2 + \omega_3 = 0$. The pseudo-periodicity of $\zeta(z)$ with respect to $2\omega_3$ is then expressed by the equation

$$\zeta(z + 2\omega_3) = \zeta(z) + 2\eta_3,$$

where $\eta_1 + \eta_2 + \eta_3 = 0$.

From the equation $\zeta(z + 2\omega_1) = \zeta(z) + 2\eta_1$, we deduce by integration that

$$\sigma(z + 2\omega_1) = Ae^{2\eta_1 z}\sigma(z),$$

where A is a constant. Putting $z = -\omega_1$, we have

$$A = e^{2\eta_1\omega_1}\frac{\sigma(\omega_1)}{\sigma(-\omega_1)} = -e^{2\eta_1\omega_1},$$

so that

$$\sigma(z + 2\omega_1) = -e^{2\eta_1(z + \omega_1)}\sigma(z).$$

Similarly we can show that

$$\sigma(z + 2\omega_2) = -e^{2\eta_2(z + \omega_2)}\sigma(z),$$

$$\sigma(z + 2\omega_3) = -e^{2\eta_3(z + \omega_3)}\sigma(z).$$

These three equations exhibit the pseudo-periodicity of $\sigma(z)$ when z is increased by a period of $\wp(z)$.

Example. Show that

$$\eta_2\omega_3 - \eta_3\omega_2 = \eta_3\omega_1 - \eta_1\omega_3 = \eta_1\omega_2 - \eta_2\omega_1 = \tfrac{1}{2}\pi i.$$

13.4. The algebraic relation connecting two elliptic functions

We shall now prove the important theorem that *if two elliptic functions have a pair of common periods whose ratio is not real, they are connected by an algebraic relation.*

Let $f(z)$ and $g(z)$ be two elliptic functions having in common a pair of periods $2\Omega_1$ and $2\Omega_2$, whose ratio is not real. From these periods we can construct, as in § 13.13, a primitive pair of periods $2\omega_1$ and $2\omega_2$ with the property that every common period of $f(z)$ and $g(z)$ is of the form $2m\omega_1 + 2n\omega_2$, where m and n are integers. We are not necessarily supposing that $2\omega_1$ and $2\omega_2$ form a pair of primitive periods for both functions; the theorem will still be true, for example, if ω_1 and $2\omega_2$ are a primitive pair of periods of $f(z)$, and $2\omega_1$ and ω_2 are a primitive pair of periods of $g(z)$.

Denote by $a_1, a_2, \ldots, a_m$ the points in the parallelogram with vertices $0, 2\omega_1, 2\omega_1 + 2\omega_2, 2\omega_2$ which are poles either of $f(z)$ or of $g(z)$ or of both functions. Let μ_r be the order of the pole at a_r; if a_r is a pole of both functions, let μ_r be the greater order.

We now consider a polynomial $F(\xi, \eta)$, of degree n in ξ and η, which has no constant term; such a polynomial involves $\frac{1}{2}n(n+3)$ arbitrary constants. The function

$$\Phi(z) = F\{f(z), g(z)\}$$

is, therefore, an elliptic function of primitive periods $2\omega_1$ and $2\omega_2$, having poles at some or all of the points a_r.

Since the order of the pole a_r cannot exceed $n\mu_r$, we can make the principal part of $\Phi(z)$ at each pole identically zero by choosing the $\frac{1}{2}n(n+3)$ coefficients to satisfy a certain set of $n(\mu_1 + \mu_2 + \ldots + \mu_m)$ homogeneous linear equations. If

$$n+3 > 2(\mu_1 + \mu_2 + \ldots + \mu_m),$$

there will be fewer equations than coefficients to be determined and so a suitable set of coefficients can always be found.† But if the coefficients are chosen in this manner, $\Phi(z)$ is an elliptic

---

† In some cases it is possible to find suitable coefficients by taking
$$n+3 = 2(\mu_1 + \mu_2 + \ldots + \mu_m).$$
An example of this is provided by the differential equation of § 13.41.

function without singularities and is therefore a constant. In other words, there exists a polynomial $F(\xi, \eta)$ such that

$$F\{f(z), g(z)\}$$

is a constant, which is the required result.

13.41. The differential equation satisfied by $\wp(z)$

It follows from the general theorem of § 13.4 that there exists an algebraic relation connecting the two elliptic functions $\wp(z)$, $\wp'(z)$, since they have the same primitive periods $2\omega_1$ and $2\omega_2$. This relation, which we shall now determine, is a differential equation satisfied by the function $\wp(z)$.

The function $\wp(z) - z^{-2}$ is regular in a neighbourhood of the origin and so can be represented there by a power series

$$\wp(z) - z^{-2} = \sum_0^\infty a_n z^n.$$

It follows from Taylor's theorem that all the odd coefficients a_{2n+1} vanish and that

$$a_0 = 0, \qquad a_2 = 3 \sum' \Omega_{m,n}^{-4}, \qquad a_4 = 5 \sum' \Omega_{m,n}^{-6}$$

and so on. Thus

$$\wp(z) = z^{-2} + a_2 z^2 + a_4 z^4 + O(z^6),$$

where $O(z^n)$ denotes a function which is regular in a neighbourhood of the origin and has a zero of order n at the origin. From this equation it follows that

$$\wp'(z) = -2z^{-3} + 2a_2 z + 4a_4 z^3 + O(z^5).$$

We now construct a polynomial in $\wp(z)$ and its derivative which is regular at the origin. To do this, we observe that

$$\wp^3(z) = z^{-6} + 3a_2 z^{-2} + 3a_4 + O(z^2),$$

$$\wp'^2(z) = 4z^{-6} - 8a_2 z^{-2} - 16a_4 + O(z^2),$$

whence

$$\wp'^2(z) - 4\wp^3(z) = -20a_2 z^{-2} - 28a_4 + O(z^2)$$

$$= -20a_2 \wp(z) - 28a_4 + O(z^2).$$

We have thus proved that the function

$$\Phi(z) = \wp'^2(z) - 4\wp^3(z) + 20a_2 \wp(z) + 28a_4$$

is regular in a neighbourhood of the origin and has a double zero at the origin.

Now $\Phi(z)$ is an elliptic function with periods $2\omega_1$ and $2\omega_2$. Hence it is regular in a neighbourhood of each of the points $\Omega_{m,n}$. But as the only possible singularities of $\Phi(z)$ are the points $\Omega_{m,n}$, $\Phi(z)$ is an elliptic function with no singularities, and so is a constant. The value of this constant is zero, since $\Phi(z)$ has a double zero at the origin. Hence $\wp(z)$ is a solution of the differential equation

$$\wp'^2(z) = 4\wp^3(z) - 20a_2\,\wp(z) - 28a_4,$$

where $\qquad a_2 = 3 \sum' \Omega_{m,n}^{-4}, \qquad a_4 = 5 \sum' \Omega_{m,n}^{-6}.$

For many purposes it is more convenient to write

$$g_2 = 20a_2 = 60 \sum' \Omega_{m,n}^{-4}, \qquad g_3 = 28a_4 = 140 \sum' \Omega_{m,n}^{-6},$$

the constants g_2 and g_3 being called the invariants† of $\wp(z)$. We have thus proved that $w = \wp(z)$ satisfies the differential equation

$$\left(\frac{dw}{dz}\right)^2 = 4w^3 - g_2\,w - g_3.$$

Example 1. Show that $w = \wp(z)$ satisfies the differential equation $d^2w/dz^2 = 6w^2 - \frac{1}{2}g_2$.

The function $\wp(z) - z^{-2}$ possesses a Taylor expansion of the form

$$\wp(z) - z^{-2} = c_1 z^2 + c_2 z^4 + \ldots + c_n z^{2n} + \ldots$$

valid near the origin. Show that the coefficients are connected by the relation
$$(n-2)(2n+3)c_n = 3(c_1 c_{n-2} + c_2 c_{n-3} + \ldots + c_{n-2} c_1)$$
for $n = 3, 4, 5, \ldots$. Hence prove that c_n is a polynomial in g_2 and g_3 whose coefficients are positive rational numbers.

Example 2. Prove that

$$\sigma(z) = z + b_1 z^5 + b_2 z^7 + \ldots + b_n z^{2n+3} + \ldots,$$

where the coefficients b_n are polynomials in g_2 and g_3 whose coefficients are rational numbers. In particular, show that

$$b_1 = -g_2/240, \qquad b_2 = -g_3/840.$$

Example 3. Show that

$$\sigma(\lambda z | \lambda\omega_1, \lambda\omega_2) = \lambda\sigma(z | \omega_1, \omega_2),$$
$$\zeta(\lambda z | \lambda\omega_1, \lambda\omega_2) = \lambda^{-1}\zeta(z | \omega_1, \omega_2),$$
$$\wp(\lambda z | \lambda\omega_1, \lambda\omega_2) = \lambda^{-2}\wp(z | \omega_1, \omega_2).$$

Prove also that the invariants of $\wp(\lambda z | \lambda\omega_1, \lambda\omega_2)$ are $\lambda^{-4}g_2$, $\lambda^{-6}g_3$.

---

† The reason for the name will be evident after reading § 13.7.

13.42. The constants e_1, e_2, and e_3

We shall now show that, if g_2 and g_3 are the invariants associated with $\wp(z)$, the three roots e_1, e_2, and e_3 of the equation $4w^3 - g_2 w - g_3 = 0$ are all distinct.

To prove this we make use of the fact that e_1, e_2, and e_3 are the values taken by $\wp(z)$ at the points where its derivative vanishes. Now since $\wp'(z)$ is an odd elliptic function, we have

$$\wp'(\omega_1) = \wp'(\omega_1 - 2\omega_1) = \wp'(-\omega_1) = -\wp'(\omega_1)$$

and so $\wp'(z)$ vanishes at ω_1; similarly it vanishes at ω_2. But $\wp'(z)$ is an elliptic function of order 3 with a triple pole at each of the points $\Omega_{m,n}$; consequently the sum of the affixes of its irreducible zeros is a period. Since $\omega_1 + \omega_2 + \omega_3 = 0$, the points ω_1, ω_2, and ω_3 form a set of irreducible zeros of $\wp'(z)$. It follows that

$$e_1 = \wp(\omega_1), \qquad e_2 = \wp(\omega_2), \qquad e_3 = \wp(\omega_3)$$

are the three roots of the cubic equation in question.

Now $\wp(z) - e_1$, being an elliptic function of order 2 with a double zero at $z = \omega_1$, cannot vanish at any other point in the primitive period-parallelogram; in particular, $e_1 \neq e_2$ and $e_1 \neq e_3$. Similarly we can show that $e_2 \neq e_3$, so that the three constants e_1, e_2, and e_3 are all distinct.

13.43. The solution of a differential equation

Let us consider the problem of finding the function w defined by the differential equation

$$\frac{dw}{dz} = (4w^3 - g_2 w - g_3)^{1/2},$$

where g_2 and g_3 are given constants. This problem can be presented in a somewhat different form; z is given as a function of w by the equation

$$z + \alpha = \int (4w^3 - g_2 w - g_3)^{-1/2}\, dw,$$

where α is a constant of integration. If we could carry out the integration and solve the resulting equation, w would be determined.

If the discriminant $g_2^3 - 27g_3^2$ of the cubic $4w^3 - g_2 w - g_3$

vanishes, the cubic has a multiple zero, w_0 say, and the integral becomes

$$2(z+\alpha) = \int \frac{dw}{(w-w_0)(w-w_1)^{1/2}},$$

which can be evaluated by the elementary methods of the integral calculus. It follows that, in this case, z can be expressed in terms of w by means of the elementary functions of analysis.

If the discriminant of the cubic is not zero, the cubic possesses distinct linear factors. We shall show that, if we can find two numbers ω_1 and ω_2, whose ratio is not real, such that[†]

$$g_2 = 60 \sum' \Omega_{m,n}^{-4}, \qquad g_3 = 140 \sum' \Omega_{m,n}^{-6},$$

the integral can be evaluated[‡] by means of the transformation $w = \wp(\zeta|\omega_1,\omega_2)$.

Assuming, then, that ω_1 and ω_2 have been found, we have

$$z+\alpha = \int \{4\wp^3(\zeta)-g_2\,\wp(\zeta)-g_3\}^{-1/2}\wp'(\zeta)\,d\zeta$$

$$= \pm \int d\zeta = \pm\zeta,$$

and so $\qquad w = \wp(\zeta|\omega_1,\omega_2) = \wp(z+\alpha|\omega_1,\omega_2).$

In particular, $\qquad \displaystyle\int\limits_{w}^{\infty} (4w^3-g_2\,w-g_3)^{-1/2}\,dw$

is equal to $z+\Omega_{m,n}$, where z is the point at which $\wp$ takes the value w. The period $\Omega_{m,n}$ depends on the manner in which the path of integration loops round the branch-points e_1, e_2, and e_3 of the integrand.

13.5. The addition-theorem for $\wp(z)$

The elliptic functions $\wp(u)$ and $\wp(u+v)$, regarded as functions of the complex variable u, have the same pair of primitive periods and so, by § 13.4, are connected by an algebraic relation.

To determine this relation we consider the function

$$f(z) = \wp'(z)+A\wp(z)+B,$$

where A and B are constants. This is an elliptic function of order 3, with a triple pole at each of the points $\Omega_{m,n}$; it has,

---

[†] The existence of such numbers ω_1, ω_2, when $g_2^3-27g_3^2$ is not zero, is proved in § 15.31.

[‡] It cannot, however, be evaluated in terms of the elementary functions of analysis. See, for example, Hardy, *Integration of Functions of a Single Variable* (Cambridge tract, 1905).

therefore, three irreducible zeros, the sum of whose affixes is a period.

Now if u and v are such that none of the numbers u, v, $u \pm v$ is a period of $\wp(z)$, we can choose the constants A and B' so that

$$\wp'(u) + A\wp(u) + B = 0,$$
$$\wp'(v) + A\wp(v) + B = 0.$$

When this is done, the function $f(z)$ has simple zeros at the points congruent to u and v; the third irreducible zero is therefore congruent to $-u-v$. Hence we have

$$\wp'(-u-v) + A\wp(-u-v) + B = 0.$$

Eliminating A and B from these equations, we obtain

$$\begin{vmatrix} \wp(u) & \wp'(u) & 1 \\ \wp(v) & \wp'(v) & 1 \\ \wp(u+v) & -\wp'(u+v) & 1 \end{vmatrix} = 0.$$

Now the derivatives occurring in this equation can be expressed algebraically in terms of $\wp(u)$, $\wp(v)$, $\wp(u+v)$ by means of the differential equation for $\wp(z)$, and so we have really expressed $\wp(u+v)$ algebraically in terms of $\wp(u)$ and $\wp(v)$.

An analytic function $F(z)$ is said to possess an addition-theorem if there exists a formula which expresses $F(u+v)$ algebraically·in terms of $F(u)$ and $F(v)$. Although we only set out to express $\wp(u+v)$ algebraically in terms of $\wp(u)$, we have actually proved the important result that $\wp(z)$ possesses an addition-theorem. It should be noticed that Weierstrass[†] proved in his lectures that a function $F(z)$ which possesses an addition-theorem is either an algebraic function of z, or an algebraic function of $\exp(\pi z i/\omega)$, where ω is a suitably chosen constant, or an algebraic function of $\wp(z|\omega_1, \omega_2)$, ω_1 and ω_2 being suitably chosen.

An alternative form of the addition-theorem for $\wp(z)$ can be obtained by considering the elliptic function

$$F(z) \equiv \wp'^2(z) - \{A\wp(z) + B\}^2$$
$$= 4\wp^3(z) - A^2\wp^2(z) - (2AB + g_2)\wp(z) - (g_3 + B^2),$$

† An account of Weierstrass's lectures is given by Schwarz, *Formeln und Lehrsätze zum Gebrauche der elliptischen Funktionen* (Berlin, 1893). The theorem to which we have just referred is stated there without proof. Proofs have been published by Phragmén, *Acta math.* 7 (1885), 33–42, Koebe, *Berlin Dissertation* (1905); and Falk, *Nova Acta Soc. Upsal.* (4), 1 (1907).

where the constants A and B have the same values as before. This is an elliptic function of order 6, with six irreducible zeros at the points $\pm u$, $\pm v$, $\pm(u+v)$. Since $\wp(z)$ is an even function, it follows that the cubic equation

$$4p^3 - A^2 p^2 - (2AB + g_2)p - (g_3 + B^2) = 0$$

has the three roots $\wp(u)$, $\wp(v)$, and $\wp(u+v)$. From this we deduce that

$$\wp(u) + \wp(v) + \wp(u+v) = \tfrac{1}{4}A^2.$$

But if we solve the equations defining A and B, we obtain

$$A = -\frac{\wp'(u) - \wp'(v)}{\wp(u) - \wp(v)}.$$

Hence we have

$$\wp(u+v) = \frac{1}{4}\left\{\frac{\wp'(u) - \wp'(v)}{\wp(u) - \wp(v)}\right\}^2 - \wp(u) - \wp(v),$$

a relation which expresses $\wp(u+v)$ explicitly in terms of $\wp(u)$ and $\wp(v)$.

Example 1. Prove that the functions

(i) $\quad f(z) = \begin{vmatrix} \wp(z) & \wp'(z) & 1 \\ \wp(\alpha) & \wp'(\alpha) & 1 \\ \wp(z+\alpha) & -\wp'(z+\alpha) & 1 \end{vmatrix},$

(ii) $\quad g(z) = \left\{\dfrac{\wp'(z) - \wp'(\alpha)}{\wp(z) - \wp(\alpha)}\right\}^2 - 4\wp(z) - 4\wp(z+\alpha)$

are elliptic functions with no singularities. Deduce the two forms of the addition-theorem.

Example 2. Show that

$$\wp(2z) = \frac{1}{4}\left\{\frac{\wp''(z)}{\wp'(z)}\right\}^2 - 2\wp(z).$$

(This result is called the *duplication formula* for $\wp(z)$.)

Example 3. Prove that, if

$$\wp(u) = p_1, \qquad \wp(v) = p_2, \qquad \wp(w) = p_3,$$

where $u+v+w = 0$, then

$$(p_1+p_2+p_3)(4p_1 p_2 p_3 - g_3) = (p_1 p_2 + p_2 p_3 + p_3 p_1 + \tfrac{1}{4}g_2)^2.$$

13.51. The formula for $\wp(z+\omega_1)$ in terms of $\wp(z)$

By the second form of the addition-theorem for $\wp(z)$, we have

$$\wp(z+\omega_1) = \frac{1}{4}\left\{\frac{\wp'(z) - \wp'(\omega_1)}{\wp(z) - \wp(\omega_1)}\right\}^2 - \wp(z) - \wp(\omega_1)$$

$$= \frac{\wp'^2(z)}{4\{\wp(z) - e_1\}^2} - \wp(z) - e_1$$

$$= \frac{\{\wp(z)-e_2\}\{\wp(z)-e_3\}}{\wp(z)-e_1} - \wp(z)-e_1$$

$$= \frac{e_1^2+e_2 e_3 - \wp(z)(e_2+e_3)}{\wp(z)-e_1}.$$

But since $e_1+e_2+e_3 = 0$, this relation can be written in the form

$$\wp(z+\omega_1) = e_1 + \frac{(e_1-e_2)(e_1-e_3)}{\wp(z)-e_1}.$$

Similarly we can show that

$$\wp(z+\omega_2) = e_2 + \frac{(e_2-e_1)(e_2-e_3)}{\wp(z)-e_2},$$

$$\wp(z+\omega_3) = e_3 + \frac{(e_3-e_1)(e_3-e_2)}{\wp(z)-e_3}.$$

13.6. The expression of an elliptic function in terms of Sigma functions

In the next few pages we shall consider the problem of expressing a general elliptic function in terms of the periodic or pseudo-periodic functions of Weierstrass. The simplest method is to express such a function as a quotient of products of Sigma functions, the resulting expression being analogous to the formula

$$g(z)e^{ikz} \prod_{r=1}^{m} \sin(z-z_r) \Big/ \prod_{r=1}^{n} \sin(z-p_r)$$

for a simply-periodic function with assigned zeros and poles.

Let us consider an elliptic function $f(z)$ of order n and primitive periods $2\omega_1$, $2\omega_2$, of which $z_1, z_2,..., z_n$ is a set of irreducible zeros, a multiple zero being repeated in the set according to its order. If $p_1, p_2,..., p_{n-1}, p_n'$ is a set of irreducible poles, a multiple pole being repeated according to its order, we know that

$$z_1+z_2+...+z_n = p_1+p_2+...+p_{n-1}+p_n'+\Omega,$$

where Ω is a period. If we replace $p_n'+\Omega$ by p_n, we obtain a set of irreducible poles $p_1, p_2,..., p_n$, the sum of whose affixes is equal to the sum of the affixes of the given set of zeros.

We now construct the function

$$F(z) = \prod_{r=1}^{n} \frac{\sigma(z-z_r)}{\sigma(z-p_r)},$$

which has the same poles and zeros as $f(z)$. Hence $f(z)/F(z)$ is an integral function. But, by the pseudo-periodicity of $\sigma(z)$, we have

$$\frac{F(z+2\omega_1)}{F(z)} = \prod_{r=1}^{n} \frac{\exp\{2\eta_1(z-z_r+\omega_1)\}}{\exp\{2\eta_1(z-p_r+\omega_1)\}} = 1,$$

so that $F(z)$ is of period $2\omega_1$; similarly $2\omega_2$ is also a period. Hence $F(z)$ is an elliptic function. This implies that $f(z)/F(z)$ is an elliptic function with no singularities and so is a constant, A say. We have thus proved that

$$f(z) = A \prod_{r=1}^{n} \frac{\sigma(z-z_r)}{\sigma(z-p_r)},$$

a formula which exhibits the manner in which the elliptic function $f(z)$ depends on its zeros and poles.

Example. $f(z)$ is an elliptic function of order n, with irreducible zeros $z_1, z_2,..., z_n$, and irreducible poles $p_1, p_2,..., p_n$. Show that, if

$$z_1+z_2+...+z_n = p_1+p_2+...+p_n+2l\omega_1+2m\omega_2,$$

then

$$f(z) = Ae^{2(l\eta_1+m\eta_2)z} \prod_{r=1}^{n} \frac{\sigma(z-z_r)}{\sigma(z-p_r)},$$

where A is a constant.

13.61. A formula for $\wp(z)-\wp(\alpha)$

As an example on the theorem of § 13.6, we shall express the elliptic function $F(z) = \wp(z)-\wp(\alpha),$

where α is not a period, as a quotient of products of Sigma functions.

We suppose, in the first instance, that 2α is not a period. Then $F(z)$ is of order 2, and has a pair of irreducible simple zeros α and $-\alpha$. Since $F(z)$ has a double pole at the origin and all congruent points, it follows at once that

$$\wp(z)-\wp(\alpha) = A \frac{\sigma(z-\alpha)\sigma(z+\alpha)}{\sigma^2(z)},$$

where A is a constant.

To determine the value of A, we consider how the expressions on each side of this equation behave near the origin. For sufficiently small values of $|z|$,

$$\wp(z)-\wp(\alpha) = z^{-2}-\wp(\alpha)+O(z^2).$$

Moreover, by Taylor's theorem,

$$\sigma(z+\alpha) = \sigma(\alpha)+z\sigma'(\alpha)+O(z^2)$$

and $$\sigma(z-\alpha) = -\sigma(\alpha)+z\sigma'(\alpha)+O(z^2).$$

Using the result of § 13.41, Ex. 2, it follows that

$$\frac{\sigma(z-\alpha)\sigma(z+\alpha)}{\sigma^2(z)} = -\frac{\sigma^2(\alpha)}{z^2} + O(1).$$

Equating coefficients of z^{-2} in the equation

$$\wp(z)-\wp(\alpha) = A\frac{\sigma(z-\alpha)\sigma(z+\alpha)}{\sigma^2(z)},$$

we find that $A = -1/\sigma^2(\alpha)$. We have thus shown that

$$\wp(z)-\wp(\alpha) = -\frac{\sigma(z-\alpha)\sigma(z+\alpha)}{\sigma^2(z)\sigma^2(\alpha)},$$

provided that 2α is not a period.

The expressions on each side of this equation are, however, analytic functions of α, regular save when α is a point of the set $\Omega_{m,n}$. Hence, by the principle of analytical continuation, the formula holds provided that α is not a period of $\wp(z)$.

Example 1. Prove that

(i) $\wp'(z) = -\dfrac{\sigma(2z)}{\sigma^4(z)}$,   (ii) $\wp'(z) = 2\dfrac{\sigma(z-\omega_1)\sigma(z-\omega_2)\sigma(z-\omega_3)}{\sigma^3(z)\sigma(\omega_1)\sigma(\omega_2)\sigma(\omega_3)}.$

Deduce that

$$\sigma(2z) = -2\{\sigma(z)\sigma(z-\omega_1)\sigma(z-\omega_2)\sigma(z-\omega_3)\}/\{\sigma(\omega_1)\sigma(\omega_2)\sigma(\omega_3)\}.$$

Example 2. Show that

$$\frac{\sigma(2z)}{\sigma(z)} = 2\sigma'^3(z)-3\sigma(z)\sigma'(z)\sigma''(z)+\sigma^2(z)\sigma'''(z).$$

13.611. The functions $\{\wp(z)-e_r\}^{1/2}$

We now define $\{\wp(z)-e_r\}^{1/2}$ as meaning that square root which has a simple pole of residue $+1$ at the origin. Since the principal part of $\wp'(z)$ is $-2/z^3$ near the origin, this definition implies that

$$\wp'(z) = -2\{\wp(z)-e_1\}^{1/2}\{\wp(z)-e_2\}^{1/2}\{\wp(z)-e_3\}^{1/2}.$$

In order to express $\{\wp(z)-e_r\}^{1/2}$ explicitly in terms of Sigma functions, we write $\alpha = -\omega_r$ in the formula of the last section and obtain

$$\wp(z) - e_r = -\frac{\sigma(z-\omega_r)\sigma(z+\omega_r)}{\sigma^2(z)\sigma^2(\omega_r)} = e^{-2\eta_r z}\frac{\sigma^2(z+\omega_r)}{\sigma^2(z)\sigma^2(\omega_r)}$$

by the pseudo-periodicity of $\sigma(z)$. Hence we have

$$\{\wp(z) - e_r\}^{1/2} = \pm e^{-\eta_r z}\frac{\sigma(z+\omega_r)}{\sigma(z)\sigma(\omega_r)}.$$

A consideration of the behaviour of the function near the origin shows that the upper sign must be taken, and so

$$\{\wp(z) - e_r\}^{1/2} = e^{-\eta_r z}\frac{\sigma(z+\omega_r)}{\sigma(z)\sigma(\omega_r)} \qquad (r = 1, 2, 3).$$

We see from this formula that $\{\wp(z) - e_r\}^{1/2}$ has simple poles at the points $\Omega_{m,n}$ and simple zeros at the points $\omega_r + \Omega_{m,n}$.

In particular, we shall always understand by $(e_r - e_s)^{1/2}$ the value taken by $\{\wp(z) - e_s\}^{1/2}$ at the point ω_r; thus

$$(e_r - e_s)^{1/2} = e^{-\eta_s \omega_r}\frac{\sigma(\omega_r + \omega_s)}{\sigma(\omega_r)\sigma(\omega_s)}.$$

Example 1. Prove that $\{\wp(z) - e_1\}^{1/2}$ is an elliptic function of periods $2\omega_1$ and $4\omega_2$ and of order two, which has 0, $2\omega_2$ as a set of irreducible poles and ω_1, $\omega_1 + 2\omega_2$ as a set of irreducible zeros. Determine also the corresponding results for $\{\wp(z) - e_2\}^{1/2}$ and $\{\wp(z) - e_3\}^{1/2}$.

Example 2. Show that

$$(e_1 - e_2)^{1/2} = i(e_2 - e_1)^{1/2}, \qquad (e_2 - e_3)^{1/2} = i(e_3 - e_2)^{1/2},$$
$$(e_3 - e_1)^{1/2} = i(e_1 - e_3)^{1/2}.$$

Example 3. Prove, by using Sigma functions, that

$$\wp(\tfrac{1}{2}\omega_1) = e_1 + \{(e_1 - e_2)(e_1 - e_3)\}^{1/2}$$
$$\wp(\tfrac{1}{2}\omega_1 + \omega_2) = e_1 - \{(e_1 - e_2)(e_1 - e_3)\}^{1/2}.$$

Example 4. Prove the formula of § 13.51 by expressing

$$\{\wp(z) - e_1\}^{1/2}\{\wp(z+\omega_1) - e_1\}^{1/2}$$

in terms of Sigma functions.

Example 5. Show that

$$\frac{\wp'(z+\omega_1)}{\wp'(z)} = -\left\{\frac{\wp(\tfrac{1}{2}\omega_1) - \wp(\omega_1)}{\wp(z) - \wp(\omega_1)}\right\}^2.$$

13.612. The functions $\sigma_r(z)$

By the introduction of the functions

$$\sigma_r(z) = e^{-\eta_r z}\frac{\sigma(z+\omega_r)}{\sigma(\omega_r)} \qquad (r = 1, 2, 3),$$

the formulae of the preceding section take the simple forms

$$\{\wp(z)-e_r\}^{1/2} = \frac{\sigma_r(z)}{\sigma(z)},$$

$$(e_r-e_s)^{1/2} = \frac{\sigma_s(\omega_r)}{\sigma(\omega_r)},$$

which will prove to be of great importance in the theory of Jacobi's elliptic functions.

The function $\sigma_r(z)$ is an integral function with simple zeros at the points $\omega_r+\Omega_{m,n}$. Moreover, it possesses pseudo-periodic properties analogous to those of $\sigma(z)$; these are expressed by the two equations

$$\sigma_r(z+2\omega_r) = -e^{2\eta_r(z+\omega_r)}\sigma_r(z),$$

$$\sigma_r(z+2\omega_s) = e^{2\eta_s(z+\omega_s)}\sigma_r(z),$$

where $r \neq s$. The proof of these formulae is left to the reader.

Example 1. Prove that $\sigma_r(z)$ is an even function and that its Taylor expansion is

$$\sigma_r(z) = 1-\tfrac{1}{2}e_r z^2+\tfrac{1}{48}(g_2-6e_r^2)z^4+\dots.$$

Example 2. Show that

    (i) $\sigma_r^2(z)-\sigma_s^2(z) = (e_s-e_r)\sigma^2(z)$,

    (ii) $(e_2-e_3)\sigma_1^2(z)+(e_3-e_1)\sigma_2^2(z)+(e_1-e_2)\sigma_3^2(z) = 0$.

13.62. The expression of an elliptic function in terms of Zeta functions

It can be shown that, if $f(z)$ is a simply-periodic function of period π whose only singularities in the strip $0 < \mathrm{Rl}\,z \leqslant \pi$ are simple poles $p_1, p_2,\dots, p_n$ of residue $c_1, c_2,\dots, c_n$ respectively, then[†]

$$f(z) = g(z)+ \sum_{r=1}^{n} c_r \cot(z-p_r),$$

where $g(z)$ is a simply-periodic integral function. We now propose to determine the analogous formula in the theory of elliptic functions, where Weierstrass's pseudo-periodic function $\zeta(z)$ plays a part similar to that of $\cot z$ in the simpler theory[‡].

Now although $\zeta(z)$ is not an elliptic function, we can easily

[†] See Ex. 42 on p. 157.

[‡] $\zeta(z)$ is the logarithmic derivative of $\sigma(z)$, just as $\cot z$ is the logarithmic derivative of $\sin z$.

choose the constants a_r so that

$$\phi(z) = \sum_{r=1}^{n} a_r \zeta(z-p_r)$$

is doubly-periodic. For

$$\phi(z+2\omega_1)-\phi(z) = \sum_{r=1}^{n} a_r\{\zeta(z+2\omega_1-p_r)-\zeta(z-p_r)\}$$

$$= 2\eta_1 \sum_{r=1}^{n} a_r = 0,$$

if $\sum_{1}^{n} a_r$ is zero; similarly

$$\phi(z+2\omega_2)-\phi(z) = 0.$$

Thus $\phi(z)$ is an elliptic function with simple poles at the points of the set $p_r+\Omega_{m,n}$.

Using this result, we can express any elliptic function in terms of Zeta functions and their derivatives if we are given a set of irreducible poles and the principal part of the function near each pole.

To prove this, consider an elliptic function $f(z)$ of primitive periods $2\omega_1$ and $2\omega_2$, having a set of irreducible poles $p_1, p_2,...,$ p_n. If the principal part of $f(z)$ in the neighbourhood of p_k is

$$\sum_{s=1}^{m_k} a_{k,s}(z-p_k)^{-s},$$

we must have

$$\sum_{k=1}^{n} a_{k,1} = 0,$$

since the sum of the residues of $f(z)$ at a set of irreducible poles is zero. It follows, as we have just seen, that

$$\sum_{k=1}^{n} a_{k,1} \zeta(z-p_k)$$

is an elliptic function.

We now construct the function

$$F(z) = f(z) - \sum_{k=1}^{n} \sum_{s=1}^{m_k} (-1)^{s-1} \frac{a_{k,s}}{(s-1)!} \zeta^{(s-1)}(z-p_k),$$

where $\zeta^{(s)}(z)$ denotes the sth derivative of $\zeta(z)$. If we remember that $\zeta^{(1)}(z) = -\wp(z)$, we see at once that $F(z)$ is an elliptic function. It is, moreover, an integral function, since the principal part of $F(z)$ at each irreducible pole has been made identically zero. Hence, by Liouville's theorem, $F(z)$ is a constant, A say. Thus the function $f(z)$ can be expanded in the form

$$f(z) = A + \sum_{k=1}^{n} \sum_{s=1}^{m_k} (-1)^{s-1} \frac{a_{k,s}}{(s-1)!} \zeta^{(s-1)}(z-p_k).$$

This result is of particular importance when we wish to integrate an elliptic function. It gives immediately

$$\int f(z)\, dz = \sum_{k=1}^{n} a_{k,1} \log \sigma(z-p_r) +$$

$$+ \sum_{k=1}^{n} \sum_{s=2}^{m_k} (-1)^{s-1} \frac{a_{k,s}}{(s-1)!} \zeta^{(s-2)}(z-p_k) + Az + B,$$

where B is the constant of integration.

Example 1. Prove that

$$\frac{\wp'(z)-\wp'(\alpha)}{\wp(z)-\wp(\alpha)} = 2\zeta(z+\alpha) - 2\zeta(z) - 2\zeta(\alpha).$$

Deduce that†, if $u+v+w = 0$,

$$\{\zeta(u)+\zeta(v)+\zeta(w)\}^2 + \zeta'(u) + \zeta'(v) + \zeta'(w) = 0.$$

Example 2. Prove that

$$\wp(z-\alpha)\wp(z-\beta) = \wp(\alpha)\wp(\beta) + \wp(\alpha-\beta)\{\wp(z-\alpha)+\wp(z-\beta)-\wp(\alpha)-\wp(\beta)\} +$$

$$+ \wp'(\alpha-\beta)\{\zeta(z-\alpha)-\zeta(z-\beta)+\zeta(\alpha)-\zeta(\beta)\}.$$

Example 3. Show that

$$\zeta(z-\alpha)-\zeta(z-\beta)-\zeta(\alpha-\beta)+\zeta(2\alpha-2\beta)$$

is an elliptic function of periods $2\omega_1$ and $2\omega_2$. Prove that it is equal to

$$\frac{\sigma(z-2\alpha+\beta)\sigma(z-2\beta+\alpha)}{\sigma(2\beta-2\alpha)\sigma(z-\alpha)\sigma(z-\beta)}.$$

13.63. The expression of an elliptic function in terms of $\wp(z)$

Let us consider, in the first instance, an even elliptic function of primitive periods $2\omega_1$ and $2\omega_2$, which is regular and non-zero at each point of the set $\Omega_{m,n}$. The order of such a function is necessarily an even integer, $2k$ say.

Now if z_r is a zero of $f(z)$ in a certain cell, the point in the cell congruent to $-z_r$ is also a zero of the same order as z_r. We can, therefore, choose k zeros $z_1, z_2, ..., z_k$ in this cell, each

† This result is a quasi-addition theorem for $\zeta(z)$. It is not a true addition theorem, since $\zeta'(z)$ is not an algebraic function of $\zeta(z)$.

multiple zero being repeated according to its order, in such a way that they, together with the points in the cell congruent to $-z_1, -z_2, \ldots, -z_k$, form an irreducible set. Similarly we can choose k poles $p_1, p_2, \ldots, p_k$, so that they, together with the points of the cell congruent to $-p_1, -p_2, \ldots, -p_k$, form an irreducible set of poles.

When the zeros and poles have been chosen in this manner, the function

$$F(z) = \prod_{r=1}^{k} \frac{\wp(z) - \wp(z_r)}{\wp(z) - \wp(p_r)},$$

where $\wp(z)$ has primitive periods $2\omega_1$ and $2\omega_2$, is an elliptic function having the same poles and zeros as $f(z)$. Hence $f(z)/F(z)$ is an elliptic function with no singularities and so is a constant A. Thus

$$f(z) = A \prod_{r=1}^{k} \frac{\wp(z) - \wp(z_r)}{\wp(z) - \wp(p_r)}.$$

We next remove the restriction that $f(z)$ is regular and non-zero at each of the points $\Omega_{m,n}$. If $f(z)$ has a pole (or zero) at the origin and congruent points, such a pole (or zero) must be of even order. Hence, if the positive or negative integer s be suitably chosen, $f(z)\{\wp(z)\}^s$ is an even elliptic function which is regular and non-zero at each of the points $\Omega_{m,n}$, and so is expressible in the above form. We have thus proved that *an even elliptic function of periods $2\omega_1$ and $2\omega_2$ can be expressed as a rational function of $\wp(z|\omega_1, \omega_2)$.*

From this it is easy to deduce that *an elliptic function of primitive periods $2\omega_1$ and $2\omega_2$ can be expressed in the form*

$$F\{\wp(z)\} + \wp'(z)G\{\wp(z)\},$$

where $\wp(z)$ has the same primitive periods $2\omega_1$ and $2\omega_2$, and $F(\lambda)$ and $G(\lambda)$ denote rational functions of λ. For any elliptic function $f(z)$ can be written in the form

$$f(z) = \tfrac{1}{2}\{f(z) + f(-z)\} + \tfrac{1}{2}\{f(z) - f(-z)\}.$$

The first term on the right-hand side of this equation is an even elliptic function, and so is a rational function $F\{\wp(z)\}$ of $\wp(z)$. The second term is, however, odd; but since $\wp'(z)$ is also odd $\tfrac{1}{2}\{f(z) - f(-z)\}/\wp'(z)$ is even, and is, therefore, a rational function $G\{\wp(z)\}$ of $\wp(z)$. The result stated now follows immediately

An important consequence of this result is that *every elliptic function possesses an addition theorem.* For an elliptic function $f(z)$ is, as we have seen, expressible in the form

$$f(z) = F\{\wp(z), \wp'(z)\},$$

where F denotes a rational function. Hence, writing

$$\wp(u) = p_1, \qquad \wp'(u) = p_1', \qquad \wp(v) = p_2, \qquad \wp'(v) = p_2',$$

we have

$$f(u) = F(p_1, p_1'), \tag{i}$$
$$f(v) = F(p_2, p_2'), \tag{ii}$$
$$f(u+v) = F\{\wp(u+v), \wp'(u+v)\}.$$

But by the addition theorem for $\wp(z)$, we can express $\wp(u+v)$ and $\wp'(u+v)$ as rational functions of p_1, p_2, p_1', and p_2', and so

$$f(u+v) = G(p_1, p_2, p_1', p_2'), \tag{iii}$$

where G denotes a rational function. If we now eliminate p_1, p_2, p_1', and p_2' from the equations (i), (ii), and (iii), by the aid of the identities

$$p_1'^2 = 4p_1^3 - g_2 p_1 - g_3, \qquad p_2'^2 = 4p_2^3 - g_2 p_2 - g_3,$$

we obtain an algebraic relation connecting $f(u+v)$, $f(u)$, and $f(v)$; this proves the theorem.

Example. Show that

$$\wp(z-\alpha) - \wp(z+\alpha) = \wp'(z)\wp'(\alpha)\{\wp(z) - \wp(\alpha)\}^{-2}.$$

13.7. The evaluation of elliptic integrals

An integral of the form $\int F(t, u)\, dt$, where F denotes a rational function† of t and u, and where

$$u^2 = a_0 t^4 + 4a_1 t^3 + 6a_2 t^2 + 4a_3 t + a_4$$

is a quartic or cubic function of t without repeated factor,‡ is called an *elliptic integral*. For example, the integral

$$a \int \frac{(1 - k^2 t^2)\, dt}{\sqrt{\{(1 - t^2)(1 - k^2 t^2)\}}},$$

which is equal to the length of arc of an ellipse of eccentricity

---

† It must be genuinely a rational function of t and u, and not a rational function of t and u^2. In the latter case the integral can be expressed in terms of the elementary functions of analysis.

‡ If u^2 has repeated factor, we can evaluate the integral by means of elementary functions. See Hardy's tract cited on p. 362.

k and major axis $2a$, is of this type; it is from this fact that the class of elliptic integrals derives its name.

We shall now prove the important theorem that any elliptic integral can be evaluated in terms of Weierstrass's periodic and pseudo-periodic functions, combined with the elementary functions of analysis. The first step in the proof is to transform the integral into a canonical form

$$\int G(w, v) \, dw,$$

where G denotes a rational function of w and v, and

$$v^2 = 4w^3 - g_2 w - g_3,$$

where $g_2^3 - 27g_3^2$ is not zero.

Let us consider how the expression

$$f \equiv a_0 x^4 + 4a_1 x^3 y + 6a_2 x^2 y^2 + 4a_3 xy^3 + a_4 y^4$$

behaves under the transformation $x = lX + mY$, $y = l'X + m'Y$, where $\Delta = lm' - l'm$ is not zero. The quantities

$$g_2 = a_0 a_4 - 4a_1 a_3 + 3a_2^2,$$

$$g_3 = \begin{vmatrix} a_0 & a_1 & a_2 \\ a_1 & a_2 & a_3 \\ a_2 & a_3 & a_4 \end{vmatrix}$$

are known to be invariants† with respect to this transformation. This means that, if

$$f \equiv A_0 X^4 + 4A_1 X^3 Y + 6A_2 X^2 Y^2 + 4A_3 X Y^3 + A_4 Y^4,$$

and if G_2 and G_3 are the same expressions in the coefficients A_s as g_2 and g_3 are in a_s, then $G_2 = \Delta^4 g_2$ and $G_3 = \Delta^6 g_3$. Moreover, since f has no repeated factors, $g_2^3 - 27g_3^2$ is not zero. We now show that the transformation can be chosen so that A_0 and A_2 vanish.

It is easily seen that A_0 vanishes if $l = l't_0$, where t_0 is a root of the equation

$$\phi(t) \equiv a_0 t^4 + 4a_1 t^3 + 6a_2 t^2 + 4a_3 t + a_4 = 0.$$

When t_0 has been chosen in this way, A_2 vanishes if the ratio of m to m' is given by

$$\phi_0'' m^2 + (6\phi_0' - 2t_0 \phi_0'')mm' + (t_0^2 \phi_0'' - 6t_0 \phi_0')m'^2 = 0,$$

† See, for example, Elliott, *Algebra of Quantics* (Oxford, 1913), 8, 21.

where ϕ_0' denotes the value of $d\phi/dt$ when $t = t_0$, and similarly for ϕ_0''. Hence

$$m = m't_0, \quad \text{or} \quad m\phi_0'' = m'(t_0\,\phi_0'' - 6\phi_0').$$

The first value of $m : m'$ provides a trivial transformation which makes Δ zero. Since ϕ_0' is not zero by hypothesis, the second value is non-trivial and gives the transformation

$$x = t_0(X + \lambda Y) - Y, \qquad y = X + \lambda Y,$$

where $6\lambda = \phi_0''/\phi_0'$. The corresponding value of f is

$$4A_1 X^3 Y + 4A_3 X Y^3 + A_4 Y^4,$$

where $A_1 = -\tfrac{1}{4}\phi_0'$. Since $\Delta = 1$, the invariance of g_2 and g_3 gives the other coefficients $A_3 = -\tfrac{1}{4}g_2/A_1$, $A_4 = -g_3/A_1^2$.

If we now write $x = ty$, $X = wY/A_1$, we find that

$$y^4\phi(t) \equiv f \equiv Y^4(4w^3 - g_2 w - g_3)/A_1^2,$$

where

$$y = \frac{Y}{A_1}(w + \lambda A_1), \qquad t = t_0 - \frac{A_1}{w + \lambda A_1}.$$

Finally, if we substitute for y in terms of Y and replace the values of A_1 and λ, we obtain

$$\phi(t) = \frac{\tfrac{1}{16}\phi_0'^2}{(w - \tfrac{1}{24}\phi_0'')^4}(4w^3 - g_2 w - g_3),$$

where

$$t = t_0 + \frac{\tfrac{1}{4}\phi_0'}{w - \tfrac{1}{24}\phi_0''}.$$

With this change of variable, the general elliptic integral is brought to the canonical form

$$\int G(w, v)\,dw,$$

where G denotes a rational function of w and v, and

$$v^2 = 4w^3 - g_2 w - g_3,$$

where $g_2^3 - 27g_3^2$ is not zero. Assuming that we can determine numbers ω_1 and ω_2 whose ratio is not real, such that[†]

$$g_2 = 60 \sum{}' \Omega_{m,n}^{-4}, \qquad g_3 = 140 \sum{}' \Omega_{m,n}^{-6},$$

we make the transformation $w = \wp(z\,|\,\omega_1, \omega_2)$, which gives

$$\int G(w, v)\,dw = \int G\{\wp(z), \wp'(z)\}\wp'(z)\,dz.$$

† A proof of the validity of this assumption is given in Chapter XV.

As the integrand is now an elliptic function of periods $2\omega_1$ and $2\omega_2$, it can be evaluated in terms of Weierstrass's periodic and pseudo-periodic functions by the method of § 13.62. This proves the theorem.

Example. Prove that, in the above notation, the equation

$$\zeta = \int_{t_0} \{\phi(t)\}^{-1/2} dt$$

implies that $\quad t = t_0 + \tfrac{1}{4}\phi'(t_0)\{\wp(\zeta; g_2, g_3) - \tfrac{1}{24}\phi''(t_0)\}^{-1}.$

REFERENCES

H. A. Schwarz, *Formeln und Lehrsätze zum Gebrauche der elliptischen Funktionen* (Berlin, 1893).

J. Tannery and J. Molk, *Fonctions elliptiques* (Paris, 1893–1902).

MISCELLANEOUS EXAMPLES

1. Prove, by the use of Liouville's theorem or otherwise, that
$$\wp(z) = \wp(2z) + \{\wp(2z) - e_2\}^{1/2}\{\wp(2z) - e_3\}^{1/2} + $$
$$+ \{\wp(2z) - e_3\}^{1/2}\{\wp(2z) - e_1\}^{1/2} + \{\wp(2z) - e_1\}^{1/2}\{\wp(2z) - e_2\}^{1/2}.$$

Deduce that
$$\wp'(\tfrac{1}{2}\omega_1) = -2(e_1 - e_2)^{1/2}(e_1 - e_3)^{1/2}\{(e_1 - e_2)^{1/2} + (e_1 - e_3)^{1/2}\}.$$

2. Show that, if 3α be a period of $\wp(z)$,
$$\{\wp(z) - \wp(\alpha)\}\{\wp(z+\alpha) - \wp(\alpha)\}\{\wp(z+2\alpha) - \wp(\alpha)\} = -\wp'^2(\alpha).$$

3. Prove that,† if $z_1 + z_2 + z_3 + z_4 = 0$,
$$(e_2 - e_3)\prod_{r=1}^{4}\{\wp(z_r) - e_1\}^{1/2} + (e_3 - e_1)\prod_{r=1}^{4}\{\wp(z_r) - e_2\}^{1/2} + $$
$$+ (e_1 - e_2)\prod_{r=1}^{4}\{\wp(z_r) - e_3\}^{1/2}$$
$$= -(e_1 - e_2)(e_2 - e_3)(e_3 - e_1).$$

4. Prove that, if $\alpha + \beta + \gamma = 0$,
$$\frac{\wp(\beta)\wp'(\gamma) - \wp'(\beta)\wp(\gamma)}{\wp(\beta) - \wp(\gamma)} = \frac{\wp(\gamma)\wp'(\alpha) - \wp'(\gamma)\wp(\alpha)}{\wp(\gamma) - \wp(\alpha)} = \frac{\wp(\alpha)\wp'(\beta) - \wp'(\alpha)\wp(\beta)}{\wp(\alpha) - \wp(\beta)}$$
$$= \tfrac{1}{3}\{\wp'(\alpha) + \wp'(\beta) + \wp'(\gamma)\} + \tfrac{2}{3}\{\wp(\alpha) + \wp(\beta) + \wp(\gamma)\}^{3/2}$$
$$= \{4\wp(\alpha)\wp(\beta)\wp(\gamma) - g_3\}^{1/2}.$$

5. Show that
$$\wp'(z)\wp'(z+\omega_1)\wp'(z+\omega_2)\wp'(z+\omega_3) = g_2^3 - 27g_3^2,$$
where g_2 and g_3 are the invariants of $\wp(z)$.

† The simplest method is to write $z_1 = z$, $z_2 = \alpha$, $z_3 = \beta$, $z_4 = \gamma - z$, where $\alpha + \beta + \gamma = 0$, and then to regard the expression on the left-hand side as an elliptic function of z, whilst α, β, and γ are constant parameters.

6. Prove that, if n is an integer, $\wp(nu)$ can be expressed as a rational function of $\wp(u)$. Show, in particular, that

$$\text{(i)} \quad \wp(2u) = \frac{\wp^4 + \frac{1}{2}g_2\wp^2 + 2g_3\wp + \frac{1}{16}g_2^2}{4\wp^3 - g_2\wp - g_3},$$

$$\text{(ii)} \quad \wp(3u) = \wp(u) + \frac{\wp'^2(\wp'^4 - \psi\wp'')}{\psi^2},$$

where $\psi = \wp'^2(u)[\wp(u) - \wp(2u)]$.

7. If

$$F(z) = \sigma(z+a)\sigma(z-a)\sigma(b+c)\sigma(b-c) + \sigma(z+b)\sigma(z-b)\sigma(c+a)\sigma(c-a) +$$
$$+ \sigma(z+c)\sigma(z-c)\sigma(a+b)\sigma(a-b),$$

prove, by considering the function $F(z)/\sigma^2(z)$ or otherwise, that $F(z)$ is identically zero.

8. Prove that

$$\begin{vmatrix} 1 & \wp(z) & \wp'(z) \\ 1 & \wp(a) & \wp'(a) \\ 1 & \wp(b) & \wp'(b) \end{vmatrix} = -2\frac{\sigma(z+a+b)\sigma(z-a)\sigma(z-b)\sigma(a-b)}{\sigma^3(z)\sigma^3(a)\sigma^3(b)}.$$

9. Show that

$$\begin{vmatrix} 1 & \wp(u_0) & \wp'(u_0) & . & . & . & \wp^{(n-1)}(u_0) \\ 1 & \wp(u_1) & \wp'(u_1) & . & . & . & \wp^{(n-1)}(u_1) \\ 1 & \wp(u_2) & \wp'(u_2) & . & . & . & \wp^{(n-1)}(u_2) \\ . & . & . & . & . & . & . \\ . & . & . & . & . & . & . \\ 1 & \wp(u_n) & \wp'(u_n) & . & . & . & \wp^{(n-1)}(u_n) \end{vmatrix}$$
$$= (-1)^{n(n-1)/2}\frac{1!\,2!\ldots n!\,\sigma(u_0+u_1+\ldots+u_n)\prod\sigma(u_\lambda-u_\mu)}{\sigma^{n+1}(u_0)\sigma^{n+1}(u_1)\ldots\sigma^{n+1}(u_n)},$$

where the product is extended over all pairs of integers λ and μ from 0 to n, with the restriction that $\lambda < \mu$.

Deduce that

$$\begin{vmatrix} \wp(u)-\wp(v) & \wp'(u)-\wp'(v) & \wp''(u)-\wp''(v) \\ \wp'(u) & \wp''(u) & \wp'''(u) \\ \wp'(v) & \wp''(v) & \wp'''(v) \end{vmatrix} = -12\frac{\sigma(2u+2v)\sigma^4(u-v)}{\sigma^8(u)\sigma^8(v)}.$$

(Oxford, 1925.)

10. Prove that

$$\begin{vmatrix} \wp'(u) & \wp''(u) & . & . & . & . & \wp^{(n-1)}(u) \\ \wp''(u) & \wp'''(u) & . & . & . & . & \wp^{(n)}(u) \\ . & . & . & . & . & . & . \\ . & . & . & . & . & . & . \\ \wp^{(n-1)}(u) & \wp^{(n)}(u) & . & . & . & . & \wp^{(2n-3)}(u) \end{vmatrix}$$
$$= (-1)^{n-1}\{1!\,2!\ldots(n-1)!\}^2\frac{\sigma(nu)}{\{\sigma(u)\}^{n^2}}.$$

(KIEPERT.)

11. Prove that

$$\begin{vmatrix} \sigma_1(2u) & \sigma_1(2v) & \sigma_1(2w) \\ \sigma_2(2u) & \sigma_2(2v) & \sigma_2(2w) \\ \sigma_3(2u) & \sigma_3(2v) & \sigma_3(2w) \end{vmatrix}$$

$$= 4ie^{(\eta_1\omega_1+\eta_2\omega_2+\eta_3\omega_3)} \frac{\sigma(u-v)\sigma(u+v)\sigma(v+w)\sigma(v-w)\sigma(w+u)\sigma(w-u)}{\sigma^2(\omega_1)\sigma^2(\omega_2)\sigma^2(\omega_3)}.$$

12. Prove that, if the numbers α, β, γ denote 1, 2, 3 in some order,

(i) $\sigma(u+a)\sigma(u-a) = \sigma^2(u)\sigma_\alpha^2(a) - \sigma_\alpha^2(u)\sigma^2(a)$,

(ii) $\sigma_\alpha(u+a)\sigma_\alpha(u-a) = \sigma_\alpha^2(u)\sigma_\alpha^2(a) - (e_\alpha-e_\beta)(e_\alpha-e_\gamma)\sigma^2(u)\sigma^2(a)$,

(iii) $\sigma_\alpha(u+a)\sigma_\alpha(u-a) = \sigma_\alpha^2(u)\sigma_\beta^2(a) - (e_\alpha-e_\beta)\sigma^2(a)\sigma_\gamma^2(u)$.

Deduce the result of Ex. 1 from equation (iii).

(TANNERY and MOLK.)

13. Prove that $\sigma(z+a)/\sigma(a)$ is equal to

$$\exp\{z\zeta(a) - \tfrac{1}{2}z^2\wp(a)\} \prod_{m,n} \left\{\left(1 - \frac{z}{\Omega_{m,n}-a}\right)\exp\left(\frac{z}{\Omega_{m,n}-a} + \frac{1}{2}\frac{z^2}{(\Omega_{m,n}-a)^2}\right)\right\},$$

where multiplication is extended over all positive and negative integral and zero values of m and n without exception.

Deduce that

$$\sigma_r(z) = \exp(-\tfrac{1}{2}e_r z^2) \prod_{m,n} \left\{\left(1 - \frac{z}{\Omega_{m,n}-\omega_r}\right)\exp\left(\frac{z}{\Omega_{m,n}-\omega_r} + \frac{1}{2}\frac{z^2}{(\Omega_{m,n}-\omega_r)^2}\right)\right\}.$$

14. Show that, if $q = e^{\pi i \omega_2/\omega_1}$ so that $|q| < 1$, the function

$$\Sigma(z) = \exp\left(\frac{\eta_1 z^2}{2\omega_1}\right)\sin\left(\frac{\pi z}{2\omega_1}\right) \prod_{n=1}^{\infty} \left\{1 - 2q^{2n}\cos\frac{\pi z}{\omega_1} + q^{4n}\right\}$$

is an integral function with the same zeros as $\sigma(z)$.

By showing that $\Sigma(z)/\sigma(z)$ is an elliptic function without singularities, deduce that

$$\sigma(z) = \frac{2\omega_1}{\pi}\exp\left(\frac{\eta_1 z^2}{2\omega_1}\right)\sin\left(\frac{\pi z}{2\omega_1}\right) \prod_{n=1}^{\infty} \left\{\frac{1 - 2q^{2n}\cos\pi z/\omega_1 + q^{4n}}{(1-q^{2n})^2}\right\}.$$

15. Prove that

$$\sigma_1(z) = \exp\left(\frac{\eta_1 z^2}{2\omega_1}\right)\cos\left(\frac{\pi z}{2\omega_1}\right) \prod_{n=1}^{\infty} \left\{\frac{1 + 2q^{2n}\cos\pi z/\omega_1 + q^{4n}}{(1+q^{2n})^2}\right\},$$

$$\sigma_2(z) = \exp\left(\frac{\eta_1 z^2}{2\omega_1}\right) \prod_{n=1}^{\infty} \left\{\frac{1 - 2q^{2n-1}\cos\pi z/\omega_1 + q^{4n-2}}{(1-q^{2n-1})^2}\right\},$$

$$\sigma_3(z) = \exp\left(\frac{\eta_1 z^2}{2\omega_1}\right) \prod_{n=1}^{\infty} \left\{\frac{1 + 2q^{2n-1}\cos\pi z/\omega_1 + q^{4n-2}}{(1+q^{2n-1})^2}\right\}.$$

16. Show that, if $|q| < 1$ and

$$q_0 = \prod_{n=1}^{\infty} (1-q^{2n}), \qquad q_1 = \prod_{n=1}^{\infty} (1+q^{2n}), \qquad q_2 = \prod_{n=1}^{\infty} (1+q^{2n-1}),$$

$$q_3 = \prod_{n=1}^{\infty} (1-q^{2n-1}),$$

then $q_1 q_2 q_3 = 1$.

Prove that, if $q = e^{\pi i \omega_2/\omega_1}$,

$$(e_1-e_2)^{1/2} = \frac{\pi}{2\omega_1} q_0^2 q_2^4, \cdot (e_3-e_2)^{1/2} = -\frac{\pi}{2\omega_1} 4q^{1/2} q_0^2 q_1^4, \quad (e_1-e_3)^{1/2} = \frac{\pi}{2\omega_1} q_0^2 q_3^4.$$

Deduce that

$$16 q q_1^8 = q_2^8 - q_3^8.$$

17. Prove that, if $\omega_2/\omega_1 = i\lambda$, where λ is real and positive, then e_1, e_2, e_3 are real, and $e_1 > e_3 > e_2$.

18. Determine the limiting forms, as $\lambda \to +\infty$, of the four Sigma functions with parameters $\omega_1 = \pi$, $\omega_2 = \pi\lambda i$.

19. Prove that

$$\sigma(z) = \frac{2\omega_1}{\pi} \exp\left(\frac{\eta_1 z^2}{2\omega_1}\right) \sin\frac{\pi z}{2\omega_1} \prod_{n=1}^{\infty} \left(1 - \frac{\sin^2(\pi z/2\omega_1)}{\sin^2(n\pi\omega_2/\omega_1)}\right),$$

$$\zeta(z) = \frac{\eta_1 z}{\omega_1} + \frac{\pi}{2\omega_1} \cot\frac{\pi z}{2\omega_1} + \frac{\pi}{2\omega_1} \sum_{-\infty}^{\infty}{}' \left\{\cot\frac{\pi(z-2n\omega_2)}{2\omega_1} + \cot\frac{n\pi\omega_2}{\omega_1}\right\},$$

$$\wp(z) = \frac{\pi^2}{4\omega_1^2}\left\{-\frac{1}{3} + \sum_{-\infty}^{\infty} \operatorname{cosec}^2\frac{\pi(z-2n\omega_2)}{2\omega_1} - \sum_{-\infty}^{\infty}{}' \operatorname{cosec}^2\frac{n\pi\omega_2}{\omega_1}\right\}.$$

20. Prove that $\sigma(z|\tfrac{1}{2}\omega_1, \omega_2) = \exp(\tfrac{1}{2}e_1 z^2)\sigma(z)\sigma_1(z)$.

Deduce that $\wp(z|\tfrac{1}{2}\omega_1, \omega_2) = \wp(z) + \wp(z+\omega_1) - e_1$.

21. Prove that $w = \wp(z|\tfrac{1}{2}\omega_1, \omega_2)$ satisfies the differential equation

$$\left(\frac{dw}{dz}\right)^2 = 4w^3 - G_2 w - G_3,$$

where $G_2 = 60e_1^2 - 4g_2$, $G_3 = 14e_1 g_2 + 22g_3$. (Oxford, 1922.)

22. Show that if $4w = \int_z^{\infty} \frac{dz}{(z+a)^{1/2}(z+b)^{3/4}}$,

then $z+b = \wp^2(w)$, where the invariants of $\wp(w)$ are $g_2 = 4(b-a)$ and $g_3 = 0$.

CHAPTER XIV

JACOBI'S ELLIPTIC FUNCTIONS

14.1. The construction of elliptic functions with two simple poles in each cell

In the previous chapter we saw that the order of an elliptic function cannot be less than two and we considered in detail Weierstrass's function $\wp(z)$, which is of order two and has one double pole in each cell. We now introduce three other elliptic functions of order two, which differ from $\wp(z)$ in that each of them has two simple poles in every cell; these are essentially the elliptic functions of Jacobi. Whilst Jacobi's functions are slightly more complicated than $\wp(z)$, they possess, as we shall see, distinct advantages when we wish to obtain numerical results in problems involving elliptic functions.

Let us consider the functions

$$S(z) = (e_1 - e_2)^{1/2} \frac{\sigma(z)}{\sigma_2(z)}, \qquad C(z) = \frac{\sigma_1(z)}{\sigma_2(z)}, \qquad D(z) = \frac{\sigma_3(z)}{\sigma_2(z)},$$

in the notation of the previous chapter. If we make use of the pseudo-periodic properties of $\sigma(z)$ we find that, when z is increased by $2\omega_r$, $S(z)$, $C(z)$, and $D(z)$ are reproduced, save for a multiplier ± 1, as indicated below.

	$2\omega_1$	$2\omega_2$	$2\omega_3$
$S(z)$	-1	$+1$	-1
$C(z)$	-1	-1	$+1$
$D(z)$	$+1$	-1	-1

It follows that each of the functions is doubly-periodic, though each has a different primitive period-parallelogram.

The only singularities of $S(z)$ are the points at which $\sigma_2(z)$ vanishes, and these are simple poles at the points of the set $\omega_2 + \Omega_{m,n}$. Thus $S(z)$, and similarly $C(z)$ and $D(z)$, are elliptic functions.

The three functions are not, however, independent. For since $4\omega_1$ and $4\omega_2$ are periods of each of them, it follows by the theorem of § 13.4 that $C(z)$ and $D(z)$ can be expressed as algebraic functions of $S(z)$. The explicit formulae are easily obtained when we observe that

$$S(z) = \left\{\frac{e_1-e_2}{\wp(z)-e_2}\right\}^{1/2}, \quad C(z) = \left\{\frac{\wp(z)-e_1}{\wp(z)-e_2}\right\}^{1/2}, \quad D(z) = \left\{\frac{\wp(z)-e_3}{\wp(z)-e_2}\right\}^{1/2}.$$

We find, in fact, that

$$C(z) = \{1-S^2(z)\}^{1/2}, \qquad D(z) = \left\{1-\frac{e_3-e_2}{e_1-e_2}S^2(z)\right\}^{1/2},$$

the square roots being chosen so that $C(z)$ and $D(z)$ have the value $+1$ at the origin, where $S(z)$ vanishes.

The latter relation is usually written in the form

$$D(z) = \{1-k^2S^2(z)\}^{1/2},$$

where
$$k = -\frac{(e_3-e_2)^{1/2}}{(e_1-e_2)^{1/2}}.$$

k is called the *modulus* of the functions $S(z)$, $C(z)$, and $D(z)$. Since e_1, e_2, and e_3 are distinct, k is finite and cannot have the values 0 or ± 1.

Similarly, it must also be possible to express the derivative of $S(z)$ algebraically in terms of the three functions. Now

$$S'(z) = -\frac{(e_1-e_2)^{1/2}\wp'(z)}{2\{\wp(z)-e_2\}^{3/2}},$$

and so, by § 13.611,

$$S'(z) = \frac{(e_1-e_2)^{1/2}\{\wp(z)-e_1\}^{1/2}\{\wp(z)-e_3\}^{1/2}}{\wp(z)-e_2},$$

which gives
$$S'(z) = (e_1-e_2)^{1/2}C(z)D(z).$$

From this we deduce that

$$C'(z) = -(e_1-e_2)^{1/2}D(z)S(z),$$

$$D'(z) = -(e_1-e_2)^{1/2}k^2S(z)C(z),$$

by using the formulae expressing $C(z)$ and $D(z)$ in terms of $S(z)$.

14.11. General description of the functions $S(z)$, $C(z)$, and $D(z)$

The function $S(z)$ is an elliptic function with periods $4\omega_1$ and $2\omega_2$, the points 0, $4\omega_1$, $4\omega_1+2\omega_2$, $2\omega_2$, taken in order, being the vertices of a primitive period-parallelogram. It is, moreover, an odd function; for

$$S(-z) = (e_1-e_2)^{1/2}\frac{\sigma(-z)}{\sigma_2(-z)} = -(e_1-e_2)^{1/2}\frac{\sigma(z)}{\sigma_2(z)} = -S(z),$$

since $\sigma(z)$ is odd and $\sigma_2(z)$ even.

$S(z)$ vanishes only when $\sigma(z) = 0$; thus the only zeros of $S(z)$ are simple ones at the points of the set $\Omega_{m,n}$. As two of these zeros occur in every cell, $S(z)$ is an elliptic function of order two. Similarly the only singularities of $S(z)$ are the points at which $\sigma_2(z)$ vanishes, and so are simple poles at the points congruent to ω_2 or to $2\omega_1+\omega_2$ (mod $4\omega_1, 2\omega_2$).

The residue of $S(z)$ at ω_2 is equal to

$$\lim_{z\to\omega_2}\left\{(e_1-e_2)^{1/2}\sigma(z)\frac{z-\omega_2}{\sigma_2(z)}\right\} = (e_1-e_2)^{1/2}\frac{\sigma(\omega_2)}{\sigma_2'(\omega_2)}.$$

But
$$\sigma_2(z) = e^{\eta_2 z}\sigma(\omega_2-z)/\sigma(\omega_2),$$

and so
$$\sigma_2'(\omega_2) = -e^{\eta_2\omega_2}/\sigma(\omega_2).$$

If we remember that

$$(e_1-e_2)^{1/2} = -e^{-\eta_2\omega_1}\frac{\sigma(\omega_3)}{\sigma(\omega_1)\sigma(\omega_2)},$$

we see that the required residue is

$$e^{-\eta_2(\omega_1+\omega_2)}\frac{\sigma(\omega_2)\sigma(\omega_3)}{\sigma(\omega_1)} = -e^{\eta_2\omega_3}\frac{\sigma(\omega_2)\sigma(\omega_3)}{\sigma(\omega_2+\omega_3)} = -(e_3-e_2)^{-1/2}.$$

Moreover, since the sum of the residues of an elliptic function at its poles in any cell is zero, the residue at $2\omega_1+\omega_2$ is $(e_3-e_2)^{-1/2}$.

The function $C(z)$, however, is obviously an even elliptic function with periods $4\omega_2$ and $2\omega_3$. The points $0, 4\omega_2, 4\omega_2+2\omega_3, 2\omega_3$, taken in order, are the vertices of a primitive period-parallelogram for $C(z)$; the lattice† of period-parallelograms associated with $C(z)$ is thus different from that of $S(z)$. The only zeros of $C(z)$ are found to be simple ones at the points of the set

---

† The reader is advised to draw a diagram of the lattice of period-parallelograms associated with each of the functions $S(z)$, $C(z)$, and $D(z)$. He will see that the three lattices considered here are not the only possible ones; for example, we might have taken the points $0, 4\omega_1, 4\omega_1-2\omega_3, -2\omega_3$ as the vertices of a primitive period-parallelogram of $C(z)$.

The three lattices of period-parallelograms considered here are probably the simplest, since each is derived from the preceding one by a cyclic permutation of ω_1, ω_2, and ω_3.

$\omega_1 + \Omega_{m,n}$; as there are two of these in each cell, $C(z)$ is of order two.

The singularities of $C(z)$ fall into two sets; they are simple poles at points congruent to ω_2 or $3\omega_2$ (mod $4\omega_2, 2\omega_3$). The residue at ω_2 and congruent points is

$$\lim_{z \to \omega_2} \left\{ \frac{(z-\omega_2)\sigma_1(z)}{\sigma_2(z)} \right\} = \frac{\sigma_1(\omega_2)}{\sigma_2'(\omega_2)} = -e^{\eta_3 \omega_2} \frac{\sigma(\omega_2)\sigma(\omega_3)}{\sigma(\omega_2+\omega_3)} = i(e_3-e_2)^{-1/2}.$$

From this it follows that the residue at each pole of the second set is $-i(e_3-e_2)^{-1/2}$.

Finally, as the reader will easily show, $D(z)$ is an even elliptic function with periods $4\omega_3$ and $2\omega_1$, the points $0, 4\omega_3, 4\omega_3+2\omega_1$, $2\omega_1$, taken in order, being the vertices of a primitive period-parallelogram. It has a simple zero at each point of the set $\omega_3 + \Omega_{m,n}$; as two zeros lie in every cell, $D(z)$ is of order two. Moreover, its only singularities are simple poles at points congruent to ω_2 or to $\omega_2+2\omega_3$ (mod $4\omega_3, 2\omega_1$), the residue at each pole of the first set being $-i(e_1-e_2)^{-1/2}$, and at each pole of the second set $i(e_1-e_2)^{-1/2}$.

14.12. The complementary modulus

The complementary modulus k' associated with $S(z)$, $C(z)$, and $D(z)$ is defined by the equation

$$k' = \frac{(e_1-e_3)^{1/2}}{(e_1-e_2)^{1/2}},$$

and so is connected with the modulus k by the relation

$$k^2 + k'^2 = 1.$$

Moreover, k' is finite and is not equal to 0 or ± 1.

Example. Prove that

$$S(\omega_1) = 1, \qquad C(\omega_1) = 0, \qquad D(\omega_1) = k',$$
$$S(\omega_3) = -1/k, \qquad C(\omega_3) = -ik'/k, \qquad D(\omega_3) = 0.$$

14.2. Jacobi's elliptic functions

The occurrence of the factor $(e_1-e_2)^{1/2}$ in the formulae for the derivatives of $S(z)$, $C(z)$, and $D(z)$ suggests that it would be advantageous to change the independent variable from z to u, where $u = (e_1-e_2)^{1/2}z$.

Accordingly, we define Jacobi's elliptic functions† by the equations

$$\text{sn}\,u = S\{(e_1-e_2)^{-1/2}u\}, \qquad \text{cn}\,u = C\{(e_1-e_2)^{-1/2}u\},$$
$$\text{dn}\,u = D\{(e_1-e_2)^{-1/2}u\},$$

and the identities of § 14.1 now take the simple forms

$$\text{cn}\,u = (1-\text{sn}^2u)^{1/2}, \qquad \text{dn}\,u = (1-k^2\,\text{sn}^2u)^{1/2},$$

$$\frac{d}{du}\,\text{sn}\,u = \text{cn}\,u\,\text{dn}\,u, \qquad \frac{d}{du}\,\text{cn}\,u = -\text{dn}\,u\,\text{sn}\,u,$$

$$\frac{d}{du}\,\text{dn}\,u = -k^2\,\text{sn}\,u\,\text{cn}\,u.$$

If we add $4\omega_1(e_1-e_2)^{1/2}$ or $4\omega_2(e_1-e_2)^{1/2}$ to u, the three functions $\text{sn}\,u$, $\text{cn}\,u$, and $\text{dn}\,u$ are unaltered. Accordingly we call the numbers

$$K = \omega_1(e_1-e_2)^{1/2}, \qquad iK' = \omega_2(e_1-e_2)^{1/2}$$

the quarter-periods‡ of Jacobi's elliptic functions. It follows from § 14.1 that, when u is increased by a half-period $2K$, $2iK'$, or $2K+2iK'$, $\text{sn}\,u$, $\text{cn}\,u$, and $\text{dn}\,u$ are reproduced, save for a multiplier ± 1, as shown below.

	$2K$	$2iK'$	$2K+2iK'$
$\text{sn}\,u$	-1	$+1$	-1
$\text{cn}\,u$	-1	-1	$+1$
$\text{dn}\,u$	$+1$	-1	-1

Finally, the equations defining Jacobi's elliptic functions now take the form

$$\text{sn}(Kz/\omega_1) = \frac{K}{\omega_1}\frac{\sigma(z)}{\sigma_2(z)}, \quad \text{cn}(Kz/\omega_1) = \frac{\sigma_1(z)}{\sigma_2(z)}, \quad \text{dn}(Kz/\omega_1) = \frac{\sigma_3(z)}{\sigma_2(z)}.$$

Example 1. Show that

$$\text{sn}\,0 = 0, \qquad \text{sn}\,K = 1, \qquad \text{sn}(K+iK') = 1/k,$$
$$\text{cn}\,0 = 1, \qquad \text{cn}\,K = 0, \qquad \text{cn}(K+iK') = -ik'/k,$$
$$\text{dn}\,0 = 1, \qquad \text{dn}\,K = k', \qquad \text{dn}(K+iK') = 0.$$

† This notation is due to Gudermann (1838). Jacobi wrote sin am u, cos am u, Δ am u for sn u, cn u, dn u, when he published his discoveries in his *Fundamenta Nova Theoriae Functionum Ellipticarum* in 1829; he regarded sn u, cn u, and dn u as the sine, cosine, and derivative of a function am u defined by the equation $\int_0^{\text{am}\,u} (1-k^2\sin^2\theta)^{-1/2}\,d\theta = u$. Cf. § 14.41.

‡ It should be observed that $\text{Rl}(K'/K) > 0$ since $\text{Im}(\omega_2/\omega_1) > 0$.

Example 2. Prove that Jacobi's elliptic functions have the Taylor expansions

$$\operatorname{sn} u = u - \frac{1}{3!}(1+k^2)u^3 + \frac{1}{5!}(1+14k^2+k^4)u^5 - \dots,$$

$$\operatorname{cn} u = 1 - \frac{1}{2!}u^2 + \frac{1}{4!}(1+4k^2)u^4 - \dots,$$

$$\operatorname{dn} u = 1 - \frac{1}{2!}k^2u^2 + \frac{1}{4!}(4k^2+k^4)u^4 - \dots,$$

valid near the origin.

Example 3. Show that

$$k = e^{(\eta_1-\eta_3)\omega_2}\sigma^2(\omega_1)/\sigma^2(\omega_3), \qquad k' = e^{(\eta_2-\eta_3)\omega_1}\sigma^2(\omega_2)/\sigma^2(\omega_1),$$

$$K = \omega_1 e^{-\eta_2\omega_1}\frac{\sigma(\omega_1+\omega_2)}{\sigma(\omega_1)\sigma(\omega_2)}, \qquad K' = \omega_2 e^{-\eta_1\omega_2}\frac{\sigma(\omega_1+\omega_2)}{\sigma(\omega_1)\sigma(\omega_2)}.$$

Example 4. Show that,† if $\tau = \omega_2/\omega_1$ and $q = e^{\pi i \tau}$,

$$k = 4q^{1/2}\prod_{n=1}^{\infty}\{(1+q^{2n})/(1+q^{2n-1})\}^4,$$

$$k' = \prod_{n=1}^{\infty}\{(1-q^{2n-1})/(1+q^{2n-1})\}^4,$$

$$K = \tfrac{1}{2}\pi\prod_{n=1}^{\infty}\{(1-q^{2n})^2(1+q^{2n-1})^4\},$$

$$iK' = \tfrac{1}{2}\pi\tau\prod_{n=1}^{\infty}\{(1-q^{2n})^2(1+q^{2n-1})^4\}.$$

Deduce that, when τ is purely imaginary, the four numbers k, k', K, K' are real and positive and that k, k' are less than unity.

Example 5. Prove that,‡ as $\operatorname{Im}\tau \to +\infty$,

$$k \to 0, \qquad k' \to 1, \qquad K \to \tfrac{1}{2}\pi, \qquad K' - \log(4/k) \to 0.$$

14.21. The general properties of the functions $\operatorname{sn} u$, $\operatorname{cn} u$, and $\operatorname{dn} u$

It is convenient at this stage to translate into the new notation the properties of $S(z)$, $C(z)$, and $D(z)$ discussed in § 14.11. The only real difficulty is the determination of the residues.

We have already seen that

$$S(z) = -\frac{1}{(e_3-e_2)^{1/2}(z-\omega_2)} + \Phi,$$

† Use the result of Ex. 16 on p. 379.
‡ We shall see in § 14.4 that, when k is given, the principal value of τ is determined, and that, when $k \to 0$, the imaginary part of this principal value tends to infinity. Thus $k \to 0$ implies that $K \to \tfrac{1}{2}\pi$ and $K' - \log(4/k) \to 0$.

where Φ denotes a function which is regular at $z = \omega_2$. It follows that

$$\operatorname{sn} u = -\frac{(e_1-e_2)^{1/2}}{(e_3-e_2)^{1/2}(u-iK')} + \Phi = \frac{1}{k(u-iK')} + \Phi,$$

where Φ is regular at $u = iK'$. Thus $\operatorname{sn} u$ has a simple pole of residue $1/k$ at every point congruent to iK' (mod $4K, 2iK'$); similarly, it also has a simple pole of residue $-1/k$ at every point congruent to $2K+iK'$. The residues of $\operatorname{cn} u$ and $\operatorname{dn} u$ are obtained in the same way.

We see, therefore, that $\operatorname{sn} u$ is an odd elliptic function of order two with primitive periods $4K$ and $2iK'$. Its only singularities are at points congruent to iK' or to $2K+iK'$ (mod $4K, 2iK'$); these are simple poles with residues $1/k$ and $-1/k$ respectively. Its only zeros are simple ones at points congruent to 0 or $2K$.

A slight difficulty occurs when we come to translate into the new notation the properties of $\operatorname{cn} u$ and $\operatorname{dn} u$. It will be remembered that the lattices of period-parallelograms of $C(z)$ and $D(z)$ were obtained from that of $S(z)$ by cyclic permutations of the parameters ω_1, ω_2, and ω_3. In the theory of Jacobi's functions there is no special symbol for $\omega_3(e_1-e_2)^{1/2}$, and a certain lack of symmetry results. We could, if we wished, take the parallelogram with vertices 0, $4iK'$, $-2K+2iK'$, $-2K-2iK'$ as fundamental for $\operatorname{cn} u$. But since every period of $\operatorname{cn} u$ is of the form $4mK+2n(K+iK')$, it is usually found more convenient to take the points 0, $4K$, $4K+2(K+iK')$, $2K+2iK'$ as the vertices of the primitive period-parallelogram of $\operatorname{cn} u$.

The function $\operatorname{cn} u$ is, then, an even elliptic function of order two with primitive periods $4K$ and $2K+2iK'$. Its only singularities are at points congruent to iK' or to $2K+iK'$ (mod $4K$, $2K+2iK'$); these are simple poles, with residues $-i/k$, i/k respectively. Its only zeros are simple ones at points congruent to K or $3K$.

Finally, $\operatorname{dn} u$ is an even elliptic function of order two with primitive periods $2K$ and $4iK'$. Its only singular points are congruent to iK' or to $3iK'$ (mod $2K, 4iK'$); these are simple poles of residue $-i$ and $+i$ respectively. Its only zeros are simple ones at points congruent to $K+iK'$ or $K+3iK'$.

14.22. Glaisher's notation for quotients of Jacobi's functions

It is convenient to have a notation for the reciprocals and quotients of Jacobi's elliptic functions. We shall write

$$1/\operatorname{sn} u = \operatorname{ns} u, \qquad 1/\operatorname{cn} u = \operatorname{nc} u, \qquad 1/\operatorname{dn} u = \operatorname{nd} u,$$
$$\operatorname{sn} u/\operatorname{cn} u = \operatorname{sc} u, \qquad \operatorname{sn} u/\operatorname{dn} u = \operatorname{sd} u, \qquad \operatorname{cn} u/\operatorname{dn} u = \operatorname{cd} u,$$
$$\operatorname{cn} u/\operatorname{sn} u = \operatorname{cs} u, \qquad \operatorname{dn} u/\operatorname{sn} u = \operatorname{ds} u, \qquad \operatorname{dn} u/\operatorname{cn} u = \operatorname{dc} u.$$

This notation is due to Glaisher.†

14.3. The addition theorem

Since $\operatorname{sn} u$, $\operatorname{cn} u$, and $\operatorname{dn} u$ are elliptic functions, each of these functions possesses an addition theorem whose form we shall now determine.‡

Let us consider the function

$$F(u) = \operatorname{cn} u \operatorname{cn}(u-\alpha) + A \operatorname{sn} u \operatorname{sn}(u-\alpha),$$

where A and α are constants. It is an elliptic function whose primitive periods are $2K$ and $2iK'$. If α is not congruent to K, iK' or $K+iK'$ (mod $2K, 2iK'$), each term in $F(u)$ has two simple poles in each cell at points congruent to iK' and $\alpha+iK'$.

We can, however, choose the constant A so that the principal part of $F(u)$ at iK' and congruent points is identically zero; thus $F(u)$ is an elliptic function with only one pole in each cell and so is a constant, by Liouville's theorem. Putting $u = 0$, we see that $F(u) = \operatorname{cn} \alpha$.

The appropriate value of the constant A is determined by observing that, when $|u|$ is small,

$$F(u) = \operatorname{cn} \alpha + u \operatorname{dn} \alpha \operatorname{sn} \alpha - uA \operatorname{sn} \alpha + O(u^2).$$

Hence $A = \operatorname{dn} \alpha$ and so

$$\operatorname{cn} u \operatorname{cn}(u-\alpha) + \operatorname{sn} u \operatorname{sn}(u-\alpha)\operatorname{dn} \alpha = \operatorname{cn} \alpha. \qquad \text{(i)}$$

This formula is true provided that α is not congruent to iK', the restrictions that α is not congruent to K or $K+iK'$ being relaxed by an appeal to the principle of analytical continuation.

† *Messenger of Math.* **11** (1882), 86.
‡ The method of proof given here is a slight modification of that of Hurwitz and Courant, *Funktionentheorie* (3rd edition) (Berlin, 1929).

In a similar manner we can show that, when α is not congruent to iK',

$$\operatorname{dn} u \operatorname{dn}(u-\alpha) + k^2 \operatorname{sn} u \operatorname{sn}(u-\alpha)\operatorname{cn}\alpha = \operatorname{dn}\alpha. \qquad \text{(ii)}$$

If we now put $\alpha = u+v$ in equations (i) and (ii), we obtain

$$c_1 c_2 - s_1 s_2 \operatorname{dn}(u+v) = \operatorname{cn}(u+v),$$

and

$$d_1 d_2 - k^2 s_1 s_2 \operatorname{cn}(u+v) = \operatorname{dn}(u+v),$$

where, for brevity, we have written $s_1 = \operatorname{sn} u$, $d_2 = \operatorname{dn} v$, and so on. These equations give at once

$$\operatorname{cn}(u+v) = \frac{c_1 c_2 - d_1 d_2 s_1 s_2}{1 - k^2 s_1^2 s_2^2}, \qquad \operatorname{dn}(u+v) = \frac{d_1 d_2 - k^2 s_1 s_2 c_1 c_2}{1 - k^2 s_1^2 s_2^2}.$$

Finally, writing $\alpha = -v$ in equation (i), we obtain

$$s_1 d_2 \operatorname{sn}(u+v) = c_2 - c_1 \operatorname{cn}(u+v),$$

from which it follows that

$$\operatorname{sn}(u+v) = \frac{s_1 c_2 d_2 + s_2 c_1 d_1}{1 - k^2 s_1^2 s_2^2}.$$

Now this last equation can be written in the form

$$\operatorname{sn}(u+v) = \frac{s_1(1-s_2^2)^{1/2}(1-k^2 s_2^2)^{1/2} + s_2(1-s_1^2)^{1/2}(1-k^2 s_1^2)^{1/2}}{1 - k^2 s_1^2 s_2^2},$$

on using the identities connecting the functions $\operatorname{sn} u$, $\operatorname{cn} u$, and $\operatorname{dn} u$. This equation expresses $\operatorname{sn}(u+v)$ as an algebraic function of $\operatorname{sn} u$ and $\operatorname{sn} v$, and so is the addition theorem for $\operatorname{sn} u$. Similar remarks apply to the formulae for $\operatorname{cn}(u+v)$ and $\operatorname{dn}(u+v)$.

We have thus shown that the Jacobian elliptic functions possess the addition theorems

$$\operatorname{sn}(u+v) = \frac{\operatorname{sn} u \operatorname{cn} v \operatorname{dn} v + \operatorname{sn} v \operatorname{cn} u \operatorname{dn} u}{1 - k^2 \operatorname{sn}^2 u \operatorname{sn}^2 v},$$

$$\operatorname{cn}(u+v) = \frac{\operatorname{cn} u \operatorname{cn} v - \operatorname{dn} u \operatorname{dn} v \operatorname{sn} u \operatorname{sn} v}{1 - k^2 \operatorname{sn}^2 u \operatorname{sn}^2 v},$$

$$\operatorname{dn}(u+v) = \frac{\operatorname{dn} u \operatorname{dn} v - k^2 \operatorname{sn} u \operatorname{sn} v \operatorname{cn} u \operatorname{cn} v}{1 - k^2 \operatorname{sn}^2 u \operatorname{sn}^2 v}.$$

Example 1. Prove that

$$\operatorname{sn}(u+K) = \operatorname{cd} u, \qquad \operatorname{cn}(u+K) = -k' \operatorname{sd} u, \qquad \operatorname{dn}(u+K) = k' \operatorname{nd} u,$$
$$\operatorname{sn}(u+K+iK') = k^{-1}\operatorname{dc} u, \qquad \operatorname{cn}(u+K+iK') = -ik'k^{-1}\operatorname{nc} u,$$
$$\operatorname{dn}(u+K+iK') = ik'\operatorname{sc} u.$$

Example 2. Deduce from Ex. 1 that

$$\operatorname{sn}(u+iK') = k^{-1}\operatorname{ns}u, \qquad \operatorname{cn}(u+iK') = -ik^{-1}\operatorname{ds}u,$$
$$\operatorname{dn}(u+iK') = -i\operatorname{cs}u.$$

Hence show that, when $|u|$ is small,

$$\operatorname{sn}(u+iK') = \frac{1}{ku} + \frac{1+k^2}{6k}u + \dots,$$

$$\operatorname{cn}(u+iK') = -\frac{i}{ku} + \frac{2k^2-1}{6k}iu + \dots,$$

$$\operatorname{dn}(u+iK') = -\frac{i}{u} + \frac{2-k^2}{6}iu + \dots.$$

Example 3. Prove that

$$\operatorname{sn}(u+\alpha)\operatorname{sn}(u-\alpha) = (\operatorname{sn}^2u - \operatorname{sn}^2\alpha)/(1-k^2\operatorname{sn}^2u\operatorname{sn}^2\alpha),$$
$$\operatorname{cn}(u+\alpha)\operatorname{cn}(u-\alpha) = (\operatorname{cn}^2\alpha - \operatorname{dn}^2\alpha\operatorname{sn}^2u)/(1-k^2\operatorname{sn}^2u\operatorname{sn}^2\alpha),$$
$$\operatorname{dn}(u+\alpha)\operatorname{dn}(u-\alpha) = (\operatorname{dn}^2\alpha - k^2\operatorname{cn}^2\alpha\operatorname{sn}^2u)/(1-k^2\operatorname{sn}^2u\operatorname{sn}^2\alpha).$$

Example 4. Writing s, c, d, S, C, D for $\operatorname{sn}u, \operatorname{cn}u, \operatorname{dn}u, \operatorname{sn}2u, \operatorname{cn}2u,$ $\operatorname{dn}2u$ respectively, prove that

$$S = \frac{2scd}{1-k^2s^4}, \qquad C = \frac{1-2s^2+k^2s^4}{1-k^2s^4}, \qquad D = \frac{1-2k^2s^2+k^2s^4}{1-k^2s^4}.$$

Deduce that

$$s^2 = \frac{1-C}{1+D}, \qquad c^2 = \frac{D+C}{1+D}, \qquad d^2 = \frac{D+C}{1+C}. \quad \text{(Glaisher.)}$$

Example 5. Show that†

$$\operatorname{sn}\tfrac{1}{2}K = 1/\sqrt{(1+k')}, \qquad \operatorname{cn}\tfrac{1}{2}K = \sqrt{k'}/\sqrt{(1+k')}, \qquad \operatorname{dn}\tfrac{1}{2}K = \sqrt{k'}.$$

Example 6. Prove that

$$\operatorname{sn}(u+\tfrac{1}{2}K) = (1+k')^{-1/2}\frac{k'\operatorname{sn}u + \operatorname{cn}u\operatorname{dn}u}{\operatorname{cn}^2u + k'\operatorname{sn}^2u}.$$

14.4. Jacobi's elliptic functions of given modulus

Weierstrass's elliptic function

$$\wp(z) = \frac{1}{z^2} + \sum' \left\{ \frac{1}{(z-\Omega_{m,n})^2} - \frac{1}{\Omega_{m,n}^2} \right\}$$

is obviously a homogeneous function of the three variables z, ω_1, and ω_2 of degree -2; in particular, the constants e_1, e_2, and e_3 are homogeneous functions of ω_1 and ω_2 of the same degree. Hence the function

$$S(z) = \left\{ \frac{e_1-e_2}{\wp(z)-e_2} \right\}^{1/2}$$

---

† In this result, the branches of the square roots of k' and $1+k'$ are defined by requiring them to be positive when $0 < k < 1$.

is homogeneous of degree zero in z, ω_1, and ω_2, and so is of the form $F(z/\omega_1, \tau)$, where $\tau = \omega_2/\omega_1$. But this gives

$$\operatorname{sn} u \equiv S\{u(e_1-e_2)^{-1/2}\} = F\{u(e_1-e_2)^{-1/2}/\omega_1, \tau\}.$$

As $\omega_1(e_1-e_2)^{1/2}$ is a function of τ alone, it follows that $\operatorname{sn} u$ depends only on the independent variable u and the parameter τ; similarly for $\operatorname{cn} u$ and $\operatorname{dn} u$.

This means that, when τ is assigned, we obtain the same Jacobian elliptic functions, no matter what pair of parameters ω_1 and ω_2 we employ in their construction, so long as the ratio ω_2/ω_1 is equal to τ.

Similarly the quantities

$$k = -\frac{(e_3-e_2)^{1/2}}{(e_1-e_2)^{1/2}}, \qquad k' = \frac{(e_1-e_3)^{1/2}}{(e_1-e_2)^{1/2}},$$

$$K = \omega_1(e_1-e_2)^{1/2}, \qquad iK' = \omega_2(e_1-e_2)^{1/2}$$

are functions of τ alone; moreover, the explicit formulae, found in § 14.2, Ex. 4, show that they are analytic functions, regular when $\operatorname{Im} \tau > 0$.

Conversely, when k^2 has a given value c different from 0 or 1, the Jacobian elliptic functions are uniquely determined. (This fact is often emphasized by denoting them by $\operatorname{sn}(u, k)$, and so on.†) To prove this, we need to show that the equation $(e_3-e_2)/(e_1-e_2) = c$ always has a root τ whose imaginary part is positive, and also that every root of this equation leads to the same set of Jacobian elliptic functions.

This problem is completely solved in Chapter XV. We show there that the equation always has a root τ_0 lying in a certain 'fundamental region' of the upper half of the τ-plane, and that any other solution is of the form $(a\tau_0+2b)/(2c\tau_0+d)$, where a, b, c, and d are integers such that $ad-4bc = 1$. From this it is deduced that the functions $\operatorname{sn}(u, k)$, $\operatorname{cn}(u, k)$, and $\operatorname{dn}(u, k)$ are uniquely determined when k^2 is given.

The equation $(e_3-e_2)/(e_1-e_2) = c$ defines τ as a many-valued function of c, with branch-points at $c = 0, 1, \infty$. Each branch is regular in the c-plane supposed cut along the real axis from $-\infty$ to 0 and from 1 to $+\infty$. As $c \to 0$ the principal branch τ_0 tends to infinity along a line parallel to the imaginary axis.

† The notation is rather unfortunate, as k^2 is given, not k.

These branch-points of τ, regarded as a function of c, are such that $e^{\pi i \tau}$ has branch-points only at $c = 1$ and $c = \infty$, and is regular in the c-plane supposed cut only along the real axis from 1 to $+\infty$.

Finally, since†

$$K = \tfrac{1}{2}\pi \prod_{n=1}^{\infty} \{(1-q^{2n})^2(1+q^{2n-1})^4\}, \qquad iK' = \tau K,$$

where $q = e^{\pi i \tau}$, these results imply that K is an analytic function of c, regular in the cut c-plane, and that K' is also regular provided that an additional cut is made‡ along the real axis from $-\infty$ to 0.

14.41. The evaluation of an elliptic integral

When k^2 is not equal to 0 or 1, the expression

$$\int_0^s (1-z^2)^{-1/2}(1-k^2z^2)^{-1/2}\, dz$$

is an elliptic integral. We now show that, when the path of integration does not pass through a branch-point of the integrand, we can evaluate this integral by means of the substitution $z = \mathrm{sn}(w, k)$.

The equation $z = \mathrm{sn}(w, k)$ defines w as a many-valued function of z. For if $w = f(z)$ is any solution of this equation, then

$$w = f(z)+4mK+2niK'$$

and

$$w = 2K-f(z)+4mK+2niK'$$

are also solutions for all positive and negative integral and zero values of m and n. Since

$$\frac{dw}{dz} = (1-z^2)^{-1/2}(1-k^2z^2)^{-1/2},$$

the only singularities of w are branch-points at $z = \pm 1$ and $z = \pm 1/k$.

There is, however, a unique solution of the equation which is regular in a neighbourhood of the origin and vanishes at the origin. The existence of this solution $w = F(z)$, say, is a consequence of the inverse-function theorem of § 6.22, since $\mathrm{sn}(w, k)$ has a simple zero at the origin and is regular when $|w|$ is small.

---

† See § 14.2, Ex. 4.
‡ Actually the cut from $c = 1$ to $c = +\infty$ is unnecessary in the case of K'. See § 14.44.

As the path of integration does not pass through a branch-point of the many-valued function $w(z)$, we can continue $F(z)$ analytically along it. Accordingly the transformation $w = F(z)$ determines a definite path of integration in the w-plane, which starts at the origin and ends at a point v, where v is a certain solution of the equation $\text{sn}(v, k) = s$. The particular solution v which has to be taken evidently depends on the manner in which the path of integration in the z-plane passes between the branch-points ± 1 and $\pm 1/k$.

If we now make the substitution $z = \text{sn}(w, k)$ and suppose that the integrand has the value $+1$ at the origin, we obtain

$$\int_0^s (1-z^2)^{-1/2}(1-k^2z^2)^{-1/2}\, dz = \int_0^v dw = v.$$

Example 1. Prove that

$$\text{(i)}\quad u = \int_{\text{cn}\, u}^{1} (1-t^2)^{-1/2}(k'^2+k^2t^2)^{-1/2}\, dt,$$

$$\text{(ii)}\quad u = \int_{\text{dn}\, u}^{1} (1-t^2)^{-1/2}(t^2-k'^2)^{-1/2}\, dt,$$

$$\text{(iii)}\quad u = \int_{\text{cs}\, u}^{\infty} (t^2+1)^{-1/2}(t^2+k'^2)^{-1/2}\, dt,$$

$$\text{(iv)}\quad u = \int_{0}^{\text{sd}\, u} (1-k'^2t^2)^{-1/2}(1+k^2t^2)^{-1/2}\, dt.$$

Example 2. Show that, if k^2 is not equal to 0 or 1,

$$\int_0^\theta (1-k^2\sin^2 t)^{-1/2}\, dt = v,$$

where v is a solution of the equation $\text{sn}(v, k) = \sin\theta$. (This equation was used by Jacobi as the definition of his function $\theta = \text{am}\, v$.)

14.42. The expression of K in terms of k

We saw in § 14.4 that K is an analytic function of c $(= k^2)$, regular in the c-plane supposed cut along the real axis from $+1$ to $+\infty$. We shall now show that the equation

$$\int_0^1 (1-x^2)^{-1/2}(1-cx^2)^{-1/2}\, dx = K,$$

where the path of integration is a straight line, holds everywhere in this cut c-plane.

By § 14.41, the value of this integral is $u+4mK+2niK'$, where m and n are integers and u is a zero of $1-\operatorname{sn} u$. But as $1-\operatorname{sn} u$ is an elliptic function of order two with a double zero at $u = K$, we have

$$\int_0^1 (1-x^2)^{-1/2}(1-cx^2)^{-1/2}\, dx = (4m+1)K+2niK',$$

where m and n are integers to be determined.

Let us consider first the case when $0 < c < 1$, so that the value of the integral is real and positive. In this case the principal value of τ is purely imaginary, and therefore K and K' are also real and positive. This implies that $m \geqslant 0$ and $n = 0$. But if m were positive, there would exist a number x_0 between 0 and 1, such that

$$\int_0^{x_0} (1-x^2)^{-1/2}(1-cx^2)^{-1/2}\, dx = K;$$

we should then have $\operatorname{sn} K = x_0 < 1$, which is impossible. Hence $m = 0$.

We have thus shown that

$$\int_0^1 (1-x^2)^{-1/2}(1-cx^2)^{-1/2}\, dx = K$$

when $0 < c < 1$. The truth of this formula when c lies anywhere in the cut plane immediately follows by the principle of analytical continuation.

14.43. K expressed as a hypergeometric function

If we write $x = \sin\theta$ in the integral-formula for K, we find that

$$K = \int_0^{\frac{1}{2}\pi} (1-c\sin^2\theta)^{-1/2}\, d\theta,$$

when c lies in the cut plane. When $|c| < 1$, we can expand the integrand as a series of ascending powers of c which converges uniformly† with respect to θ and so can be integrated term by

† By Weierstrass's M-test, since $0 \leqslant \sin^2\theta \leqslant 1$.

term. This gives immediately

$$K = \tfrac{1}{2}\pi F(\tfrac{1}{2}, \tfrac{1}{2}; 1; c),$$

where $c = k^2$.

By the principle of analytical continuation, this formula holds everywhere in the c-plane, supposed cut along the real axis from $+1$ to $+\infty$, since the expressions on each side of the equation are both regular all over the cut plane.

14.44. The expression of K' in terms of k'

We now prove that K' is the same function of k' as K is of k, by considering the effect of renaming the parameters ω_1 and ω_2 which occur in the definition of Jacobi's elliptic functions. If we write $\omega_1' = -\omega_2$, $\omega_2' = \omega_1$, $\omega_1' + \omega_2' + \omega_3' = 0$, the set of points $2m'\omega_1' + 2n'\omega_2'$, where m' and n' take all positive and negative integral and zero values, is identical with the set of periods $2m\omega_1 + 2n\omega_2$ of Weierstrass's function $\wp(z|\omega_1, \omega_2)$. It follows that

$$\wp(z|\omega_1', \omega_2') = \wp(z|\omega_1, \omega_2), \qquad \zeta(z|\omega_1', \omega_2') = \zeta(z|\omega_1, \omega_2),$$

and

$$\sigma(z|\omega_1', \omega_2') = \sigma(z|\omega_1, \omega_2).$$

On the other hand, the constants which occur in the equations expressing the pseudo-periodicity of $\zeta(z|\omega_1', \omega_2')$ and $\sigma(z|\omega_1', \omega_2')$ are no longer η_1 and η_2. For, if

$$\zeta(z + 2\omega_1'|\omega_1', \omega_2') = 2\eta_1' + \zeta(z|\omega_1', \omega_2'),$$

then

$$\eta_1' = \zeta(\omega_1'|\omega_1', \omega_2') = \zeta(-\omega_2|\omega_1, \omega_2) = -\eta_2,$$

and similarly

$$\eta_2' = \eta_1, \qquad \eta_3' = 2\eta_2 + \eta_3.$$

Hence we obtain a different set of Jacobian elliptic functions if we use the parameters ω_1' and ω_2' instead of ω_1 and ω_2.

Next we find the modulus and quarter-periods of this new set of elliptic functions. Using an obvious notation, we have

$$k(\omega_1', \omega_2')$$

$$= -\frac{(e_3' - e_2')^{1/2}}{(e_1' - e_2')^{1/2}} = -\frac{\{\wp(\omega_3') - e_2'\}^{1/2}}{\{\wp(\omega_1') - e_2'\}^{1/2}} = -\frac{\{\wp(\omega_2 - \omega_1) - e_1\}^{1/2}}{\{\wp(-\omega_2) - e_1\}^{1/2}},$$

by the definition of $(e_r - e_s)^{1/2}$. Now $\{\wp(z) - e_1\}^{1/2}$ is an odd elliptic function with periods $2\omega_1$ and $4\omega_2$; hence

$$k(\omega_1', \omega_2') = -\frac{\{\wp(\omega_3) - e_1\}^{1/2}}{\{\wp(\omega_2) - e_1\}^{1/2}} = -\frac{(e_3 - e_1)^{1/2}}{(e_2 - e_1)^{1/2}} = \frac{(e_1 - e_3)^{1/2}}{(e_1 - e_2)^{1/2}},$$

since $(e_3 - e_1)^{1/2} = i(e_1 - e_3)^{1/2}$, $(e_2 - e_1)^{1/2} = -i(e_1 - e_2)^{1/2}$. It follows, therefore, that $k(\omega_1', \omega_2') = k'(\omega_1, \omega_2)$, and similarly that $k'(\omega_1', \omega_2') = k(\omega_1, \omega_2)$. Thus the modulus and complementary modulus are interchanged by the interchange of parameters.

Again, we have

$$K(\omega_1', \omega_2') = \omega_1'(e_1 - e_2')^{1/2} = -\omega_2\{\wp(-\omega_2) - e_1\}^{1/2} = \omega_2(e_2 - e_1)^{1/2},$$

which gives at once

$$K(\omega_1', \omega_2') = K'(\omega_1, \omega_2);$$

similarly $\qquad K'(\omega_1', \omega_2') = K(\omega_1, \omega_2).$

Hence, when $k^2(\omega_1', \omega_2')$ is not real and greater than unity,

$$K'(\omega_1, \omega_2) = K(\omega_1', \omega_2')$$

$$= \int_0^1 (1 - x^2)^{-1/2}\{1 - k^2(\omega_1', \omega_2')x^2\}^{-1/2}\, dx$$

$$= \int_0^1 (1 - x^2)^{-1/2}\{1 - k'^2(\omega_1, \omega_2)x^2\}^{-1/2}\, dx,$$

that is, $\qquad K' = \int_0^1 (1 - x^2)^{-1/2}(1 - k'^2 x^2)^{-1/2}\, dx,$

save when $k'^2 \geqslant 1$. This proves the required result.

Further, by using the result of § 14.43, we see that K' is an analytic function of $c\ (= k^2)$, regular in the c-plane supposed cut along the real axis from $-\infty$ to 0; the additional cut from $+1$ to $+\infty$, imposed in § 14.4, is unnecessary. The explicit formula for K' as a function of c is

$$K' = \tfrac{1}{2}\pi F(\tfrac{1}{2}, \tfrac{1}{2}; 1; 1 - c).$$

14.45. Jacobi's imaginary transformation

We have just seen that the primitive periods of $\operatorname{sn}(u, k')$ are $4K'$ and $2iK$, and hence those of $\operatorname{sn}(iu, k')$ are $2K$ and $4iK'$. Therefore the functions $\operatorname{sn}(u, k)$ and $\operatorname{sn}(iu, k')$ have a common pair of periods $4K$ and $4iK'$, and this implies that they are connected by an algebraic relation which we shall now determine.

By definition, we have

$$\operatorname{sn}\!\left(\frac{zK'}{\omega_1'}, k'\right) = \frac{K'}{\omega_1'}\,\frac{\sigma(z|\omega_1', \omega_2')}{\sigma_2(z|\omega_1', \omega_2')} = \frac{K'}{\omega_1'}\,\frac{\sigma(z|\omega_1', \omega_2')\sigma(\omega_2'|\omega_1', \omega_2')}{e^{-\eta_2'z}\sigma(z + \omega_2'|\omega_1', \omega_2')}$$

$$= \frac{K'}{\omega_1'}\,\frac{\sigma(z)\sigma(\omega_1)}{e^{-\eta_1 z}\sigma(z + \omega_1)} = \frac{K'}{\omega_1'}\,\frac{\sigma(z)}{\sigma_1(z)}.$$

But $iK'/K = \omega_2/\omega_1$, and so $K'/\omega_1' = -K'/\omega_2 = iK/\omega_1$. Hence

$$\operatorname{sn}\left(\frac{iKz}{\omega_1}, k'\right) = \frac{iK}{\omega_1}\frac{\sigma(z)}{\sigma_2(z)}\Big/\frac{\sigma_1(z)}{\sigma_2(z)} = i\operatorname{sc}\left(\frac{Kz}{\omega_1}, k\right).$$

Putting $Kz = \omega_1 u$, we obtain

$$\operatorname{sn}(iu, k') = i\operatorname{sc}(u, k),$$

which is the required algebraic relation. From this it follows that

$$\operatorname{cn}(iu, k') = \operatorname{nc}(u, k), \qquad \operatorname{dn}(iu, k') = \operatorname{dc}(u, k).$$

These three equations constitute Jacobi's imaginary transformation[†] of his elliptic functions.

Example 1. Deduce Jacobi's imaginary transformation from the equation

$$\int_0^{\operatorname{sn}(iu, k')} (1-z^2)^{-1/2}(1-k'^2 z^2)^{-1/2}\, dz = iu,$$

by the substitution $z = it/(1-t^2)^{1/2}$.

Example 2. Prove by the aid of Jacobi's imaginary transformation that

$$\operatorname{sn}\tfrac{1}{2}iK' = i/\sqrt{k}, \qquad \operatorname{cn}\tfrac{1}{2}iK' = \sqrt{(1+k)}/\sqrt{k}, \qquad \operatorname{dn}\tfrac{1}{2}iK' = \sqrt{(1+k)},$$

the square roots being positive when $0 < k < 1$.

Example 3. Prove that

$$\operatorname{sn}(u + \tfrac{1}{2}iK') = k^{-1/2}\frac{(1+k)\operatorname{sn} u + i\operatorname{cn} u\operatorname{dn} u}{1 + k\operatorname{sn}^2 u}.$$

14.46. Landen's transformation

The theory of the transformations of elliptic functions is concerned with the expression of the Jacobian functions of parameter τ' in terms of those of parameter τ, where

$$\tau' = (a\tau + b)/(c\tau + d),$$

a, b, c, and d being integers such that $ad - bc$ is positive. A very simple instance[‡] of this is provided by Jacobi's imaginary transformation, in which $\tau' = -1/\tau$.

The general theory of these transformations is beyond the scope of the present book;[§] we shall consider only Landen's

---

† *Fundamenta Nova*, 34–5.
‡ For others, see Ex. 18 on p. 416.
§ See, however, Tannery and Molk, *Fonctions elliptiques*, **2** (Paris, 1896), 195–232.

transformation, defined by $\tau' = 2\tau$. This is of historical interest, being the first case ever discussed.†

In order to determine Landen's transformation,‡ we consider first the connexion between Weierstrass's Sigma functions $\sigma(z|\omega_1, \omega_2)$ and $\sigma(z|\omega_1', \omega_2')$, where $\omega_1' = \tfrac{1}{2}\omega_1$ and $\omega_2' = \omega_2$, since these give

$$\tau' = \frac{\omega_2'}{\omega_1'} = 2\frac{\omega_2}{\omega_1} = 2\tau.$$

It is easily shown that§

$$\sigma(z|\omega_1', \omega_2') = e^{\frac{1}{2}e_1 z^2 - \eta_1 z}\sigma(z)\sigma(z+\omega_1)/\sigma(\omega_1),$$

it being understood that the parameters of $\sigma(z)$ are ω_1 and ω_2, unless the contrary is explicitly indicated. From this it follows that

$$\zeta(z|\omega_1', \omega_2') = e_1 z - \eta_1 + \zeta(z) + \zeta(z+\omega_1),$$

and hence that

$$\eta_1' = \tfrac{1}{2}e_1\omega_1 - \eta_1 + \zeta(\tfrac{1}{2}\omega_1) + \zeta(\tfrac{3}{2}\omega_1) = \tfrac{1}{2}e_1\omega_1 + \eta_1,$$

and

$$\eta_2' = e_1\omega_2 - \eta_1 + \zeta(\omega_2) + \zeta(\omega_1+\omega_2) = e_1\omega_2 + 2\eta_2.$$

Let us now suppose that the Jacobian elliptic functions constructed from $\sigma(z|\omega_1', \omega_2')$ have quarter-periods L, iL' and modulus l. Then

$$\operatorname{sn}\!\left(\frac{2zL}{\omega_1}, l\right) = \operatorname{sn}\!\left(\frac{zL}{\omega_1'}, l\right)$$

$$= \frac{L}{\omega_1'}\,\frac{\sigma(z|\omega_1', \omega_2')\sigma(\omega_2'|\omega_1', \omega_2')}{e^{-\eta_2' z}\sigma(z+\omega_2'|\omega_1', \omega_2')}$$

$$= \frac{2L}{\omega_1}\,\frac{\sigma(z)\sigma(z+\omega_1)\sigma(\omega_2)\sigma(\omega_1+\omega_2)}{\sigma(z+\omega_2)\sigma(z+\omega_1+\omega_2)\sigma(\omega_1)}\exp\{(2\eta_2+e_1\omega_2)z+\tfrac{1}{2}e_1 z^2 - $$
$$-\eta_1 z + \tfrac{1}{2}e_1\omega_2^2 - \eta_1\omega_2 - \tfrac{1}{2}e_1(z+\omega_2)^2 + \eta_1(z+\omega_2)\}$$

$$= \frac{2L}{\omega_1}\,e^{2\eta_2 z}\frac{\sigma(z)\sigma(z+\omega_1)\sigma(\omega_2)\sigma(\omega_1+\omega_2)}{\sigma(z+\omega_2)\sigma(z+\omega_1+\omega_2)\sigma(\omega_1)}$$

† Landen, *Phil. Trans.* **65** (1775), 285. Landen, however, deals only with elliptic integrals, the idea of 'inverting' an elliptic integral to obtain an elliptic function (due to Abel and Jacobi) not having been introduced until 1826.

‡ A simpler but less obvious method of finding Landen's transformation is suggested in Ex. 2 at the end of this section.

§ See Ex. 20 on p. 379.

$$= \frac{2L}{\omega_1} \frac{\sigma(z)\sigma_1(z)}{\sigma_2(z)\sigma_3(z)}$$

$$= \frac{2L}{K} \operatorname{sn}\!\left(\frac{Kz}{\omega_1}, k\right)\operatorname{cd}\!\left(\frac{Kz}{\omega_1}, k\right).$$

Writing $Kz = \omega_1 u$, we have

$$K \operatorname{sn}(2Lu/K, l) = 2L \operatorname{sn}(u, k)\operatorname{cd}(u, k). \tag{i}$$

It remains to determine the relations connecting the quarter-periods and moduli of the two sets of Jacobian functions.

The relations connecting the quarter-periods are found by putting $u = \tfrac{1}{2}K$ in this equation. This gives

$$K \operatorname{sn}(L, l) = 2L \operatorname{sn}(\tfrac{1}{2}K, k)\operatorname{cd}(\tfrac{1}{2}K, k),$$

and hence, by § 14.3, Ex. 5,

$$L = \tfrac{1}{2}(1+k')K.$$

Using this value of L/K, equation (i) becomes

$$\operatorname{sn}\{(1+k')u, l\} = (1+k')\operatorname{sn}(u, k)\operatorname{cd}(u, k).$$

Moreover, since

$$2L/L' = 2i\omega_1'/\omega_2' = i\omega_1/\omega_2 = K/K',$$

we also have $L' = (1+k')K'.$

Again, if we write equation (i) in the form

$$L' \operatorname{sn}(u, k)\operatorname{cd}(u, k) = K' \operatorname{sn}(L'u/K', l)$$

and then put $u = v+iK'$, we obtain

$$\frac{L' \operatorname{dc}(v, k)}{k^2 \operatorname{sn}(v, k)} = \frac{K'}{l \operatorname{sn}(L'v/K', l)}.$$

Multiplying the expressions on each side of this equation by v and then making v tend to zero, we have

$$\frac{L'}{k^2} = \frac{K'^2}{L'l},$$

and so $l = \dfrac{k^2 K'^2}{L'^2} = \dfrac{k^2}{(1+k')^2} = \dfrac{1-k'}{1+k'}.$

We have thus proved that

$$\operatorname{sn}\{(1+k')u, l\} = (1+k')\operatorname{sn}(u, k)\operatorname{cd}(u, k)$$

where $l = (1-k')/(1+k')$. This is the result known as Landen's transformation.

Example 1. Prove that, in the notation of the previous section,

$$\operatorname{cn}\{(1+k')u, l\} = \{1-(1+k')\operatorname{sn}^2(u, k)\}\operatorname{nd}(u, k),$$
$$\operatorname{dn}\{(1+k')u, l\} = \{1-(1-k')\operatorname{sn}^2(u, k)\}\operatorname{nd}(u, k).$$

Example 2. Show that Landen's transformation is equivalent to

$$\int_0^{\phi_1} (1-l^2\sin^2\phi)^{-1/2}\, d\phi = (1+k')\int_0^{\theta_1} (1-k^2\sin^2\theta)^{-1/2}\, d\theta,$$

where
$$\sin\phi_1 = (1+k')\sin\theta_1\cos\theta_1(1-k^2\sin^2\theta_1)^{-1/2}.$$

Obtain this result also by a direct transformation of the integrals.

14.5. Legendre's three kinds of elliptic integral

We shall now show that the problem of evaluating the general elliptic integral $\int F(t, u)\, dt$, where $F(t, u)$ denotes a rational function of t and u, and u^2 is a quartic or cubic polynomial in t without repeated factors, can be reduced to the evaluation of three very simple types of elliptic integral.

Since $F(t, u)$ is a rational function of t and u, we can write

$$F(t, u) \equiv N(t, u)/D(t, u),$$

where N and D denote polynomials in t and u. Now $D(t, u)\, D(t, -u)$ is a polynomial in t and u^2, since it does not alter when we change the sign of u, and so becomes a polynomial in t alone when we substitute for u^2 in terms of t. Thus

$$uF(t, u) \equiv uN(t, u)D(t, -u)/G(t),$$

where G denotes a polynomial in t.

If we multiply out $uN(t, u)D(t, -u)$ and substitute for u^2 in terms of t, we obtain ultimately

$$uN(t, u)D(t, -u) \equiv \Phi(t)+u\Psi(t),$$

where Φ and Ψ denote polynomials in t. Hence

$$F(t, u) \equiv \frac{1}{u}\frac{\Phi(t)}{G(t)}+\frac{\Psi(t)}{G(t)}.$$

As the second term in this expression for $F(t, u)$ can be integrated by means of elementary functions, the problem of evaluating the general elliptic integral has been reduced to the discussion of the simpler integral

$$\int \frac{\Phi(t)}{G(t)}\frac{dt}{u}.$$

Let us suppose, in the first instance, that

$$u^2 = (t-\alpha)(t-\beta)(t-\gamma)(t-\delta),$$

where α, β, γ, and δ are, by hypothesis, distinct. Making the transformation†

$$z^2 = \{(\beta-\delta)(t-\alpha)\}/\{(\alpha-\delta)(t-\beta)\},$$

we easily find that

$$\sqrt{\{(\alpha-\gamma)(\beta-\delta)\}}\,\frac{dt}{u} = \frac{2dz}{\sqrt{\{(1-z^2)(1-k^2z^2)\}}},$$

where $k^2 = \{(\alpha-\delta)(\beta-\gamma)\}/\{(\alpha-\gamma)(\beta-\delta)\}$. If, however, u^2 is a cubic in t, say $u^2 = (t-\alpha)(t-\beta)(t-\gamma),$

the appropriate transformation is $z^2 = (t-\alpha)/(t-\beta)$; this gives at once

$$\sqrt{(\alpha-\gamma)}\,\frac{dt}{u} = \frac{2dz}{\sqrt{\{(1-z^2)(1-k^2z^2)\}}},$$

where $k^2 = (\beta-\gamma)/(\alpha-\gamma)$. Hence, no matter whether u^2 be a quartic or cubic, we have now shown that

$$\int \frac{\Phi(t)}{G(t)}\,\frac{dt}{u} = \int R(z^2)\{(1-z^2)(1-k^2z^2)\}^{-1/2}\,dz,$$

where $R(z^2)$ is a rational function of z^2, and k^2 is a finite constant, not equal to 0 or 1.

The next step is to express $R(z^2)$ as a sum of partial fractions in z^2. The general elliptic integral is thus reduced to a sum of integrals of the following types,

$$\int z^{2r}\{(1-z^2)(1-k^2z^2)\}^{-1/2}\,dz,$$

$$\int (1+\nu z^2)^{-s}\{(1-z^2)(1-k^2z^2)\}^{-1/2}\,dz,$$

where r and s are integers, s being positive, and ν is a constant.

Finally, by using well-known methods of the integral calculus, it is easy to obtain reduction formulae by means of which each of the above integrals can be expressed in terms of one of the

† For an alternative method which only involves the use of a homographic transformation, see Ex. 29 at the end of the present chapter.

three standard forms of Legendre:

$$\int \{(1-z^2)(1-k^2z^2)\}^{-1/2}\, dz,$$

$$\int z^2\{(1-z^2)(1-k^2z^2)\}^{-1/2}\, dz,$$

$$\int (1+\nu z^2)^{-1}\{(1-z^2)(1-k^2z^2)\}^{-1/2}\, dz.$$

These are called the elliptic integrals of the first, second, and third kinds respectively. The evaluation of the integral of the first kind has already been discussed in § 14.41.

14.51. The elliptic integral of the second kind

If we make the substitution $z = \operatorname{sn}(u,k)$ in Legendre's integral $\int z^2\{(1-z^2)(1-k^2z^2)\}^{-1/2}\, dz$, we find that it becomes $\int \operatorname{sn}^2(u,k)\, du$. But since

$$\int \operatorname{dn}^2(u,k)\, du = u-k^2 \int \operatorname{sn}^2(u,k)\, du,$$

the latter integral could equally well be taken as the standard elliptic integral of the second kind, and this proves to be more convenient. It is usual to write

$$E(u,k) = \int_0^u \operatorname{dn}^2(u,k)\, du,$$

it being supposed that the path of integration does not pass through a pole of the integrand. When it is unnecessary to emphasize the modulus k, we shall denote the function more briefly by $E(u)$.

We shall now show that $E(u)$ is an odd analytic function of u, regular save for simple poles of residue $+1$ at the points $2mK+(2n+1)iK'$.

To prove this, we observe that $\operatorname{dn}^2 u$ is an even elliptic function of periods $2K$, $2iK'$ whose only singularity in any cell is a double pole of residue zero at the point congruent to iK'. It follows that the integral of $\operatorname{dn}^2 u$ round any closed contour which does not pass through a pole is zero, and hence that $E(u)$ is a one-valued function. Moreover, since the derivative of $E(u)$ is $\operatorname{dn}^2 u$, $E(u)$ is an odd function whose only possible singularities are the poles of $\operatorname{dn}^2 u$. We know, however, that, if α is a pole of $\operatorname{dn}^2 u$,

$$\operatorname{dn}^2 u = -(u-\alpha)^{-2}+\phi(u),$$

D d

where $\phi(u)$ is regular at α; hence

$$E(u) = (u-\alpha)^{-1} + \Phi(u),$$

where $\Phi(u)$ is regular at α. Thus α is a simple pole of $E(u)$, of residue $+1$.

It should be noticed that $E(u)$ is not an elliptic function, since the sum of its residues at any set of its poles can never be zero. We can, however, show that, when u is increased by $2K$ or $2iK'$, $E(u)$ is reproduced, save for an additive constant.

For we have

$$E(u+2K) - E(u) = \int_u^{u+2K} \mathrm{dn}^2 u \, du = \int_0^{2K} \mathrm{dn}^2 u \, du,$$

since $2K$ is a period of the integrand, and hence

$$E(u+2K) - E(u) = E(2K).$$

Putting $u = -K$, we find that $E(2K) = 2E(K)$.

Similarly we can show that

$$E(u+2iK') - E(u) = E(2iK'),$$

but no simpler form of the constant can be obtained at the present stage, since iK' is a pole of $E(u)$.

14.511. The complete elliptic integral of the second kind

The constant $E(K)$ is called the complete elliptic integral of the second kind, and is usually denoted by E. If we write $\mathrm{sn}\, u = \sin\theta$ in the equation

$$E = \int_0^K \mathrm{dn}^2 u \, du,$$

we find that

$$E = \int_0^{\pi/2} (1 - c\sin^2\theta)^{1/2} \, d\theta,$$

where $c = k^2$. From this it can be shown† that E is an analytic function of c, regular in the c-plane supposed cut along the real axis from $+1$ to $+\infty$, and that

$$E = \tfrac{1}{2}\pi F(-\tfrac{1}{2}, \tfrac{1}{2}; 1; c).$$

We write E' for $E(K', k')$. Since E' is the same function of k' as E is of k, it is regular in the c-plane supposed cut along

† Cf. § 14.43.

the real axis from $-\infty$ to 0, and can be written in the form

$$E' = \tfrac{1}{2}\pi F(-\tfrac{1}{2}, \tfrac{1}{2}; 1; 1-c).$$

Example 1. Show that, as $k \to 0$,

$$E \to \tfrac{1}{2}\pi, \qquad E' \to 1, \qquad (K-E)/k^2 \to \tfrac{1}{4}\pi.$$

Example 2. Prove that

$$2\frac{dE}{dc} = \frac{E-K}{c}, \qquad 2\frac{dK}{dc} = \frac{E-Kc'}{cc'},$$

$$2\frac{dE'}{dc} = \frac{K'-E'}{c'}, \qquad 2\frac{dK'}{dc} = \frac{K'c-E'}{cc'},$$

where $c = k^2$, $c' = k'^2$.

Example 3. Show, by using the results of Ex. 2, that

$$EK' + E'K - KK'$$

is independent of c, and find its value by making $c \to 0$.

14.512. Jacobi's imaginary transformation of $E(u)$

To find the effect of Jacobi's imaginary transformation on the function $E(u, k)$, we write

$$E(iu, k) = \int_0^{iu} \mathrm{dn}^2(t, k)\, dt = i\int_0^u \mathrm{dn}^2(iu, k)\, du = i\int_0^u \mathrm{dc}^2(u, k')\, du,$$

and so

$$E(iu, k) + iE(u, k') = i\int_0^u [\mathrm{dc}^2(u, k') + \mathrm{dn}^2(u, k')]\, du$$

$$= i\int_0^u \left[1 + \frac{d}{du}\{\mathrm{sn}(u, k')\mathrm{dc}(u, k')\}\right] du.$$

From this it follows that

$$E(iu, k) = iu + i\,\mathrm{sn}(u, k')\mathrm{dc}(u, k') - iE(u, k').$$

In particular, by putting $u = 2K'$, we obtain the formula

$$E(2iK', k) = 2iK' - iE(2K', k') = 2i(K' - E').$$

Hence, by § 14.51,

$$E(u + 2iK', k) = E(u, k) + 2i(K' - E').$$

14.513. Legendre's relation

Since the only singularities of $E(u)$ are simple poles of residue $+1$ at the points $2mK + (2n+1)iK'$,

$$\int_C E(u)\, du = 2\pi i,$$

when C is the parallelogram with vertices K, $K+2iK'$, $-K+2iK'$, and $-K$. Hence

$$2\pi i = \int_{-K}^{K} \{E(u)-E(u+2iK')\}\,du + \int_{0}^{2iK'} \{E(u+K)-E(u-K)\}\,du.$$

When we make use of the pseudo-periodic properties of $E(u)$, this becomes

$$2\pi i = -4iK(K'-E')+4iK'E,$$

or $$EK'+E'K-KK' = \tfrac{1}{2}\pi.$$

This relation, which is due to Legendre, is the analogue of the formula $\eta_1\omega_2-\eta_2\omega_1 = \tfrac{1}{2}\pi i$ which occurs in the theory of the integral $\zeta(z)$ of Weierstrass's function $\wp(z)$.

14.514. The quasi-addition theorem for $E(u)$

Let us consider the expression

$$F(u) = E(u)+E(v)-E(u+v),$$

regarded as a function of u. By the pseudo-periodicity of $E(u)$, it is an elliptic function with periods $2K$ and $2iK'$. It has a pair of irreducible simple poles iK', $iK'-v$, and two irreducible simple zeros 0, $-v$. But $\operatorname{sn}u\operatorname{sn}(u+v)$ is an elliptic function of periods $2K$ and $2iK'$, with the same irreducible poles and zeros as $F(u)$; thus $\operatorname{sn}u\operatorname{sn}(u+v)/F(u)$ is an elliptic function without singularity and so is a constant.

When $|u|$ is small, we have

$$\frac{\operatorname{sn}u\operatorname{sn}(u+v)}{F(u)} = \frac{u\operatorname{sn}v+O(u^2)}{u\{1-E'(v)\}+O(u^2)} = \frac{\operatorname{sn}v}{1-\operatorname{dn}^2v}\{1+O(u)\},$$

and therefore

$$\frac{\operatorname{sn}u\operatorname{sn}(u+v)}{F(u)} = \frac{\operatorname{sn}v}{1-\operatorname{dn}^2v} = \frac{1}{k^2\operatorname{sn}v},$$

for all values of u.

We have thus shown that

$$E(u)+E(v)-E(u+v) = k^2\operatorname{sn}u\operatorname{sn}v\operatorname{sn}(u+v),$$

which is the quasi-addition theorem for $E(u)$. There can be no true addition theorem, as $E(u)$ is only pseudo-periodic.

14.515. Jacobi's Zeta function $Z(u)$

For some purposes it is desirable to have a function which is of the same general character as $E(u)$, but is simply-periodic. Such a function is Jacobi's function $Z(u)$, defined by the equation

$$Z(u) = E(u) - uE/K.$$

It is easily verified that

$$Z(u+2K) = Z(u), \qquad Z(u+2iK') = Z(u) - \pi i/K,$$

on taking into account Legendre's relation. Thus $Z(u)$ is simply-periodic with period $2K$.

Example. Show that

$$Z(u) + Z(v) - Z(u+v) = k^2 \operatorname{sn} u \operatorname{sn} v \operatorname{sn}(u+v).$$

14.52. Jacobi's Theta function $\Theta(u)$

We now introduce Jacobi's function $\Theta(u)$, which plays a part in the present theory similar to that of $\sigma(z)$ in the work of Weierstrass.† This function is defined by the equation

$$\Theta(u) = \Theta(0) \exp \int_0^u Z(u)\,du,$$

where $\Theta(0)$ is a constant which we shall choose later. We show that $\Theta(u)$ is an even integral function of period $2K$, whose only zeros are simple ones at the points $2mK + (2n+1)iK'$.

For if α is a pole of $Z(u)$ we know that $Z(u) = (u-\alpha)^{-1} + \phi(u)$, where $\phi(u)$ is regular at α, and so two determinations of $\int_0^u Z(u)\,du$, along different paths of integration, differ by a multiple of $2\pi i$. Hence $\log \Theta(u)$ is a many-valued function, but $\Theta(u)$ itself is one-valued. Moreover, as $Z(u)$ is an odd function, $\Theta(u)$ is even.

The only possible singularities of $\Theta(u)$ are the poles of $Z(u)$. But

$$\log \Theta(u) = \log(u-\alpha) + \int \phi(u)\,du = \log(u-\alpha) + \Phi,$$

where $\Phi(u)$ is regular at α, and so

$$\Theta(u) = (u-\alpha)e^{\Phi(u)}.$$

† In fact, we shall show that $\Theta(Kz/\omega_1)$ and $\sigma_2(z)$ differ only in an exponential factor.

Hence $\Theta(u)$ has a simple zero at each pole of $Z(u)$. Since, however, any pole or zero of $\Theta(u)$ is a pole† of $Z(u)$, it follows that $\Theta(u)$ is an integral function whose only zeros are simple ones at the poles of $Z(u)$.

Finally, since $Z(u+2K) = Z(u)$, we have

$$\Theta(u+2K) = A\,\Theta(u),$$

where A is a constant. If we put $u = -K$ and remember that $\Theta(u)$ is an even function, we find that $A = 1$; thus $\Theta(u)$ is simply-periodic‡ with period $2K$. This completes the proof of the fundamental properties of $\Theta(u)$.

14.521. The Fourier series for $\Theta(u)$

Since $\Theta(u)$ is an integral function of period $2K$, it can be represented by a Fourier series§

$$\Theta(u) = \sum_{-\infty}^{\infty} a_n\, e^{n\pi i u/K},$$

which converges uniformly and absolutely in any bounded closed domain of the u-plane. We shall deduce the values of the coefficients a_n from the important identity

$$\Theta(u+2iK') = -q^{-1}e^{-\pi i u/K}\Theta(u),$$

where $q = e^{-\pi K'/K}$.

To prove this identity we integrate the equation

$$Z(u+2iK') = Z(u)-\pi i/K.$$

This gives $\Theta(u+2iK') = Ae^{-\pi i u/K}\Theta(u),$

where A is a constant of integration. To find A, we put $u = v-iK'$; we then have

$$Aqe^{-\pi i v/K} = \frac{\Theta(iK'+v)}{\Theta(-iK'+v)} = \frac{\Theta(iK'+v)}{\Theta(iK'-v)}.$$

But, when $|v|$ is small, $\Theta(iK'+v) = \Theta'(iK')v+O(v^2)$, and $\Theta'(iK')$ does not vanish, since $\Theta(u)$ has only a simple zero at iK'. Hence, when $v \to 0$, we obtain $Aq = -1$, and so

$$\Theta(u+2iK') = -q^{-1}e^{-\pi i u/K}\Theta(u).$$

---

† Since $Z(u) = \Theta'(u)/\Theta(u)$.

‡ If it were doubly-periodic, it would be a constant, which is certainly not the case.

§ See Ex. 10 on p. 89.

Substituting in this identity the two series

$$\Theta(u) = \sum_{-\infty}^{\infty} a_n e^{n\pi i u/K}, \qquad \Theta(u+2iK') = \sum_{-\infty}^{\infty} a_n q^{2n} e^{n\pi i u/K},$$

and equating coefficients of $e^{(n-1)\pi i u/K}$, we find that

$$a_n = -a_{n-1} q^{2n-1}.$$

From this it follows that $a_n = (-1)^n a_0 q^{n^2}$, for all positive and negative values of n. Hence

$$\Theta(u) = a_0 \sum_{-\infty}^{\infty} (-1)^n q^{n^2} e^{n\pi i u/K}.$$

The constant a_0 is at our disposal, since, in the definition of Jacobi's Theta function, $\Theta(0)$ was left undetermined. We now fix $\Theta(0)$ by taking $a_0 = 1$. This gives

$$\Theta(u) = \sum_{-\infty}^{\infty} (-1)^n q^{n^2} e^{n\pi i u/K} \equiv 1+2 \sum_{1}^{\infty} (-1)^n q^{n^2} \cos(n\pi u/K).$$

This series provides a valuable method of computing $\Theta(u)$; for since $\mathrm{Rl}(K'/K) > 0$, we have $|q| < 1$, so that the series converges rapidly.

14.53. The elliptic integral of the third kind

Making the substitution $z = \mathrm{sn}(u,k)$ in Legendre's elliptic integral of the third kind, we obtain

$$\int \frac{(1+\nu z^2)^{-1}}{\{(1-z^2)(1-k^2z^2)\}^{1/2}} \, dz = \int \frac{du}{1+\nu\,\mathrm{sn}^2 u} = u - \nu \int \frac{\mathrm{sn}^2 u}{1+\nu\,\mathrm{sn}^2 u} \, du.$$

If $\nu = -1$ or $-k^2$, the evaluation can be completed in terms of the elliptic integral of the second kind. For other values of ν, we choose a so that $\nu = -k^2 \mathrm{sn}^2 a$, and we have to evaluate

$$u + k^2 \mathrm{sn}^2 a \int \frac{\mathrm{sn}^2 u}{1 - k^2 \mathrm{sn}^2 a\,\mathrm{sn}^2 u} \, du.$$

We shall take as the fundamental elliptic integral of the third kind Jacobi's function

$$\Pi(u,a) = \int_0^u \frac{k^2 \mathrm{sn}\,a\,\mathrm{cn}\,a\,\mathrm{dn}\,a\,\mathrm{sn}^2 u}{1 - k^2 \mathrm{sn}^2 a\,\mathrm{sn}^2 u} \, du,$$

and this can be expressed in terms of Jacobi's Theta function.

For, using the addition theorems for sn u and $Z(u)$, we have

$$\Pi(u,a) = \tfrac{1}{2} \int_0^u k^2 \operatorname{sn} u \operatorname{sn} a \{ \operatorname{sn}(u+a) + \operatorname{sn}(u-a) \}\, du$$

$$= \tfrac{1}{2} \int_0^u \{ Z(u-a) - Z(u+a) + 2Z(a) \}\, du.$$

Hence $$\Pi(u,a) = \tfrac{1}{2} \log \frac{\Theta(u-a)}{\Theta(u+a)} + u Z(a).$$

14.6. The expressions for $E(u)$ and $Z(u)$ in terms of Weierstrass's Zeta function

The function $\operatorname{dn}^2 u$ is an elliptic function of periods $2K$ and $2iK'$, with one double pole per cell at the point congruent to iK', the principal part at iK' being $-(u-iK')^{-2}$. If we substitute $u = Kz/\omega_1$, and suppose that $\omega_2/\omega_1 = iK'/K$, we find that $(K/\omega_1)^2 \operatorname{dn}^2(Kz/\omega_1)$ is an elliptic function of periods $2\omega_1$, $2\omega_2$ with one double pole per cell at the point congruent to ω_2. As the principal part of this function at ω_2 is $-(z-\omega_2)^{-2}$, it follows, by § 13.62, that

$$\frac{K^2}{\omega_1^2} \operatorname{dn}^2 \frac{Kz}{\omega_1} = \zeta'(z+\omega_2) + A,$$

where A is a constant.

When we integrate the expressions on each side of this equation, we find that

$$\frac{K}{\omega_1} E\!\left(\frac{Kz}{\omega_1}\right) = \zeta(z+\omega_2) + Az - \eta_2,$$

the constant of integration being determined by the fact that $E(0) = 0$. To find the constant A, we put $z = \omega_1$. This gives

$$EK/\omega_1 = \zeta(\omega_1+\omega_2) + A\omega_1 - \eta_2 = A\omega_1 - \eta_2 - \eta_3 = A\omega_1 + \eta_1,$$

and so $$A = \frac{EK}{\omega_1^2} - \frac{\eta_1}{\omega_1}.$$

We have thus obtained the formula

$$\frac{K}{\omega_1} E\!\left(\frac{Kz}{\omega_1}\right) = \zeta(z+\omega_2) + \frac{EK}{\omega_1^2} z - \frac{\eta_1}{\omega_1} z - \eta_2,$$

which expresses the elliptic integral of the second kind in terms of Weierstrass's Zeta function.

From this equation, it follows at once that

$$\frac{K}{\omega_1} Z\left(\frac{Kz}{\omega_1}\right) = \zeta(z+\omega_2) - \frac{\eta_1}{\omega_1} z - \eta_2.$$

14.61. The connexion between $\Theta(u)$ and $\sigma(z)$

To show the connexion between $\Theta(u)$ and $\sigma(z)$, we write the last equation of § 14.6 in the form

$$\frac{d}{dz} \log \Theta\left(\frac{Kz}{\omega_1}\right) = \frac{d}{dz} \log \sigma_2(z) - \frac{\eta_1 z}{\omega_1},$$

and integrate between the limits 0 and z. This gives

$$\Theta(Kz/\omega_1) = \Theta(0)\exp(-\tfrac{1}{2}\eta_1 z^2/\omega_1)\sigma_2(z).$$

If we now use the result of Ex. 15 on p. 378, we deduce from this equation that

$$\Theta(u) = G \prod_1^\infty \{1-2q^{2n-1}\cos(\pi u/K)+q^{4n-2}\},$$

where $q = e^{-\pi K'/K}$ and G depends only on q. As this formula is of great importance, we give in the next section a proof of it which is independent of the theory of Sigma functions and which gives incidentally a very simple expression for G.

14.62. The infinite product formula for $\Theta(u)$

If $|q| < 1$, the infinite product

$$F(t) = \prod_1^\infty \{(1-q^{2n-1}t)(1-q^{2n-1}t^{-1})\}$$

converges uniformly and absolutely in any bounded closed domain not containing the origin. Hence $F(t)$ is regular in every annulus $0 < \alpha \leqslant |t| \leqslant \beta$ and can be represented there by a uniformly and absolutely convergent Laurent series

$$F(t) = \sum_{-\infty}^\infty a_n t^n.$$

Moreover, since $qt\,F(q^2t) = -F(t)$, we can show, as in § 14.521, that $a_n = (-1)^n q^{n^2} a_0$. It remains to determine a_0.

Now the function

$$f(t) = \prod_1^\infty (1-q^{2n-1}t)$$

is an integral function, expansible as a Taylor series

$$f(t) = \sum_0^\infty b_n t^n,$$

where $b_0 = 1$. Since $F(t) = f(t)f(t^{-1})$, we can express a_n in terms of the coefficients b_r by multiplying together the series for $f(t)$ and $f(t^{-1})$ and then equating powers of t^n; this gives

$$a_n = b_n + b_1 b_{n+1} + b_2 b_{n+2} + \dots.$$

But if we substitute the Taylor series in the identity $(1-qt)f(q^2t) = f(t)$ and equate coefficients, we find that the coefficients b_n are connected by the recurrence formula

$$b_n = -b_{n-1} q^{2n-1}/(1-q^{2n}),$$

from which it follows that

$$b_n = (-1)^n q^{n^2}/c_n,$$

where

$$c_n = (1-q^2)(1-q^4)\dots(1-q^{2n}).$$

Hence

$$(-1)^n q^{n^2} a_0 = a_n = (-1)^n \left\{ \frac{q^{n^2}}{c_n} + \sum_{r=1}^\infty \frac{q^{(n+r)^2} q^{r^2}}{c_r c_{n+r}} \right\},$$

and so

$$a_0 = \frac{1}{c_n} + \sum_{r=1}^\infty \frac{q^{2(nr+r^2)}}{c_r c_{n+r}}.$$

As a_0 is independent of n, it is necessarily equal to the limit as n tends to infinity of the expression on the right-hand side of this equation.

Since $|q| < 1$, c_n tends to a finite non-zero limit as $n \to \infty$, and so $1/c_n$ is a bounded function of n. Hence we have

$$\left| \sum_{r=1}^n \frac{q^{2(nr+r^2)}}{c_r c_{n+r}} \right| \leqslant A |q|^{2n} \sum_{r=1}^\infty |q|^{2r^2},$$

where A is independent of n. Since $\sum_{r=1}^\infty |q|^{2r^2}$ is convergent, this inequality shows that

$$\lim_{n \to \infty} \sum_{r=1}^\infty \frac{q^{2(nr+r^2)}}{c_r c_{n+r}} = 0,$$

and so

$$a_0 = \lim_{n \to \infty} 1/c_n = 1 \Big/ \prod_1^\infty (1-q^{2n}).$$

We have thus shown that

$$\prod_1^\infty \{(1-q^{2n})(1-q^{2n-1}t)(1-q^{2n-1}t^{-1})\} = \sum_{-\infty}^\infty (-1)^n q^{n^2} t^n.$$

Putting $t = \exp(\pi i u/K)$, we obtain

$$\Theta(u) = \prod_1^\infty \{(1-q^{2n})(1-2q^{2n-1}\cos(\pi u/K)+q^{4n-2})\},$$

the required formula for $\Theta(u)$.

14.63. Jacobi's Eta function H(u)

Closely associated with Jacobi's function $\Theta(u)$ is his Eta function, defined by

$$H(u) = -iq^{1/4}\exp(\tfrac{1}{2}\pi i u/K)\,\Theta(u+iK').$$

The relation between $\Theta(u)$ and $H(u)$ is a reciprocal one; for

$$\Theta(u) = -iq^{1/4}\exp(\tfrac{1}{2}\pi i u/K)\,H(u+iK'),$$

as the reader will easily verify by using the formula for $\Theta(u+2iK')$.

$H(u)$ is an odd integral function which possesses simple zeros at the points of the set $2mK+2niK'$. The effect of increasing u by $2K$ or $2iK'$ is given by the equations

$$H(u+2K) = -H(u), \qquad H(u+2iK') = -q^{-1}e^{-\pi i u/K}H(u).$$

Thus $H(u)$ is a simply-periodic function of period $4K$.

Example. Show that

(i) $\quad H(u) = 2\sum_{n=0}^\infty (-1)^n q^{(2n+1)^2/4}\sin\{(n+\tfrac{1}{2})\pi u/K\},$

(ii) $\quad H(u) = 2q^{1/4}\sin(\tfrac{1}{2}\pi u/K)\prod_{n=1}^\infty \{(1-q^{2n})(1-2q^{2n}\cos(\pi u/K)+q^{4n})\}.$

14.64. The expression of Jacobi's elliptic functions in terms of $\Theta(u)$ and H(u)

It follows at once from the formulae of §§ 14.521, 14.63 that the function $H(u)/\Theta(u)$ is reproduced with multipliers -1 or $+1$ when u is increased by $2K$ or $2iK'$ respectively, and so is an elliptic function of periods $4K$ and $2iK'$. In any cell it has two simple zeros (the zeros of $H(u)$) at points congruent to 0 and $2K$, and two simple poles (the zeros of $\Theta(u)$) at points congruent to iK' and $2K+iK'$. Hence $\operatorname{sn}u\,\Theta(u)/H(u)$ is an elliptic function with no singularities, and so is a constant whose value $\Theta(K)/H(K)$ is found by putting $u = K$. We have thus shown that

$$\operatorname{sn}u = \frac{\Theta(K)H(u)}{H(K)\Theta(u)}.$$

Similarly it can be proved that

$$\operatorname{cn} u = \frac{\Theta(0)\mathrm{H}(u+K)}{\mathrm{H}(K)\Theta(u)}, \qquad \operatorname{dn} u = \frac{\Theta(0)\Theta(u+K)}{\Theta(K)\Theta(u)}.$$

Example. Prove that

$$\sqrt{k} = \mathrm{H}(K)/\Theta(K), \qquad \sqrt{k'} = \Theta(0)/\Theta(K),$$

and deduce that

$$\operatorname{sn} u = \sqrt{(1/k)}\mathrm{H}(u)/\Theta(u), \qquad \operatorname{cn} u = \sqrt{(k'/k)}\mathrm{H}(u+K)/\Theta(u),$$
$$\operatorname{dn} u = \sqrt{k'}\Theta(u+K)/\Theta(u).$$

Show also that $\qquad \sqrt{(2K/\pi)} = \Theta(K).$

14.7. The numerical evaluation of elliptic functions

The simplest method of computing the numerical values of Jacobi's elliptic functions, when q is given, is provided by the formulae of § 14.64, which express them as quotients of Θ and H functions. For, in the formulae

$$\sqrt{k}\operatorname{sn} u = \frac{2\displaystyle\sum_{n=0}^{\infty}(-1)^n q^{(n+\frac{1}{2})^2}\sin\dfrac{(2n+1)\pi u}{2K}}{1+2\displaystyle\sum_{n=1}^{\infty}(-1)^n q^{n^2}\cos\dfrac{n\pi u}{K}},$$

etc., we have $|q| < 1$ so that the initial terms of these rapidly convergent series give very accurate approximations to the values of $\operatorname{sn} u$, $\operatorname{cn} u$, and $\operatorname{dn} u$.

Usually, however, it is the modulus k, and not q, which is given. When this is the case we have to determine the values of K and q before we can calculate the values of the elliptic functions. Now it is possible to calculate K and K' in terms of k by using the hypergeometric series

$$K = \tfrac{1}{2}\pi F(\tfrac{1}{2},\tfrac{1}{2};1;k^2), \qquad K' = \tfrac{1}{2}\pi F(\tfrac{1}{2},\tfrac{1}{2};1;1-k^2)$$

when $|k^2|$ and $|1-k^2|$ are less than unity, and thence to find q from the formula $q = e^{-\pi K'/K}$. But as k^2 and $1-k^2$ are never small simultaneously, at least one of these series converges far too slowly to be of much use.

An alternative procedure, due to Weierstrass, gives q immediately in terms of k. We know that

$$\sqrt{k'} = \frac{\Theta(0)}{\Theta(K)} = \frac{1-2q+2q^4-2q^9+\dots}{1+2q+2q^4+2q^9+\dots}$$

and so
$$\frac{1-\sqrt{k'}}{1+\sqrt{k'}} = \frac{2q+2q^9+2q^{25}+\ldots}{1+2q^4+2q^{16}+\ldots}.$$

If we write $2\epsilon = (1-\sqrt{k'})/(1+\sqrt{k'})$ and apply the ordinary methods for the reversal of series, we find that[†]

$$q = \epsilon+2\epsilon^5+15\epsilon^9+150\epsilon^{13}+\ldots,$$

the first term omitted. being of the order of ϵ^{17}. This series is convergent when $|\epsilon| < \frac{1}{2}$, a condition which is certainly satisfied in the case of greatest practical importance, namely that in which k lies between 0 and 1.

The power of this method for calculating q is seen from the fact that, when $0 < k^2 \leqslant \frac{1}{2}$, $\epsilon < 1/23$. The second term in the series for q is thus less than 10^{-6} and can, in general, be omitted.[‡]

When q has been found, K is then calculated from the formula

$$\sqrt{(2K/\pi)} = \Theta(K) = 1+2q+2q^4+2q^9+\ldots,$$

and finally K' from the equation

$$\pi K' = K \log q^{-1}.$$

Having found q, K, and K', the computation of Jacobi's elliptic functions can be readily carried out.[§]

14.8. The four Theta functions

In his later work, Jacobi denoted the functions $\mathrm{H}(u)$, $\mathrm{H}(u+K)$, $\Theta(u+K)$, and $\Theta(u)$ of the *Fundamenta Nova* by $\vartheta_1(z,q)$, $\vartheta_2(z,q)$, $\vartheta_3(z,q)$, and $\vartheta_4(z,q)$ respectively,[∥] where $2Kz = \pi u$. For our purposes Jacobi's older notation was preferable.

Another method of introducing the elliptic functions of Jacobi is to determine, from first principles, the properties of the four Theta functions defined by means of infinite series, and thence to deduce the whole theory of Jacobi's elliptic functions, defined as quotients of Theta functions. For an account of this very

[†] See Weierstrass, *Werke*, **2** (1895), 276, or Schwarz's account of Weierstrass's lectures, *Formeln und Lehrsätze zum Gebrauche der elliptischen Funktionen* (Berlin, 1893), 54.

[‡] If $\frac{1}{2} < k^2 < 1$, it is probably best to interchange k and k' and determine $e^{-\pi K/K'}$, and thence find q.

[§] For an example of this, see Whittaker's discussion of a problem in rigid dynamics, soluble in terms of elliptic functions, in his *Analytical Dynamics* (Cambridge, 1917), 144–9.

[∥] This notation, which is a slight modification of Jacobi's, is the one now in general use. Jacobi himself wrote $\vartheta(z,q)$ for $\vartheta_4(z,q)$.

beautiful theory, we must, with regret, refer the reader elsewhere.†

REFERENCES

C. G. J. JACOBI, *Fundamenta Nova Theoriae Functionum Ellipticarum* (Königsberg, 1829); reprinted in his *Ges. Math. Werke*, **1** (1881), 49–239.

A. CAYLEY, *Elliptic Functions* (London, 1895).

J. TANNERY and J. MOLK, *Fonctions elliptiques* (Paris, 1893–1902).

E. T. WHITTAKER and G. N. WATSON, *Modern Analysis* (Cambridge, 1920), Chaps. XXI–XXII.

MISCELLANEOUS EXAMPLES

1. Show that $\operatorname{sn} u$, $\operatorname{cn} u$, and $\operatorname{dn} u$ tend to $\sin u$, $\cos u$, and 1 respectively as $k \to 0$, and to $\tanh u$, $\operatorname{sech} u$, and $\operatorname{sech} u$ respectively as $k \to 1$.

2. Prove that
$$\left(\frac{\operatorname{cn}^3 u}{\operatorname{sn} u \operatorname{dn} u} - \frac{k'^2 \operatorname{sn}^3 u}{\operatorname{cn} u \operatorname{dn} u}\right)^2, \qquad \left(\frac{\operatorname{dn}^3 u}{\operatorname{sn} u \operatorname{cn} u} + \frac{k^2 k'^2 \operatorname{sn}^3 u}{\operatorname{cn} u \operatorname{dn} u}\right)^2$$
are elliptic functions of periods K, iK'.

3. Show that, if $z = \operatorname{sn}^2(w, k)$, where $0 < k < 1$, the curves in the z-plane on which the real and imaginary parts of $w = u + iv$ are constant form two orthogonal families of Cartesian ovals, whose equations are
$$|z-1| - |z| \operatorname{dn}(2u, k) = \operatorname{cn}(2u, k),$$
$$|z-1| \operatorname{cn}(2v, k') + |z| \operatorname{dn}(2v, k') = 1.$$

4. Prove that, if $0 < k < 1$, the transformation $z = \sqrt{k} \operatorname{sn} w$ maps conformally the interior of the rectangle with vertices $w = \pm K \pm \frac{1}{2} iK'$ on the interior of the circle $|z| = 1$, provided with cuts along the real axis from $\sqrt{k}$ to 1 and from $-\sqrt{k}$ to -1.

5. Show that the part of the w-plane within the ellipse $u^2/a^2 + v^2/b^2 = 1$, where $w = u + iv$, is mapped conformally on the interior of the circle $|z| = 1$ by the relation
$$z = \sqrt{k} \operatorname{sn}\left[\frac{2K}{\pi} \arcsin \frac{w}{\sqrt{(a^2 - b^2)}}\right],$$
where Jacobi's parameter q is given by $q = (a-b)^2/(a+b)^2$. (SCHWARZ.‡)

6. Prove that
$$\{1 + \operatorname{sn}(u+v)\}\{1 + \operatorname{sn}(u-v)\} = (\operatorname{cn} v + \operatorname{sn} u \operatorname{dn} v)^2/D,$$
$$\{1 + \operatorname{cn}(u+v)\}\{1 + \operatorname{cn}(u-v)\} = (\operatorname{cn} u + \operatorname{cn} v)^2/D,$$
$$\{1 + \operatorname{dn}(u+v)\}\{1 + \operatorname{dn}(u-v)\} = (\operatorname{dn} u + \operatorname{dn} v)^2/D,$$
where $D = 1 - k^2 \operatorname{sn}^2 u \operatorname{sn}^2 v$.

† See, for example, Whittaker and Watson, *Modern Analysis* (Cambridge), Chapter XXI, or Tannery and Molk, *Fonctions elliptiques*, **2** (Paris, 1896). The notation in the latter book is slightly different from that given above.

‡ See Forsyth, *Theory of Functions* (1918), 614–15.

7. Show that
$$\mathrm{sn}(u+v)\mathrm{cn}(u-v)+\mathrm{sn}(u-v)\mathrm{cn}(u+v)$$
$$= 2\,\mathrm{sn}\,u\,\mathrm{cn}\,u\,\mathrm{dn}\,v/(1-k^2\,\mathrm{sn}^2 u\,\mathrm{sn}^2 v),$$
$$\mathrm{cn}(u+v)\mathrm{cn}(u-v)+\mathrm{sn}(u+v)\mathrm{sn}(u-v)$$
$$= (\mathrm{cn}^2 v-\mathrm{sn}^2 v\,\mathrm{dn}^2 u)/(1-k^2\,\mathrm{sn}^2 u\,\mathrm{sn}^2 v).$$

8. Show that, if $\tanh U = k\,\mathrm{sn}^2 u$, $\tanh V = k\,\mathrm{sn}^2 v$, then
$$\tanh(U-V) = k\,\mathrm{sn}(u+v)\mathrm{sn}(u-v).$$
Deduce that
$$\mathrm{sn}(v+w)\mathrm{sn}(v-w)+\mathrm{sn}(w+u)\mathrm{sn}(w-u)+\mathrm{sn}(u+v)\mathrm{sn}(u-v)+$$
$$+k^2\,\mathrm{sn}(v+w)\mathrm{sn}(w+u)\mathrm{sn}(u+v)\mathrm{sn}(v-w)\mathrm{sn}(w-u)\mathrm{sn}(u-v) = 0.$$

(GLAISHER.)

9. AB is a fixed diameter of a circle. P, Q are variable points on the circle such that $\angle PAB = \mathrm{am}(u+\alpha)$, $\angle QAB = \mathrm{am}(u-\alpha)$, where α is a constant. Prove that the chord PQ envelopes a circle. (JACOBI.†)

10. P, Q are points on the ellipse $x^2/a^2+y^2/b^2 = 1$ of eccentric angle $\mathrm{am}(u\pm\alpha)$. Show that, if α is constant and u variable, the locus of the pole of PQ is the ellipse
$$\frac{x^2}{a^2}\mathrm{cn}^2\alpha+\frac{y^2}{b^2}\mathrm{sn}^2(K-\alpha) = 1.$$

11. Prove that $\mathrm{sn}\tfrac{2}{3}K = \mathrm{cd}\tfrac{1}{3}K$, $\mathrm{cn}\tfrac{2}{3}K = k'\,\mathrm{sd}\tfrac{1}{3}K$. Deduce that $\mathrm{sn}\tfrac{1}{3}K+\mathrm{cn}\tfrac{2}{3}K = 1$.

12. Show that $\mathrm{sn}\,u+\alpha\,\mathrm{cn}\,u+\beta\,\mathrm{dn}\,u+\gamma$, where α, β, γ are constants, is an elliptic function of periods $4K$, $4iK'$ and of order 4 and that the sum of the affixes of its zeros in any cell is congruent to 0 $(\mathrm{mod}\,4K, 4iK')$. Deduce that, if $u_1+u_2+u_3+u_4 = 0$,
$$\begin{vmatrix} s_1 & c_1 & d_1 & 1 \\ s_2 & c_2 & d_2 & 1 \\ s_3 & c_3 & d_3 & 1 \\ s_4 & c_4 & d_4 & 1 \end{vmatrix} = 0,$$
where $s_r = \mathrm{sn}\,u_r$, $c_r = \mathrm{cn}\,u_r$, $d_r = \mathrm{dn}\,u_r$.
Hence or otherwise show that
$$\frac{c_1 d_2-c_2 d_1}{s_1-s_2} + \frac{c_3 d_4-c_4 d_3}{s_3-s_4} = 0.$$

(CAYLEY.)

13. Determine the periods and order of the elliptic function
$$\mathrm{sn}\,u\,\mathrm{sn}(u+K)+\alpha\,\mathrm{sn}(u+K)+\beta\,\mathrm{sn}\,u+\gamma,$$

† This result is of importance in Jacobi's discussion of Poncelet's poristic polygons (*Journal für Math.* **3** (1828), 376). See also Forsyth, *Messenger of Math.* **12** (1882), 100.

where α, β, γ are constants. Hence show that, if $u_1+u_2+u_3+u_4 = 2K$,

$$\begin{vmatrix} s_1c_1 & s_1d_1 & c_1 & d_1 \\ s_2c_2 & s_2d_2 & c_2 & d_2 \\ s_3c_3 & s_3d_3 & c_3 & d_3 \\ s_4c_4 & s_4d_4 & c_4 & d_4 \end{vmatrix} = 0.$$

(Oxford, 1923.)

14. Prove, by using Liouville's theorem or otherwise, that, if $u_1+u_2+u_3+u_4 = 0$,

$$k'^2 - k^2k'^2s_1s_2s_3s_4 + k^2c_1c_2c_3c_4 - d_1d_2d_3d_4 = 0.$$

(GUDERMANN.)

15. Deduce from Ex. 14 that, if $u_1+u_2+u_3+u_4 = 0$,

(i) $k^2s_1s_2c_3c_4 - d_1d_2 = k^2c_1c_2s_3s_4 - d_3d_4$,

(ii) $d_1d_2c_3c_4 + k'^2s_1s_2 = c_1c_2d_3d_4 + k'^2s_3s_4$,

(iii) $s_1s_2d_3d_4 - c_1c_2 = d_1d_2s_3s_4 - c_3c_4$.

(H. J. S. SMITH.)

16. Show that, if $\operatorname{sn} u$, $\operatorname{cn} u$, and $\operatorname{dn} u$ are denoted by s, c, and d respectively,

$$\frac{1-\operatorname{sn} 3u}{1+\operatorname{sn} 3u} = \frac{1+s}{1-s}\left(\frac{1-2s+2k^2s^3-k^2s^4}{1+2s-2k^2s^3-k^2s^4}\right)^2,$$

$$\frac{1-\operatorname{cn} 3u}{1+\operatorname{cn} 3u} = \frac{1-c}{1+c}\left(\frac{k'^2+2k'^2c+2k^2c^3+k^2c^4}{k'^2-2k'^2c-2k^2c^3+k^2c^4}\right)^2,$$

$$\frac{1-\operatorname{dn} 3u}{1+\operatorname{dn} 3u} = \frac{1-d}{1+d}\left(\frac{k'^2+2k'^2d-2d^3-d^4}{k'^2-2k'^2d+2d^3-d^4}\right)^2.$$

17. If the nine roots of $\operatorname{cn} 3u = a$, regarded as an equation in $\operatorname{cn} u$, are $c_1, c_2, ..., c_9$, prove that

$$3k^4 \prod_1^9 c_r + k'^4 \sum_1^9 c_r = 0.$$

18. By considering the four transformations (i) $\tau' = \tau/(1+\tau)$, (ii) $\tau' = -1/(1+\tau)$, (iii) $\tau' = -(1+\tau)/\tau$, (iv) $\tau' = 1+\tau$, prove that

$$\operatorname{sn}\left(ku, \frac{1}{k}\right) = k\operatorname{sn}(u, k),$$

$$\operatorname{sn}\left(ik'u, \frac{1}{k'}\right) = ik'\operatorname{sc}(u, k),$$

$$\operatorname{sn}\left(iku, \frac{ik'}{k}\right) = ik\operatorname{sd}(u, k),$$

$$\operatorname{sn}\left(k'u, \frac{k}{ik'}\right) = k'\operatorname{sd}(u, k).$$

Deduce the corresponding transformations of $\operatorname{cn} u$ and $\operatorname{dn} u$.

19. Prove the results of Ex. 18 by direct transformation of the integral formula

$$u = \int_0^{\mathrm{sn}(u,k)} (1-z^2)^{-1/2}(1-k^2z^2)^{-1/2}\, dz.$$

20. Prove Gauss's transformation, viz. that if $\lambda = 2\sqrt{k}/(1+k)$,

$$\mathrm{sn}\{(1+k)u,\lambda\} = (1+k)\mathrm{sn}(u,k)/\{1+k\,\mathrm{sn}^2(u,k)\},$$
$$\mathrm{cn}\{(1+k)u,\lambda\} = \mathrm{cn}(u,k)\mathrm{dn}(u,k)/\{1+k\,\mathrm{sn}^2(u,k)\},$$
$$\mathrm{dn}\{(1+k)u,\lambda\} = \{1-k\,\mathrm{sn}^2(u,k)\}/\{1+k\,\mathrm{sn}^2(u,k)\}.$$

Show also that, if 4Λ, $2i\Lambda'$ are the periods of $\mathrm{sn}(u,\lambda)$,

$$\Lambda = (1+k)K, \qquad \Lambda' = \tfrac{1}{2}(1+k)K'.$$

21. a and b are two real positive numbers. Two sequences of real numbers, $a_1, a_2, a_3,...$ and $b_1, b_2, b_3,...$, are defined by the equations

$$a_1 = \tfrac{1}{2}(a+b), \qquad b_1 = \sqrt{(ab)},$$
$$a_{r+1} = \tfrac{1}{2}(a_r+b_r), \qquad b_{r+1} = \sqrt{(a_r b_r)}.$$

Show that, as $n \to \infty$, a_n and b_n tend to the same finite limit, $M(a,b)$ say. (This limit is called the arithmetico-geometric mean of a and b.)

22. Prove that, in the notation of Ex. 21,

$$\int_0^{\pi/2} \frac{d\theta}{(a^2\cos^2\theta+b^2\sin^2\theta)^{1/2}} = \int_0^{\pi/2} \frac{d\phi}{(a_1^2\cos^2\phi+b_1^2\sin^2\phi)^{1/2}}.$$

Deduce that, if $0 < k < 1$,

$$K = \tfrac{1}{2}\pi/M(1,k'), \qquad K' = \tfrac{1}{2}\pi/M(1,k).$$

23. Show that the arc s of the lemniscate $r^2 = a^2\cos 2\theta$, measured from the point of polar coordinates $(a, 0)$, is given by $r = a\,\mathrm{cn}(s\sqrt{2}/a, 1/\sqrt{2})$.

Prove that, for the elliptic functions of modulus $1/\sqrt{2}$, $q = 0\cdot04321$, $K = K' = 1\cdot854$, correct to four significant figures. Deduce that the length of a complete loop of the lemniscate is $2\cdot62a$, approximately.

24. A rigid body is performing finite oscillations about a fixed horizontal axis, under the action of gravity. Show that, if its angle of swing is 2α, its period of oscillation is $4K\sqrt{(l/g)}$, where $k = \sin\tfrac{1}{2}\alpha$ and l is the length of the equivalent simple pendulum.

If gravity is suddenly reversed when the pendulum is at the end of a swing, show that the new period is $4K'\sqrt{(l/g)}$.

25. Show that

$$\int \mathrm{sn}\,u\, du = \frac{1}{2k}\log\frac{\mathrm{dn}\,u-k\,\mathrm{cn}\,u}{\mathrm{dn}\,u+k\,\mathrm{cn}\,u},$$
$$\int \mathrm{cn}\,u\, du = \frac{1}{k}\arctan(k\,\mathrm{sd}\,u),$$
$$\int \mathrm{dn}\,u\, du = \mathrm{am}\,u.$$

Deduce the integrals of the other elliptic functions of Jacobi by increasing u in turn by K, iK', $K+iK'$.

26. Prove that the integrals of ns^2u, nc^2u, nd^2u, sc^2u, cs^2u, sd^2u, ds^2u, cd^2u, dc^2u can all be expressed in terms of $E(u)$, Jacobi's elliptic functions, and u.

27. Show that

$$\frac{d}{du}(k^2 \,\text{sn}\, u \,\text{cn}\, u \,\text{dn}^{n-1}u)$$
$$= (n+1)\text{dn}^{n+2}u - n(1+k'^2)\text{dn}^n u + (n-1)\text{dn}^{n-2}u.$$

Hence obtain reduction formulae for

$$\int_0^u \text{dn}^n u \, du, \qquad \int_0^K \text{dn}^n u \, du.$$

Find also similar formulae for $\text{sn}^n u$, $\text{cn}^n u$.

28. Prove that

$$\int_0^{2K} u\,\text{nd}^2u \, du = \frac{2KE}{k'^2}, \qquad \int_0^{2K} u\,\text{nd}^3u \, du = \frac{\pi}{2k'^3}(1+k'^2)K,$$

$$\int_0^{2K} u\,\text{nd}^4u \, du = \frac{2K}{3k'^4}\{2(1+k'^2)E - K\}.$$

29. Show that any quartic or cubic polynomial in x without repeated factor can be expressed in the form

$$w^2 = \{A(x-\alpha)^2 + B(x-\beta)^2\}\{C(x-\alpha)^2 + D(x-\beta)^2\},$$

where A, B, C, D, α, and β are real if the coefficients of the quartic are real.

Hence prove, by using the homographic transformation

$$t = (x-\alpha)/(x-\beta),$$

that an elliptic integral $\int R(x,w) \, dx$ can be evaluated in terms of Legendre's three kinds of elliptic integral, together with the elementary functions of analysis.†

30. Express x in terms of u when

$$u = \int_0^x (1+t^2 - 2t^4)^{-1/2} \, dt. \qquad \text{(Math. Trip., 1914.)}$$

31. Prove that

$$\Pi(u,v) - \Pi(v,u) = u\text{Z}(v) - v\text{Z}(u).$$

32. Show that

$$\Pi(u,a) + \Pi(v,a) - \Pi(u+v,a) = \tfrac{1}{2}\log\frac{1 - k^2 \,\text{sn}\, a \,\text{sn}\, u \,\text{sn}\, v \,\text{sn}(u+v-a)}{1 + k^2 \,\text{sn}\, a \,\text{sn}\, u \,\text{sn}\, v \,\text{sn}(u+v+a)}.$$

† The advantage of this method of reduction is that it always gives a real modulus when the coefficients in w^2 are real, unlike the reduction of § 14.5.

33. Prove that

$$\Pi(iu, ia+K, k) = \Pi(u, a+K', k').$$

34. Show that

$$\Pi(u,a)+\Pi(u,b)-\Pi(u,a+b)$$
$$= \tfrac{1}{2}\log\frac{1-k^2\operatorname{sn}a\operatorname{sn}b\operatorname{sn}u\operatorname{sn}(a+b-u)}{1+k^2\operatorname{sn}a\operatorname{sn}b\operatorname{sn}u\operatorname{sn}(a+b+u)}+uk^2\operatorname{sn}a\operatorname{sn}b\operatorname{sn}(a+b).$$

35. By integrating round a cell of $\operatorname{sn}u$, prove that

$$\int_{-2K}^{2K}\operatorname{sn}u\exp(\tfrac{1}{2}n\pi iu/K)\,du = \frac{2\pi iq^{n/2}}{k(1-q^n)}\{1-(-1)^n\}.$$

Deduce that $\operatorname{sn}u$ is expansible as a Fourier series

$$\operatorname{sn}u = \frac{2\pi}{Kk}\sum_0^\infty\frac{q^{n+1/2}}{1-q^{2n+1}}\sin(n+\tfrac{1}{2})\pi u/K,$$

valid in the strip $|\operatorname{Im}(u/K)| < \operatorname{Rl}(K'/K)$.

36. Prove that the expansions

$$\operatorname{cn}u = \frac{2\pi}{Kk}\sum_0^\infty\frac{q^{n+1/2}}{1+q^{2n+1}}\cos(n+\tfrac{1}{2})\pi u/K,$$

$$\operatorname{dn}u = \frac{\pi}{2K}+\frac{2\pi}{K}\sum_1^\infty\frac{q^n}{1+q^{2n}}\cos n\pi u/K,$$

hold in the strip $|\operatorname{Im}(u/K)| < \operatorname{Rl}(K'/K)$.

37. Deduce from Exx. 35, 36 the Fourier series for $\operatorname{cd}u$, $\operatorname{sd}u$, and $\operatorname{nd}u$.

38. Show that

$$\operatorname{ns}u = \frac{\pi}{2K}\operatorname{cosec}\frac{\pi u}{2K}+\frac{2\pi}{K}\sum_0^\infty\frac{q^{2n+1}}{1-q^{2n+1}}\sin(n+\tfrac{1}{2})\pi u/K,$$

the Fourier series on the right-hand side being convergent in the strip $|\operatorname{Im}(u/K)| < 2\operatorname{Rl}(K'/K)$.

39. Prove that the expansion

$$\operatorname{dn}^2u = \frac{E}{K}+\frac{2\pi^2}{K^2}\sum_{n=1}^\infty\frac{nq^n}{1-q^{2n}}\cos n\pi u/K$$

holds in the strip $|\operatorname{Im}(u/K)| < \operatorname{Rl}(K'/K)$.

Deduce that the formula

$$Z(u) = \frac{2\pi}{K}\sum_1^\infty\frac{q^n}{1-q^{2n}}\sin n\pi u/K$$

is valid in the same strip.

40. Prove that, if $u_1+u_2+u_3+u_4 = 0$,

$$Z(u_1)+Z(u_2)+Z(u_3)+Z(u_4) = -\frac{k^2 s_1 s_2 s_3 s_4}{1+k^2 s_1 s_2 s_3 s_4} \sum \frac{c_r d_r}{s_r}$$

$$= \frac{k^2 c_1 c_2 c_3 c_4}{k^2 c_1 c_2 c_3 c_4 - k'^2} \sum \frac{d_r s_r}{c_r} = \frac{k^2 d_1 d_2 d_3 d_4}{k'^2 + d_1 d_2 d_3 d_4} \sum \frac{s_r c_r}{d_r}.$$

41. Prove that $\prod_{r=1}^{4} \Theta(u_r) + \prod_{r=1}^{4} H(u_r)$

is invariant under the transformation $2u'_r = u_1+u_2+u_3+u_4-2u_r$. Deduce that

$$\Theta(u_1)\Theta(u_2)H(u_3)H(u_4)+H(u_1)H(u_2)\Theta(u_3)\Theta(u_4)$$

and

$$\Theta(u_1+K)\Theta(u_2+K)\Theta(u_3)\Theta(u_4)-H(u_1+K)H(u_2+K)H(u_3)H(u_4)$$

are also invariant.

42. Show that, in the notation of Ex. 41,

$$\Theta(u_1+K)\Theta(u_2+K)\Theta(u_3)\Theta(u_4)+H(u_1+K)H(u_2+K)H(u_3)H(u_4)$$
$$= \Theta(u'_4+K)\Theta(u'_3+K)\Theta(u'_2)\Theta(u'_1)+H(u'_4+K)H(u'_3+K)H(u'_2)H(u'_1).$$

43. Prove that $\dfrac{(1-k\,\mathrm{sn}\,u_1\,\mathrm{sn}\,u_2)(1-k\,\mathrm{sn}\,u_3\,\mathrm{sn}\,u_4)}{(1+k\,\mathrm{sn}\,u_1\,\mathrm{sn}\,u_2)(1+k\,\mathrm{sn}\,u_3\,\mathrm{sn}\,u_4)}$

is invariant under the transformation of Ex. 41. Deduce that

$$\frac{1-k\,\mathrm{sn}(t-x)\mathrm{sn}(y-z)}{1+k\,\mathrm{sn}(t-x)\mathrm{sn}(y-z)}\;\frac{1-k\,\mathrm{sn}(t-y)\mathrm{sn}(z-x)}{1+k\,\mathrm{sn}(t-y)\mathrm{sn}(z-x)}\;\frac{1-k\,\mathrm{sn}(t-z)\mathrm{sn}(x-y)}{1+k\,\mathrm{sn}(t-z)\mathrm{sn}(x-y)}$$

is equal to unity.

CHAPTER XV

THE ELLIPTIC MODULAR FUNCTIONS AND PICARD'S THEOREM

15.1. The construction of elliptic functions of given modulus

It was seen in the previous chapter that the problem of evaluating an elliptic integral is solved if we can construct Jacobian elliptic functions when c, the square of the modulus, is given. By the first formula of Ex. 4 on p. 385, we have to show that, when c has any given value different from 0 or 1, we can find a number τ whose imaginary part is positive, which satisfies the equation

$$16q \prod_1^\infty \left(\frac{1+q^{2n}}{1+q^{2n-1}} \right)^8 = c,$$

where $q = e^{\pi i \tau}$, and, moreover, that each solution of this equation leads to the same set of Jacobian elliptic functions.

An equivalent form of this problem is the determination of two parameters ω_1 and ω_2, such that $\mathrm{Im}(\omega_2/\omega_1)$ is positive, which satisfy the equation

$$\frac{\wp(\omega_1+\omega_2|\omega_1, \omega_2)-\wp(\omega_2|\omega_1, \omega_2)}{\wp(\omega_1|\omega_1, \omega_2)-\wp(\omega_2|\omega_1, \omega_2)} = c.$$

Actually a precise value for ω_1 cannot be determined from this equation, since the expression on the left-hand side is a function of $\tau = \omega_2/\omega_1$ alone; but this is immaterial, since ω_1 disappears when we construct the Jacobian elliptic functions by means of Weierstrass's Sigma functions.

If, however, we reduce the elliptic integral to Weierstrass's form, as in § 13.7, we are given three constants e_1, e_2, and e_3 whose sum is zero, and have to determine ω_1 and ω_2 such that

$$e_1 = \wp(\omega_1), \qquad e_2 = \wp(\omega_2), \qquad e_3 = \wp(\omega_1+\omega_2)$$

and $\mathrm{Im}(\omega_2/\omega_1) > 0$. But when we take into account the homogeneity of $\wp(z)$, we find that this problem is precisely the same as the one we have just stated.

15.2. The primitive periods of an elliptic function

In § 13.2, the periods $2\omega_1$ and $2\omega_2$ of an elliptic function were said to be a pair of primitive periods if $\mathrm{Im}(\omega_2/\omega_1)$ is positive and if every other period of the function is of the form $2m\omega_1+2n\omega_2$, where m and n are positive or negative integers or zero. When this is the case, the parallelogram with vertices 0, $2\omega_1$, $2\omega_1+2\omega_2$, $2\omega_2$ is a primitive period-parallelogram; if the affix of a point within or on this parallelogram is a period, the point is necessarily one of the vertices.

There are obviously an infinite number of pairs of primitive periods. If $2\omega_1$ and $2\omega_2$ form one pair, the numbers

$$2\omega_1' = 2d\omega_1+2c\omega_2, \qquad 2\omega_2' = 2b\omega_1+2a\omega_2$$

form another if and only if $\mathrm{Im}(\omega_2'/\omega_1') > 0$ and

$$\omega_1 = p\omega_1'+q\omega_2', \qquad \omega_2 = r\omega_1'+s\omega_2',$$

where p, q, r, and s are integers. It is easily seen that $\mathrm{Im}(\omega_2'/\omega_1')$ has the same sign as $ad-bc$, and so $ad-bc > 0$. If we solve the first set of equations for ω_1 and ω_2, we obtain

$$(ad-bc)\omega_1 = a\omega_1'-c\omega_2', \qquad (ad-bc)\omega_2 = -b\omega_1'+d\omega_2',$$

and so
$$\frac{a}{p} = \frac{b}{-r} = \frac{c}{-q} = \frac{d}{s} = (ad-bc).$$

From this it follows that $(ad-bc)(ps-qr) = 1$ and hence that $ad-bc = 1$. We have thus shown that *if $2\omega_1$ and $2\omega_2$ form a pair of primitive periods of an elliptic function, so also do*

$$2\omega_1' = 2d\omega_1+2c\omega_2, \qquad 2\omega_2' = 2b\omega_1+2a\omega_2$$

if and only if a, b, c, and d are integers such that $ad-bc = 1$.

Out of the infinite number of pairs of primitive periods of the given elliptic function, we now choose a particular pair of special importance, in the following manner.

There are two, four, or six periods of least modulus. (i) If there are two, let 2ω be the one of least argument. In the set of periods $2\omega'$ such that 2ω and $2\omega'$ form a pair of primitive periods, there are at most two nearer the origin than the rest. If there is only one such period $2\omega'$, call it $2\omega\tau$; if there are two, let $2\omega\tau$ be the one which gives the smaller value of $\arg(\omega'/\omega)$. (ii) If there are more than two periods of least modulus, any pair whose sum is not zero form a pair of primitive periods; we take as 2ω and $2\omega\tau$ the particular pair which is such that

$0 < \arg \tau \leqslant \frac{1}{2}\pi$ and $\arg \omega$ is least. The unique pair of primitive periods chosen in this way is called *the fundamental pair of primitive periods* of the given elliptic function, and the corresponding period-parallelogram the *fundamental primitive period-parallelogram*.

Obviously $|\tau| \geqslant 1$, and, if $|\tau| = 1$, then $0 < \arg \tau \leqslant \frac{1}{2}\pi$. Moreover, as 2ω and $2\omega + 2\omega\tau$ also form a pair of primitive periods of the function, we have $|1+\tau| \geqslant |\tau|$; but since $0 < \arg(1+\tau) < \arg \tau$ when $\operatorname{Im} \tau > 0$, the sign of equality is not permissible, and so $|1+\tau| > |\tau|$. Similarly we can show that $|\tau-1| \geqslant |\tau|$, where, however, the sign of equality can now occur.

Therefore if 2ω and $2\omega\tau$ form the fundamental pair of primitive periods of an elliptic function, τ lies in the region defined by the inequalities $|\tau| \geqslant 1$, $|\tau+1| > |\tau|$, $|\tau-1| \geqslant |\tau|$. This region is bounded by an arc of the circle $|\tau| = 1$ and the straight lines $\operatorname{Rl} \tau = \pm\frac{1}{2}$; the only boundary points which belong to the region are those for which the real part of τ is not negative.

15.21. The modular group of transformations

If $2\omega, 2\omega\tau$ and $2\omega', 2\omega'\tau'$ are two pairs of primitive periods of an elliptic function, there exist, as we have just seen, integers a, b, c, and d, connected by the relation $ad - bc = 1$, such that

$$\omega'\tau' = a\omega\tau + b\omega, \qquad \omega' = c\omega\tau + d\omega.$$

When, therefore, we change from one pair of primitive periods to another, the quotient τ undergoes the homographic transformation

$$\tau' = \frac{a\tau + b}{c\tau + d}.$$

A transformation of this type, where a, b, c, and d are integers connected by the relation $ad - bc = 1$, is called a *modular transformation*.

The set of all modular transformations forms a group, since it possesses the two characteristic properties of a group, namely:

  (i) If $\tau' = (a\tau + b)/(c\tau + d)$ is a modular transformation, so also is the inverse transformation $\tau = -(d\tau' - b)/(c\tau' - a)$.

(ii) If $\tau_1 = (a_1\tau+b_1)/(c_1\tau+d_1)$, $\tau_2 = (a_2\tau_1+b_2)/(c_2\tau_1+d_2)$ are two modular transformations, so also is the transformation

$$\tau_2 = \frac{(a_1a_2+c_1b_2)\tau+(b_1a_2+d_1b_2)}{(a_1c_2+c_1d_2)\tau+(b_1c_2+d_1d_2)},$$

which is obtained by the successive application of the given transformations.

The group of modular transformations is called the *modular group*.

Two points in the τ-plane are said to be congruent with respect to the modular group whenever their affixes are connected by a modular transformation. If $\operatorname{Im}\tau > 0$, there is evidently no point congruent to τ in the lower half-plane; moreover, if a point is congruent to a point on the real axis, it is either the point at infinity or else lies on the real axis. We shall only consider the effect of modular transformations on sets of points in the upper half-plane, as the corresponding results for the lower half-plane can be obtained by a reflection in the real axis.

It follows immediately from the work of the preceding section that if $\operatorname{Im}\tau'$ is positive, there exists a point τ which is congruent to τ' with respect to the modular group and which lies in the region defined by (i) $|\tau| > 1$ and $-\tfrac{1}{2} < \operatorname{Rl}\tau < 0$ or (ii) $|\tau| \geqslant 1$ and $0 \leqslant \operatorname{Rl}\tau \leqslant \tfrac{1}{2}$. This region is called the *fundamental region* of the modular group.

We have not, however, shown that τ is the only point of the fundamental region congruent to τ'. Now if τ_1 were another point of the fundamental region congruent to τ', τ_1 would be congruent to τ; this is impossible, as we shall now show.

Let us suppose, then, that τ_1 and τ are connected by a modular transformation $\tau_1 = (a\tau+b)/(c\tau+d)$ and that τ lies in the fundamental region; we consider separately the cases $c = 0$, $c^2 = 1$, and $c^2 > 1$.

If $c = 0$, the transformation becomes $\tau_1 = \tau+n$, where n is an integer, and so τ_1 does not lie in the fundamental region.† The point at infinity is invariant under this transformation.

If $c^2 = 1$, the transformation is of the form $\tau_1 - m = -1/(\tau-n)$,

---

† It must be remembered here that boundary points on the line $\operatorname{Rl}\tau = -\tfrac{1}{2}$ do not belong to the fundamental region.

where m and n are positive or negative integers or zero. Now the inequality $|\tau - n| > 1$ holds for all points of the fundamental region if $n \neq 0$ or 1, and for all save certain boundary points if $n = 0$ or 1. In these cases $|\tau_1 - m| < 1$, so that τ is certainly outside the fundamental region. When $n = 0$, we have to consider the boundary points $\tau = e^{\theta i}$, where $\frac{1}{3}\pi \leqslant \theta \leqslant \frac{1}{2}\pi$, and so $\tau_1 - m = e^{(\pi - \theta)i}$. It follows that τ_1 belongs to the fundamental region only when $m = 0$ and $\theta = \frac{1}{2}\pi$, or when $m = 1$ and $\theta = \frac{1}{3}\pi$; in both cases, τ_1 is identical with τ. Again, when $n = 1$, $|\tau - 1| > 1$ save when $\tau - 1 = e^{2\pi i/3}$; this gives $\tau_1 - m = e^{\pi i/3}$, so that τ_1 lies in the fundamental region only when $m = 0$, in which case τ_1 and τ are identical.

Finally, when $c^2 > 1$, the transformation can be written in the form

$$\tau_1 - \frac{a}{c} = -\frac{1}{c^2}\left(\tau + \frac{d}{c}\right)^{-1}.$$

But

$$\left|\tau + \frac{d}{c}\right| \geqslant \frac{\sqrt{3}}{2},$$

so that

$$\left|\tau_1 - \frac{a}{c}\right| \leqslant \frac{2}{\sqrt{3}c^2} \leqslant \frac{1}{2\sqrt{3}} < \frac{\sqrt{3}}{2};$$

hence τ_1 is certainly not in the fundamental region.

We have thus shown that, *if* $\mathrm{Im}\,\tau'$ *is positive, there exists a unique point* τ *which lies in the fundamental region of the modular group and is congruent to* τ' *with respect to that group.*

A modular transformation $\tau' = U(\tau)$, being homographic, maps the fundamental region conformally on a region of the upper half-plane bounded by three circular arcs (or straight lines) intersecting at angles $\frac{1}{3}\pi$, $\frac{1}{3}\pi$, 0. It is convenient to denote this region by U, which is also the symbol of the transformation producing it; we denote the fundamental region by I.

Every point of the upper half-plane lies in at least one of the regions congruent to I, so that they completely fill the upper half-plane; we shall show that they do so without any overlapping.

For suppose that τ_1' is a point common to the regions U and V, produced from I by the modular transformations $\tau' = U(\tau)$, $\tau' = V(\tau)$; let τ_1 be the point of I congruent to τ_1'. Then, if $\tau = U^{-1}(\tau')$ is the transformation inverse to $\tau' = U(\tau)$, we have

$$\tau_1 = U^{-1}(\tau_1') = U^{-1}V(\tau_1),$$

so that τ_1 is a point of I which is invariant under the modular transformation $\tau' = U^{-1}V(\tau)$.

We have, however, just seen that at most one point of I is invariant under a modular transformation and that such a point has affix $e^{\pi i/3}$, $e^{\pi i/2}$, or ∞. Hence the regions U and V can have at most one point in common, and so do not overlap.

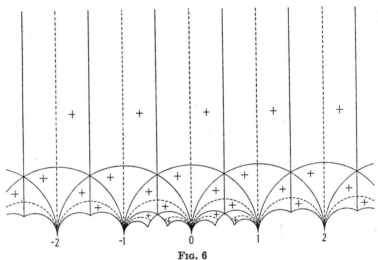

FIG. 6

In the above figure are shown the fundamental region and a number of the regions congruent to it. In each case the dotted curve is congruent to the imaginary axis; it divides each region into two parts and corresponding parts are marked with crosses. At first sight, it appears that two adjacent regions would have a whole side in common, contrary to what we have just proved. This is not the case, since part of the boundary of each region does not belong to it.

15.22. The elliptic modular functions

An analytic function $f(\tau)$, regular save for poles when $\operatorname{Im} \tau > 0$, is called an *elliptic modular function*† if there exists an algebraic relation between the functions $f(\tau)$ and $f(\tau')$ whenever τ and τ' are connected by a transformation of the modular

---

† The standard work on elliptic modular functions is Klein and Fricke, *Theorie der elliptischen Modulfunktionen* (Leipzig, 1890).

group. If $f(\tau) \equiv f(\tau')$ for all modular transformations, $f(\tau)$ is said to be an *automorphic function*† of the modular group.

We can easily construct an elliptic modular function out of the invariants g_2, g_3 of Weierstrass's function $\wp(z|\omega, \omega\tau)$, which are unaltered when we replace 2ω and $2\omega\tau$ by any other pair of primitive periods $2\omega'$ and $2\omega'\tau'$. But since

$$g_2(\omega, \omega\tau) = \omega^{-4}g_2(1, \tau), \qquad g_3(\omega, \omega\tau) = \omega^{-6}g_3(1, \tau),$$

it follows g_2^3/g_3^2 is a function of τ which is invariant when τ undergoes a modular transformation. As g_2^3/g_3^2 can be shown to be regular in the fundamental region, save for one simple pole, it is an automorphic function of the modular group.

On the other hand, the function

$$\lambda(\tau) = 16q \prod_1^\infty \left(\frac{1+q^{2n}}{1+q^{2n-1}}\right)^8,$$

where $q = e^{\pi i \tau}$, is an elliptic modular function, but not an automorphic function of the modular group. To prove this, we observe that, as we saw in § 15.1,

$$\lambda(\tau) = (e_3 - e_2)/(e_1 - e_2),$$

where e_1, e_2, and e_3 are the values taken by $\wp(z|\omega, \omega\tau)$ when $z = \omega$, $\omega\tau$, and $\omega + \omega\tau$. Now when we change to a new pair of primitive periods, $2\omega'$ and $2\omega'\tau'$ say, the numbers e_1', e_2', e_3' are a permutation of e_1, e_2, e_3. Hence, when τ' is connected with τ by a modular transformation, $\lambda(\tau')$ is equal to one of the six functions

$$\lambda(\tau), \quad 1-\lambda(\tau), \quad \frac{1}{\lambda(\tau)}, \quad \frac{1}{1-\lambda(\tau)}, \quad \frac{\lambda(\tau)}{\lambda(\tau)-1}, \quad 1-\frac{1}{\lambda(\tau)},$$

obtained by permuting e_1, e_2, and e_3. Since $\lambda(\tau)$ is regular when $|q| < 1$, that is, when $\text{Im}\,\tau > 0$, we have thus shown that $\lambda(\tau)$ is an elliptic modular function.

15.23. The λ-group

A group of transformations A is said to be a sub-group of another group B, if every transformation of A belongs to B although there are transformations of B which do not belong

† For the theory of automorphic functions in general, see, for example, L. R. Ford, *Automorphic Functions* (New York, 1929), or Forsyth, *Theory of Functions* (Cambridge, 1918).

to A. We now show that the elliptic modular function $\lambda(\tau)$ is an automorphic function of a certain sub-group of the modular group.

We have seen that $\lambda(\omega_2/\omega_1) = \lambda(\omega_2'/\omega_1')$ if $2\omega_1'$, $2\omega_2'$ form a pair of primitive periods of $\wp(z|\omega_1, \omega_2)$, such that $\wp(\omega_1') = e_1$, $\wp(\omega_2') = e_2$, and $\wp(\omega_3') = e_3$. This is the case if

$$\omega_1' = d\omega_1 + 2c\omega_2, \qquad \omega_2' = 2b\omega_1 + a\omega_2,$$

where a, b, c, and d are integers such that $ad - 4bc = 1$, a and d being odd.† Writing $\omega_2 = \omega_1\tau$, $\omega_2' = \omega_1'\tau'$, we find that $\lambda(\tau') = \lambda(\tau)$ when $\tau' = (a\tau + 2b)/(2c\tau + d)$, where a, b, c, and d are integers such that $ad - 4bc = 1$.

We shall call a modular transformation of this special type a λ-transformation. The set of all λ-transformations evidently constitutes a group, which is a sub-group of the modular group; we call it the λ-group. The elliptic modular function $\lambda(\tau)$ is, therefore, an automorphic function of the λ-group.

15.24. The fundamental region of the λ-group

Two points in the τ-plane are said to be congruent with respect to the λ-group if their affixes are connected by a λ-transformation. As two congruent points are necessarily both on the real axis or both on the same side of that axis, it suffices to consider only the effect of λ-transformations on sets of points in the region $\operatorname{Im}\tau \geqslant 0$.

We show first of all that the λ-group possesses a fundamental region by considering the periods $2\Omega_1$ and $2\Omega_2$ of $\wp(z|\omega_1, \omega_2)$ such that $\wp(\Omega_1) = e_1$, $\wp(\Omega_2) = e_2$, the ratio ω_2/ω_1 being an assigned number τ' whose imaginary part is positive.

The fundamental primitive period-parallelogram of $\wp(z)$ contains either one or two points of the set Ω_1. If there is only one, we call it ω. If there are two, they are the midpoints of opposite sides of the parallelogram; we take as ω the one nearer the origin. In this way, ω is uniquely defined and satisfies the condition $|\omega| \leqslant |\omega + \Omega_{m,n}|$, where $\Omega_{m,n}$ is any period of $\wp(z)$.

We next consider the points ω' of the set Ω_2, such that 2ω and $2\omega'$ form a pair of primitive periods of $\wp(z)$. These points ω' lie on a straight line parallel to the line through $\pm\omega$, and at

† It will be seen that the condition $ad - 4bc = 1$ itself implies that a and d are odd.

most two of them are nearer to the origin than the rest. If there is only one, we call it $\omega\tau$. If there are two, we take as $\omega\tau$ the one which gives the smaller (positive) value of $\arg(\omega'/\omega)$. Thus $\omega\tau$ is uniquely defined and satisfies the condition

$$|\omega\tau| \leqslant |\omega\tau + \Omega_{m,n}|,$$

where $\Omega_{m,n}$ is any period of $\wp(z)$.

In this way we have found a number τ which is congruent to the given number τ' with respect to the λ-group, and which satisfies the inequalities

$$1 \leqslant |2m+1+2n\tau|, \qquad |\tau| \leqslant |2p+(2q+1)\tau|,$$

for all positive or negative integer or zero values of m, n, p, and q. Each of these inequalities is satisfied if

$$1 \leqslant |2\tau+1|, \qquad |\tau| \leqslant |\tau+2|,$$
$$1 \leqslant |2\tau-1|, \qquad |\tau| \leqslant |\tau-2|.$$

The point τ lies, therefore, in a region bounded by the straight lines $\mathrm{Rl}\,\tau = \pm 1$ and the semicircles $|2\tau\pm 1| = 1$; moreover, it is easily verified† that the only boundary points which belong to the region are those for which $\mathrm{Rl}\,\tau \geqslant 0$. We call the region defined in this way the fundamental region of the λ-group.

We have thus shown that, when $\mathrm{Im}\,\tau' > 0$, there exists a point in this fundamental region which is congruent to τ' with respect to the λ-group. It is not, however, obvious that τ is the only point of the fundamental region congruent to τ'. If there were another such point τ_1, τ and τ_1 would be two points in the fundamental region congruent with respect to the λ-group, and this can be shown to be impossible.‡ Hence, *if* $\mathrm{Im}\,\tau' > 0$, *there exists a unique point τ in the fundamental region of the λ-group which is congruent to τ' with respect to that group.*

Each λ-transformation maps the fundamental region conformally on a region in the upper half-plane, bounded by four semicircles (or straight lines) all orthogonal to the real axis. It can be shown, just as in the case of the modular group, that these 'quadrilaterals' congruent to the fundamental region fill the upper half-plane completely without any overlapping. Two

---

† By finding τ when $\tau' = \pm 1 + iy$ and when $2\tau' = \pm 1 + e^{\theta i}$.

‡ The proof is omitted, since it is a simple modification of that given in § 15.21 in connexion with the modular group.

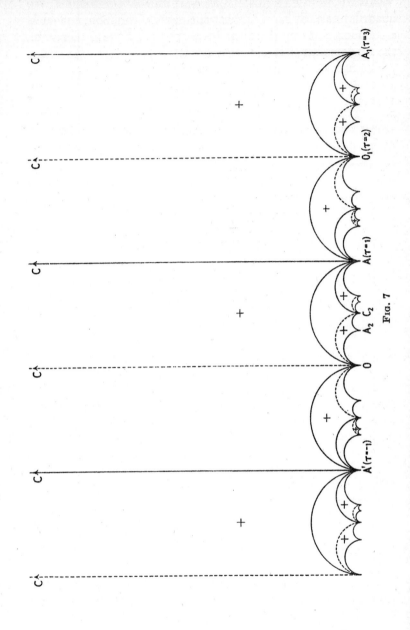

FIG. 7

quadrilaterals can have at most one point in common, and such a common point is congruent to one of the points 0, 1, or ∞ of the fundamental region.[†]

The figure given opposite shows the fundamental region and a number of the regions congruent to it with respect to the λ-group.

15.3. The behaviour of $\lambda(\tau)$ in the fundamental region

The function $\lambda(\tau)$ is regular in any bounded closed domain in the upper half of the τ-plane and never takes there the values 0 and 1. We now show that these exceptional values 0, 1, and ∞ are the limits to which $\lambda(\tau)$ tends as τ moves in the fundamental region of the λ-group up to one of the corners 0, ± 1, or ∞.

Now
$$\lambda(\tau) = 16q \prod_1^\infty \left(\frac{1+q^{2n}}{1+q^{2n-1}} \right)^8,$$

where $q = e^{\pi i \tau}$. Hence, if $\tau = u + iv$, where $v \geqslant 1$, we have
$$|q| = e^{-\pi v} \leqslant e^{-\pi}$$

and so
$$|\lambda(\tau)| \leqslant 16e^{-\pi v} \prod_1^\infty \left(\frac{1+e^{-2n\pi}}{1-e^{-(2n+1)\pi}} \right)^8 < Ae^{-\pi v},$$

where A is independent of u and v. Therefore $\lambda(u+iv) \to 0$ as $v \to \infty$, uniformly with respect to u. In particular, $\lambda(\tau) \to 0$ as $\tau \to \infty$ in the fundamental region.

Now as τ moves to the origin in the fundamental region, the point $-1/\tau$ tends to infinity in the same region. But, by Jacobi's imaginary transformation, we have
$$\lambda(\tau) = 1 - \lambda(-1/\tau), \tag{i}$$

and so $\lambda(\tau) \to 1$ as $\tau \to 0$ in the fundamental region.

Again, since[‡]
$$\lambda(\tau) = \frac{\lambda(\tau+1)}{\lambda(\tau+1)-1} = \frac{\lambda(\tau-1)}{\lambda(\tau-1)-1}, \tag{ii}$$

the function $\lambda(\tau)$ tends to infinity as $\tau \to \pm 1$ in the fundamental region.

When τ lies on the imaginary axis, q is real and hence $\lambda(\tau)$ is also real. But $\lambda(iv)$ is a continuous function of the real variable

---

† The proofs of these statements are omitted, as they can be easily supplied by the reader.

‡ See Ex. 18 on p. 416.

v; therefore $\lambda(\tau)$ assumes all real values between 0 and 1 on the imaginary axis. Using formulae (ii), we deduce that $\lambda(\tau)$ is also real and takes all values between $-\infty$ and 0 on each of the lines $\mathrm{Rl}\,\tau = \pm 1$. Finally, by formula (i), we see that $\lambda(\tau)$ is real and takes all values between 1 and $+\infty$ on each of the semicircles $|2\tau \pm 1| = 1$.

15.31. The zeros† of $\lambda(\tau) - c$

If Γ is a closed contour in the upper half of the τ-plane on which $\lambda(\tau)$ never takes an assigned value c, different from 0 or 1,

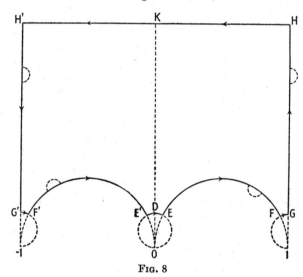

Fig. 8

the function $\lambda(\tau) - c$ has N zeros within Γ, where

$$2\pi i N = \int_{\Gamma} \frac{\lambda'(\tau)}{\lambda(\tau) - c}\, d\tau.$$

We suppose, in the first place, that c is not real, so that $\lambda(\tau) - c$ has no zeros on the boundary of the fundamental region, and we take Γ to be the boundary of that part of the fundamental region for which

$$\mathrm{Im}\,\tau \leqslant 1/2\epsilon, \qquad |\tau - i\epsilon| \geqslant \epsilon, \qquad |\tau \pm 1 - i\epsilon| \geqslant \epsilon,$$

where $\epsilon > 0$. This contour is shown in the figure above. Since

† The analysis of this section is essentially the same as that given by Whittaker and Watson, *Modern Analysis* (Cambridge, 1920), 481–3.

$\lambda(\tau) \to 0, 1, \infty$ as $\tau \to \infty, 0, \pm 1$ respectively in the fundamental region, we can make ϵ so small that no zero of the function occurs in the part of the fundamental region outside Γ. The value of the contour integral then remains constant as ϵ decreases; we find its value by considering the limit as $\epsilon \to 0$.

Now when τ moves along the arc $F'E'$, its affix is $-\tfrac{1}{2}+\tfrac{1}{2}e^{(\pi-\theta)i}$, where θ increases. The congruent point of the fundamental region has affix $\tfrac{1}{2}+\tfrac{1}{2}e^{\theta i}$, and so describes the arc FE. It follows that the integrals along $F'E'$ and EF cancel. Similarly the sum of the integrals along GH and $H'G'$ is zero.

The value of the contour integral is thus equal to the sum of the integrals along HH', $G'F'$, $E'E$, and FG. We consider these parts separately.

Now when $\operatorname{Im}\tau \geqslant 1$, $\lambda(\tau)$ is regular since $|q| \leqslant e^{-\pi}$. We can therefore express it as a power series

$$\lambda(\tau) = 16q(1+a_1 q+a_2 q^2+...)$$

which converges uniformly with respect to τ when $\operatorname{Im}\tau \geqslant 1$. Hence we have

$$\lambda'(\tau) = 16\pi i q(1+2a_1 q+3a_2 q^2+...),$$

and so the function

$$\frac{\lambda'(\tau)}{\lambda(\tau)-c} = \frac{16\pi i q(1+2a_1 q+3a_2 q^2+...)}{-c+16q(1+a_1 q+a_2 q^2+...)}$$

tends to zero as $\operatorname{Im}\tau \to \infty$, uniformly with respect to $\operatorname{Rl}\tau$, provided that c is not zero. From this it follows that the integral along HH' tends to zero with ϵ, since $\operatorname{Im}\tau = 1/(2\epsilon)$ on HH'.

When τ moves along the arc $E'E$, the point $\tau_1 = -1/\tau$ describes the straight line HH', and hence

$$\int_{E'E} \frac{1}{\lambda(\tau)-c} \frac{d\lambda(\tau)}{d\tau}\,d\tau = \int_{HH'} \frac{1}{\lambda(\tau)-c} \frac{d\lambda(\tau)}{d\tau_1}\,d\tau_1.$$

But, by Jacobi's imaginary transformation, $\lambda(\tau) = 1-\lambda(\tau_1)$, and so

$$\int_{E'E} \frac{\lambda'(\tau)}{\lambda(\tau)-c}\,d\tau = \int_{HH'} \frac{\lambda'(\tau_1)}{\lambda(\tau_1)-(1-c)}\,d\tau_1.$$

By the same argument as before, this tends to zero with ϵ, since $1-c$ is, by hypothesis, not zero.

F f

Again, when τ describes the arc FG, the point $\tau_1 = -1/(\tau-1)$ moves along the right-hand half of the line HH', so that

$$\int_{FG} \frac{1}{\lambda(\tau)-c} \frac{d\lambda(\tau)}{d\tau}\, d\tau = \int_{HK} \frac{1}{\lambda(\tau)-c} \frac{d\lambda(\tau)}{d\tau_1}\, d\tau_1.$$

But, by Ex. 18 of p. 416,

$$\lambda(\tau) = 1 - \frac{1}{\lambda(\tau_1)},$$

which gives

$$\int_{FG} \frac{\lambda'(\tau)}{\lambda(\tau)-c}\, d\tau = \int_{HK} \frac{1}{(1-c)\lambda(\tau_1)-1} \frac{\lambda'(\tau_1)}{\lambda(\tau_1)}\, d\tau_1.$$

Similarly, by using the transformation $\tau_1 = -1/(\tau+1)$, we can show that

$$\int_{G'F'} \frac{\lambda'(\tau)}{\lambda(\tau)-c}\, d\tau = \int_{KH'} \frac{1}{(1-c)\lambda(\tau_1)-1} \frac{\lambda'(\tau_1)}{\lambda(\tau_1)}\, d\tau_1.$$

Combining these results, we find that, so far, we have shown that

$$2\pi i N = \lim_{\epsilon \to 0} \int_{HH'} \frac{1}{(1-c)\lambda(\tau)-1} \frac{\lambda'(\tau)}{\lambda(\tau)}\, d\tau.$$

The integrand can, however, be written in the form

$$-\pi i \cdot \frac{(1+2a_1 q + 3a_2 q^2 + \ldots)}{(1+a_1 q + a_2 q^2 + \ldots)\{1-(1-c)\lambda(\tau)\}},$$

and this tends to $-\pi i$ as $\operatorname{Im}\tau \to +\infty$, uniformly with respect to $\operatorname{Rl}\tau$. From this it follows that $2\pi i N = 2\pi i$, and so $N = 1$.

We have thus proved that, when c is not real, the function $\lambda(\tau)-c$ has one zero in the fundamental region of the λ-group. It remains to consider the case when c is a real number not equal to 0 or 1. In this case, $\lambda(\tau)-c$ will have a finite† number of zeros on the sides EF, $E'F'$, GH, and $G'H'$ of Γ, and none in the part of the fundamental region outside Γ, provided that ϵ be sufficiently small. Now $F'E'$ does not belong to the fundamental region, but is congruent to FE with respect to the λ-group; a similar remark applies to the sides $G'H'$ and GH.

---

† It cannot have an infinite number, since $\lambda(\tau)-c$ is regular within and on Γ.

Accordingly these zeros occur in pairs which are symmetrically placed with respect to the imaginary axis.

We now cut out each zero on $E'F'$ and $G'H'$ by an indentation whose radius is so small that it cuts out no other zero† of $\lambda(\tau)-c$. The zeros on EF and GH are then brought within Γ by circular arcs congruent to these indentations, as shown in the figure. We then apply the same argument to the modified contour, observing that the integrals along the indentations and the congruent circular arcs cancel, and conclude that $\lambda(\tau)-c$ has one zero within the modified contour. Since, however, points on $E'F'$ or $G'H'$ do not belong to the fundamental region, this means that the function has precisely one zero in that region.

Hence it follows that, *if c is any number not equal to 0 or 1, the elliptic modular function $\lambda(\tau)$ takes the value c once in the fundamental region of the λ-group.*

In particular, we see that $\lambda(\tau)$ increases steadily from $-\infty$ to 0 as τ moves along the straight line from 1 to $1+\infty i$, then from 0 to 1 as τ describes the imaginary axis from ∞i to 0, and finally from 1 to $+\infty$ as τ moves along the semicircle joining the points of affix 0 and 1.

15.32. The solution of the problem of § 15.1

We now show that the Jacobian elliptic functions are uniquely determined when the square of the modulus is assigned.

For we know that the equation $\lambda(\tau) = k^2$ has an infinite number of roots; each root τ is connected with the root τ_0 in the fundamental region of the λ-group by an equation

$$\tau_0 = (a\tau+2b)/(2c\tau+d),$$

where a, b, c, and d are integers such that $ad-4bc = 1$.

If we construct two sets of Jacobian elliptic functions from the Weierstrassian functions $\wp(z|2c\tau+d, a\tau+2b)$ and $\wp(z|1, \tau)$, the square of the modulus k has the same value for each set. But since the two Weierstrassian functions are identical, the two sets of Jacobian elliptic functions are also identical. Thus, when k^2 is given, $\mathrm{sn}(u,k)$, $\mathrm{cn}(u,k)$, and $\mathrm{dn}(u,k)$ are uniquely determined.

† This is possible, since the zeros of a regular analytic function are isolated.

15.4. Conformal mapping by $\lambda(\tau)$

In the fundamental region of the λ-group, the function $\lambda(\tau)$ is real only on the sides of the curvilinear triangle† OAC. Hence the imaginary part of $\lambda(\tau)$ is always of the same sign within this 'triangle'. To determine this sign, we observe that

$$\lambda(\tau) = 16q\{1+f(q)\},$$

where $f(q)$ can be made as small as we please by taking $\operatorname{Im}\tau$ sufficiently large, and so $\operatorname{Im}\lambda(\tau)$ has the same sign as $\operatorname{Im}q$. But if $\tau = u+iv$,

$$\operatorname{Im} q = \operatorname{Im}(e^{\pi iu-\pi v}) = \sin \pi u \, e^{-\pi v},$$

and this is positive within OAC. Thus *the imaginary part of $\lambda(\tau)$ is positive within the curvilinear 'triangle' OAC, and vanishes on its boundary.* Similarly we see that the imaginary part of $\lambda(\tau)$ is negative within the curvilinear 'triangle' $OA'C$ and vanishes on its boundary; in fact, by Schwarz's principle of symmetry,‡ $\lambda(\tau)$ takes conjugate complex values at points which are symmetrical with respect to the imaginary axis.

Since $\lambda(\tau)$ is regular and simple within the fundamental region and takes there every value save real values between $-\infty$ and 0 and between 1 and $+\infty$, the transformation $z = \lambda(\tau)$ maps the interior of this region conformally on the whole z-plane, supposed cut along the real axis from $-\infty$ to 0 and from 1 to $+\infty$. The upper sides of the two cuts correspond to AC and OA respectively, the lower sides to $A'C$ and OA'. There exists, therefore, a unique inverse function $\tau = \nu(z)$ which is regular in the cut z-plane, and maps it conformally on the fundamental region of the λ-group.

15.41. The inverse function $\nu(z)$

The equation $z = \lambda(\tau)$ defines τ as a many-valued function of z. We call the function $\nu(z)$, which we have just defined, the fundamental branch of τ; any branch of τ is connected with $\nu(z)$ by a λ-transformation. We now consider how these other branches of τ can be obtained by continuing analytically the function $\nu(z)$ across the cuts in the z-plane. We do this by using certain results in Chapter XIV which depended on showing that

---

† See the figure of § 15.24.   ‡ See § 8.4.

the Jacobian elliptic functions are uniquely determined when the square of the modulus is given; the work of the present chapter has completely justified this assumption.

Now $\nu(z) = iK'/K$, where K and iK' are the quarter-periods of the Jacobian elliptic functions of modulus $z^{1/2}$. But K has branch-points at $z = 1$ and $z = \infty$, and K' at $z = 0$ and $z = \infty$; this follows from their expressions as hypergeometric functions. Hence $\nu(z)$ has branch-points at $0, 1, \infty$.

To determine the nature of these branch-points, we use the equation

$$\nu'(z) = \frac{d}{dz}\left(\frac{iK'}{K}\right) = \frac{\pi}{4iK^2 z(1-z)},$$

which follows immediately from the result of § 14.511, Ex. 2. When $|z| < 1$, this equation can be written in the form†

$$\nu'(z) = \frac{1}{\pi i z} + a_0 + a_1 z + a_2 z^2 + ...,$$

the infinite series having $|z| = 1$ as circle of convergence. Hence

$$\nu(z) = \frac{1}{\pi i}\log z + \phi(z),$$

where $\phi(z)$ is regular when $|z| < 1$.

The function $\nu(z)$ has, therefore, a logarithmic branch-point at the origin. When we continue $\nu(z)$ analytically once round $z = 0$ in the positive sense, we obtain a new branch $\tau = \nu(z) + 2$ of the inverse function‡; this branch maps the cut z-plane conformally on the interior of the 'quadrilateral' $CAO_1 A_1$ of the figure of § 15.24.

On the other hand, we have

$$\frac{d}{dz}\left(\frac{1}{\nu(z)}\right) = -\frac{\nu'(z)}{\nu^2(z)} = \frac{\pi}{4iK'^2 z(1-z)}.$$

We deduce from this, in a similar manner, that

$$\frac{1}{\nu(z)} = \frac{1}{\pi i}\log(1-z) + \psi(z),$$

where $\psi(z)$ is regular when $|1-z| < 1$.

† Since $1/\{(1-z)K^2\}$ is regular when $|z| < 1$ and has the value $4/\pi^2$ at the origin.

‡ It should be observed that this implies that $e^{\pi i\tau}$, regarded as a function of z, has no branch-point at the origin, but has a simple zero there.

The singularity of $v(z)$ at $z = 1$ is therefore most simply explained by saying that $1/v(z)$ has a logarithmic branch-point at $z = 1$. When we continue $v(z)$ analytically round $z = 1$ once in the positive sense, we obtain a new branch τ of the inverse function, given by the equation

$$\frac{1}{\tau} = \frac{1}{v(z)} + 2,$$

so that

$$\tau = \frac{v(z)}{2v(z)+1}.$$

This branch maps the cut plane conformally on the interior of the 'quadrilateral' OAC_2A_2 of the figure, which is obtained from the fundamental region by the λ-transformation $\tau' = \tau/(2\tau+1)$.

The point at infinity is the only other branch-point of $v(z)$. But as a circuit about the point at infinity is the same as a circuit about $z = 0$ and $z = 1$, there is no need to consider this any further.

All the branches of the function τ defined by the equation $\lambda(\tau) = z$ can therefore be obtained by repeated circuits about $z = 0$ and $z = 1$ in appropriate orders. Each such branch maps the cut z-plane conformally on the interior of a 'quadrilateral' congruent to the fundamental region of the λ-group. It follows that every transformation of the λ-group can be generated by repeated applications of the two transformations $\tau' = \tau+2$ and $\tau' = \tau/(2\tau+1)$. For this reason, these transformations are called the *generating transformations* of the λ-group.

15.5. Picard's theorem

It is well known that a polynomial takes any assigned finite value n times, where n is the degree of the polynomial. As a polynomial is an integral function with a pole at infinity, we naturally ask whether every integral function actually attains any given value.

The theorem of Weierstrass, proved in § 4.55, does not really answer this question. It merely shows that we can find a sequence of points at which the integral function approaches as near as we please to the given value.

The answer to this question was first given by Picard,[†] who

† *Comptes rendus*, **88** (1879), 1024–7.

proved that *an integral function actually attains every finite value, save one exceptional value at most*. This result is known as Picard's theorem.

We know that the equation $e^z = a$ has an infinite number of roots for any given finite value of a, save $a = 0$; but if $a = 0$, the equation has no roots at all. Thus zero is an exceptional value of e^z. On the other hand, there exist integral functions with no exceptional values; the function $\sin z$ is a simple example of this.

In order to prove Picard's theorem, we have to show that an integral function $F(z)$, which never takes two given values, a or b say, must be a constant. The simplest proof of this is Picard's original proof, by means of the function $\nu(z)$ introduced in § 15.41.

The function
$$f(z) = \frac{F(z) - a}{b - a}$$

is an integral function which never takes the values 0 or 1. We now consider the function $\tau = \nu\{f(z)\}$, where τ lies initially in the fundamental region of the λ-group when $z = 0$.

When z describes a closed curve C, the point $t = f(z)$ describes a closed curve Γ, since $f(z)$ is one-valued. This curve Γ cannot enclose either of the points 0 or 1; for if it enclosed the point $t = 0$ (or 1), we could make Γ pass through $t = 0$ (or 1) by deforming C, and this is impossible by hypothesis. Thus $\nu(t)$ returns to its original value when t describes Γ, and so $\nu\{f(z)\}$ is a one-valued function of z.

The point $\tau = \nu\{f(z)\}$ lies, therefore, in the fundamental region for all values of z, and τ is always finite, since $f(z)$ is never zero. Hence $\nu\{f(z)\}$ is an integral function whose imaginary part is positive.

It follows that the function
$$\phi(z) = e^{i\nu\{f(z)\}}$$

is also an integral function. But since
$$|\phi(z)| = e^{-\operatorname{Im}\nu\{f(z)\}} < 1,$$

we see, by applying Liouville's theorem, that $\phi(z)$ is a constant. Hence $f(z)$ is also a constant. This completes the proof of Picard's theorem.

15.51. Elementary proofs of Picard's theorem

Although Picard's proof of his theorem is quite simple, it involves the rather difficult theory of the elliptic modular function $\lambda(\tau)$. It is, however, possible to prove the theorem by elementary methods without the use of the modular function.

The first elementary proof was due to Borel.† More recently, other elementary proofs have been given by Bloch‡ and R. Nevanlinna.§ These proofs are of great interest, as they have been the starting-points of new methods in the theory of functions.‖

For an account of the application of the modular function to the discussion of the behaviour of a function near an isolated essential singularity, we refer the reader to Julia's tract†† in the Borel collection.

15.52. Landau's theorem

Let $f(z)$ be an analytic function which is regular and never takes the values 0 or 1 when $|z| < R$. If this were true for all values of R, no matter how large, $f(z)$ would be an integral function with two exceptional values, and this is impossible by Picard's theorem. The set of permissible values of R possesses, therefore, a finite upper bound L; if $R' > L$, the function $f(z)$ is either not regular everywhere in $|z| < R'$ or else takes there one of the values 0, 1.

In 1904 Landau‡‡ discovered a remarkable extension of Picard's theorem when he found that this upper bound L depends only on the first two non-vanishing coefficients in the expansion of $f(z)$ as a Taylor series in powers of z.

Landau proved his theorem by elementary methods. The best proof, however, is that due to Carathéodory,§§ which gives

---

† *Comptes rendus*, **122** (1896), 1045–8; *Acta Math.* **20** (1897), 357–96.

‡ *Comptes rendus*, **178** (1924), 1593. An account of Bloch's method is given by Landau, *Darstellung und Begründung einiger neuerer Ergebnisse der Funktionentheorie* (Berlin, 1929).

§ *Acta Soc. Scient. Fennicae*, **50** (1924), vi. See also his Borel tract, *Le Théorème de Picard-Borel* (Paris, 1929).

‖ See, for example, Bloch's tract in the series, *Mémorial des sciences mathématiques*, fascicule xx (Paris, 1926).

†† *Leçons sur les fonctions uniformes* (Paris, 1924).

‡‡ *Berliner Sitzungsberichte* (1904), 1118–33.

§§ *Comptes rendus*, **141** (1905), 1213–15.

the 'best possible' value for L; it involves the use of the function $\nu(z)$. We give here Carathéodory's proof in the case when $f'(0)$ is not zero; the proof in the general case follows the same lines.

The function $\qquad f(z) = a_0 + a_1 z + a_2 z^2 + \dots,$

where a_1 is not zero, is regular and never takes the values 0 or 1 in the region $|z| < R$. As in the proof of Picard's theorem, we consider the function $\nu\{f(z)\}$, where $\nu\{a_0\}$ is understood to mean the fundamental value; this function is one-valued and regular in $|z| < R$, where its imaginary part is positive.

Now the transformation $w = (\tau - \alpha)/(\tau - \bar{\alpha})$, where $\operatorname{Im} \alpha > 0$, maps the region $\operatorname{Im} \tau > 0$ conformally on $|w| < 1$ and turns $\tau = \alpha$ into $w = 0$. Hence the function

$$w(z) = \frac{\nu\{f(z)\} - \alpha}{\nu\{f(z)\} - \bar{\alpha}},$$

where $\nu(a_0) = \alpha$, vanishes at $z = 0$ and is regular in $|z| < R$, where it takes only values for which $|w| < 1$.

As $w(z)$ satisfies all the conditions of Schwarz's lemma (§ 8.32), the inequality

$$\left| \frac{\nu\{f(z)\} - \alpha}{\nu\{f(z)\} - \bar{\alpha}} \right| \leqslant \frac{|z|}{R},$$

holds when $|z| < R$. If we divide through by $|z|$ and then make $|z| \to 0$, we find that

$$\frac{1}{R} \geqslant \lim_{z \to 0} \left| \frac{\nu\{f(z)\} - \nu\{f(0)\}}{z} \, \frac{1}{\nu\{f(z)\} - \bar{\alpha}} \right|$$

$$= \frac{1}{|\alpha - \bar{\alpha}|} \left| \frac{d}{dz} \nu\{f(z)\} \right|_{z=0} = \frac{1}{2 \operatorname{Im} \nu(a_0)} |\nu'(a_0) f'(0)|$$

$$= \frac{|a_1| |\nu'(a_0)|}{2 \operatorname{Im} \nu(a_0)},$$

and so $\qquad\qquad R \leqslant \dfrac{2 \operatorname{Im} \nu(a_0)}{|a_1| |\nu'(a_0)|}.$

We have thus proved Landau's theorem, that *if*

$$f(z) = a_0 + a_1 z + a_2 z^2 + \dots \qquad (a_1 \neq 0)$$

is regular and never takes the values 0 *or* 1 *in the region* $|z| < R$, *then* $R \leqslant L$, *where*

$$L = \frac{2 \operatorname{Im} \nu(a_0)}{|a_1| |\nu'(a_0)|}.$$

If we replace L by any smaller function of a_0 and a_1, the theorem is false. For we can actually construct a function satisfying the conditions of the theorem with $R = L$, by taking

$$f(z) = \lambda\left\{\frac{z\bar{\alpha}-L\alpha}{z-L}\right\},$$

where $\alpha = \nu(a_0)$ and λ denotes the elliptic modular function of § 15.22. The result contained in Carathéodory's formulation of Landau's theorem is thus a 'best possible' one.

REFERENCES

Elliptic Modular Functions:

A. R. FORSYTH, *Theory of Functions of a Complex Variable* (Cambridge, 1918), Chaps. XXI, XXII.

L. R. FORD, *Automorphic Functions* (New York, 1929), Chap. VII.

F. KLEIN and R. FRICKE, *Vorlesungen über die Theorie der elliptischen Modulfunktionen* (Leipzig, 1890).

Picard's Theorem:

G. JULIA, *Leçons sur les fonctions uniformes* (Paris, 1924).

E. LANDAU, *Darstellung und Begründung einiger neuerer Ergebnisse der Funktionentheorie* (Berlin, 1929).

R. NEVANLINNA, *Le Théorème de Picard-Borel* (Paris, 1929).

MISCELLANEOUS EXAMPLES

1. Show that
$$J(\tau) = \frac{g_2^3(1,\tau)}{g_2^3(1,\tau)-27g_3^2(1,\tau)}$$
is an automorphic function of the modular group, which takes every finite value exactly once in the fundamental region of that group.

2. Prove that
$$J(\tau) = \frac{4(1-\lambda+\lambda^2)^3}{27\lambda^2(1-\lambda)^2},$$
where λ denotes the elliptic modular function $\lambda(\tau)$.

3. Show that any transformation of the modular group can be generated by successive applications of the transformations $\tau' = \tau+1$ and $\tau' = -1/\tau$.

4. Prove that $\lambda(\tau) \to 1$ as $\tau \to 0$, uniformly with respect to $\arg\tau$ in any angle $\epsilon \leqslant \arg\tau \leqslant \pi-\epsilon$, where ϵ is positive.

5. Show that the only points on the real axis which are congruent, with respect to the λ-group, to points of the fundamental region, are those of rational affix.

6. Prove that the function which is equal to $\nu(z)$ when $\operatorname{Im}z > 0$, and is equal to $\nu(z)+2$ when $\operatorname{Im}z < 0$, is regular in the z-plane supposed cut along the real axis from 0 to $+\infty$, and that it maps this cut plane conformally on the 'quadrilateral' $COAO_1$ of § 15.24.

7. Obtain a function regular in the z-plane, supposed cut along the real axis from $-\infty$ to $+1$, which maps this cut plane conformally on the 'quadrilateral' COC_2A.

8. The function $F(z)$ is regular save for poles in any finite region of the z-plane. Show that there exist at most two values of c such that the equation $F(z) = c$ has no roots.

9. The function
$$f(z) = a_0 + a_n z^n + a_{n+1} z^{n+1} + \dots,$$
where a_n is not zero, is regular and never takes the values 0 or 1 when $|z| < R$. Prove that $R \leqslant L$, where
$$L = \left[\frac{2 \operatorname{Im} \nu(a_0)}{|a_n||\nu'(a_0)|} \right]^{1/n}.$$

10. The function
$$f(z) = a_0 + a_1 z + a_2 z^2 + \dots$$
is regular and never takes the values 0 or 1 when $|z| < R$. θ is a constant between 0 and 1. Show that there exists a function $S(a_0, \theta)$, depending on a_0 and θ alone, such that, when $|z| \leqslant \theta R$,
$$1/S(a_0^{-1}, \theta) \leqslant |f(z)| \leqslant S(a_0, \theta),$$
$$1/S\{(1-a_0)^{-1}, \theta\} \leqslant |1-f(z)| \leqslant S(1-a_0, \theta). \quad \text{(SCHOTTKY.)}$$

11. Show that, under the conditions of Ex. 10, there exists a function $L(k, \theta)$, depending on k and θ alone, such that, if $|a_0| \leqslant k$, the inequality $|f(z)| \leqslant L(k, \theta)$ holds when $|z| \leqslant \theta R$. (LANDAU.)

INDEX

The numbers refer to pages